(303) 590-7229

Olson & Associates
REPRESENTING FINE CONTRACT FURNISHING

GERALD OLSON
6387 MESEDGE DRIVE
COLORADO SPRINGS, COLORADO 80919

A Complete Guide To

The Language of Lighting

McGRAW-EDISON

Halo Lighting Division
McGraw-Edison Company
400 Busse Road
Elk Grove Village, Illinois 60007

Library of Congress Cataloging in Publication Data

McGraw-Edison Company.
    The language of lighting.

    Includes index.
    1. Electric lighting.   I.   Title.
TK4175.M36   1972   621.32'2   82-24964
ISBN 0-8359-2625-7

Printed in the United States of America

10 9 8 7 6 5 4 3 2 1

Text prepared and book designed by Robert Scharff
and Associates, Ltd.

Table of Contents

High Intensity Discharge Lamps. HID design and operation—Mercury design, performance, and color rendering—Metal Halide design, performance, and color rendering—HPS design, performance, and color rendering.

Incandescent and Fluorescent Lamps. Incandescent design and performance—General and extended service lamps—PAR, R, and ER lamps—Tungsten halogen lamps—Fluorescent lamp design and performance.

Lamp Comparisons. Lamp life and efficacy—cost—color rendering—color temperature—color rendering index—selecting lamp color—physiological considerations—final checklist.

HID Lamp Ballasts. Operating factors—Reactor ballasts—High Reactance (Autotransformer) ballasts—Constant Wattage Autotransformer ballasts—HPS lamp ballasts—remote location—fusing—data table.

Ambient Lighting. Lighting factors—indirect lighting of CRT areas—ambient lighting equipment—ambient lighting design—HID downlighting—incandescent downlighting.

Task Lighting. Problems with direct light systems—HID indirect/SPI task lighting solution—SPI task lighting concept—task light comparison.

Accent Lighting. Concept—illumination requirements—accent lighting lamps and fixtures—lighting variables—accent lighting of objects, surfaces, and spaces—lighting mirrors.

Parking Area Lighting. Illumination levels—aesthetics—economics—luminaires and lamps—design methods and tables—medium, large, and small area applications—high mast lighting.

Roadway Lighting. Concept—illumination requirements—roadway classifications and reflectances—uniformity ratios—aesthetics—lamps and luminaires—design methods and tables.

Sports Lighting. Concept—illumination levels—light quality—lamps and luminaires—design methods and layouts—application tables for base, foot, racquet, stick, combination, and other miscellaneous sports.

Sign and Building Lighting. Illumination requirements—cost factors and lamp selection—luminaires—design methods and tables—application sketches.

Security Lighting. Concept—economics—protective lighting methods—shadow and silhouette system—building-mounted systems—luminaires and lamps—design methods and table.

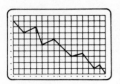

SECTION IV:
SYSTEM MAINTENANCE AND ECONOMICS **213**

> **Lighting System Maintenance.** Light loss factors—relamping and cleaning—maintenance equipment—troubleshooting HID systems—troubleshooting incandescent systems—troubleshooting fluorescent systems.
>
> **Lighting System Economics.** Using economic comparisons—cost-of-lighting-concept—lighting cost comparison—Econ II economic analysis—Econ II analysis sample problem.

PREFACE

The challenges faced by the lighting industry and lighting designers are many and varied. The problems of light control and light pollution in outdoor installations are being seriously addressed for the first time, and many communities have enacted ordinances curbing the indiscriminate use of light in outdoor areas. Indoors, many traditional lighting methods are now being questioned, and the advantages of HID indirect lighting are becoming apparent throughout the industry. For all systems, indoor and out, clients demand and deserve efficient, reliable operation, minimal maintenance costs, and pleasing aesthetic appearance.

Good lighting is a mixture of good products and sound, logical lighting design. At McGraw-Edison, our goal has always been to manufacture products capable of meeting the present and future demands of all light applications. All McGraw-Edison products are designed and tested using the most advanced optical and computer test facilities available. The luminaires resulting from this process offer the finest quality workmanship and performance characteristics found on the market today.

But a good product poorly applied will produce unsatisfactory results, an unfortunate situation McGraw-Edison believes happens far too often in our industry. This handbook was prepared to give guidance on the selection and application of McGraw-Edison products to all those involved in lighting system design. Many design methods presented rely on computer-generated information found in the various appendices at the back of the handbook. Although quite different from the methods employed in the past, I am sure you will find these new methods fast, straightforward means of attaining accurate, predictable results. I am also certain you will agree with me when I say this handbook fulfills a very real need—that of matching proven products with proven design methods to meet specific lighting needs.

Dan T. Thomson, President
Halo Lighting Division, McGraw-Edison Company

V

INTRODUCTION

The variety of modern lighting applications is almost countless. The material in this handbook was selected because I feel it represents the lighting applications most often faced by today's designers. The numerous application tables place pertinent data at the reader's fingertips, so it is possible to review equipment options and design criteria and draw up the layout in a matter of minutes. Every effort has been made to ensure fast, accurate results.

I would like to express my appreciation to all those at Halo Lighting whose work, research, and ideas are reflected in this project. I would also like to thank the staff of Robert Scharff and Associates, Ltd., for their aid in organizing and designing the book.

James L. Rhiner

James L. Rhiner
Manager, Technical Services
Halo Lighting Division, McGraw-Edison Company

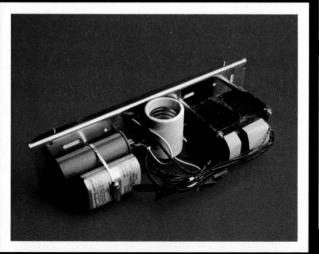

Selecting a viable luminaire design and equipping it with a lamp capable of producing the desired performance standards are large parts of any lighting design. Performance characteristics to be considered when choosing a lamp design include the lamp's light or lumen output, its maintenance factors, its initial cost, and the lamp's color rendering characteristics. As a lighting designer, you must also be concerned with the lamp's ability to meet required illumination levels, the overall lighting effect created, and any psychological or photobiological factors pertinent to the lamp choice.

There are three major lamp groups used in modern lighting: incandescent, fluorescent, and high intensity discharge designs. Of these types, high intensity discharge lamps, HIDs, have become increasingly important in recent years. Although the use of high intensity discharge lamps has dominated roadway lighting, outdoor area lighting, and some forms of indoor industrial lighting applications for some time, HIDs have now begun to replace fluorescent and incandescent installations in smaller commercial and office areas. Indirect lighting with HID lamps has a particularly promising future. While the number of high efficiency HID lamps in service is expected to increase greatly in the future, incandescent and fluorescent lamp designs will still play a prominent role in some types of lighting design, such as residential lighting and accent or task lighting.

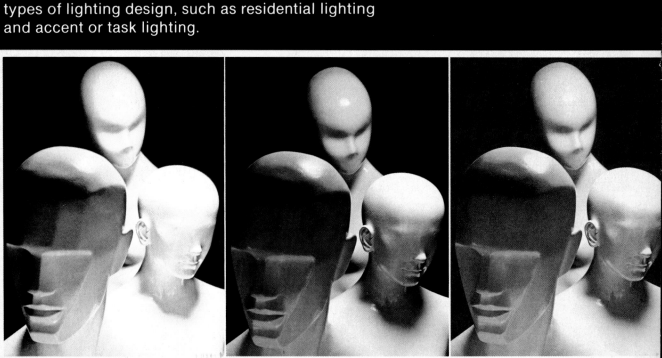

The three main types of HID lamps are named for the different material contained in the lamp's arc tube. This material affects lamp light coloring. Mercury lamps (left) generate more wavelengths in the blue-green area of the spectrum. High pressure sodium lamps (right) highlight the red-yellow range. While all HID sources render color adequately, the coloring characteristics of metal halide lamps (center) are considered the most natural.

Fluorescent lighting creates an even, blanketing effect. Incandescent and high intensity discharge light sources provide "point source" illumination. Point source illumination offers increased optical control and can dramatize merchandising displays by adding sparkle, highlights, and shadows.

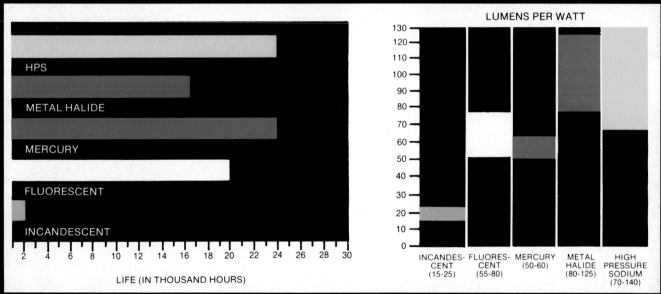

LUMENS PER WATT

HPS

METAL HALIDE

MERCURY

FLUORESCENT

INCANDESCENT

2 4 6 8 10 12 14 16 18 20 22 24 26 28 30

LIFE (IN THOUSAND HOURS)

INCANDES-CENT (15-25)	FLUORES-CENT (55-80)	MERCURY (50-60)	METAL HALIDE (80-125)	HIGH PRESSURE SODIUM (70-140)

High efficiency and long lamp life are two desirable light source characteristics. The above illustration indicates why systems employing HID lighting have moved to the forefront of current lighting design.

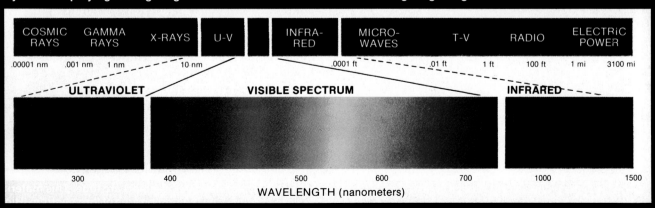

COSMIC RAYS	GAMMA RAYS	X-RAYS	U-V		INFRA-RED	MICRO-WAVES	T-V	RADIO	ELECTRIC POWER
.00001 nm	.001 nm 1 nm	10 nm			.0001 ft	.01 ft	1 ft	100 ft	1 mi 3100 mi

ULTRAVIOLET   VISIBLE SPECTRUM   INFRARED

300   400   500   600   700   1000   1500

WAVELENGTH (nanometers)

The color spectrum. Besides the visible wavelengths a light source generates, the lighting designer must be aware of any

High Intensity Discharge (HID)

The high intensity discharge lamp group is by far the most important lamp group used in modern lighting. HID light sources are highly regarded for their long life and high efficacy. The compactness of these lamps increases optical control and allows for a great deal of flexibility in the area of luminaire design.

HID Design

The HID lamp group can be broken down into three distinct categories based on the type of arc metal used in the generation of light. These categories are mercury, metal halide, and high pressure sodium. All HID lamps (Fig. 1) contain a sealed arc tube which houses two main electrodes. Mercury and metal halide arc tubes also house a separate starting electrode. Small amounts of arc metal (mercury, halide compounds, or sodium) and a special starting gas are contained within the arc tube.

The HID lamp produces light in much the same manner as a lightning bolt, except that instead of a brief flash, the bolt or arc generated within the arc tube is continually sustained. When the lamp is energized, individual particles of the starting gas are electrically charged through the presence of an electrical field existing between the starting and main electrodes of the lamp. As these charged particles fill the arc tube, the resistance across the starting gap is reduced, allowing electrons to flow readily through the gap. The flow of charged particles begins to ionize particles of the arc metal which have been altered by the electrical current. The heat generated by the arc causes more of the arc metal material to evaporate and ionize. When there is a sufficient number of ionized particles in the tube, the resistance between the main electrodes is reduced to a point where the voltage from the lamp's ballast can strike an arc between the main electrodes. The arc current continues to increase until the current rating of the lamp is attained, a process which may require several minutes to reach stabilization.

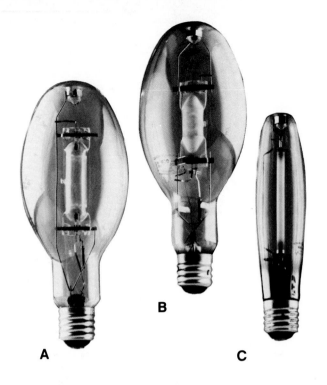

Fig. 1: The three types of high intensity discharge lamps: (A) mercury lamp, the original HID lamp; (B) metal halide lamp, known for its fine color rendering; and (C) high pressure sodium lamp, the most efficient HID lamp.

The current in this arc consists of an extremely rapid flow of both electrons and ions of the arc metal. During this rapid movement, a great many collisions occur between particles. One result of these collisions is that the particles release energy of a specific wavelength. This energy appears to us as light. Since the number of particles in the arc tube are so great and the number of collisions so frequent, it appears that the entire arc path continuously generates light at each of the wavelengths characteristic of the arc material. The apparent color of the light emitted from a particular lamp will differ, depending on whether mercury, metal halides, or sodium is the main metal used in establishing the arc.

All three types of HID lamps require the use of a ballast to assist in starting and to regulate the current across the arc once the arc has been struck. If a ballast were not used, the arc discharge would draw an unlimited amount of current and be quickly destroyed. To prevent this, a ballast is inserted between the lamp and the power supply to limit the electric current flow through the arc discharge. Since the dynamic characteristics of each type of HID lamp are different, each requires its own specific type of ballast. Detailed ballast information is given later in Section I.

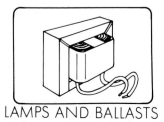

HID Lamp Operation

Certain operational characteristics are common to all high intensity discharge lamps. For example, with any HID type, sufficient starting current must be supplied to the lamp during the first half minute or so of operation. Too little current results in the lamp never warming up properly, while too much current reduces lamp life.

Voltage Considerations. The operating voltage of HID lamps tends to rise during the life of the lamp. This rise will be minimal when lamp watts are kept close to desired ratings and bulb temperatures well below the maximum permissible. The operating voltage of mercury lamps rises approximately 1% per 5,000 hours of operation. The voltage rise of metal halide lamps is roughly 1.5% per 1,000 operating hours. High pressure sodium lamps have the greatest voltage increase, about 3% per 1,000 operating hours.

Because of differing manufacturers' tolerances, individual lamps may have a somewhat wide range of operating voltages. For example, a 400-watt mercury lamp has a nominal operating voltage of 135 volts. However, the voltages of a group of lamps may vary from 120 volts to 150 volts. Depending upon the type of ballast employed, lamp wattage may vary considerably with the lamp voltage.

Also, all HID lamps will operate at their nominal wattages only if the lamps' voltage and the line voltage are nominal. Theoretically, these variables can cause a lamp wattage variation of up to 20%; however, almost all of the lamps in a large group will vary no more than 10% away from their nominal ratings.

Voltage Interruption. If the HID lamp circuit is turned off, if a momentary power outage occurs, or if the lamp voltage drops below that required to sustain the arc, the metallic particles in the arc tube deionize and the light ceases. The lamp will not restart immediately because it requires more voltage than the ballast can provide to reionize the gases when they are not under pressure. Depending on the lamp wattage, operating characteristics, and the temperature characteristics of the fixture, a cooldown period of 3 to 6 minutes is required before the arc tube pressure drops to a point where the arc can restrike.

Wattage Considerations. HID lamps should not be operated at higher-than-rated wattages. While this practice may result in a higher light output, the excess wattage imposes excessive temperatures on electrodes, arc tubes, and perhaps outer bulb walls. This may result in bulging of the arc tube and possible shattering. Lumen maintenance and lamp life are also drastically shortened.

Temperature Considerations. Due to the insulating effect of the lamp's outer bulb and the fixture enclosure, the output of high intensity discharge lamps is not affected by ambient temperature. Low ambient temperature may produce a pressure condition in the arc tubes in which the lamps will not start at normal line voltages or will fail to warm up to acceptable levels. This is essentially a ballasting problem, and ballast manufacturers are careful to publish the minimum temperatures at which their equipment will produce satisfactory system starting.

MERCURY LAMPS

First developed during the 1930s, mercury lamps are the oldest of the HID groups. While mercury lamps are favored over incandescent designs in certain applications, they cannot match the overall efficacy of the fluorescents and other HID lamps. The overall importance of mercury lamps has diminished to a certain point. The main advantages of mercury lamps are their good lumen maintenance characteristics and their exceptionally long burning life (24,000+ hours). For these reasons, mercury lamps still maintain their position in outdoor lighting as long life, lower first cost lamps.

Mercury lamps are primarily used in luminaires with built-in optical control. Due to the small physical size of their arc tube, mercury lamps exhibit the optical characteristics of a point light source, such as a typical incandescent lamp. Mercury lamps are available with clear outer bulbs which produce the finest optical control or with phosphor coated outer bulbs which improve the lamp's color rendering capabilities.

While mercury lamps are no longer a wise choice for many of the outdoor applications they once dominated, such as parking, roadway, and sports lighting, they have become more acceptable for some general lighting needs normally associated with incandescent lamps. These applications include interior downlighting, recessed luminaire lighting, and wall washing. The long life of mercury lamps, the longest of all HID sources, is particularly attractive where relamping is expensive and/or difficult.

Mercury Lamp Design

Most mercury lamps contain arc tubes of fused quartz (Fig. 2). The elements contained within the arc tube are mercury with a small amount of easily ionized argon as a starting gas. The lamp's outer

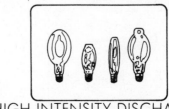

bulb is filled with an inert gas (usually nitrogen) which forms a protective layer around the inner arc tube. Mercury arcs produce both near- and far-ultraviolet energy as well as visible light. General service mercury lamps have a quartz arc tube contained within an outer bulb usually formed of heat resistant glass. The outer bulb absorbs the ultraviolet energy and narrows the spectral output of the lamp to only those energies provided by the sun.

Burning Position. Mercury lamps can operate in any burning position. However, in a vertical position, the initial lumen output of the lamp is slightly higher (2-3 lumens per watt) than it would be if the lamp were operated in a horizontal position.

Mercury Lamp Performance

The initial vertical and horizontal lumen outputs of various mercury lamps are listed in Table 1. The efficacy (lumens generated per watt of electricity consumed) of mercury systems far outdistances that of a corresponding incandescent system. For example, in similar systems equipped with 500-watt

Table 1: Mercury DX (Color Improved) Lamps

Lamp Type	Life Span (hours)	Initial Lumens	
		Vertical	Horizontal
100E23-1/2	24,000+	4,200	4,000
175E28	24,000+	8,600	8,150
250E28	24,000+	12,100	11,500
400E37	24,000+	22,500	21,500
1000BT56	24,000+	63,000	60,000

extended service incandescents and 250-watt phosphor coated mercury lamps, the mercury system will require approximately 40% less energy to run while producing about 30% more light. The mercury system will also have a rated life span nine times greater than the incandescent system.

When compared to fluorescent and other HID sources, the mercury lamps do not fair as well. The efficacy of fluorescent lamps easily surpasses mercury lamps, and for other types of HID sources this gap is even greater. For example, replacing 400-watt mercury fixtures with comparable 400-watt high

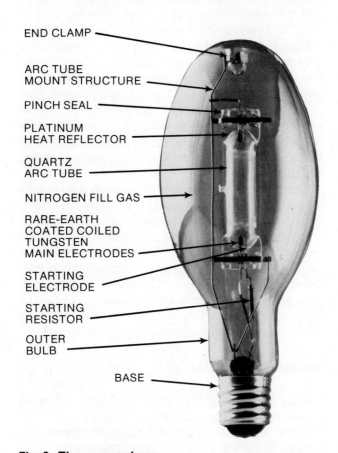

END CLAMP
ARC TUBE MOUNT STRUCTURE
PINCH SEAL
PLATINUM HEAT REFLECTOR
QUARTZ ARC TUBE
NITROGEN FILL GAS
RARE-EARTH COATED COILED TUNGSTEN MAIN ELECTRODES
STARTING ELECTRODE
STARTING RESISTOR
OUTER BULB
BASE

Fig. 2: The mercury lamp.

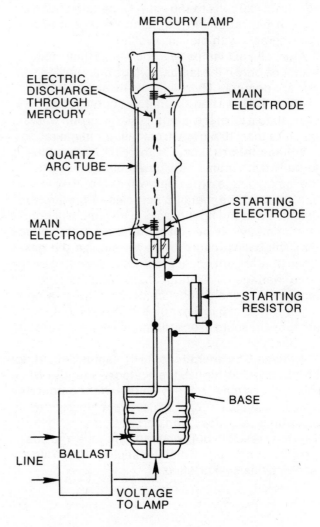

MERCURY LAMP
ELECTRIC DISCHARGE THROUGH MERCURY
MAIN ELECTRODE
QUARTZ ARC TUBE
STARTING ELECTRODE
MAIN ELECTRODE
STARTING RESISTOR
BASE
LINE
BALLAST
VOLTAGE TO LAMP

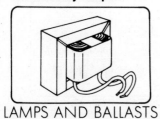

pressure sodium fixtures will result in two and one-half times more initial light generated. See Table 20 (page 25) for full efficacy comparisons of all lamp types.

Lumen Maintenance. During its life span, every electric light source changes somewhat in its electrical characteristics and light output. In a mercury lamp, the depreciation which occurs in light output is usually the result of the combined effects of physical changes occurring in the arc tube. The decline in lumens over the rated life of a mercury lamp is shown in Table 2.

Lamp Life. One of the main advantages of mercury lamps is their long lamp life. As indicated in Table 1, lamps in the 100 to 1000-watt range have average rated lives of 24,000+ hours. These ratings are based on operation with properly designed ballasts and an average of 10 or more burning hours per start. More frequent starting may reduce life significantly (Table 3).

Table 2: Mercury Lamp Lumen Depreciation

Burning Time		Percent of Initial Lumens	
Percent of Lamp Life	Hours	Vertical	Horizontal
0	0	100	100
8	2,000	94	91
17	4,000	90	88
33	8,000	83	80
50*	12,000	76	71
67	16,000	69	63
83	20,000	61	55
100	24,000	54	48

*Mean lumen value equal to the lamp lumen depreciation at 50% of the rated lamp life.

Table 3: Mercury Lamp Life vs. Hours/Start

Hours per Start	Estimated Average Lamp Life
continuous operation	24,000+
10	24,000
5	18,000
2.5	13,500
1.2	10,000

Note: The lumen depreciation percentages listed in Table 1 also apply to the estimated lamp life values listed above.

The rated lamp life of 24,000+ hours has an important meaning. Normally at average rated life, 50% of a large test group of lamps no longer operates. For mercury lamps, the point of 50% burnout occurs at a time in excess of 24,000 hours. However, the lumen output of the mercury lamp at the 24,000 hour mark has deteriorated to such a low level that this point was chosen to indicate an "economic life" based on lamp maintenance.

Color Rendering

Mercury lamps with clear outer bulbs generate the light that has a distinct greenish, white-blue appearance effect on neutral surfaces. While their color rendering is quite satisfactory in the area of blacks, whites, and grays, the scarcity of red and the high concentrations of blue, green, and yellow wavelengths make mercury lamps a poor source for producing the familiar appearances of warm colors. The atmosphere produced by clear bulb mercury lamps is very cool and greenish, while red and orange colors appear grayed. Overall, the color rendering capabilities of clear mercury lamps are very poor.

As mentioned earlier, mercury lamps are also available with phosphor coatings on the inside of their outer bulbs. When activated by the near-ultraviolet energy given out by the arc tube, these phosphors emit visible energy or light at wavelengths in the red portion of the light spectrum. This reddish light has a tendency to offset some of the greenish effect created by the mercury arc. The result is a lamp with moderate color rendering capabilities quite suitable for many indoor commercial lighting applications.

METAL HALIDE LAMPS

Metal halide lamps are the most popular HID light source for both indoor and outdoor applications. Their wide acceptance is a reflection of their excellent color rendering capability, the most natural of all HID sources. The small physical size of the metal halide arc tube leads to increased optical control. These lamps can be installed in surface or recess mounted luminaires of varying designs provided the luminaires are equipped with built-in optical control.

Applications for metal halide lamps are numerous and diverse. They include interior direct and indirect lighting for commercial, industrial, office, school, merchandising, and accent applications. Outdoors, these lamps are an effective choice for roadway illumination, parking, industrial storage and area lighting, all types of floodlighting, and sign lighting. Metal halide lamps are extremely important in the field of interior and exterior sports lighting, where meeting the requirements of optical control and color rendition are critical. In cases where optical control is not critical, phosphor coated metal halide lamps offer increased color rendering qualities.

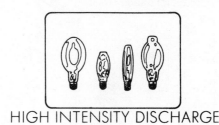

Metal Halide Lamp Design

Development of metal halide lamps stems from research conducted in the early 1960s which led to the first viable system for adding other metals to a standard mercury mixture or discharge. These additional metals improve the lamp's lighting characteristics and overall efficiency.

Metal halide lamps are distinctly similar to conventional mercury lamps in overall physical appearance with the exception of several internal design differences which can be seen by comparing Fig. 2 (page 6) and Fig. 3. The arc tube of a metal halide lamp is constructed of fused quartz and one or both of the tube ends are treated with a special reflective coating. This coating serves to redirect light energy in such a manner to achieve a more uniform temperature over the entire arc tube. This minimizes variations in lumen output and color rendering from lamp to lamp.

The arc tube contains argon as a starting gas, mercury, and one or several metal halide additives. Unlike mercury lamps, the amounts of these materials exceed those needed to stabilize the arc. Therefore, a *pool* of excess amalgam exists somewhere within the arc tube. The position of the pool is dependent on gravity and temperature. The temperature of the pool determines the lamp's color characteristics or chromaticity. It also affects the lamp's light output. Because of this, metal halide lamps, unlike mercury lamps, are sensitive to wattage variations.

A bimetal switch is also employed to short circuit the starter electrode to the adjacent main electrode after the arc has been struck. This switch must be located in the hottest portion of the lamp. When the lamp's operating position is base-up, the switch must be located close to the base. When the lamp is used in a base-down position, the bimetal switch must be positioned close to the end opposite the base.

The lamp's outer bulb is made of heat resistant glass which absorbs the ultraviolet energy generated by the arc. If the outer bulb is broken and the exposed bare arc tube continues to operate, the lamp should be turned off immediately, allowed to cool, and removed from the socket.

Metal Halide Lamp Performance

Metal halide lamps have the second highest lumen production of the three HID designs (Table 4). Although they fall short of the light production of comparable high pressure sodium lamps, these lamps operate at substantially higher efficacy than

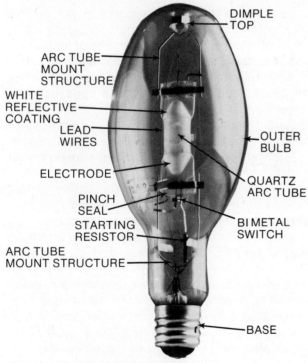

Fig. 3: The metal halide lamp.

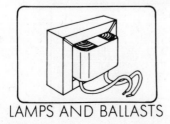

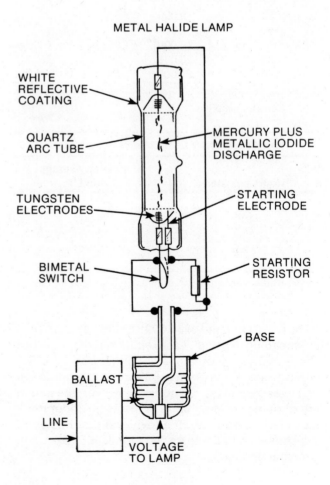

mercury lamps. For example, the approximate initial lumen output of a standard 400-watt metal halide lamp is 34,000 lumens, while the initial output of a 400-watt clear mercury lamp is approximately 21,000 lumens. While a 1000-watt metal halide lamp will initially produce around 110,000 lumens, a clear mercury lamp with a 1000-watt rating will only generate 57,000 initial lumens. In the first case, light produced per energy dollar will be about 63% more if metal halide lamps are utilized. In the latter case, light per energy dollar is almost increased by 93% through the use of metal halide lamps.

Tilt Angle. As explained in the section on lamp design, most sizes of metal halide lamps are made in two types, base-up and base-down designs. As Table 5 indicates, operating metal halide lamps at angles away from vertical can significantly decrease initial lumen output. This decrease in output must be considered in design computations when a position other than vertical is employed such as in floodlighting luminaires. Operating lamps at angles away from vertical can also adversely affect lamp life.

Lumen Maintenance. Metal halide lamps have good lumen maintenance characteristics, with the decline in light output over lamp life being gradual. The three major causes of lumen decline are:

1. Deterioration of electrodes over time.
2. Loss of transmission of the arc tube due to blackening.
3. Shifts in the chemical balance of the additive metals.

Lumen maintenance is best when the lamps are burned for longer periods of time between each start, and the best maintenance will result from continuous operation. Lumen maintenance data for several types of metal halide lamps is given in Table

Table 4: Metal Halide Lamps				
	Life Span (hours)		Initial Lumens	
Lamp Type	Vertical	Horizontal	Vertical	Horizontal
MXR175	10,000	—	16,600	—
MVR175/U	7,500	6,000	14,200	12,000
MS175/HOR*	—	10,000	—	15,000
MVR175/C/U	7,500	6,000	14,200	12,000
MS175/C/HOR*	—	10,000	—	15,000
MS175/3K/HOR*	—	10,000	—	14,000
MVR250/U	10,000	10,000	20,500	19,500
MS250/HOR*	—	10,000	—	23,000
MVR250/C/U	10,000	10,000	20,500	19,500
MS250/C/HOR*	—	10,000	—	23,000
MS250/3K/HOR*	—	10,000	—	21,500
MVR400/U	20,000	15,000	34,000	32,000
MVR400/C/U	20,000	15,000	34,000	32,000
MVR400/HOR	—	20,000	—	40,000
MVR400/C/HOR	—	20,000	—	40,000
MVR400/VBU or D	20,000	—	40,000	—
MVR400/C/VBU or D	20,000	—	40,000	—
MS400/HOR*	—	20,000	—	40,000
MS400/C/HOR*	—	20,000	—	40,000
MS400/3K/HOR*	—	20,000	—	37,000
MVR1000/U	10,000	10,000	110,000	107,800
MVR1000C/U	10,000	10,000	105,000	100,000
MVR1000/VBU or D	10,000	—	115,000	—
MS1000/VBU or D*	10,000	—	125,000	—
MVR1500/HBU-D	3,000	3,000	155,000	150,000

*Sylvania Super Metal Arc Lamps. All other lamps are General Electric.
Key: C = Phosphor Coated
         U = Universal Operating Position
    HOR = Horizontal Operating Position Only
    VBU = Vertical Base Up Only
    VBD = Vertical Base Down Only
    HBU = Horizontal Base To Base Up Positions
    HBD = Horizontal Base To Base Down Positions

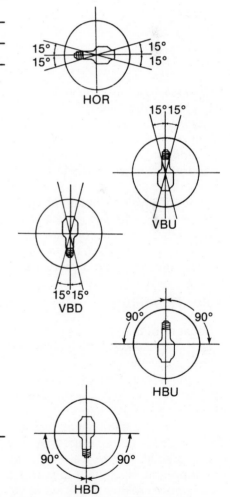

Metal halide lamp operating positions.

Table 5:   Metal Halide Lamp Tilt Factors

Operating Angle from Vertical	Percent of Initial Lumens			Operating Angle from Horizontal
	400 Watt	1000 Watt	1500 Watt	
0°	100	100	100	90°
5°	98.3	98.3	98.3	85°
10°	96.7	96.7	96.7	80°
15°	95	95	95	75°
20°	94.7	94.7	94.7	70°
25°	94.3	94.3	94.3	65°
30°	94	94	94	60°
35°	92.7	92.7	93.7	55°
40°	91.3	91.3	93.3	50°
45°	90	90	93	45°
50°	89.3	89.3	91.3	40°
55°	88.7	88.7	89.7	35°
60°	88	88	88	30°
65°	87.7	87.7	87.7	25°
70°	87.3	87.3	87.3	20°
75°	87	87	87	15°
80°	89.3	89.3	90.3	10°
85°	91.7	91.7	93.7	5°
90°	94	98	97	0°

6. There is an additional light depreciation in lamps with phosphor coatings.

Lamp Life.   Metal halide lamps have a life span rating of anywhere from 10,000 to around 20,000 hours depending on lamp type, size, and the hours of operation per start (Table 4, page 9 and Table 7, page 12).

Although lives of metal halide lamps are not as long as those of mercury lamps of the same wattages, improvements constantly being made in design and manufacturing techniques will continue to improve the life rating of metal halide lamps.

Color Rendering

Because of the properties of the added metal halides, the light waves of metal halide lamps occur at different wavelengths, a fact that enhances overall color rendering. Since sodium is the metal additive which emits light waves in the most sensitive portion of the human eye's sensitivity curve, it affects the color of metal halide lamps the most dramatically. The lamp's appearance effect on neutral surfaces is one of greenish white. It strengthens yellow, green, and blue colors, while it grays or dulls reds. The atmosphere created under metal halides is moderately cool and greenish. This crisp atmosphere is usually related to areas of higher light level and activity such as industrial plants, offices, schools, and many types of store settings.

As mentioned, variations in line voltage can affect color rendering. Operation at lower than rated wattages results in less sodium being ionized and a loss of yellow and red energy. The result is a marked shift toward green and blue in the light being emitted. Operation at higher than rated wattages results in more sodium being ionized and a more pinkish-red color rendering. Metal halide lamps also shift color as they age. A darkening of the tube ends creates a more blue-green color rendering. In modern metal halide designs, color variations from lamp to lamp are generally not a problem.

HIGH PRESSURE SODIUM (HPS) LAMPS

High pressure sodium lamps, the newest HID source to be developed, generate the greatest number of lumens per watt of all HID light sources. Due to this high efficacy, HPS lamps have become the most popular HID source for general outdoor lighting applications such as parking area, industrial storage space, and roadway lighting. HPS sources are also an excellent choice for building floodlighting and sign illumination. In addition, high pressure sodium lamps are rapidly becoming the finest economic choice for many outdoor sports lighting projects.

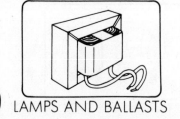

Table 6: Metal Halide Lamp Lumen Depreciation

Lamp Type and Description	Hours Burned	Percent of Initial Lumens†			
		Clear		Phosphor Coated	
		Vertical	Horizontal	Vertical	Horizontal
MXR175	100	100	—	100	—
	4,000	82	—	82	—
	8,000	73	—	73	—
	10,000	66	—	66	—
MVR175/U	100	100	100	100	100
	2,000	84	72	81	71
	4,000	74	62	71	61
	6,000	68	57	65	56
	7,500	67	—	64	—
MVR250/U MS250/HOR** MS175/HOR**	100	100	100	100	100
	2,000	93	81	87	78
	4,000	83	72	78	69
	6,000	78	67	73	64
	8,000	73	63	68	58
	10,000	68	60	64	55
MVR400/U MS400/HOR**	100	100	100	100	100
	4,000	83	79	82	77
	8,000	74	71	71	68
	12,000	69	66	66	63
	16,000	66	65	61	58
	20,000	64	64	59	57
MVR400/HOR** MVR400/VBU or D***	100	100	100	100	100
	4,000	83	83	82	82
	8,000	75	75	72	72
	12,000	64	69	66	66
	16,000	66	66	61	61
	20,000	64	64	59	59
MVR1000/U	100	100	100	100	100
	2,000	87	87	87	87
	4,000	80	80	78	78
	6,000	75	75	72	72
	8,000	73	73	68	68
	10,000	70	70	65	65
MVR1000/VBU or D MS1000/VBU or D	100	100	100	—	—
	2,000	87	87	—	—
	4,000	80	80	—	—
	6,000	75	75	—	—
	8,000	72	72	—	—
	10,000	70	70	—	—
MVR1500/HBU or D	600	95	95	—	—
	1,200	90	90	—	—
	1,800	85	85	—	—
	2,400	82	82	—	—
	3,000	80	80	—	—

†See Table 4 (page 9) for actual initial lumen output of the lamps listed above.
*Horizontal lamp life is 15,000 hours.
**For horizontal only lamps, only horizontal lumen output percentages apply.
***For MVR400/VBU or D, only vertical lumen output percentages apply.

Table 7:	Metal Halide Lamp Life vs. Hours/Start		
		Estimated Average Lamp Life	
Lamp Type	**Hours per Start**	**Vertical**	**Horizontal**
MXR175	continuous operation	10,000	—
	10	10,000	—
	5	7,500	—
	2.5	5,600	—
	1.2	4,200	—
MVR175/U	continuous operation	7,500	6,000
	10	7,500	6,000
	5	5,600	4,500
	2.5	4,200	3,400
	1.2	3,200	2,500
MVR250/U MS250/HOR MS175/HOR	continuous operation	10,000	
	10	10,000	
	5	7,500	
	2.5	5,600	
	1.2	4,200	
MVR400/U MS400/HOR	continuous operation	20,000	15,000
	10	20,000	15,000
	5	15,000	11,000
	2.5	11,000	8,500
	1.2	8,500	6,000
MVR400/HOR MVR400/UBU or D	continuous operation	20,000	
	10	20,000	
	5	15,000	
	2.5	11,000	
	1.2	8,500	
MVR1000/U	continuous operation	10,000	
	10	10,000	
	5	7,500	
	2.5	5,600	
	1.2	4,200	
MVR1000/VBU or D	continuous operation	10,000	
	10	10,000	
	5	7,500	
	2.5	5,600	
	1.2	4,200	
MVR1500/HBU or D	continuous operation	3,000	
	10	3,000	
	5	3,000	
	2.5	2,200	
	1.2	1,700	

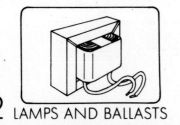

Indoors, HPS lamps are employed in both direct and indirect lighting designs for commercial, industrial, school, and sporting areas where high efficiency is of prime importance and color rendition is a secondary consideration. Many people find the lamp's golden-white coloring pleasing and relaxing, and luminaire systems equipped with both high pressure sodium and metal halide lamps have excellent coloring characteristics.

As with the other HID lamp types, high pressure sodium lamps can often be utilized in point source applications. HPS lamps must also be installed in luminaires with built-in optical control such as reflectors, refractors, lenses, or diffusers.

High Pressure Sodium Lamp Design

The heart of a high pressure sodium lamp is an arc tube constructed of a special ceramic compound (Fig. 4). This ceramic can withstand extremely high temperatures in service (1,300°C as compared to 1,000°C for quartz and 400°C for borosilicate glass). Unlike most other ceramics, it also has a high transmittance of visible wavelengths—over 90%.

Like the metal halide lamps described, high pressure sodium lamps are *excess amalgam lamps*. The amount of amalgam not held in a gaseous state remains condensed in an external amalgam reservoir located in the coolest spot in the lamp. As before, the amount of amalgam remaining in a liquid state depends upon the total energy in the arc and the arc's thermal environment. Unlike the metal halides, the lumen output of high pressure sodium lamps is not affected by the lamp's burning position or tilt angle.

The smaller diameter of the high pressure sodium arc tube does not permit the use of a starting electrode. The ballast used in conjunction with this lamp must provide this function. The ballast must contain a special starting circuit capable of ionizing the xenon across the main electrode gap by means of a low-energy, high-voltage pulse of electrical power. Most ballasts are designed so that the starting pulse ceases once this xenon arc has been struck. As the heat and pressure build up in the arc tube, more and more sodium is affected and the color shifts from bluish-white (ionized mercury and xenon), to yellow, to the final golden-white color discussed previously.

HPS Lamp Performance

The light producing efficacy of high pressure sodium lamps is up to 140 lumens per watt. This is about 50% higher efficacy than either metal halide or fluorescent sources, over twice the efficacy of mercury sources, and up to six times the efficacy of incandescent sources (Table 8, page 14 and Table 20, page 25).

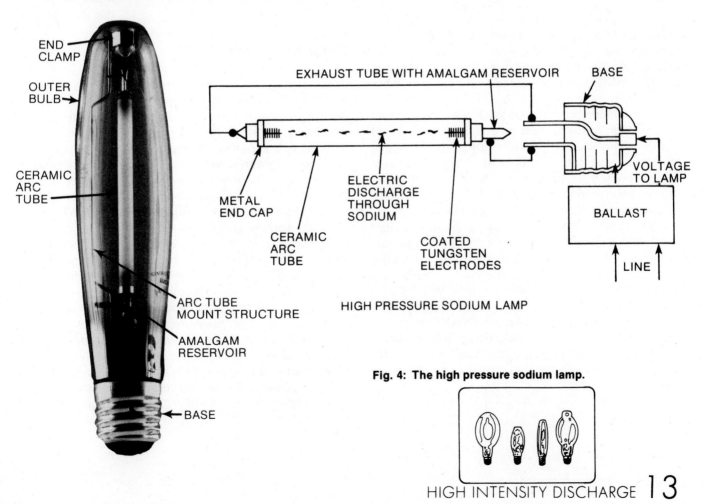

END CLAMP

OUTER BULB

CERAMIC ARC TUBE

ARC TUBE MOUNT STRUCTURE

AMALGAM RESERVOIR

BASE

EXHAUST TUBE WITH AMALGAM RESERVOIR

BASE

METAL END CAP

CERAMIC ARC TUBE

ELECTRIC DISCHARGE THROUGH SODIUM

COATED TUNGSTEN ELECTRODES

VOLTAGE TO LAMP

BALLAST

LINE

HIGH PRESSURE SODIUM LAMP

Fig. 4: The high pressure sodium lamp.

Table 8: High Pressure Sodium Lamps

Lamp Type	Life Span (hours)	Initial Lumens	
		Clear	Diffuse
35W—E17*	16,000	2,250	2,150
50W—E23-1/2	24,000	4,000	3,800
70W—E23-1/2	24,000	5,800	5,400
100W—E23-1/2	24,000	9,500	8,800
150W—E23-1/2	24,000	16,000	15,000
200W—E18	24,000	22,000	—
250W—E18	24,000	27,500	26,000
250W—E18(S)	24,000	30,000	—
310W—E18	24,000	37,000	—
400W—E18/E37	24,000	50,000	47,500
1000W—E25	24,000	140,000	—

*Med. base. All others mogul base.

Table 9: High Pressure Sodium Lamp Lumen Depreciation

Burning Time		Percent of Initial Lumens	
Percent of Lamp Life	Hours	Clear	Diffuse
0.4	100	100	100
17	4,000	98	98
33	8,000	95	95
50*	12,000	90	90
67	16,000	84	84
83	20,000	79	79
100	24,000	73	73

*Mean lumen value equal to the lamp lumen depreciation at 50% of the rated lamp life.

Table 10: High Pressure Sodium Lamp Life vs. Hours/Start

Hours per Start	Estimated Average Lamp Life
continuous operation	24,000+
10	24,000+
5	18,000
2.5	13,500
1.2	10,000

Note: Lumen maintenance and lamp life data for HPS lamps also applies for the life values in the above table.

To fully appreciate the light producing capacity of this new lamp design, consider that a 250-watt high pressure sodium fixture can replace a 400-watt mercury unit with a 50% increase in light output and a 37% reduction in energy consumption. Four-hundred-watt high pressure sodium fixtures can replace 1000-watt mercury units with only a slight sacrifice in total light output and a corresponding 60% reduction in power consumption. These comparisons can be extended to lower wattage fixtures as well.

In situations where a high lighting level is required, high pressure sodium lamps can satisfy the need at a much lower operating cost than other lamp designs. New installations also receive the additional benefits of reduced installation cost due to a reduction in the number of luminaires needed and load circuit requirements generated.

Lumen Maintenance. Of the three types of HID lamps, high pressure sodium lamps offer the finest lumen maintenance characteristics. The average mean lumens for typical high pressure sodium lamps are about 90% of the lamp's rated initial lumens. Common lumen maintenance data for high pressure sodium lamps is illustrated in Table 9.

Lamp Life. The life of a high pressure sodium lamp is dependent on the rate of lamp voltage rise. As previously mentioned, the lamp volts rise as the lamp ages, until they reach the limit of the ballast voltage available. At this point the lamp will cycle *on* and *off,* and its effective life will be over. Normal mortality for most high pressure sodium lamps will occur at approximately 24,000 hours, a range comparable to mercury lamps. As shown in Table 10, HPS lamp life is also affected by the burning time per start.

Color Rendering

As its name implies, this lamp generates basically a sodium arc which is strongest in the yellow and orange ranges of the light spectrum and weakest in the blue-green areas. For this reason, a small amount of mercury is added to the amalgam to help strengthen the blue-green wavelengths. The lamp's appearance effect on neutral surfaces is golden white, and both reds and blues appear grayed. However, the higher pressures (1 to 1.5 atmospheres) used in high pressure sodium lamps result in a more even color pattern over the yellow-orange range of the spectrum. (The essentially obsolete low pressure sodium lamps operate at considerably lower atmospheres and generate a monochromatic or single orange color which is totally unacceptable in modern applications.) While high pressure sodium lamps should still be utilized in situations where color rendering is secondary to efficacy, their golden-white color offers many new application opportunities for the designer. Design improvements are also continually improving this lamp's color rendering capabilities.

Incandescent & Fluorescent

While the increased acceptance of high intensity discharge lamps has displaced the use of incandescents in certain ambient lighting and floodlighting situations, incandescent lamps will continue to be viable sources for many applications.

INCANDESCENT LAMPS

The incandescent lamp group utilizes the simplest and oldest method of producing artificial electric light—passage of an electric current through a tungsten filament contained within a glass bulb. Edison's original lamp was an incandescent, and other than improvements in materials and manufacturing techniques, the incandescent lamp has changed little over the years.

Incandescents are the least efficient of all lamp types. Yet, sales of incandescent lamps account for nearly half of the dollars spent for large lamps each year. There are a number of reasons for the incandescent lamp's maintained popularity. Of all major lighting groups, incandescent lighting systems are the easiest to install and least expensive in terms of initial equipment investment. All incandescent lamps are available in a wide range of wattages—from as low as 2 watts in some cases up to 1000 watts and above. Incandescent lighting is also extremely flexible. In many cases, the light generated in a particular luminaire can be increased or decreased simply by changing lamp size (wattage). In contrast, the ballast and other auxiliary equipment associated with fluorescent and HID lamps often limit these systems to a single lamp wattage. In addition, incandescent lamps accent the warm colors, such as reds, oranges, and yellows, and create an atmosphere most people are accustomed to and comfortable in. The overall color rendering characteristics of incandescent lamps are very good.

For these reasons, incandescent lamps have remained the mainstay of the residential lighting industry over the years. They have strong commercial applications in areas such as accent lighting, downlighting, and task lighting. They are the finest type of lamps for the washing or grazing of textured walls or surfaces. Incandescents are often the best choice in cases where a high amount of sparkle or reflectance is desired, such as in the showcasing of glassware, silverware, or jewelry. Low level, warm atmosphere, lighting situations, such as those found in restaurants and lounges, rely heavily on incandescents. Incandescent lamps are also manufactured in numerous designs, sizes, shapes, and colors for all types of indoor and outdoor sign lighting and decorative lighting applications.

Incandescent Lamp Design

There are several types or designs of incandescent lamps. Among these are general and extended service lamps, projector (PAR) lamps, reflector (R) lamps, and elliptical reflector (ER) lamps. All of these lamp types exhibit certain common design characteristics.

Incandescent lamps can be broken down into two groups—conventional tungsten and tungsten halogen. Conventional tungsten lamps contain a tungsten filament encased in a glass bulb filled with a mixture of inert gases (Fig. 5). As an electrical current is passed through the lamp, the filament provides an impedance to electrical flow, which causes the filament to heat and glow. As the lamp operates, the tungsten filament slowly evaporates and deposits on the interior of the lamp bulb. The purpose of the inert gases, usually argon or krypton with a small amount of nitrogen, is to reduce bulb blackening caused by evaporation. Regardless of the inert gases used, the lamp bulb darkens and the lamp eventually fails due to tungsten loss.

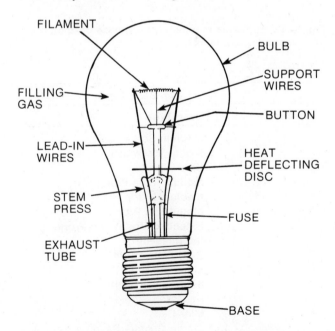

Fig. 5: The components of the conventional tungsten filament incandescent lamp.

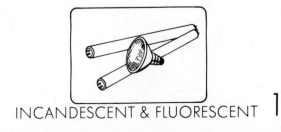

Tungsten halogen lamps attempt to reduce tungsten evaporation by introducing small amounts of bromine into the bulb atmosphere. Bromine causes the tungsten to redeposit on the filament. If the tungsten always redeposited exactly where it evaporated from, the lamp would have an infinite life. Unfortunately, this does not occur in tungsten halogen lamps. Nevertheless, lamp life is approximately twice that of conventional tungsten lamps.

Nearly all large incandescent lamps use a metal screw base (Fig. 6). The medium base is by far the most often used base. Larger general service lamps have mogul bases. Nonscrew type bases, such as the bayonet type, have been developed where accurate positioning of the filament is necessary, as in spotlighting applications. Lamp base types are listed in Table 11.

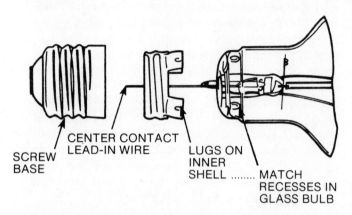

Fig. 6: **Components of a metal screw base used on most large incandescent lamps.**

Table 11:   Lamp Base Types

Abbreviation	Base Type
Med	Medium Screwshell
Mog	Mogul Screwshell
ST	Screw Terminal
MSP	Medium Side Prong
Med Bi Pin	Medium Bi Pin
MEP	Mogul End Prong
EMEP	Extended Mogul End Prong
Inter	Intermediate
BPM	Bi Pin Miniature
Mini Bi Pin	Miniature Bi Pin
4 Pin	4 Pins Clustered
RSC	Recessed Single Contact
MC	Mini-Can
SC Bay	Single Contact Bayonet
DC Bay	Double Contact Bayonet

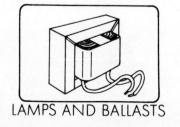

Incandescent Lamp Performance

The efficacy of incandescent light sources is the lowest of all modern light groups. Lamps for general service have ratings ranging from 15 to 25 lumens/watt. When lighting efficiency is of primary concern, the HID light source is a logical choice over any type of incandescent system.

Filament evaporation throughout the lamp's life results in a thinner filament which consumes less power and produces less light. The curve shown in Fig. 7 illustrates the range of lumen depreciation among typical incandescent lamp designs. As shown, most incandescents are still producing between 80% and 90% of their initial lumens at the termination of their rated life.

The average rated life spans of conventional tungsten and tungsten halogen lamps are listed in the various tables on the following pages. As you can see, these life ratings are considerably shorter than those associated with either HID or fluorescent light sources.

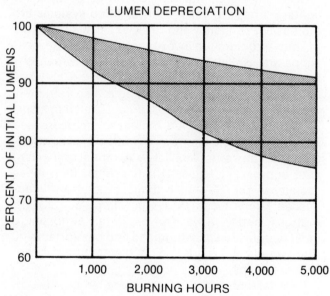

Fig. 7: **Incandescent lamp lumen depreciation characteristics.**

GENERAL AND EXTENDED SERVICE LAMPS

General and extended service lamps are those designed with the familiar teardrop or pear-shaped bulb (Fig. 8). While these lamps are available in an extremely wide range of wattages (5 to 10,000 in special cases), the characteristics of those most commonly used in commercial and residential appli-

Watts	Bulb Type	Base Type	Designation	Initial Lumens	Average Rated Life (hours)	Color Temperature (degrees Kelvin)	Color Rendering Index
15	A15	Med	15A15	126	2,500	—	—
25	A19	Med	25A	235	2,500	2,550	—
40	A19	Med	40A	455	1,500	2,650	—
50	A19	Med	50A	680	1,000	—	—
60	A19	Med	60A	860	1,000	2,790	—
75	A19	Med	75A	1,180	750	2,840	—
100	A19	Med	100A	1,740	750	2,905	97
100	A21	Med	100A21	1,690	750	2,880	—
150	A21	Med	150A	2,880	750	2,960	—
150	A23	Med	150A23	2,780	750	2,925	—
200	A23	Med	200A	4,000	750	2,980	—
200	PS25	Med	200/PS25	3,800	750	—	—
200	PS30	Med	200/IF	3,700	750	2,925	—
300	PS30	Med	300M/IF	6,100	750	3,000	97
300	PS30	Mog	300AX/IF	5,960	1,000	—	—
300	PS35	Mog	300/IF	5,860	1,000	2,980	—

Table 12: General Service Incandescent Lamps (115, 120, and 125 Volts)

Energy Efficient General Service Lamps (120, 130 Volts)

Watts	Bulb Type	Base Type	Designation	Initial Lumens	Average Rated Life (hours)
34	A19	Med	40A/34	410	1,500
52	A19	Med	60A/52	800	1,000
67	A19	Med	75A/67	1,130	750
90	A21	Med	100A/90	1,620	750
135	A21	Med	150A/135	2,580	750

Notes: 1. Lamp lumen depreciation is measured as the percentage of initial lumens produced after the lamp has been in service for 70% of its rated life. For general service lamps, an average of 87% of initial lumens are still generated at this point in lamp life.

2. Color temperature, color rendering index, lamp wattage, initial lumens, and lumen depreciation are based upon operation at the lamp's rated voltage.

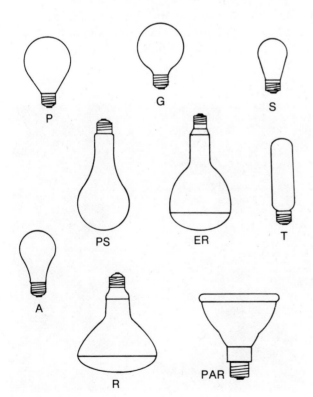

Incandescent lamp bulb shapes.

Fig. 8: Various general and extended service lamps.

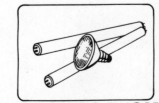

Watts	Bulb Type	Base Type	Designation	Initial Lumens	Average Rated Life (hours)
15	A-15	Med	15A15	125	2,500
40	A-19	Med	40A/99	420	2,500
60	A-19	Med	60A/99	775	2,500
75	A-19	Med	75A/99	1,000	2,500
100	A-19	Med	100A/99	1,490	2,500
100	A-21	Med	100A21/99	1,450	2,500
150	A-23	Med	100A23/99	2,350	2,500
160	PS-25	Med	150/99	2,300	2,500
200	A-23	Med	200A/99	3,410	2,500
200	A-25	Med	200A25/99	3,250	2,500
200	PS-25	Med	200PS25/99XL	3,220	2,500
200	PS-30	Med	200/99	3,260	2,500
300	PS-30	Med	300M/99	5,190	2,500
300	PS-35	Mog	300/99	5,190	2,500

Notes: 1. Lamp lumen depreciation is measured as the percentage of initial lumens produced after the lamp has been in service for 70% of its rated life. For extended service lamps, an average of 87% of initial lumens are still generated at this point in lamp life.

2. Lamp wattage, initial lumens, and lumen depreciation are based upon operation at the lamp's rated voltage.

3. Color temperature and the color rendering index are essentially the same as those of general service lamps of similar wattages.

cations are listed in Tables 12 and 13. These incandescents must be used in luminaires with built-in optical control such as those equipped with lenses, reflectors, refractors, or diffusers. Traditionally the major light source for residential lighting, general and extended service lamps also find use in certain types of office, retail, accent, task, and commercial area lighting.

PROJECTOR (PAR) LAMPS

Projector lamps are directional light sources with built-in reflectors for optical control. This means PAR lamps are extremely efficient in baffled or dark cone downlights, louvered units, and other interior and exterior luminaires which do not have built-in optical control. They are available in a wide range of wattages and beam spreads (Table 14). Applications for these lamps include general interior and downlighting, such as track lighting, decorative lighting in color, and display lighting. It is also possible to use projector lamps for building floodlighting and landscape lighting. Depending on the application, fixtures for these lamps range from simple lamp holders to precision engineered luminaires designed to control brightness and assure visual comfort.

Bulbs for projector lamps are made of hard, heat resistant glass that is pressed into two molds, one for the reflector portion of the lamp and one which forms the lens (Fig. 9). The reflector portion is thinly coated with aluminum, the inner workings are mounted in place, and the two sections are then fused together. The result is a lamp with better beam control than reflector lamps. In addition, many PARs are weather resistant.

Fig. 9: Projector or PAR lamp design.

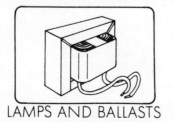

Table 14: Projector, Reflector, and Elliptical Reflector Lamps

Projector (PAR) Lamps

Watts	Bulb Type	Base Type	Volts	Designation and Description	Average Rated Life (hours)	Beam Spread (degrees at 10% of Maximum Candlepower)	Average Maximum Candlepower (candelas)	Beam Initial Lumens	Total Initial Lumens
25	PAR36	ST	5.5	25PAR36VNSP	1,000	4.5° × 5.5°	30,000	—	—
25	PAR36	ST	12	25PAR36NSP	2,000	17° × 19°	4,500	—	—
25	PAR36	ST	12	25PAR36WFL	2,000	41° × 44°	500	—	—
25	PAR36	ST	12	25PAR36VWFL	2,000	80° × 82°	250	—	—
25	PAR46	ST	5.5	25PAR36VNSP	1,000	4.5° × 5.5° *	55,000	—	—
50	PAR36	ST	12	50PAR36VNSP	2,000	5.5° × 5.5°	20,160	—	—
50	PAR36	ST	12	50PAR36NSP (Z3)†	2,000	17° × 20°	9,200	—	—
50	PAR36	ST	12	50PAR36WFL	2,000	41° × 48°	1,300	—	—
50	PAR36	ST	12	50PAR36VWFL	2,000	80° × 80°	600	—	—
75	PAR38	Med/MSP	120	75PAR38/SP	2,000	27° × 27°	4,500	540	760
75	PAR38	Med/MSP	120	75PAR38/FL	2,000	57° × 57°	1,750	690	765
150	PAR38	Med/MSP	120	150PAR38/SP	2,000	28° × 28°	11,500	1,200	1,740
150	PAR38	Med/MSP	120	150PAR38/FL	2,000	60° × 60°	4,000	1,690	1,740
200	PAR46	MSP	120	200PAR46/3NSP	2,000	19° × 23°	31,000	1,000	2,300
200	PAR46	MSP	120	200PAR46/3MFL	2,000	23° × 38°	11,500	1,300	2,300
300	PAR56	MEP	120	300PAR56/NSP	2,000	14° × 20°	68,000	1,800	3,840
300	PAR56	MEP	120	300PAR56/MFL	2,000	19° × 34°	24,000	2,100	3,840
300	PAR56	MEP	120	300PAR56/WFL	2,000	28° × 53°	11,000	2,200	3,840
500	PAR64	EMEP	120	500PAR64/NSP	2,000	14° × 19°	110,000	3,000	6,500
500	PAR64	EMEP	120	500PAR64/MFL	2,000	19° × 35°	37,000	3,300	6,500
500	PAR64	EMEP	120	500PAR64/WFL	2,000	32° × 55°	13,000	3,400	6,500

Reflector (R) Lamps

Watts	Bulb Type	Base Type	Volts	Designation and Description	Average Rated Life (hours)	Beam Spread (degrees at 10% of Maximum Candlepower)	Average Maximum Candlepower (candelas)	Beam Initial Lumens	Total Initial Lumens
15	R14	SC Bay	12	15R14SC/SP	2,000	31°	800	—	140
15	R14	SC Bay	12	15R14SC/FL	2,000	102°	120	─┐	140
25	R14	SC Bay	12	25R14SC/SP	2,000	32°	1,200	—	230
25	R14	SC Bay	12	25R14SC/FL	2,000	102°	200	—	235
25	R14	Inter	120	25R14/N (Z11)†	1,500	120°	150	—	190
25	R12	Inter	120	25R12/N	1,500	160°	90	—	200
30	R20	Med	120	30R20/FL	2,000	92°	300	170	210
40	R16	Med	120	40R16/FL (Z9)†	1,000	80°**	180	—	445
50	R20	Med	120	50R20/FL	2,000	95°	530	350	440
75	R30	Med	120	75R30/SP	2,000	78°	1,540	760	900
75	R30	Med	120	75R30/FL	2,000	136°	400	730	900
100	R25	Med	120	100R25/FL (Z10)†	2,000	70°	60	—	1,400
150	R40	Med	120	150R/SP	2,000	49°	5,400	1,550	1,900
150	R40	Med	120	150R/FL	2,000	124°	1,040	1,650	1,900
300	R40	Med	120	300R/SP	2,000	60°	8,900	3,100	3,650
300	R40	Med	120	300R/FL	2,000	123°	1,950	3,200	3,650

Elliptical Reflector (ER) Lamps

Watts	Bulb Type	Base Type	Volts	Designation and Description	Average Rated Life (hours)	Beam Spread (degrees at 10% of Maximum Candlepower)	Average Maximum Candlepower (candelas)	Beam Initial Lumens	Total Initial Lumens
50	ER30	Med	120	50ER30	2,000	—	—	—	525
75	ER30	Med	120	75ER30	2,000	70°	1,800	748	850
120	ER40	Med	120	120ER40	2,000	76°	2,900	—	1,475

*At 50% of maximum candlepower (used in Pinspot track luminaires).

**At 50% of maximum candlepower.

†Halo Lighting catalog number.

Notes: 1. For PAR lamp beam spreads, the vertical angle is listed before the horizontal angle.

2. Lamp lumen depreciation and color temperatures are approximately the same as those given for general service lamps in Table 12 (page 17).

REFLECTOR (R) AND ELLIPTICAL REFLECTOR (ER) LAMPS

Reflector and elliptical reflector lamps have built-in reflectors. They are most efficient in luminaires with partial or no optical control, such as multiplying cone downlights. Both lamp types are used for commercial general lighting needs, display lighting, wall washing, decorative lighting, and supplementary lighting.

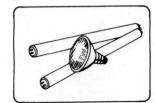

Bulbs of reflector lamps are mold blown, and most are made of soft glass intended for interior applications (Fig. 10A). Some R lamps are available in hard, heat resistant glass for indoor applications where contact with moisture is possible or in outdoor applications if adequate protection against the elements is provided. The inner surface of the bulb is thinly coated with silver which has higher reflectance than aluminum. Bulbs can be frosted to attain beam diffusion.

As their name implies, the reflector bulbs of elliptical reflector lamps are elliptical rather than parabolic in contour (Fig. 10B). This shape focuses the light reflected from the bulb wall at a point external to the lamp (Fig. 10C).

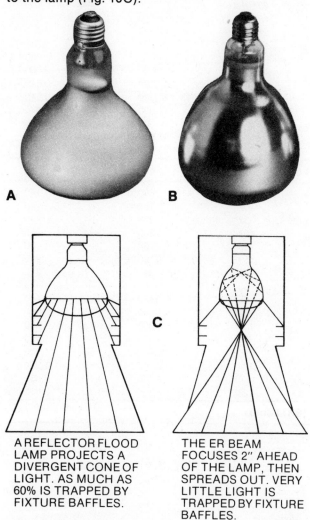

A REFLECTOR FLOOD LAMP PROJECTS A DIVERGENT CONE OF LIGHT. AS MUCH AS 60% IS TRAPPED BY FIXTURE BAFFLES.

THE ER BEAM FOCUSES 2" AHEAD OF THE LAMP, THEN SPREADS OUT. VERY LITTLE LIGHT IS TRAPPED BY FIXTURE BAFFLES.

Fig. 10: (A) Standard reflector lamp, (B) the elliptical reflector lamp design, and (C) the light pattern produced by each type. Note how the ER lamp focuses the light at a point some 2" ahead of the lamp and then spreads it out. In this way, very little light is trapped inside the fixture.

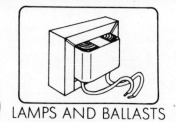

The advantages of such a light beam (Table 14) are apparent in stacked-baffle and stepped-ring downlights, pinhole and small aperture spotlights, and in other luminaire designs which trap a high percentage of the light emitted by the lamp. ER lamps dramatically increase the amount of light emitted from these luminaires. For instance, in some deep-baffle downlights, use of the 75-watt ER lamp in place of a 150-watt reflector flood lamp provides useful light while cutting energy consumption by one-half.

The elliptical bulb shape also gives the ER lamp a relatively low brightness when seen from normal viewing angles (as compared to reflector lamps of comparable or even higher wattages). In shallow downlights, ER lamps should be chosen over reflector lamps for increased visual comfort.

Special Application Incandescents

Incandescent lamps are manufactured in a wide variety of decorative and special purpose designs. Table 15 lists just a few of the lamps used for decorative, showcase, step, corridor, and exit lighting.

TUNGSTEN HALOGEN LAMPS

Lamps utilizing the tungsten halogen design offer the advantages of longer lamp life, better maintenance, and increased light output when compared to conventional incandescents. Single end T- or tube-type designs (Table 16) are commonly used to replace general and extended service A- and PS-type lamps. They must be used in fixtures with built-in optical control, and applications include many types of interior lighting, stage and studio lighting, and some exterior floodlighting.

Tungsten halogen PAR lamps are used in fixtures requiring no optical control. These lamps can replace conventional PAR, R, and ER lamps with substantial economic savings. Tungsten halogen PARs (Fig. 11) can be used for all types of commercial interior lighting as well as some industrial and exterior floodlighting, and fountain lighting applications. Special purpose reflector lamps (Table 17, page 22) are extremely effective in high and low level accent lighting and special display applications.

FLUORESCENT LAMPS

Fluorescent lamps are extremely popular, useful, and diverse lamps with numerous residential and commercial applications. They are used for both general and task lighting and are currently the most

Table 15: Decorative and Special Purpose Incandescent Lamps

Incandescent Decorative Lamps

Watts	Bulb	Base	Volts	Average Rated Life (hours)	Initial Lumens
25	G25	Medium	120	1,500	240
40	G40	Medium	120	2,500	348
60	G40	Medium	120	2,500	576
100	G40	Medium	120	2,500	1,230
150	G40	Medium	120	2,500	—

Incandescent Special Purpose* Lamps

Watts	Bulb	Base	Volts	Average Rated Life (hours)	Initial Lumens
6	S-6	Inter	120	1,500	44
20	T6-1/2	DC Bay	120	10,000+	92
25	T-10	Medium	120	1,000	248
40	T-10	Medium	120	1,000	420
60	T-10	Medium	120	1,000	745

*Showcases, steps, corridors, exits.

Table 16: Tungsten Halogen (Quartz) Lamps (Single End Design)

Watts	Bulb Type	Base Type	Volts	Designation	Average Rated Life (hours)	Initial Lumens	Color Temperature (degrees Kelvin)
100	T4 Clear	DC Bay or MC	120	Q100CL/MC or DC	1,000	1,800	—
100	T4 Frosted	DC Bay or MC	120	Q100/MC or DC	1,000	1,750	—
150	T4 Clear	DC Bay or MC	120	Q150CL/MC or DC (Z19)†	1,500	2,800	3,000
150	T4 Frosted	DC Bay or MC	120	Q150/MC or DC	1,500	2,700	3,000
250	T4 Clear	DC Bay or MC	120	Q250 CL/MC or DC	2,000	5,000	2,950
250	T4 Frosted	DC Bay or MC	120	Q250/MC or DC	2,000	4,800	2,950

†Halo Lighting catalog number.

Note: Lamp lumen depreciation is measured as the percentage of initial lumens produced after the lamp has been in service for 70% of its rated life. For 100- and 150-watt tungsten halogen lamps, an average of 93% of initial lumens are still generated at this point in lamp life. For 250-watt lamps, this percentage is 97%.

Fig. 11: Cross section of a tungsten halogen incandescent PAR lamp.

popular lamp used in office lighting. However, the overall advantages of both direct and indirect HID lighting systems are reducing the use of fluorescents in many indoor industrial, commercial, office, and school lighting systems. Also, certain design problems, such as decreased light output in colder temperatures and poor beam control, have virtually eliminated fluorescent lamps from modern exterior applications.

Fluorescent luminaires must have built-in optical control, such as reflectors or reflectors with lenses or diffusers. Luminaires can be either surface or recess mounted and are usually considerably larger than those used for incandescent lamps. Due to their larger size, fluorescents cannot be considered for use as a point source.

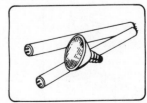

Parabolic Projector Lamps

Watts	Bulb Type	Base Type	Volts	Designation and Description	Average Rated Life (hours)	Beam Spread at 10% of Maximum Candlepower	Average Maximum Candlepower** Candelas	Initial Lumens	Color Temperature (degrees Kelvin)
250	PAR38	Med	120	Q250PAR38/SP	6,000	24° × 24°	40,000	3,200	2,900
250	PAR38	Med	120	Q250PAR38/FL	6,000	60° × 60°	7,000	3,200	2,900
500	PAR56	MEP	120	Q500PAR56NSP	4,000	15° × 32°	96,000*	8,000	2,950
500	PAR56	MEP	120	Q500PAR56MFL	4,000	20° × 42°	43,000	8,000	2,950
500	PAR56	MEP	120	Q500PAR56WFL	4,000	34° × 66°	19,000	8,000	2,950

Special Purpose MR-16 Reflector Lamps

Watts	Bulb Type	Base Type	Volts	Designation and Description	Average Rated Life (hours)	Beam Spread at 10% of Maximum Candlepower	Average Maximum Candlepower** Candelas	Initial Lumens	Color Temperature (degrees Kelvin)
20	MR-16	BPM	12	ESXNSP (Z30)†	2,000	12° × 14°	3,500	—	2,925
20	MR-16	BPM	12	BABFL (Z35)†	2,000	38° × 36°	500	—	2,925
42	MR-16	BPM	12	EPZNSP (Z20)†	5,000	12° × 15°	5,900	—	3,020
42	MR-16	BPM	12	EYRNSP* (Z20)†	2,500	12.5° × 15°	5,900	—	3,000
42	MR-16	BPM	12	EYSSP* (Z25)†	2,500	21° × 22°	2,200	—	3,000
42	MR-16	BPM	12	EYSNFL (Z25)†	3,000	23° × 24°	2,200	—	3,000
50	MR-16	BPM	12	EXTNSP —	3,000	12° × 14°	10,200	—	3,025
50	MR-16	BPM	12	EXZNFL (Z26)†	3,000	21° × 27°	3,350	—	3,025
50	MR-16	BPM	12	EXNFL (Z31)†	3,000	38° × 39°	1,600	—	3,050
75	MR-16	BPM	12	EYENSP	3,500	12° × 13°	14,500	—	3,050
75	MR-16	BPM	12	EYCFL	3,500	39° × 39°	2,200	—	3,050

†Halo Lighting catalog number.
*Sylvania Lamps. All others listed are General Electric.
**Average in 5° cone for narrow spot (NSP) and spot (SP), 10° cone for flood (FL).
Notes: 1. For beam spreads, the vertical angle is listed before the horizontal angle.
2. Lamp lumen depreciation is measured as a percentage of initial lumens produced after the lamp has been in service for 70% of its rated life. For 250-watt PAR, this percentage is 93%. For 500-watt PAR, the average is 94%.

Fluorescent Lamp Design

A fluorescent lamp is a low-pressure mercury arc discharge light source (Fig. 12). As with high intensity discharge lamps, fluorescent lamps require the use of a correctly matched ballast to limit and regulate current flow. The lamp itself consists of a closed tube containing two cathodes, a filling gas such as argon, and a small amount of mercury. Three designs are available: T, or straight tubular; U-shaped tubular; and C, or circline (Fig. 13). The inside of the tube is coated with a special phosphor depending on the color characteristics desired. When current is supplied to the lamp in proper amounts, an arc is struck between the two cathodes. This arc emits energy which the phosphor coating on the tube converts into usable light.

Fluorescent lamps can be classified as preheat lamps, which require an automatic starter for operation, or as instant start and rapid start lamps which require no starters.

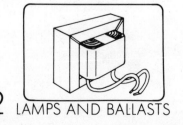

Fig. 12: Components of the fluorescent lamp design.

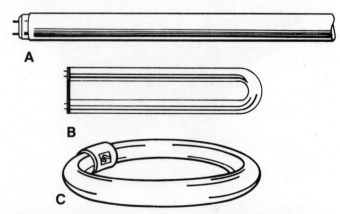

Fig. 13: The three types of fluorescent lamp shapes: (A) T, or straight tubular; (B) U-shaped tubular; and (C) C, or circline.

Fluorescent Lamp Performance

Some of the advantages of fluorescent lamps include good efficacy and lumen maintenance, long lamp life, and a relatively low brightness and heat content when compared to incandescents and other light sources with smaller surface areas (Table 18). The efficacy of these lamps averages between 55 and 80 lumens/watt, considerably higher than conventional tungsten and halogen incandescents and mercury lamps but lower than the metal halide and high pressure sodium HID lamp designs. The average rated lamp life of fluorescent lamps can be above 20,000 hours. However, frequent starting cycles will considerably shorten lamp life (Table 19). Color rendering can vary between specific lamp designs, but fluorescent lamps are available to create cool, neutral, or warm color atmospheres. The lamp's large physical size and poor beam control are the major limiting factors of its use.

Table 18: Fluorescent Lamps

Watts	Bulb Type	Base Type	Designation	Average Rated Life (hours)	Initial Lumens
8	T-51	Mini Bi Pin	F8T5/CW	7,500	400
8	T-51	Mini Bi Pin	F8T5/WW	7,500	400
14	T-6U	4 Pin	FUL14/CW	7,500	680
14	T-6U	4 Pin	FUL14/WW**	7,500	680
22	T-9C	4 Pin	FC8T9/CW/RS	12,000	1,100
32	T-10C	4 Pin	FC12T10/CW/RS	12,000	1,910
40	T-10C	4 Pin	FC16T10/CW/RS	12,000	2,640
34*	T-12	Med Bi Pin	F40CW/RS/WM	20,000+	2,850
34*	T-12	Med Bi Pin	F40WW/RS/WM	20,000+	2,850
34*	T-12	Med Bi Pin	F40CWX/RS/WM	20,000+	2,000
34*	T-12	Med Bi Pin	F40WWX/RS/WM	20,000+	1,900
40	T-12	Med Bi Pin	F40CW	20,000+	3,150
40	T-12	Med Bi Pin	F40WW	20,000+	3,150
40	T-12	Med Bi Pin	F40CWX	20,000+	2,200
40	T-12	Med Bi Pin	F40WWX	20,000+	2,150
40	T-12U	Med Bi Pin	F40CW/U	12,000+	2,900

*Energy saving lamps.

**3,000° K Color temperature.

Note: Lamp lumen depreciation is measured as the percentage of initial lumens produced when the lamp has been in service for 40% of its rated lamp life. For fluorescent lamps, the average percent of initial lumens generated at this point is 87%.

Table 19: Rapid Start Fluorescents— Average Life vs. Hours/Start

Hours per Start	Estimated Average Lamp Life (hours)
continuous operation	28,500
20	27,000
15	25,000
10	23,000
6	20,000
3	16,000

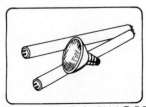

Lamp Comparisons

Previous sections contain detailed information concerning each of the three main lamp groups—high intensity discharge, incandescent, and fluorescent. The main purpose of this section will be to summarize much of this data and draw some fundamental comparisons between lamp groups.

Lamp Life and Efficacy Comparisons. Long lamp life and good efficacy (lumens produced/watt of electrical energy consumed) are desirable characteristics in any lighting system. They are often the number one consideration in outdoor area lighting, roadway lighting, and many forms of industrial and commercial illumination. Table 20 summarizes the life ranges and efficacies of the various lamp types. Note the particularly fine characteristics of the HID lamp group, especially the high pressure sodium and metal halide designs. Fluorescents fare better than mercury lamp designs, and fluorescents and all HIDs outdistance both conventional and tungsten halogen incandescents in terms of lamp life and light producing efficacy.

Cost Comparison. Energy, maintenance, and initial costs have a strong bearing on the overall viability of a lighting system. Steady, substantial increases in the cost of electrical power have made energy costs the prime economic consideration in lighting design. Maintenance costs such as relamping and luminaire cleaning expenses follow in importance. Surprisingly, initial equipment and installation costs are the least important of all major economic factors.

How much electrical power do the lamps and auxiliary equipment consume? Do they utilize this power effectively? Are the luminaires easily accessible for maintenance? Will the use of high mountings force pole costs to unreasonably high levels?

These are questions every lighting designer must answer accurately. The lamp efficacies listed in Table 20 give a good idea of the lamp's overall efficiency. Table 21 presents a more complete economic comparison. The table includes the three major cost factors involved in lamp selection—energy, maintenance, and initial—and assigns a point value

to each cost. Energy costs are assigned three points, maintenance two points, and initial costs a single point. This means that in terms of economic significance, energy costs are three times as important as initial costs, while maintenance costs are twice as significant as initial costs and two-thirds as significant as energy costs.

The three costs are also assigned comparative impact weight values. These values rank the significance of economic costs among the lamp types. Higher numbers denote increased significance. For example, energy costs are most significant (6) in incandescent systems and least significant (1) in HPS systems. Fluorescents rank third in terms of energy costs, etc.

Both the cost point values and the impact weight values are used to obtain an overall weighted cost (WC) factor for each lamp design. The WC factor is obtained by multiplying the cost point value of each individual cost by the impact weight value assigned that cost and adding the three values.

For example: Fluorescent Lamp Weight Cost Factor =

$$
\begin{array}{rcl}
\text{Energy—}3 \times 3 &=& 9 \\
\text{Maintenance—}4 \times 2 &=& 8 \\
\text{Initial—}3 \times 1 &=& 3 \\
\hline
&& 20
\end{array}
$$

The impact weight values and the weighted cost factors should be used for *general* economic comparisons. Details for making a precise economic analysis of a particular lighting design, either proposed or existing, can be found in **Section IV: System Maintenance and Economics**.

COLOR RENDERING COMPARISONS

Color is not a property that is a physical part of a viewed object. It is simply the effect of light waves bouncing off or passing through the object. The color of an object is determined by numerous factors including the characteristics of the light source under which it is viewed; the way the object absorbs, transmits, or reflects the light waves striking it; the environmental surroundings; the physical condition of the viewer's eye; and perhaps most importantly, the viewer's psychological mood, viewing experience, and color bias.

Because light and color are integral parts of everyday life, lighting designers must work up systems which produce sufficient quantities of *quality* light, that light which naturally renders the color of familiar objects. This task is made more difficult by the fact that "natural" color is a highly subjective quality. Largely due to our familiarity with them, incandescent light sources are generally regarded as producing the most natural color rendering.

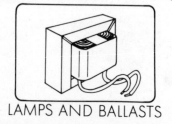

Table 20: Lamp Types—Life and Efficacy Comparisons

Type	Life Range (hours)	Efficacy (lumens/watt) Range
Incandescent Conventional Tungsten	750 to 4,000	15 to 25
Incandescent Tungsten Halogen	1,000 to 6,000	15 to 25
Fluorescent	5,000 to 20,000	55 to 80
HID Mercury	16,000 to 24,000	50 to 60
HID Metal Halide	10,000 to 20,000	80 to 125
HID High Pressure Sodium	16,000 to 24,000	70 to 140

Table 21: Lighting System Cost Comparison

Lamp Group	Impact Weight Values			Weighted Cost Factor
	Energy Costs (3 points)	Maintenance Costs (2 points)	Initial Costs (1 point)	
Incandescent Conventional Tungsten	6	6	1	31
Incandescent Tungsten Halogen	5	5	2	27
Fluorescent	3	4	3	20
HID Mercury	4	2	4	20
HID Metal Halide	2	3	5	17
HID High Pressure Sodium	1	1	6	11

While individual color preferences can strongly affect a person's reaction to the surrounding environment, some color reactions are considered universal. For instance, warm colors such as reds, oranges, and yellows are generally accepted as stimulating, while cool colors such as blues, blue-violets, and violets are considered calming colors.

When the "proper" appearance of people is important, there is a strong unconscious preference for white light sources which are rich in red light. These lamps help impart a healthy, ruddy, or tanned impression of the skin and flatter the complexion. There also are indications that people prefer warm light in areas where lower levels of illumination are involved, while cool light seems to be more acceptable for higher levels.

Where stronger, more saturated colors are involved, people generally agree that warm colors appear to advance, while cool colors recede and help support a feeling of spaciousness. In a more subtle sense, light color can alter the psychological mood of an area and create the impressions associated with warm sunlight, cool shadows, or many other familiar experiences. As a lighting designer, you must always remember that people invariably feel the psychological impact of light and color.

Colorimetry is the science of measuring and systematically designating colors. While many color measurement systems have been devised, the two most useful for comparing light source color are color temperature, or chromaticity, and the color rendering index.

Color Temperature

All objects will emit light if they are heated to a sufficiently high temperature. Also, as an object is raised in temperature, the color of the light emitted from it will change. An iron bar, for example, appears dull red when first heated, then red-orange, then white, and finally blue-white as it is heated hotter and hotter. In the same way, a tungsten filament in an incandescent lamp changes color when different voltages are applied. This phenomenon was studied by Max Planck in 1900 and is the basis for his law of blackbody radiators. A blackbody radiator is an object which will absorb all light falling upon it. A radiator is absolutely black at room temperature, red at 800° K, yellow at 3,000° K, white at 5,000° K, pale blue at 8,000° K, and brilliant blue at 60,000° K.

The law of blackbody radiators can be used to designate the relative color temperature of any heated object. A color temperature designation, applied to a light source, refers to the absolute temperature in degrees Kelvin of a blackbody whose color appearance matches that of the source in question. Tungsten filament lamps used for general lighting have color temperatures in the 2,600° K to 3,100° K range. Low wattage lamps used where luminance is

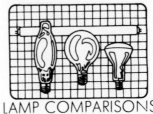

Lamp		Color Effects		Color Temperature Degrees Kelvin	Color Rendering Index
Type	Watts	Accents	Grays		
Incandescent Conventional Tungsten	300	warm colors	blues	3,000	97
Incandescent Tungsten Halogen	250	warm colors	blues	3,000	97
Fluorescent Cool White	40	yellows, blues, greens	reds	4,200	66
Fluorescent Warm White	40	yellows, greens	reds, blues	4,200	89
Fluorescent Cool White Deluxe	40	all colors	no colors	3,000	52
Fluorescent Warm White Deluxe	40	yellows, oranges, reds	blues	2,900	73
Mercury Deluxe White	100-400	reds, yellows, blues, greens	deep reds	3,900	46
Mercury Deluxe Warm White	100-400	reds, oranges, yellows, greens	deep reds, blues	3,000	52
Metal Halide Clear	175-400	yellows, greens, blues	reds	4,000-4,500	65
Metal Halide Coated	175-400	yellows, greens, blues, reds	deep reds	3,700-3,900	70
High Pressure Sodium Diffuse	100-400	yellows, oranges	deep reds, greens, blues	2,100	32
High Pressure Sodium Diffuse Deluxe	250	yellows, oranges, greens	deep reds, blues	2,400	65
Combined MH Coated/HPS Diffuse	400/250	all colors	deep reds	3,000	65

not too important operate at about 2,000° K. Such lamps as TV and studio floods operate in the 3,100° K to 3,400° K range. In most cases, actual filament temperature is slightly lower than the apparent color temperature. The complete color temperature spectrum is illustrated on page 3.

Technically, a "color temperature" designation can only apply to incandescent sources, and as such, it is a specification of both the degree of whiteness and the spectral energy composition of the source. However, the term "apparent color temperature" is often used to specify the degree of whiteness of fluorescent lamps as well as the HID types.

Unfortunately, the apparent color temperature of any light source does not give an indication of how well that light source will render certain colors. As illustrated in Table 22, two different light sources can have the same color temperature but accent and gray entirely different colors.

Color Rendering Index (CRI)

The color rendering index systematically indicates how well a light source renders colors. The

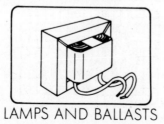

CRI assigns a numerical value between 1 and 100 to a given source as a means of comparing it to a reference source whose CRI value is 100. In most cases, the reference source closely resembles the common incandescent lamp. Like the color temperature system, the CRI system is also limited because it is meaningful only if the two sources being compared on the index scale have the same chromaticity or color temperature (within 100-300° K).

For example, it would not be meaningful to compare the CRI of an incandescent lamp having a 2,900° K value with a cool white fluorescent lamp having a 4,200° K value. However, a comparison between two different cool white fluorescents would be relevant because they have the same chromaticity value. The color rendering index values of various lamps are given in Table 22.

Selecting a Lamp Color

The most often used method of selecting a lamp based on its color rendering qualities is to first select a general color temperature range. Base this selected temperature range on the amount of warmth or coolness you wish to create in the lighted area. Low temperatures accent the warm colors such as red, orange, and yellow. Higher temperatures accent cool colors such as greens and blues. The next step is to locate all the lamps which fall within this range and to choose the lamp with the highest color rendering index number. When other qualities such as optimum lumen production or low maintenance cost are equally or more important, it may become necessary to adjust this choice to attain the best overall balance of the desired qualities. In general, lamps with better color rendering produce less light per watt of power consumed.

Another extremely important factor to consider is the color scheme of the area to be lighted. The lamps selected should always complement or accent the colors found in the area. By looking at Table 22, you can see that high pressure sodium diffuse lamps would work well in an office area decorated in yellows, oranges, and other earth tones. Using HPS lamps in predominately green or blue surroundings would create a grayed "colorless" environment which would have a psychologically depressing effect on people. However, you can also see in Table 22 that metal halide lamps would work quite adequately in a blue-green environment. Recently a revolutionary design trend has begun in which two lamps with different color renderings are used within the same system. Each lamp accents the colors the other grays. A fine example of this is the use of high pressure sodium lamps in combination with metal halide lamps in indirect indoor lighting. Obviously such a system would increase the number of acceptable color schemes for decorating purposes.

Physiological Considerations

In recent years, public concern has increased regarding the effects certain types of light have on the human body. Light is a special narrow range of electromagnetic energy capable of stimulating receptors in the eye which permit vision. The spectrum of visible radiant energy or light is very narrow, ranging from approximately 380 nanometers to 760 nanometers (15 to 30 millionths of an inch). The sun and electric lamps are considered light sources because they can transform other forms of energy into the radiant energy wavelengths known as light. But these sources also emit energy at wavelengths both shorter and longer than light waves. Ultraviolet (U-V) energy, valuable for germ killing, suntanning, and photochemical properties, has wavelengths shorter than light waves. Infrared energy waves, also referred to as heat waves, are longer than light waves. It is the possibility of extended exposure to these two types of waves which has generated the greatest concern.

Exposing the eye to infrared waves can result in retinal burn and a loss of vision. While looking at the sun for extended periods of time can cause retinal burn, the problems of infrared energy emitted from artificial light sources are not as great. Most of the problems associated with electric lamps stem from exposure to ultraviolet energy. The human eye is particularly sensitive to ultraviolet light in the 320 to 400 nanometer range, and exposure to these wavelengths for long periods of time can result in inflammation of the cornea. Symptoms of this condition include bloodshot eyes and a sandy or grainy sensation in or around the eyes.

Standard mercury lamps and fluorescent lamp designs are known to produce the highest levels of ultraviolet wavelengths of all modern lamp types. Metal halide and high pressure sodium lamps produce some U-V wavelengths, but incandescents do not produce U-V wavelengths in significant amounts.

A recent study conducted by the Food and Drug Administration compared the ultraviolet levels of high pressure sodium lamps with those of other lamps known to generate ultraviolet light. The purpose of the testing was to determine the suitability of HPS lamps for interior lighting applications. The researchers illuminated a predetermined test area to a 100 footcandle level using HPS, mercury, and 40-watt cool white fluorescent lamps in turn.

The data gathered indicated that mercury lamps generate 25 times as much U-V light as HPS lamps. Forty-watt cool white fluorescent lamps generate up to three times as much U-V light as HPS lamps. The study concluded that interior lighting designs utilizing high pressure sodium lamps pose less of an ultraviolet light threat than other commonly employed systems. It also stated that most cornea irritation attributed to HPS lamps is actually caused by exposure to glare resulting from poor lighting design.

Final Checklist

Choosing a light source requires more than a thorough knowledge of the lamps available and their performance properties. It requires a sense of lighting judgment which only the lighting designer can supply. Each individual lighting system is unique, and it is up to the designer of that system to correlate lamp and luminaire performance with the client's needs, tastes, and desires. Often one area of performance must be sacrificed to enhance performance in a more desirable area. For example, color rendering may be reduced to increase lumen output,

or higher initial costs may be paid to reduce future maintenance considerations. The previous section has supplied the raw data to make a wise lamp selection. You must supply specific details and make judgments concerning the intangible elements of light and color. The following checklist can serve as a reminder of the major factors accountable in almost every lighting system. They are not necessarily listed in order of importance.

1. Desired illumination levels.
2. Energy consumption or lamp efficacy.
3. Lamp lumen depreciation and lamp life.
4. Initial and maintenance costs.
5. Color rendering characteristics.
6. Overall lighting effect desired.
7. Psychological effects on people.
8. Physiological or photobiological effects on people.

A Power-Trac system utilizing incandescent sources creates a warm, comfortable lighting atmosphere. Its flexibility is an added advantage.

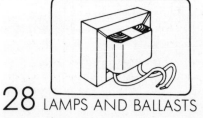

HID Lamp Ballasts

All high intensity discharge lamps require the use of a ballast for proper operation (Fig. 14). The ballast serves several important functions. Among these are:

1. To provide the correct starting current.
2. To provide the correct voltage to initiate the arc discharge.
3. To provide the correct voltage to stabilize the arc for the proper operation of the lamp.
4. To regulate the flow of current through the arc discharge.
5. To compensate for the low power factor characteristic of the arc discharge.

Proper current control (point 4) is extremely important because all arc discharge lamps exhibit negative resistance characteristics. This means that if the arc discharge is placed directly across a nonregulated voltage supply, the arc would draw unlimited current, and the lamp would be quickly destroyed. In order to control the current flow to the lamp, a positive impedance must be added to the lamp's circuit. The ballast acts as this impedance.

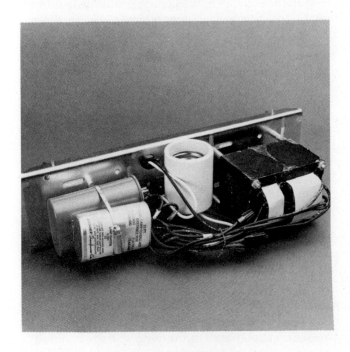

Fig. 14: The Power Drawer ballast design.

Ballasts for high pressure sodium lamps must also have special performance characteristics. As mentioned in the section describing HPS lamp design, high pressure sodium lamps have no starting electrode. Instead, they rely on a low energy, high voltage pulse of electrical power for starting. This pulse can be provided in one of two ways. A starting pulse generator separate from the lamp ballast may be used. A more common approach, however, is to employ a ballast design utilizing all or a portion of the ballast circuitry as a pulse transformer. In this way, an auxiliary starting circuit designed into the actual ballast supplies the necessary low energy, high voltage starting pulse. Also, since the HPS lamp's stabilizing voltage increases with age over a wide range, its ballast must be capable of controlling the lamp's wattages within a narrow range.

Ballast Power Factors. Ballasts are classified as having either high or normal power factors. A *high power factor ballast* is one that draws within 10% of the minimum line current for a specific power consumption. These ballasts are described as having a power factor of 90% or greater. High power factor (HPF) ballasts allow the use of a large number of luminaires and high wattage lamps on each branch circuit or specific power distribution and control equipment.

A *normal power factor ballast* is described as a ballast with a power factor of approximately 50%. This means a normal power factor ballast has almost twice the *line current* as a high power factor ballast, and thereby makes less efficient use of the distribution system. Normal power factor (NPF) ballasts are commonly associated with reactor and high reactance type ballast circuits used for both mercury and high pressure sodium lamps. They are commonly used for lower wattage lamps (150 watts or less), where the quantity of luminaires used will not affect specific branch circuit design or power distribution and control equipment.

Ballast Efficiency. No ballast delivers all of the power passing through it to the lamp it serves. Some of the power is lost in the form of heat. A ballast that is 90% efficient delivers 90% of the power to the lamp. The remaining 10% is wasted in heating the ballast. The ballast watt losses add to the total power consumed, so the lighting designer should not disregard these losses when choosing a ballast.

Line Current. For some ballast types, the line current as the lamp starts is less than the final operating current. In these cases, fuses and circuit breaker ratings should be based on the operating current value. For other ballast types, the starting current is con-

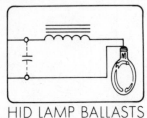

siderably higher than the operating current. Fuses or circuit breakers must be sized to accommodate this increased value.

Line Voltage Regulation. Line voltage regulation is the change in lamp watts due to variation in the line voltage. When selecting a ballast, consideration should be given the expected variation in line voltage on a particular system utilizing HID lamps. Newer systems normally operate within ± 5% of their nominal line voltage, but in older systems this variation may be up to 10% or more of the nominal voltage.

Extinction Voltage. All power systems are subject to dips in line voltage. While a well regulated distribution circuit will seldom experience voltage dips of more than 10%, dips of 20-30% are possible. If the ballast is not capable of riding through these dips, the lamp will extinguish and recycle.

Reactor Ballasts

The reactor ballast (Fig. 15A) is the most economical, smallest, and the most efficient ballast made today. It is the simplest lag circuit power frequency inductive ballast. Reactor ballasts can only be used when the line voltage is greater than the minimum required lamp starting voltage. This type of ballast provides little regulation for fluctuations in line voltage. For example, for a mercury lamp reactor ballast, a 3% change in line voltage would result in a 6% change in lamp wattage. For this reason the reactor ballast is not recommended where line fluctuations exceed 5%.

A normal power factor reactor ballast can be modified to a high power factor ballast by the addition of a capacitor across the line. This modified ballast will still have the same operating characteristics as the original NPF ballast. The capacitors used in this circuit have no ballasting function. Their only purpose is power factor correction, and these capacitors effectively increase the power factor from ± 50% to ± 90%. This allows for the use of a larger number of ballasts on a given branch circuit.

High Reactance (Autotransformer) Ballasts

In situations where the line voltage is below or above the specified lamp starting voltage range, a transformer is used in conjunction with the reactor ballast to provide proper starting voltage. This is normally accomplished through the combination of primary and secondary coils to form a one piece single high leakage reactance autotransformer (Fig. 15B). This ballast performs the functions of supplying the necessary starting voltage as well as current control and is normally the most economical ballast to perform these two tasks. High reactance ballasts are commonly associated with both mercury and HPS lamps. Their power factor is approximately 50% lagging and these ballasts have the same features and shortcomings as the NPF reactor lag circuit.

A normal power factor high reactance ballast can be modified to a high power factor ballast by adding a capacitor to its primary circuit. In order to provide a more economical system, an extra capacitor winding is normally added to the autotransformer primary. The combination of extended windings with the capacitor increases the system power factor to above 90%. The effect on input current is the same as in the HPF reactor ballast.

Constant Wattage Autotransformer (CWA) Ballasts

The constant wattage autotransformer ballast is the most widely used in modern lighting systems equipped with mercury or metal halide lamps. The fundamental electrical difference between the CWA ballast and the high reactance ballast is that a capacitor is used in series with the lamp (Fig. 15C). The capacitor used with ballast performs an important ballasting function as in all lead-type circuits. The capacitor used in lag type reactor and high reactance ballasts is purely a power factor correction component and has no ballasting property. In addition to providing a small economical package, there are many benefits of the constant wattage autotransformer ballasts. It allows the lamp to operate with a better wattage stability (better stabilized light output). Other advantages include high power factor, low line extinguishing voltage, and line starting currents that are lower than normal operating line currents (allowing maximum loading on branch circuits). A metal halide CWA ballast may be used for either mercury or metal halide lamps. A CWA ballast designed specifically for mercury lamps is not interchangeable and must only be used for mercury lamps.

High Pressure Sodium CWA Ballasts

Unlike mercury or metal halide lamps, which exhibit relatively constant lamp voltage with lamp wattage, the high pressure sodium lamp voltage increases and decreases as the lamp wattage is varied. Because of this characteristic, maximum and minimum permissible lamp wattage versus lamp voltage trapezoids have been established.

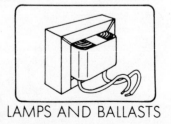

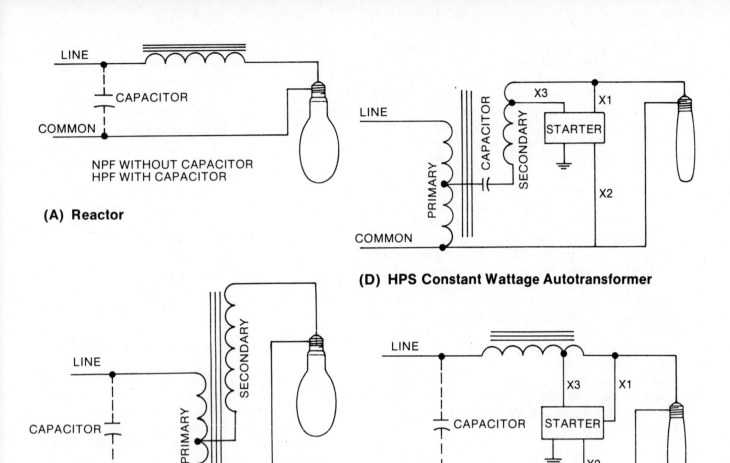

(A) Reactor

NPF WITHOUT CAPACITOR
HPF WITH CAPACITOR

(D) HPS Constant Wattage Autotransformer

(B) High Reactance (Autotransformer)

NPF WITHOUT CAPACITOR
HPF WITH CAPACITOR

(E) HPS Reactor

NPF WITHOUT CAPACITOR
HPF WITH CAPACITOR

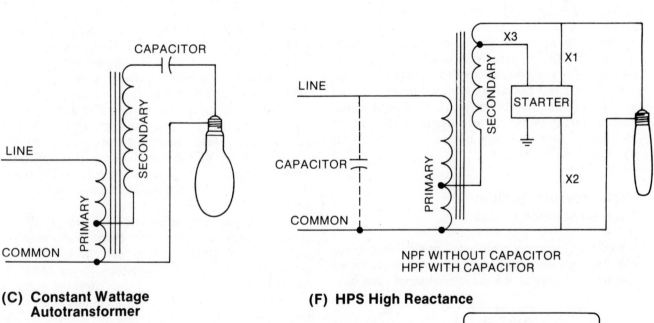

(C) Constant Wattage Autotransformer

(F) HPS High Reactance

NPF WITHOUT CAPACITOR
HPF WITH CAPACITOR

Fig. 15: Schematic drawings of the various HID ballasts.

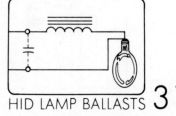

The constant wattage autotransformer or lead circuit HPS ballast circuit configuration operates with a combination of inductance and capacitance in series with the lamp (Fig. 15D). It differs in design from other CWA ballasts in that rather than maintaining a constant current through the lamp, the current decreases with increasing lamp voltage to key the lamp operating wattage within the acceptable trapezoid. This ballast type provides wattage regulation for changes both in line voltage and lamp wattage. In addition, in order to initiate the arc in the lamp arc tube, an electronic starting circuit is required to provide a pulse voltage which generates approximately 4,000 volts peak for the 1000-watt lamp and 2,500 volts peak for other wattages. This pulse occurs at least once per cycle until the lamp is started.

CWA high pressure sodium ballasts are commonly used with HPS lamps with 200- through 1000-watt ratings. The advantages of this ballast are those common to all CWA ballasts. It offers good stabilization, a high power factor, line starting currents which are lower than operating currents, and a low line extinguishing voltage. High pressure sodium CWA ballasts also allow for maximum loading on branch circuits.

High Pressure Sodium Reactor Ballasts

This ballast is basically the same as the mercury reactor ballast described earlier. The main difference is that a starting circuit is added to provide the proper pulse voltage for starting the lamp (Fig. 15E). The reactor ballast is used only when the available line voltage is greater than the minimum voltage required to sustain lamp operation. The starting current is always higher than operating current. They are generally normal power factor and are commonly used on 120-volt systems for lamps of 150 watts or less and for systems where the quantity of luminaires used will not affect specific branch circuit design or power distribution and control equipment. This ballast provides good wattage regulation for changes in lamp wattage, but poor regulation for variations in line voltage.

High Pressure Sodium High Reactance Ballasts

HPS high reactance ballasts are similar to those high reactance types used for mercury lamps. These ballasts are also of the autotransformer type, and

again this is normally accomplished through the combining of primary and secondary coils to form a one piece single high leakage reactance autotransformer. The major modification in the high pressure sodium design is the addition of a starting circuit to provide the proper pulse voltage for starting the lamp (Fig. 15F). This ballast is generally a high power factor type, created by the addition of a capacitor to the primary circuit and a capacitor to the autotransformer primary. This type of design provides an economical ballast for operation when the input voltage is maintained within ±5% of the ballast input rating. The open circuit current or starting current is always higher than the operating current. It may be operated on any of the input voltage circuits from 120 through 480 volts. It is commonly used for lamps of 150 watts or less.

Line Voltage and Lamp Wattage Ranges

A summary of the line voltage and lamp wattage ranges for reactor, high reactance, and constant wattage autotransformer ballasts used with HID lamps is presented in Table 23. A listing of the lamp wattages each particular ballast is capable of serving is also included. Always keep in mind that except where previously noted, HID ballasts are not interchangeable between lamp types or even between certain wattage ranges within the same lamp type. Any ballast chosen must be properly matched to the lamp it serves.

Remote Location of Ballasts

Due to the design of some structures, it is sometimes necessary to locate the lamp's ballast some distance away from the lamp. When working with mercury and metal halide ballasts, a correctly sized wire protected by conduit must be used to minimize voltage drop between the ballast and lamp. This is because the open circuit voltage provided by the ballast must be maintained to ensure proper starting and operation of the lamp. Refer to applicable American National Standards Institute (ANSI) standards for the exact specification voltages in each situation.

Remote ballast consideration for high pressure sodium lamps cannot be generalized in this manner due to the electronic starter and the low energy pulse required to start these lamps. Table 24 specifies the maximum distances high pressure sodium ballasts can be located away from lamps of particular wattages. If these distances are exceeded, the lamp may not start.

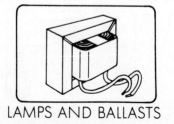

Table 23:	Line Voltage and Lamp Wattage Ranges			
Lamp Type	Ballast Type	Lamp Wattage	Line Volts Range (%)	Lamp Watt Range (%)
Mercury	HR	All	± 5	± 12
Mercury	R	All	± 5	± 12
Mercury	CWA	All	± 5	± 5
Metal Halide	CWA	175	± 10	± 7
Metal Halide	CWA	250	± 10	± 8
Metal Halide	CWA	400	± 10	± 7
Metal Halide	CWA	1000	± 10	± 10
Metal Halide	CWA	1500	± 10	± 12
HPS	R	35-150	± 5	± 12
HPS	HR	50-150	± 5	± 12
HPS	CWA	200-1000	± 10	± 10

Table 24:	Ballast Type and Distances		
Lamp Wattage	Reactor	HR (HPF)	CWA
35	15'	—	—
50	15'	35'	—
70	15'	35'	—
100	15'	35'	—
150 (55v)	15'	35'	—
150 (100v)	—	30'	—
200	—	—	42'
250	—	—	42'
310	—	—	42'
400	—	—	42'
1000	—	—	50'

Fusing of Ballasts

At times it is desirable to provide individual fuse protection for HID lamps as part of the ballast or as part of an integral-ballast luminaire. Specific recommendations best suited to individual lamp ballast combinations are listed in Table 25.

One advantage of individual fusing is that the remaining lamp fixtures of the circuit stay in operation instead of being turned off by the opening of the branch circuit fuse or circuit breaker. Also, the location of the failure is immediately evident. There are also certain safety advantages when circuits of higher voltage and current are used. For example, on a 480-volt, 50-ampere circuit, a single 400-watt lamp might be protected by a 3- or 4-ampere fuse. If a ballast should fail, this fuse would open much faster than the 50-ampere breaker or fuse, thereby reducing the amount of sparking or burning at the fixture. However, the location of luminaires or other considerations may make individual fusing inappropriate

for some installations. The advantages of such a system must be weighed against disadvantages in each case. *Note:* Consult Bussmann Division, McGraw-Edison Company, when fusing systems other than individual setups are desired.

HID LAMP BALLAST DATA TABLE

Table 25 lists the pertinent data for the most commonly used lamp ballast combinations. When using the table, the following points should be considered:

1. All ballasts are of the high power factor type (± 90%) except where designated by the symbol †.

2. The symbol * indicates a starting current less than the operating current.

3. The symbol ** indicates the recommended fusing for individual HID ballasts when specified, based on the use of KTK type (quick-blow) fuses. Consult Bussmann Division, McGraw-Edison Company, when other types of fusing are desired.

4. Size all branch circuits to accommodate line operating amps or line starting amps—whichever of the two values is higher.

5. All ballasts listed have a minimum operating temperature of –20° F (–28.9° C). Contact Halo Lighting for information concerning ballasts with lower operating temperature limits.

6. Key:
   CWA = Constant Wattage Autotransformer
   HR = High Reactance
   R   = Reactor

Note: The Halo Lighting warranty is void on any 480-volt ballast if used on systems which are not grounded due to the potential of destructive failures.

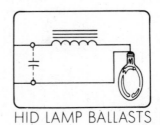

HID LAMP BALLASTS 33

Table 25: HID Lamp Ballast Data

Mercury Lamp Ballast

| Lamp Watts and ANSI Code | Ballast Circuit Type | Input Characteristics (Approximate) | | | | Total Watts | Fuse Rating— Amps** per Fuse |
| | | Rated Volts | Input Current—Amps | | | | |
			Operating	Max. Start	Lamp Out O.C.††		
50 (H46)	HR†	120	1.3	2.0	—	62	5
	CWA	120	0.67	*	.30	74	3
	CWA	208	0.39	*	.20	74	3
	CWA	240	0.33	*	.15	74	3
	CWA	277	0.29	*	.13	74	3
	CWA	480	0.16	*	.10	74	3
75 (H43)	HR†	120	1.9	2.4	—	98	10
	CWA	120	0.82	*	.50	93	3
	CWA	208	0.48	*	.29	93	3
	CWA	240	0.41	*	.25	93	3
	CWA	277	0.36	*	.22	93	3
	CWA	480	0.21	*	.13	93	3
100 (H38)	HR†	120	1.95	2.8	—	120	10
	CWA	120	1.05	*	.50	124	3
	CWA	208	0.6	*	.29	124	3
	CWA	240	0.52	*	.25	124	3
	R	240	0.56	1.25	.45	125	5
	R†	240	0.85	1.7	—	125	5
	CWA	277	0.45	*	.22	124	3
	CWA	480	0.26	*	.16	120	3
175 (H39)	HR†	120	3.3	6.0	.40	200	15
	CWA	120	1.75	*	.60	200	5
	CWA	208	1.0	*	.35	200	3
	CWA	240	0.87	*	.30	200	3
	CWA	277	0.76	*	.27	200	3
	CWA	480	0.44	*	.20	200	3
250 (H37)	HR†	120	5.4	8.3	1.90	285	20
	CWA	120	2.5	*	1.25	285	10
	CWA	208	1.45	*	.72	285	5
	CWA	240	1.25	*	.54	285	5
	CWA	277	1.10	*	.54	285	3
	CWA	480	0.62	*	.38	285	3
400 (H33)	HR†	120	6.6	13.5	.30	430	30
	CWA	120	3.9	*	.78	454	10
	CWA	208	2.2	*	.51	454	5
	CWA	240	1.95	*	.44	454	5
	CWA	277	1.70	*	.39	454	5
	CWA	480	0.98	*	.24	454	3
1000 (H36)	CWA	120	9.2	*	1.73	1080	25
	CWA	208	5.3	*	1.00	1080	15
	CWA	240	4.6	*	.87	1080	15
	CWA	277	4.0	*	.75	1080	10
	CWA	480	2.3	*	.43	1080	10

†Normal power factor.
††Open circuit.
*Starting current less than operating current.
**Recommended fusing for individual HID ballasts when specified, based on the use of KTK type fuses.

Metal Halide Lamp Ballast

Lamp Watts and ANSI Code	Ballast Circuit Type	Input Characteristics (Approximate)				Total Watts	Fuse Rating— Amps** per Fuse
		Rated Volts	Input Current—Amps				
			Operating	Max. Start	Lamp Out O.C.††		
175 (M57)	CWA	120	1.8	*	1.8	210	5
	CWA	208	1.04	*	1.04	210	3
	CWA	240	0.9	*	0.9	210	3
	CWA	277	0.78	*	0.78	210	3
	CWA	480	0.45	*	0.45	210	3
250 (M58)	CWA	120	2.60	*	2.4	294	10
	CWA	208	1.50	*	1.38	294	5
	CWA	240	1.30	*	1.20	294	5
	CWA	277	1.12	*	1.04	294	3
	CWA	480	0.65	*	0.6	294	3
400 (M59)	CWA	120	4.0	*	4.0	455	10
	CWA	208	2.3	*	2.3	455	10
	CWA	240	2.0	*	2.0	455	5
	CWA	277	1.75	*	1.75	455	5
	CWA	480	1.0	*	1.0	455	3
1000 (M47)	CWA	120	9.2	*	5.5	1080	25
	CWA	208	5.3	*	3.2	1080	15
	CWA	240	4.6	*	2.8	1080	15
	CWA	277	4.0	*	2.4	1080	10
	CWA	480	2.3	*	1.4	1080	10
1500 (M48)	CWA	120	13.5	*	4.4	1610	30
	CWA	208	7.8	*	2.5	1610	20
	CWA	240	6.75	*	2.2	1610	20
	CWA	277	5.85	*	1.9	1610	15
	CWA	480	3.4	*	1.1	1610	10

†Normal power factor.
††Open circuit.
*Starting current less than operating current.
**Recommended fusing for individual HID ballasts when specified, based on the use of KTK type fuses.

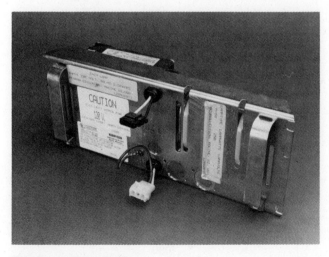

The Power Tray Ballast.

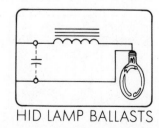

Table 25: HID Lamp Ballast Data (Continued)

High Pressure Sodium Lamp Ballast

Lamp Watts and ANSI Code	Ballast Circuit Type	Input Characteristics (Approximate)				Total Watts	Fuse Rating— Amps** per Fuse
		Rated Volts	Input Current—Amps				
			Operating	Max. Start	Lamp Out O.C.††		
35 (S76)	R†	120	0.83	1.15	—	43	3
50 (S68)	R†	120	1.18	1.80	—	60	5
	HR	120	0.61	0.65	0.99	66	5
	HR	277	0.26	0.30	0.44	66	3
70 (S62)	R†	120	1.6	2.10	—	82	8
	HR	120	0.81	0.75	1.45	88	5
	HR	208	0.47	0.45	0.85	88	3
	HR	240	0.40	0.37	0.75	88	3
	HR	277	0.35	0.35	0.65	88	3
	HR	480	0.21	0.21	0.36	88	3
100 (S54)	R†	120	2.10	2.90	—	115	10
	HR	120	1.15	1.30	2.2	130	5
	HR	208	0.67	0.76	1.27	130	5
	HR	240	0.58	0.66	1.10	130	3
	HR	277	0.50	0.60	0.85	130	3
	HR	480	0.29	0.33	0.57	130	3
150 (S55)	R†	120	3.20	4.10	—	170	15
	HR	120	1.65	2.00	2.80	188	10
	HR	208	0.95	1.15	1.60	188	5
	HR	240	0.83	1.00	1.40	188	5
	HR	277	0.72	0.85	1.25	188	5
	HR	480	0.42	0.50	0.70	188	3
200 (S66)	CWA	120	2.22	*	1.32	240	10
	CWA	208	1.28	*	0.76	240	5
	CWA	240	1.11	*	0.66	240	3
	CWA	277	0.96	*	0.57	240	3
	CWA	480	0.56	*	0.33	240	3
250 (S50)	CWA	120	2.75	*	1.50	300	10
	CWA	208	1.60	*	0.87	300	5
	CWA	240	1.38	*	0.75	300	5
	CWA	277	1.20	*	0.65	300	3
	CWA	480	0.69	*	0.37	300	3
310 (S67)	CWA	120	3.37	*	1.9	365	10
	CWA	208	1.94	*	1.1	365	5
	CWA	240	1.68	*	0.90	365	5
	CWA	277	1.45	*	0.80	365	5
	CWA	480	0.84	*	0.45	365	3
400 (S51)	CWA	120	4.3	*	1.83	465	15
	CWA	208	2.48	*	1.15	465	10
	CWA	240	2.15	*	0.84	465	10
	CWA	277	1.86	*	0.71	465	5
	CWA	480	1.07	*	0.45	465	3
1000 (S52)	CWA	120	9.2	*	4.80	1090	25
	CWA	208	5.3	*	2.80	1090	15
	CWA	240	4.6	*	2.40	1090	15
	CWA	277	4.0	*	2.10	1090	10
	CWA	480	2.3	*	1.20	1090	10

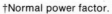

†Normal power factor.
††Open circuit.
*Starting current less than operating current.
**Recommended fusing for individual HID ballasts when specified, based on the use of KTK type fuses.

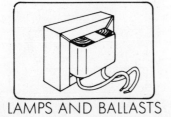

Lighting for Interiors

(Left) The Steelcase Showroom in Chicago uses a Power-Trac system to create wall washing, highlighting, and dramatic visual contrast. (Above and below) SPI ceiling fixtures provide soft, warm, no-glare lighting for less than 1-1/2 watts per square foot.

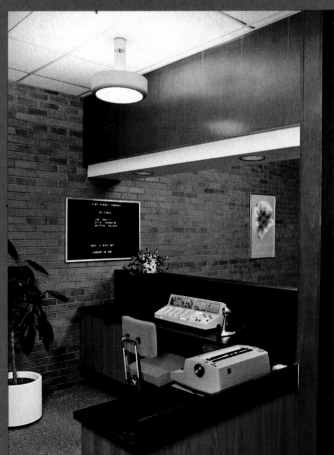

(Above) SPI portable lighting fixtures, such as the SPE Series shown here, can be positioned (and repositioned) to provide light in unique, dynamic work spaces.

(Above and right) SPI Task lighting fixtures in both wall mounted and base mounted designs.

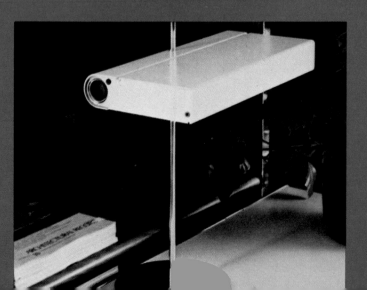

(Above) SPI portable fixtures and SPI Task lighting effectively combine to illuminate modern panel partition office areas. (Left) SPI rectangular shelf or panel mounted portable fixtures.

(Opposite page) A Power-Trac system provides the natural color rendering and design flexibility the Emilio Robba Florist Shop demands.

Two SPI Task lighting fixtures mounted at opposite ends of the work surface provide far more useful light than a single 40-watt fluorescent lamp, while using less energy.

SPR Series portable lighting fixtures.

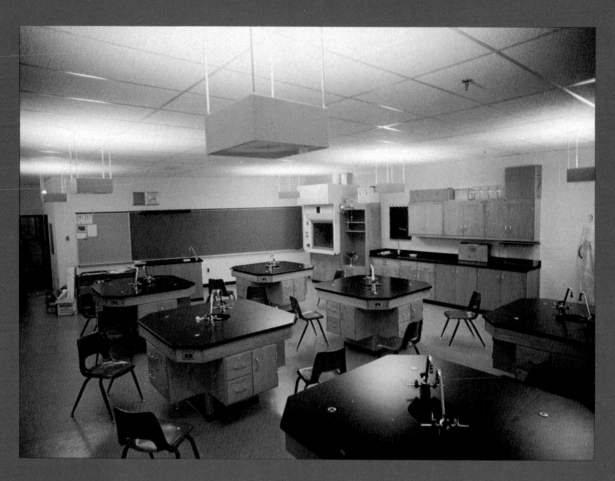

(Above) The SFD Series and (below) the SFF Series. Fewer fixtures, lower costs, and good color rendering are just some of the advantages offered by SPI Lighting.

Introduction to Interior Lighting

For too many years there has been a separation of light's scientific or functional side from its artistic or aesthetic side. Lighting as an art has always been practiced in certain settings. Those involved in theater, motion pictures, and still photography have all benefited from the varied and dramatic effects created through the use of artificial and natural light sources. The ability of light to accent or highlight particular objects or areas has made it invaluable in retail, museum, and display settings.

Yet, those who treated lighting strictly as a science often created visually bland settings of which the redeeming feature was believed to be their high uniform light levels. The principle of "more light is better light" became an industry standard, and only the most obvious glare and veiling reflectance problems were addressed. Energy costs were one of the nation's best bargains, and the architectural style of the day lent itself to uniform blankets of lighting from ceiling mounted fixtures. Task and accent lighting often were not designed into the original system, but added in the final stages to "solve" unexpected trouble areas or to create interesting lighting effects in "special" cases.

A sudden end to inexpensive energy in the early 1970s exposed the major fault of most lighting systems of the day. They were inefficient in terms of light produced per watt of energy consumed. So as the cost of electricity rose throughout the decade, the cost of running a lighting system rose with it, and we in the lighting industry realized a need to totally reassess what had become standard lighting practices.

A rapid surge in lamp and luminaire research has produced a new generation of energy-efficient lighting equipment for the 1980s. No longer can lighting designers afford to overpower lighting problems with excessive amounts of illumination. They must be able to design lighting systems which provide quality light where and when people need it. Lighting has become no less of a science, but the realization that functional light can be aesthetically pleasing has changed the face of modern lighting ideas and led to a subtle yet dynamic enhancement of all types of residential and commercial settings.

Today's lighting designers must be conscious of the human aspect in lighting. Mankind is a dynamic creature. We sit, stand, run, and move incessantly about our environment. We communicate with others through speech, gestures, expressions, or the written word. To fully communicate we must be able to hear clearly and we must be able to see clearly.

In order to provide effective lighting within a space, we must first carefully study that space and the actions of those who work and interact within it. A dynamic work force cannot function effectively in a static lighting situation. A system must be flexible, and it must provide the right light in the right place. A single uniform light level cannot satisfy the needs of a dynamic office area or commercial situation. We must design our illumination systems for all uses, all people, and all seeing tasks within a given area. We must create seeability.

THE INDOOR LIGHTING CONCEPT

The basic design concept for indoor areas consists of two distinct steps—analysis and synthesis. During the analysis, the lighting designer must identify all of the influences which will affect the operation of the lighting system and the seeing ability of the people it will serve.

What is the physical layout of the space? The actual length, width, and ceiling height are important. Where are the entrances and exits? Will the space be broken down into partitioned areas like many of today's modular office and commercial designs? What are the colors of the walls, ceiling, and floor?

Physical questions such as those in the preceding paragraph are easily answered by simple observation. The second type of analytic questions deals with seeing needs and is not as easily answered. What type of work will be done in the space? What will be the average duration of the tasks? What are the ages of the workers? Will the type of work done in one particular area change on a regular basis? Are there any particular lighting effects the client wishes to include? As you will see, all of these factors can have a marked effect on the amount and types of illumination needed within a space or subspace. In any event, the designer must provide accurate and non-fatiguing visibility.

Synthesis involves merging the data collected during the analysis into a practical lighting system. The designer must consider the entire room or building design, not just its lighting aspects. The lighting

must become an integral part of the architectural and functional systems (electrical, heating/cooling, etc.) of the entire project and be able to change and expand as needs dictate.

The Key to Success: Lighting Balance

The stress in modern lighting is placed on quality lighting. A moderate amount of high quality light can do the job of high quantities of average grade illuminance. Quality light must be used to light the task at hand, its immediate surroundings, and all areas in the peripheral field of view of the worker or occupant. In other words, the designer must provide a balanced lighting system employing three distinct types of lighting—ambient, task, and accent. **Ambient lighting** is defined as the lighting throughout an area which produces general illumination. **Task lighting** is lighting directed to a specific surface or area which provides illumination to perform a localized visual task. **Accent lighting** is directional lighting used to emphasize a particular object or draw attention to a particular field of view.

High quality, balanced illumination is achieved when proper proportions of each light type are blended together in a single lighting system. Ambient, task, and accent lighting each serve to fulfill major seeing requirements, and omitting one or more from any lighting system can result in serious seeing difficulty, eyestrain, and fatigue.

The need for lighting balance is directly related to how our eyes physically function. The human eye functions by perceiving brightness or reflected light. In low light situations, the eye's pupil will dilate or open and allow more light to enter the eye. The pupil will also constrict or close when subject to high levels of light, extreme brightness, or glare. As our eyes move about a particular field of vision, they will continuously adapt to the bright and dark areas within that field. This action, known as transient adaptation, can be very fatiguing to the eye if it occurs continuously. By designing a balanced lighting system in which brightness contrasts are closely controlled, the amount of transient adaptation the eye must undergo is kept to a minimum. Eyestrain is reduced, fatigue is less likely, and worker production is increased.

Creating balanced lighting through the use of ambient, task, and accent lighting will lead to optimum visual comfort and increased productivity in contemporary office settings.

Ambient Lighting

Good ambient lighting forms the basis of good seeing. Seeing is a matter of correctly viewing the details presented in a given task, such as reading, drawing, detailed assembly work, or any other of the thousands of tasks performed by people each day. There are five key factors which can affect our ability to view these details. They are: age of the viewer, brightness contrast in the field of view, quality of light placed on the task, duration of the task, and quantity of light placed on the task.

Viewer Age

Numerous studies conducted by the Illuminating Engineering Research Institute have shown that as the eye ages its seeing ability decreases. Figure 1 clearly indicates that as people age the lighting level at which they experience discomforting glare becomes lower and lower. Older people also require increasing levels of illumination to achieve the same levels of visibility. Figure 2 graphically illustrates how younger viewers consistently outperform older viewers in terms of task accuracy and speed at all levels of illumination. Simply providing more raw footcandles will not solve the seeing problems of the older eye, since this increase may result in more

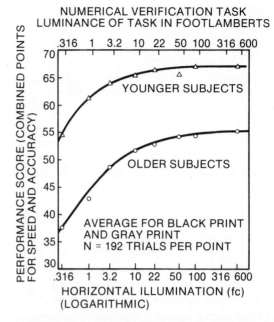

Fig. 2: This graph clearly indicates how younger workers can outperform older workers in terms of both speed and accuracy at all light levels.

discomforting glare. Increased levels of **quality light** will improve worker productivity and accuracy at all age levels.

Task Contrast

The contrast between an object and its immediate background has a marked effect on how well a viewer can see (Fig. 3). Basic research conducted by the IESRI indicates that for each 1% loss in contrast between a subject and its immediate background, 15% more light is required to maintain the same level

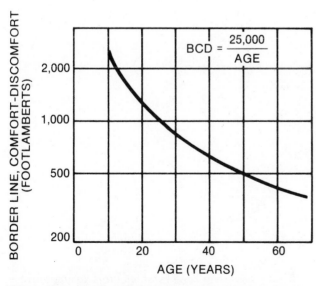

Fig. 1: This graph indicates how older viewers have a lower border line comfort-discomfort tolerance level in terms of surface brightness.

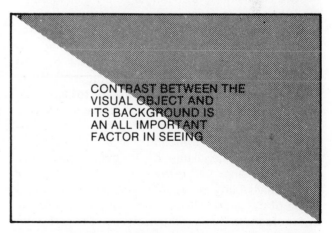

Fig. 3: A high task contrast is essential to clear, comfortable seeing. Veiling reflections can reduce task contrast.

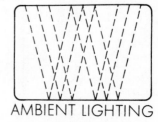

of visibility. Light reflected off the task into the viewer's eyes can greatly reduce task contrast and seeing ability. A good example of this is light reflected off the surface of a glossy magazine page. More will be said concerning contrasts and veiling reflections in the following paragraphs on light quality.

Light Quality

Light quality involves a combination of three main factors: visibility, visual comfort, and luminance ratios.

Visibility and ESI Footcandle Levels. Visibility is the measurement of how well our eyes can distinguish the contrast between an object or image and its background. Many direct lighting systems produce light source reflections which can obscure image/background contrasts (Fig. 4). As mentioned previously, these veiling reflections appear as shiny images on the surface of paper, desk tops, drawing boards, and other surfaces. Although veiling reflections are most noticed on glossy surfaces, they exist to lesser or greater degrees on all surfaces, including matte or dull finishes. In fact, veiling reflections on matte and other non-glossy surfaces are often more damaging than highly apparent reflections because the reader or worker rarely notices their presence and, therefore, makes no attempt to change the situation and improve the visibility.

Figure 5 illustrates the offending zone in which most veiling reflections occur. By carefully regulating the amount of light in this zone, the overall quality of seeability can be increased. The use of indirect lighting is one of the finest methods known of reducing light levels in the offending zone.

Because visibility is no longer solely considered a function of the raw footcandle levels, a new means of measuring visibility was developed. This new method, known as Equivalent Spherical Illuminance, accurately rates a lighting system in terms of light quality, not just light quantity. ESI footcandle levels are based on the amount of light it takes to illuminate a theoretical sphere to certain visibility levels. The lighting level is always equal throughout this theoretical sphere. ESI footcandle levels of a system state the equivalent amount of light which would have to be placed in this theoretical sphere in order to create visibility levels within the sphere equal to those of the system in question. So the higher the ESI footcandle levels within a system, the better the visibility within that system will be.

ESI can be defined as the effective lighting level, or see-ability, of a lighting system in relation to a specific task. ESI is the percentage relationship between the test system and a perfectly uniform overall luminous field generating a specific amount of illumination. ESI takes into account the degrading effect of veiling reflections.

Veiling reflections are a degrading influence because they reduce contrast between task information and background material. Veiling reflections make the task less visible.

Evaluating lighting systems in terms of effectiveness is extremely important because a 1% loss in task contrast requires an increase in illumination from 7% to 15%.

A

ESI can be defined as the effective lighting level, or see-ability, of a lighting system in relation to a specific task. ESI is the percentage relationship between the test system and a perfectly uniform overall luminous field generating a specific amount of illumination. ESI takes into account the degrading effect of veiling reflections.

Veiling reflections are a degrading influence because they reduce contrast between task information and background material. Veiling reflections make the task less visible.

Evaluating lighting systems in terms of effectiveness is extremely important because a 1% loss in task contrast requires an increase in illumination from 7% to 15%.

B

Fig. 4: (A) When light is reflected off a surface into the viewer's eyes, contrasts necessary for seeing can be obscured. (B) Controlling the amount of light reflected at these offending angles will increase visibility.

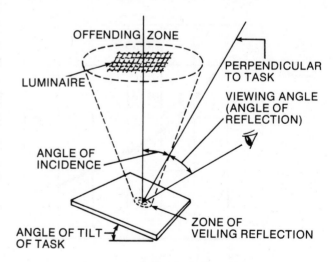

Fig. 5: The offending zone in which most veiling reflections occur.

For a clearer picture of the ESI concept, consider this example. Two entirely different lighting systems are used to light the exact same area to identical 100 footcandle illuminance levels. System A is tested and found to produce 75 ESI footcandles while System B is found to produce only 20 ESI footcandles. This means that System A produces less veiling reflectances and more usable footcandles than System B. In many cases the ESI footcandle level of a quality system will be found to be higher than the raw footcandle level or task illuminance (TI) produced. In fact, Equivalent Spherical Illuminance is such a good indicator of system quality that ESI footcandle levels up to 25% below the Illuminating Engineering Society (IES) recommended raw footcandle levels can be used to properly light a given area. In other words, if the IES recommends a raw footcandle level of 50 footcandles for a given task, a lighting system known to produce 37.5 ESI footcandles will light the area to suitable levels.

Visual Comfort. Direct glare from a lighting fixture reduces visual comfort, and since lack of visual comfort results in eyestrain, visual tension, and reduced worker concentration, it is essential to design an environment without bright light sources. The IES has established a standard by which to judge visual comfort called the visual comfort probability (VCP) factor. This factor expresses the percentage of people who, when viewing from a specified location and direction within the system, will find it acceptable in terms of visual comfort.

Since the VCP ratings are based on the eyes' reaction to fixture brightness, indirect lighting fixtures, which generate no direct fixture brightness, have a theoretical VCP factor of 100. This is another advantage of choosing indirect lighting techniques for modern lighting installations. However, from a practical viewpoint, the ceiling brightness generated with an indirect system should not exceed 500 footlamberts for a lighting system to achieve optimum visual comfort.

Luminance Ratios. The luminance relationship of various surfaces in the visual field is another important consideration in providing quality light. As explained earlier in this section, when the eyes scan a task they adapt to the brightness or luminance of that area. As the eyes leave the task and look at an area of a different luminance, there is a sudden loss in the eye's ability to see contrast details in the new area until the eye can adapt to the new light levels. So in order to see the detail of a visual task accurately, quickly, and with a minimum of eye fatigue, brightness or luminance ratios must be kept within the limits shown in Table 1.

As you can see, a 3:1 ratio should be maintained between the task and its immediate surroundings.

Table 1: Recommended Brightness or Luminance Ratios for Indoor Lighting	
Recommended Ratio	**Area**
3:1	Task to immediate surroundings.
5:1	Task to general surroundings.
10:1	Task to remote surroundings.

An example of this would be the brightness ratio between a paper that a worker is reading and the luminance of his/her desk top. The maximum/minimum brightness ratio between the task and the general surroundings should not exceed 5:1. The general surroundings include the individual work station, partitioned space, or area. Ambient and task lighting fixtures are commonly used in combination to meet immediate and general surrounding brightness ratios. The brightness ratio between the task and remote areas should not exceed 10:1. A dark wall located some distance away from the task would be a good example of a badly lighted remote area. For this reason, accent lighting is often used to light the border areas of a larger work space.

These ratios represent the maximum difference which should exist between the brightest and darkest spots within a given area. Reducing the contrast levels below these recommended maximums will result in further visual benefits. As explained later in the section on task lighting, conventional task lighting systems are among the worst offenders in terms of poor brightness ratios.

Task Duration

The duration of the task is an element that deserves some attention in the determination of acceptable lighting levels. Difficult tasks can be performed under lower light levels if task duration time is short and the tasks are performed infrequently. However, performing a rapid succession of short tasks under inadequate light will result in eye fatigue and decreased productivity if adequate levels of quality light are not provided.

Light Quantity

To help lighting designers in decisions concerning light quantity levels, the Illuminating Engineer-

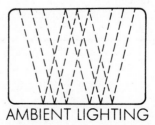

AMBIENT LIGHTING 49

ing Society has researched and adopted recommended illumination levels for numerous indoor activities. Because the precise amount of light required may vary with viewer age, task reflectances, and other sight affecting factors, the IES has established illuminance categories which state a range of footcandle levels for a particular type of activity (Table 2).

For example, from Table 2 we see that illuminance category C encompasses "work spaces where visual tasks are only occasionally performed." The range of illuminance is 10-15-20 footcandles (100-150-200 lux), and the reference work plane calls for general lighting throughout the space.

To determine which suggested light level should be used, the lighting designer must weigh various sight affecting factors as presented in Table 3. For categories A through C, two weighting factors, occupants' ages and room surface reflectances, must be considered. For categories D through I, workers' ages, the need of speed and accuracy, and the reflectance of the task background are the three weighting factors involved.

If in our example for category C, the average age of the occupants in the space is under 40 years, a weighting factor of –1 will be used. For ages 40 to 55, the weighting factor is 0; and for ages over 55, a factor of +1 is used. Room surface reflectance refers to the amount of light reflected or absorbed by the walls, ceiling, and floor of the space. Light color paints and finishes reflect the most light while dark finishes absorb it. Most modern commercial areas are finished to provide good to average surface reflectances of 30% to 70% and above. Darkly paneled and carpeted offices and lobbies are exceptions to this rule. If our example space had an average reflectancy of 80%, the room reflectance weighting factor would be –1. For reflectances of 30% to 70%, the weighting factor is 0; for those less than 30%, the factor is +1.

Once the weighting factors are found, they are added together. For example, in a high reflectance room in which the occupants' age is less than 40 (a classroom perhaps) the weighting factors would be (–1) + (–1) for a total weighting factor of –2. When the total weighting factor is –2, the lowest recommended footcandle level is used—10 footcandles in the case of illuminance category C. If, on the other hand, the occupants' age is over 55 years and the space has dark walls and a dark ceiling and floor which reflect less than 30% of the light, the total weighting factor would be (+1) + (+1) or +2 and the highest recommended footcandle level would be used—20 footcandles in the case of illuminance

Table 2: Illuminance Categories and Illuminance Values for Generic Types of Interior Activities

Type of Activity	Illuminance Category	Ranges of Illuminances		Reference Work Plane
		Footcandles	Lux	
Public spaces with dark surroundings	A	2-3-5	20-30-50	General lighting throughout spaces
Simple orientation for short, temporary visits	B	5-7.5-10	50-75-100	
Working spaces where visual tasks are only occasionally performed	C	10-15-20	100-150-200	
Performance of visual tasks of high contrast or large size	D	20-30-50	200-300-500	Illuminance on task
Performance of visual tasks of medium contrast or small size	E	50-75-100	500-750-1,000	
Performance of visual tasks of low contrast or very small size	F	100-150-200	1,000-1,500-2,000	
Performance of visual tasks of low contrast and very small size over a prolonged period	G	200-300-500	2,000-3,000-5,000	Illuminance on task, obtained by a combination of general and local (supplementary lighting)
Performance of very prolonged and exacting visual tasks	H	500-750-1,000	5,000-7,500-10,000	
Performance of very special visual tasks of extremely low contrast and small size	I	1,000-1,500-2,000	10,000-15,000-20,000	

Table 3:   Weighting Factors to Pinpoint Exact Illuminance Requirements

For Illuminance Categories A through C				For Illuminance Categories D through I			
Room and Occupant Characteristics	**Weighting Factor**			**Task and Worker Characteristics**	**Weighting Factor**		
	−1	**0**	**+1**		**−1**	**0**	**+1**
Occupant Age	Under 40	40-55	Over 55	**Occupant Age**	Under 40	40-55	Over 55
Room Surface Reflectances*	Greater than 70%	30%-70%	Less than 30%	**Speed and/or Accuracy**	Not Important	Important	Critical
				Reflectance of Task Background	Greater than 70%	30%-70%	Less than 30%

*Average of wall, floor, and ceiling reflections (weighted). If ceiling is very high and not usually important, only wall and floor reflections are used.

category C. The middle range footcandle level should be used for all other weighting factor totals— 15 footcandles in the case of category C.

The table works the same for illuminance categories D through I except the task and worker characteristics are worker's age, speed and/or accuracy, and reflectance of task background. Determining the exact speed and accuracy requirements is a rather judgmental process. For tasks such as accurately proofreading magazine copy by a certain deadline, the positive weighting factor for speed and accuracy must be used. In a drugstore, a simple error in reading a prescription could be disastrous, so accuracy in performing tasks is critical. When all the weighting factors for categories D through I are added, a total value of −2 or −3 indicates the lowest listed footcandle level should be used. Totals of +2 or +3 indicate the need for the highest footcandle level, and all other totals require the middle footcandle level illumination.

Illuminance categories A through C are for lower level lighting requirements in which the activity tends to be the same throughout the entire area. Categories D through F describe areas in which the job or task will be performed in a fixed spot within that general area. These jobs may vary in their lighting needs. For instance, in a single large office space, workers at one station may be required to read computer printouts, while at another station a clerk may work with figures printed on yellow legal paper in No. 2 pencil. Each of these stations must be lighted to its own needs based on its own set of weighting factors. A single illumination level will not fulfill the requirements of the entire space. Although the room will not be lighted to a set uniform level, the immediate, general, and remote brightness ratios listed in Table 1 (page 49) must be met at all times.

Illuminance categories G through I are for very difficult seeing tasks in which the lighting needs must be carefully assessed. It is not practical, economically feasible, or visually safe to provide ex-

tremely high light levels solely from ambient lighting fixtures. In these cases supplemental high-quality task lighting will have to be provided in the immediate work area.

Appendix A found at the end of the book lists the illuminance categories for numerous commercial, institutional, residential, and public assembly interiors. The categories in the table are listed in alphabetical order and are broken down into subdivisions to further pinpoint lighting requirements. For example, under Educational facilities we see that classrooms can be classified as science laboratories, lecture rooms, and sight saving rooms. Science laboratories require an illuminance category of E. By referring to Tables 2 and 3, a total weighting factor can be computed and the proper illuminance for a specific laboratory found.

INDIRECT LIGHTING OF CRT AREAS

Computers and their corresponding control equipment—known as CRTs, VDUs, or VDTs—often present the operator with a difficult seeing task. The mirror-like viewing screens of these units maximize the adverse effects of direct and reflected glare and veiling reflections. Pronounced and continuous veiling reflections on CRT viewing screens result in rapid eyestrain and fatigue. Because indirect lighting eliminates direct glare and produces diffuse lighting which minimizes problems with reflected glare, indirect lighting is the finest method of illuminating CRT stations.

Because CRT work is most often conducted in the normal office setting, the lighting system must provide adequate CRT viewing without detracting from the illumination needed to perform other office tasks. To provide this illumination, lighting de-

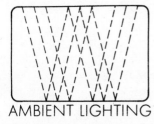

signers initially attempted to locate traditional ceiling mounted fluorescent luminaires in positions which would not be visible when looking into the mirror-like viewing screen. However, placing luminaires in these positions failed to adequately illuminate the office space behind the CRT station. Alternative attempts to light the CRT station solely with task lighting resulted in problems with extreme transient adaptation (page 46).

In a third attempt to effectively light CRT stations, lighting designers employed deep cell, parabolic reflector, louver fluorescent luminaires having 45° light cutoff. Once again, it was found that it was virtually impossible to locate the luminaire so that light reflections would not appear in the terminal screen. In addition, the ceiling area between luminaires was quite dark in comparison to the luminaires themselves, and this contrast ratio difference actually appeared on the screen in the form of a pool of light (Fig. 6A). Reflections from portable office panels and the brightness of untreated window surfaces caused other seeing difficulties. Indirect lighting was found to be the answer.

CRT Analysis

In order to effectively light a CRT station, the lighting designer must understand its basic physical design. There are three types of CRT installations. The vast majority, approximately 90%, fall into the one unit per work station category. Approximately 5% of CRT installations fall into what are classified as "medium intensity situations," where there are as many as ten units in one general location. The remaining 5% fall into the "large data center" classification where there are ten or more CRTs facing in all directions, either grouped in clusters or spread over a large area.

In all cases, CRT operators must perform other visual tasks, such as reading printouts or pencil tasks. Workers are also dynamic and move throughout the entire work area.

The National Institute of Occupational Safety and Health (NIOSH) has studied the human engineering aspects of CRT operation. In addition to making recommendations for work-rest regimens, mandatory vision tests, and flexibility in work station design, NIOSH has also made recommendations for optimum viewing angles, viewing distances, keyboard height, and glare control (Fig. 6B).

SPI Lighting has conducted several intensive studies of "on site" CRT installations and has established a set of guidelines to follow in the design of indirect lighting systems for CRT installations. The guidelines are listed here.

1. Make certain that the CRT station design follows the NIOSH recommendations for keyboard height, viewing distances, and viewing angles (Fig. 6B).
2. Recommend vision tests for all operators. Inform the examining physician that the worker will be operating a CRT unit. Perhaps corrective lenses can be prescribed according to the viewing distance.
3. Study the space from a vertical elevation in addition to the horizontal plane to determine problem areas, particularly from a reflective standpoint. This is quite important when glass or high-gloss free-standing modular office panels are used.
4. Treat windows with translucent screening materials or draperies to achieve the same brightness as the walls or adjacent vertical surface areas.
5. All surfaces in and around the station should have a matte or nonglossy finish, and surface colors should provide the following reflectances: ceilings, not less than 70%; walls and other vertical surfaces, not less than 40%; and floors, not less than 20%.
6. If certain reflective situations exist that cannot be controlled, a filter should be placed on the screen surface. Information on anti-glare filters is available from the Polaroid Corp., Cambridge, Mass.; Optical Coating Laboratory Inc., Santa Rosa, Calif.; and Sun-Flex Company Inc., Novato, Calif.
7. Illuminate the area to account for all possible viewing tasks within that area. Use the IES weighted illuminance category system described on pages 49 through 51 to account for viewer age, room reflectance, etc.
8. Use Equivalent Spherical Illuminance and Visual Comfort Probability Factors in evaluating the lighting system.
9. Minimize shadows and dark areas, particularly those on the ceiling, by providing well-diffused, uniform illumination throughout the entire area. Do not exceed the recommended brightness or luminance ratios listed in Table 1 (page 49).
10. Do not employ any lighting equipment which directs light downward in excess of 500 footlamberts at any spot on the ceiling or from any other angle. The preferred lighting technique, indirect lighting, directs all light upward toward the ceiling.
11. Illuminate the entire ceiling uniformly with a brightness ratio of 5:1 or less. When looking into the mirror-like CRT screen, areas of brightness in excess of 500 footlamberts or less than 100 footlamberts should not be visible.
12. Maintain the minimum luminaire to ceiling surface distances listed in Table 5 (page 68).

High Intensity Discharge, SPI Indirect lighting equipment can be used to meet all reflectance, lumi-

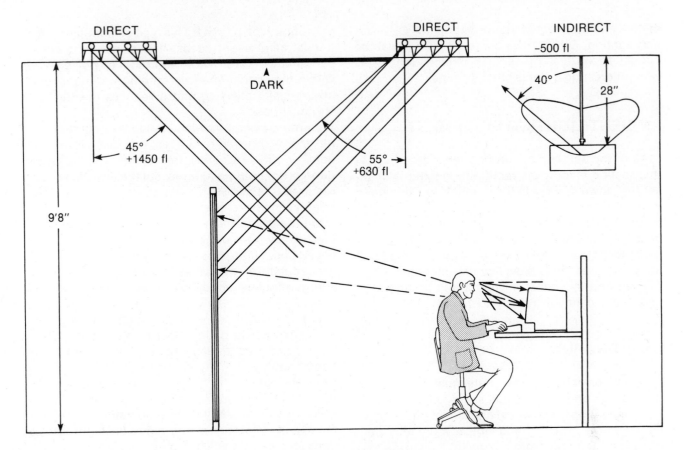

DIRECT DIRECT INDIRECT
–500 fl

DARK

40°

28"

45°
+1450 fl

55°
+630 fl

9'8"

A

CRT VIEWING
H = KEYBOARD HEIGHT = 29" TO 31"
D = VIEWING DISTANCE = 18" TO 20"
∅ = VIEWING ANGLE 10° TO 20°
    BOTTOM EDGE OF SCREEN = 10°

∅
D

H

B

Fig. 6: (A) Direct lighting systems employing parabolic reflector fluorescent luminaires direct light into the CRT viewing screen causing severe veiling reflections. Dark areas between luminaires are also a problem. Indirect lighting systems provide even, diffuse lighting which reduces veiling reflections and dark ceiling areas. All light is directed toward the ceiling, away from the CRT viewing screen. (B) The critical CRT dimensions and angles as recommended by the National Institute of Occupational Safety and Health.

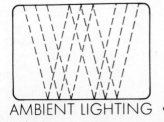

AMBIENT LIGHTING 53

nance, and illuminance requirements for CRT station lighting. Office areas containing CRTs can be lighted to normal office task illumination levels without creating adverse effects on the CRT screen.

AMBIENT LIGHTING EQUIPMENT

All of the ambient lighting systems described in this section employ indirect lighting fixtures or recessed downlighting fixtures which are equipped with high intensity discharge lamps. Of course, ambient fluorescent and incandescent systems are possible, but the light quality, economic, and flexibility advantages of HID systems far outweigh any advantages of these older lighting methods. Fluorescent and incandescent lighting is best used in task and accent lighting applications.

Lamp Selection

Two types of HID lamps, coated metal halide and diffuse high pressure sodium, are recommended for interior lighting with indirect and downlight ambient light fixtures. The lighting efficacy (lumens produced per watt of energy consumed), lumen maintenance, and lamp life of HPS and MH lamps are among the finest available. It is highly recommended that you review the information concerning these two lamps found in **Section I: Lamps and Ballasts**. The information concerning comparing lamp performance and lamp coloring characteristics is of particular importance. Because both metal halide and high pressure sodium lamps have unique color rendering capabilities, selecting a color scheme to match the light generated in that area is essential. A number of indirect lighting fixtures employ a dual lamp feature in which two lamps, one high pressure sodium and one metal halide, are used. In this way the widest range of colors will be complemented. Because of color consideration, the lighting designer must always coordinate his or her work with that of the interior designer to assure that satisfactory color rendering is achieved.

Ambient Lighting Fixture Selection

The rapid development of HID indirect lighting fixtures was triggered by a new concept in office and commercial furniture design—the open-top modular design system (Fig. 7). Refer also to the color

photograph on page 41. This type of modular design fulfills many client needs. It is portable, provides personal worker privacy, and reduces noise levels within the space. The freestanding wall concept is aesthetically pleasing and it reduces overall construction costs.

Lighting systems which could be integrated into this modular furniture concept had to be developed quickly. Initial research stressed the use of indirect fluorescent lighting fixtures, but the electrical loads required to make such systems work made indirect fluorescent systems economically impractical. The fluorescent approach was abandoned, and a completely new line of SPI indirect HID fixtures was developed. High lamp efficacy combined with advanced fixture optics make these fixtures the most energy-efficient indoor lighting equipment available today.

The housing of SPI ambient lighting fixtures is formed of heavy gauge steel or aluminum that is precision tooled to assure dimensional integrity. All components are rigidly locked together, and a heavy powder-coat acrylic finish is fused to the metal to provide lasting good appearance.

The Power Tray ballast assembly simplifies installation and maintenance and allows the fixtures to be upgraded as new HID lamp models are developed. All connections are of the plug-in type so rewiring will not be necessary, and all ballasts are acoustically engineered to operate quietly.

SPI's unique optical systems are designed to place light where it is needed. Two types of optics, symmetric and asymmetric, are available. A symmetrical light distribution pattern is one in which light is equally distributed at all points around the fixture (Fig. 8A). Light is directed smoothly and evenly over a given area for proper ambient illumination. Wide and medium symmetrical distribution pattern optics are available. Asymmetrical or forward throw optical systems distribute all of the lamp's light in front of the fixture (Fig. 8B). Forward throw optics are used in wall mounted fixtures.

Three types of SPI indirect lighting fixtures are used for interior ambient lighting: freestanding, portable, and fixed position. Figure 9 illustrates which types are best for lighting particular areas or types of space, and basic descriptions of the fixture groups are given in the following paragraphs.

SPI Freestanding Fixtures. Freestanding lighting equipment is designed to stand alone and maintain the same light source to ceiling relationship. Available in a number of square (Fig. 10A) and cylindrical (Fig. 10B) designs, freestanding units can be used to light completely open spaces, spaces containing desks and other office equipment, and partitioned spaces. Fixtures are portable so that they can be precisely positioned to provide light where it is

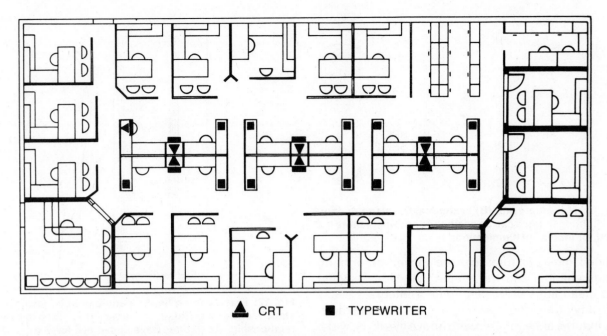

CRT ▲   TYPEWRITER ■

Fig. 7: Overhead view of a typical, modern office modular work station arrangement. The office is arranged through the use of partition panels, which provide worker privacy and reduced noise levels. The lighting in such a system must be flexible enough to meet the needs of the individual work stations.

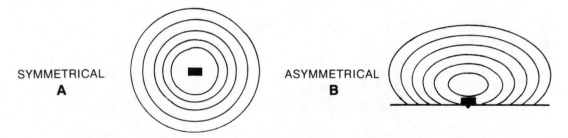

SYMMETRICAL
A

ASYMMETRICAL
B

Fig. 8: (A) A symmetrical light distribution pattern in which the light is distributed equally on all sides of the fixture. (B) Asymmetrical or forward throw optical systems distribute light to the front and sides of the fixture.

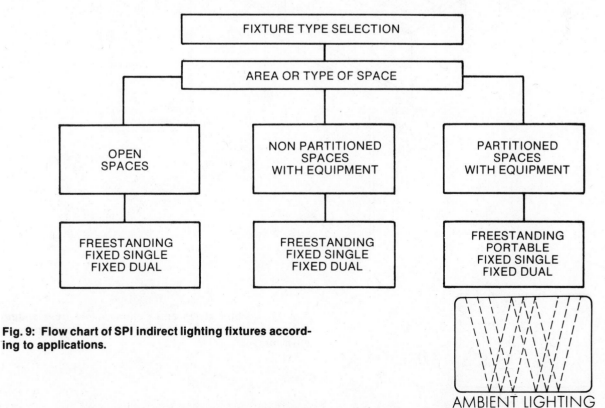

FIXTURE TYPE SELECTION

AREA OR TYPE OF SPACE

OPEN
SPACES

NON PARTITIONED
SPACES
WITH EQUIPMENT

PARTITIONED
SPACES
WITH EQUIPMENT

FREESTANDING
FIXED SINGLE
FIXED DUAL

FREESTANDING
FIXED SINGLE
FIXED DUAL

FREESTANDING
PORTABLE
FIXED SINGLE
FIXED DUAL

Fig. 9: Flow chart of SPI indirect lighting fixtures according to applications.

AMBIENT LIGHTING 55

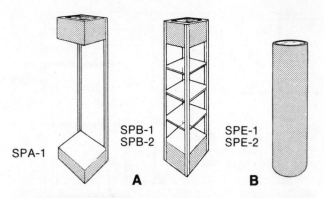

SPA-1 SPB-1 SPB-2 SPE-1 SPE-2

A   B

Fig. 10: (A) Square and (B) cylindrical freestanding indirect lighting fixtures can be positioned anywhere there is a need for increased illumination.

needed most. Fixtures can be moved as lighting needs change, and the simple, handsome styling and clean lines of this equipment integrate easily with any furnishing style (Fig. 11). All SPI freestanding fixtures are equipped with above eye level, wide, symmetric optical systems (Fig. 12).

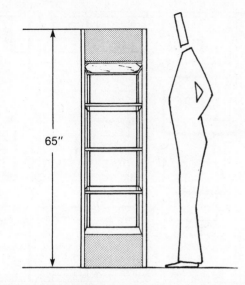

65″

Fig. 12: Freestanding lighting equipment is designed to stand alone and maintain the same light source to ceiling relationship. All fixtures have above eye level wide symmetric optical systems.

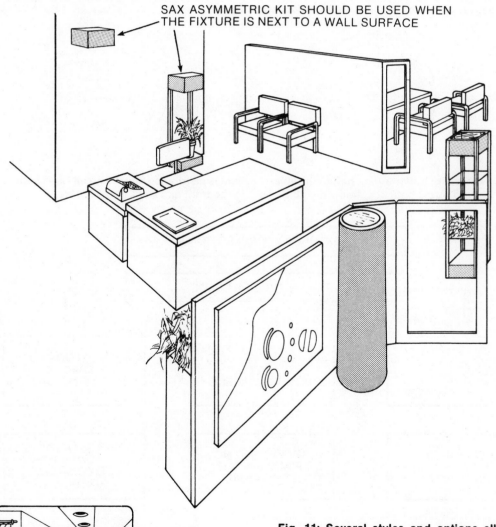

SAX ASYMMETRIC KIT SHOULD BE USED WHEN THE FIXTURE IS NEXT TO A WALL SURFACE

Fig. 11: Several styles and options allow freestanding fixtures to blend with any commercial or merchandising environment.

SPI Portable Fixtures. SPI portable fixtures are designed especially for use with partitioned office furniture systems (Figs. 13 and 14). As shown in the illustrations, these versatile units can be hung from or mounted onto panel systems in any number of ways. They also can be set on any flat surface, such as shelves, cabinets, or bins. As shown in Fig. 15, SPI portable fixtures are designed with above eye level, wide, symmetrical light distribution optics. They should always be placed at least 65″ above

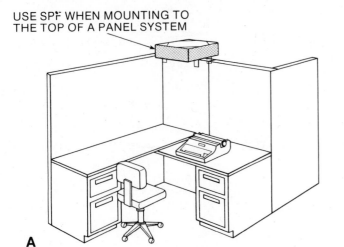

USE SPF WHEN MOUNTING TO THE TOP OF A PANEL SYSTEM

A

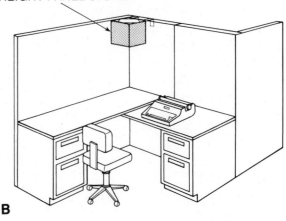

SPJ HANGING FROM THE SIDE OF A MEDIUM HEIGHT PANEL SYSTEM

B

Fig. 13: SPI portable fixtures can be (A) mounted on top of partition panels or (B) hung from partition panels.

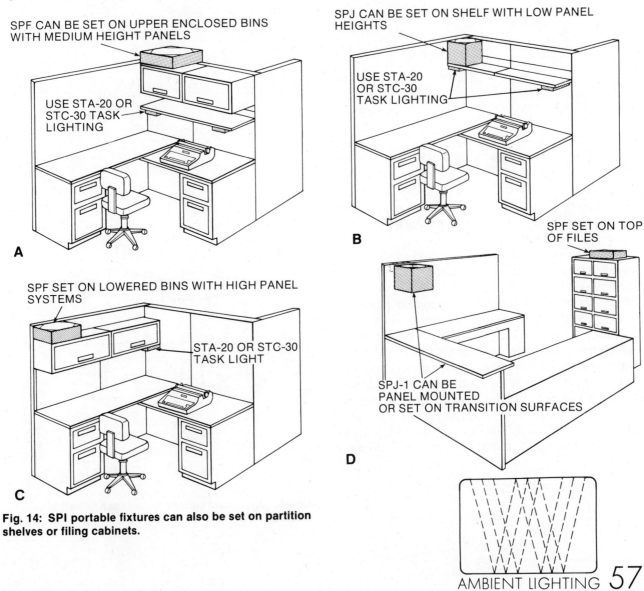

SPF CAN BE SET ON UPPER ENCLOSED BINS WITH MEDIUM HEIGHT PANELS

USE STA-20 OR STC-30 TASK LIGHTING

A

SPJ CAN BE SET ON SHELF WITH LOW PANEL HEIGHTS

USE STA-20 OR STC-30 TASK LIGHTING

B

SPF SET ON LOWERED BINS WITH HIGH PANEL SYSTEMS

STA-20 OR STC-30 TASK LIGHT

C

SPF SET ON TOP OF FILES

SPJ-1 CAN BE PANEL MOUNTED OR SET ON TRANSITION SURFACES

D

Fig. 14: SPI portable fixtures can also be set on partition shelves or filing cabinets.

AMBIENT LIGHTING 57

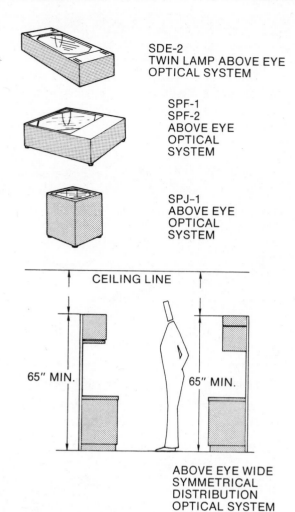

SDE-2
TWIN LAMP ABOVE EYE
OPTICAL SYSTEM

SPF-1
SPF-2
ABOVE EYE
OPTICAL
SYSTEM

SPJ-1
ABOVE EYE
OPTICAL
SYSTEM

CEILING LINE

65" MIN.   65" MIN.

ABOVE EYE WIDE
SYMMETRICAL
DISTRIBUTION
OPTICAL SYSTEM

Fig. 15: Portable lighting fixtures should be placed at least 65" above floor level so the top of a fixture is above eye level.

floor level. Like freestanding units, portable units can be arranged and rearranged to meet present and future ambient lighting needs.

SPI Fixed Position Fixtures. Fixed units can be used to provide ambient light in open or partitioned spaces. As shown in Figs. 16, 17, and 18, these fixtures can be wall, column, or gondola mounted; suspended from the ceiling; or fixed directly to the ceiling. SPI fixed position fixtures are available with symmetric or asymmetric (forward throw) optic systems, and depending upon the exact model, the ballast may be contained within the fixture or located at a remote position. SPI ceiling mounted fixtures require as little as 12" of hang-down space, so it is possible to have all the advantages of indirect lighting from fixed position fixtures in rooms with ceilings as low as 8'.

INTERIOR LIGHTING

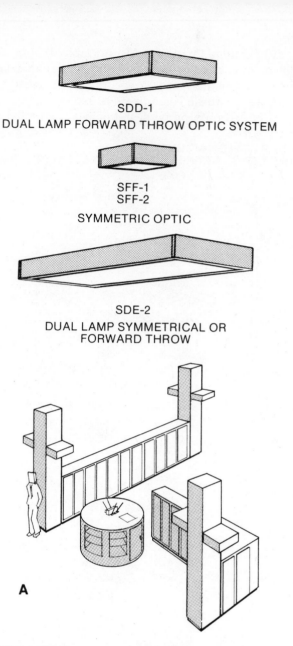

SDD-1
DUAL LAMP FORWARD THROW OPTIC SYSTEM

SFF-1
SFF-2

SYMMETRIC OPTIC

SDE-2
DUAL LAMP SYMMETRICAL OR
FORWARD THROW

A

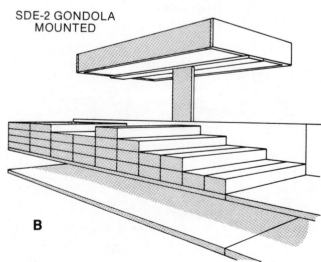

SDE-2 GONDOLA
MOUNTED

B

Fig. 16: (A) Indirect lighting fixtures can be wall or column mounted or (B) gondola mounted.

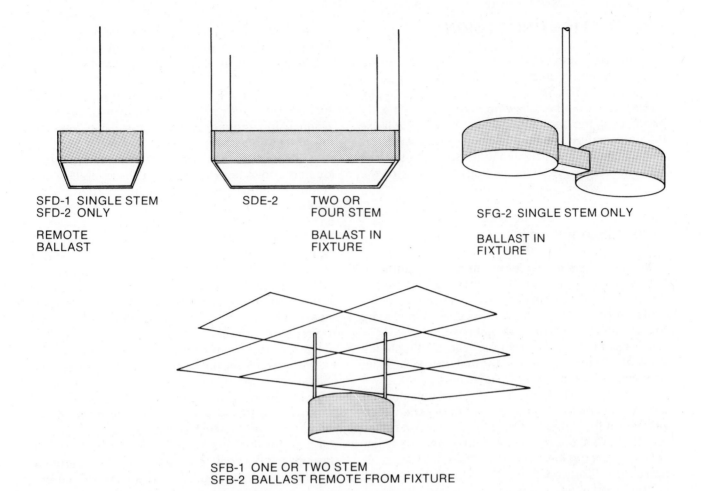

SFD-1 SINGLE STEM
SFD-2 ONLY

REMOTE
BALLAST

SDE-2   TWO OR
           FOUR STEM

BALLAST IN
FIXTURE

SFG-2 SINGLE STEM ONLY

BALLAST IN
FIXTURE

SFB-1 ONE OR TWO STEM
SFB-2 BALLAST REMOTE FROM FIXTURE

Fig. 17: Many SPI indirect fixtures can be suspended from the ceiling.

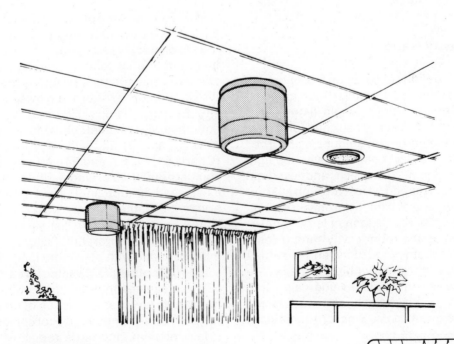

Fig. 18: SPI ceiling mounted fixtures require as little as 12″ of hang-down space.

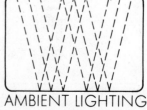

AMBIENT LIGHTING DESIGN

The key to ambient lighting design with SPI indirect lighting fixtures lies in the proper use of the application tables and isofootcandle reference plot curves found on the following pages and in the appendices at the back of the book. How you will use this information is based on the lighting levels required, the room's size and shape, and the surface reflectances of the walls, ceiling, and floor of the space.

Reflectance Values

As was discussed earlier in this section, different colors absorb and reflect different amounts of light. The amount of light reflected from the ceiling, floor, walls, and partition panels within a space plays a key role in the final lighting level achieved.

Most contemporary ceilings have a reflectance value of 70% to 90%. This means that up to 90% of the light which strikes the ceiling is reflected back down into the room. Modern wall reflectance values fall within the 30% to 80% range, and floor reflectance values run from 10% to 30%. The application tables found in this section will be based on the following set reflectance values: ceilings, 80%; walls and partition panels, 50%; and floors, 20%. These are the most common reflectance values found in interior design today. Consult Halo Lighting if the space uses unusually light or dark colors which radically alter this 80/50/20 reflectancy value.

The Room Cavity Ratio

Room size has a definite effect upon the amount of light which is absorbed by the walls, floor, and ceiling. Consider the light from a single fixture. In a small room, the light is reflected back and forth from all surfaces until the maximum amount is absorbed by all surfaces. In a larger room, however, the light will dissipate throughout the space, and less light will strike room surfaces and be lost through absorption. So the percentage of light lost from absorption will be greater in small rooms than in large rooms.

A factor known as the room cavity ratio gives a good indication of room proportions and the effect they will have upon light levels within the space. The room cavity ratio is a numerical value calculated using the length, width, height, and work plane height found in a given room. Smaller rooms have large cavity ratios, which indicate a good amount of light will be absorbed by room surfaces. Larger rooms have smaller ratios, which indicate the exact opposite is true.

Table 4 lists the room cavity ratios for various room length, width, and cavity depth measurements. When using indirect lighting, the cavity depth is found by subtracting the height of the work plane (the distance the desk, table, drafting board, etc. is located above floor level) from the overall ceiling height. So if the room ceiling height is 10.5' and the desk or work plane height is 2.5', the cavity depth will be 10.5' – 2.5' = 8'.

From the table we can see that a small room, such as a private office, measuring 14' × 14' with a cavity depth of 7' has a room cavity ratio of 5. A medium size room measuring 30' × 30' with a cavity depth of 9' has a room cavity ratio of 3, while a large room measuring 100' × 200' with a cavity depth of 14 has a room cavity ratio of 1.

Table 4 lists room cavity ratios for many dimension combinations, but as an overall rule most rooms will fall into the small, medium, or large category of 5, 3, or 1 room cavity ratio value. The design information given in this section is based on room cavity ratios of 5, 3, and 1. If you encounter rooms for which the room cavity ratio varies greatly from these values, consult the application engineering department of Halo Lighting for additional design information.

Footcandle/Spacing/Area Charts

The Footcandle/Spacing/Area Charts A through E4 found on the following pages provide a simple means of quickly laying out fixture locations for ambient lighting systems in standard small, medium, and large size rooms. The charts are based on light distribution patterns created by specific high intensity discharge lamps used in SPI indirect fixtures equipped with symmetrical wide distribution (Charts A, B, C, and D) and wide distribution dual optics (Charts E1, E2, E3, and E4). All charts assume that a standard 80/50/20 ceiling, wall, and floor reflectancy exists, and all footcandle levels are stated in initial horizontal footcandles at a work plane height of 2'6". Notes under each chart list several possible lamp alternatives with proration factors to modify results in accordance with substitute lamp performance.

Using **Footcandle/Spacing/Area Chart A** (page 62), you can see that the chart plots average initial footcandle levels as a function of luminaire spacing for SPI indirect luminaires. Plot curves are shown for small, medium, and large rooms with room cavity ratios of 5, 3, and 1 respectively.

For example, assume that a lighting designer wishes to design an ambient lighting system for a

Table 4: Room Cavity Ratios

Room Dimensions Width	Length	1.0'	1.5'	2.0'	2.5'	3.0'	3.5'	4.0'	5.0'	6.0'	7.0'	8'	9'	10'	11'	12'	14'	16'	20'	25'	30'
8'	8'	1.2	1.9	2.5	3.1	3.7	4.4	5.0	6.2	7.5	8.8	10.0	11.2	12.5	—	—	—	—	—	—	—
	10'	1.1	1.7	2.2	2.8	3.4	3.9	4.5	5.6	6.7	7.9	9.0	10.1	11.3	12.4	—	—	—	—	—	—
	14'	1.0	1.5	2.0	2.5	3.0	3.4	3.9	4.9	5.9	6.9	7.8	8.8	9.7	10.7	11.7	—	—	—	—	—
	20'	0.9	1.3	1.7	2.2	2.6	3.1	3.5	4.4	5.2	6.1	7.0	7.9	8.8	9.6	10.5	12.2	—	—	—	—
	30'	0.8	1.2	1.6	2.0	2.4	2.8	3.2	4.0	4.7	5.5	6.3	7.1	7.9	8.7	9.5	11.0	—	—	—	—
	40'	0.7	1.1	1.5	1.9	2.3	2.6	3.0	3.7	4.5	5.3	5.9	6.5	7.4	8.1	8.8	10.3	11.8	—	—	—
10'	10'	1.0	1.5	2.0	2.5	3.0	3.5	4.0	5.0	6.0	7.0	8.0	9.0	10.0	11.0	12.0	—	—	—	—	—
	14'	0.9	1.3	1.7	2.1	2.6	3.0	3.4	4.3	5.1	6.0	6.9	7.8	8.6	9.5	10.4	12.0	—	—	—	—
	20'	0.7	1.1	1.5	1.9	2.3	2.6	3.0	3.7	4.5	5.3	6.0	6.8	7.5	8.3	9.0	10.5	12.0	—	—	—
	30'	0.7	1.0	1.3	1.7	2.0	2.3	2.7	3.3	4.0	4.7	5.3	6.0	6.6	7.3	8.0	9.4	10.6	—	—	—
	40'	0.6	0.9	1.2	1.6	1.9	2.2	2.5	3.1	3.7	4.4	5.0	5.6	6.2	6.9	7.5	8.7	10.0	12.5	—	—
	60'	0.6	0.9	1.2	1.5	1.7	2.0	2.3	2.9	3.5	4.1	4.7	5.3	5.9	6.5	7.1	8.2	9.4	11.7	—	—
12'	12'	0.8	1.2	1.7	2.1	2.5	2.9	3.3	4.2	5.0	5.8	6.7	7.5	8.4	9.2	10.0	11.7	—	—	—	—
	16'	0.7	1.1	1.5	1.8	2.2	2.5	2.9	3.6	4.4	5.1	5.8	6.5	7.2	8.0	8.7	10.2	11.6	—	—	—
	24'	0.6	0.9	1.2	1.6	1.9	2.2	2.5	3.1	3.7	4.4	5.0	5.6	6.2	6.9	7.5	8.7	10.0	12.5	—	—
	36'	0.6	0.8	1.1	1.4	1.7	1.9	2.2	2.8	3.3	3.9	4.4	5.0	5.5	6.0	6.6	7.8	8.8	11.0	—	—
	50'	0.5	0.8	1.0	1.3	1.5	1.8	2.1	2.6	3.1	3.6	4.1	4.6	5.1	5.6	6.2	7.2	8.2	10.2	—	—
	70'	0.5	0.7	1.0	1.2	1.5	1.7	2.0	2.4	2.9	3.4	3.9	4.4	4.9	5.4	5.8	6.8	7.8	9.7	12.2	—
14'	14'	0.7	1.1	1.4	1.8	2.1	2.5	2.9	3.6	4.3	5.0	5.7	6.4	7.1	7.8	8.5	10.0	11.4	—	—	—
	20'	0.6	0.9	1.2	1.5	1.8	2.1	2.4	3.0	3.6	4.2	4.9	5.5	6.1	6.7	7.3	8.6	9.8	12.3	—	—
	30'	0.5	0.8	1.0	1.3	1.6	1.8	2.1	2.6	3.1	3.7	4.2	4.7	5.2	5.8	6.3	7.3	8.4	10.5	—	—
	42'	0.5	0.7	1.0	1.2	1.4	1.7	1.9	2.4	2.9	3.3	3.8	4.3	4.7	5.2	5.7	6.7	7.6	9.5	11.9	—
	60'	0.4	0.7	0.9	1.1	1.3	1.5	1.8	2.2	2.6	3.1	3.5	3.9	4.4	4.8	5.2	6.1	7.0	8.8	10.9	—
	90'	0.4	0.6	0.8	1.0	1.2	1.4	1.6	2.0	2.5	2.9	3.3	3.7	4.1	4.5	5.0	5.8	6.6	8.3	10.3	12.4
17'	17'	0.6	0.9	1.2	1.5	1.8	2.1	2.3	2.9	3.5	4.1	4.7	5.3	5.9	6.5	7.0	8.2	9.4	11.7	—	—
	25'	0.5	0.7	1.0	1.2	1.5	1.7	2.0	2.5	3.0	3.5	4.0	4.5	5.0	5.5	6.0	7.0	8.0	10.0	12.5	—
	35'	0.4	0.7	0.9	1.1	1.3	1.5	1.7	2.2	2.6	3.1	3.5	3.9	4.4	4.8	5.2	6.1	7.0	8.7	10.9	—
	50'	0.4	0.6	0.8	1.0	1.2	1.4	1.6	2.0	2.4	2.8	3.1	3.5	3.9	4.3	4.5	5.4	6.2	7.7	9.7	11.6
	80'	0.4	0.5	0.7	0.9	1.1	1.2	1.4	1.8	2.1	2.5	2.9	3.3	3.6	4.0	4.3	5.1	5.8	7.2	9.0	10.9
	120'	0.3	0.5	0.7	0.8	1.0	1.2	1.3	1.7	2.0	2.3	2.7	3.0	3.4	3.7	4.0	4.7	5.4	6.7	8.4	10.1
20'	20'	0.5	0.7	1.0	1.2	1.5	1.7	2.0	2.5	3.0	3.5	4.0	4.5	5.0	5.5	6.0	7.0	8.0	10.0	12.5	—
	30'	0.4	0.6	0.8	1.0	1.2	1.5	1.7	2.1	2.5	2.9	3.3	3.7	4.1	4.5	4.9	5.8	6.6	8.2	10.3	12.4
	45'	0.4	0.5	0.7	0.9	1.1	1.3	1.4	1.8	2.2	2.5	2.9	3.3	3.6	4.0	4.3	5.1	5.8	7.2	9.1	10.9
	60'	0.3	0.5	0.7	0.8	1.0	1.2	1.3	1.7	2.0	2.3	2.7	3.0	3.4	3.7	4.0	4.7	5.4	6.7	8.4	10.1
	90'	0.3	0.5	0.6	0.8	0.9	1.1	1.2	1.5	1.8	2.1	2.4	2.7	3.0	3.3	3.6	4.2	4.8	6.0	7.5	9.0
	150'	0.3	0.4	0.6	0.7	0.8	1.0	1.1	1.4	1.7	2.0	2.3	2.6	2.9	3.2	3.4	4.0	4.6	5.7	7.2	8.6
24'	24'	0.4	0.6	0.8	1.0	1.2	1.5	1.7	2.1	2.5	2.9	3.3	3.7	4.1	4.5	5.0	5.8	6.7	8.2	10.3	12.4
	32'	0.4	0.5	0.7	0.9	1.1	1.3	1.5	1.8	2.2	2.6	2.9	3.3	3.6	4.0	4.3	5.1	5.8	7.2	9.0	11.0
	50'	0.3	0.5	0.6	0.8	0.9	1.1	1.2	1.5	1.8	2.2	2.5	2.8	3.1	3.4	3.7	4.4	5.0	6.2	7.8	9.4
	70'	0.3	0.4	0.6	0.7	0.8	1.0	1.1	1.4	1.7	2.0	2.2	2.5	2.8	3.0	3.3	3.8	4.4	5.5	6.9	8.2
	100'	0.3	0.4	0.5	0.6	0.8	0.9	1.0	1.3	1.6	1.8	2.1	2.4	2.6	2.9	3.1	3.7	4.2	5.2	6.5	7.9
	160'	0.2	0.4	0.5	0.6	0.7	0.8	1.0	1.2	1.4	1.7	1.9	2.1	2.4	2.6	2.8	3.3	3.8	4.7	5.9	7.1
30'	30'	0.3	0.5	0.7	0.8	1.0	1.2	1.3	1.7	2.0	2.3	2.7	3.0	3.3	3.7	4.0	4.7	5.4	6.7	8.4	10.0
	45'	0.3	0.4	0.6	0.7	0.8	1.0	1.1	1.4	1.7	1.9	2.2	2.5	2.7	3.0	3.3	3.8	4.4	5.5	6.9	8.2
	60'	0.3	0.4	0.5	0.6	0.7	0.9	1.0	1.2	1.5	1.7	2.0	2.2	2.5	2.7	3.0	3.5	4.0	5.0	6.2	7.4
	90'	0.2	0.3	0.4	0.6	0.7	0.8	0.9	1.1	1.3	1.6	1.8	2.0	2.2	2.5	2.7	3.1	3.6	4.5	5.6	6.7
	150'	0.2	0.3	0.4	0.5	0.6	0.7	0.8	1.0	1.2	1.4	1.6	1.8	2.0	2.2	2.4	2.8	3.2	4.0	5.0	5.9
	200'	0.2	0.3	0.4	0.5	0.6	0.7	0.8	1.0	1.1	1.3	1.5	1.7	1.9	2.0	2.2	2.6	3.0	3.7	4.7	5.6
36'	36'	0.3	0.4	0.6	0.7	0.8	1.0	1.1	1.4	1.7	1.9	2.2	2.5	2.8	3.0	3.3	3.9	4.4	5.5	6.9	8.3
	50'	0.2	0.4	0.5	0.6	0.7	0.8	1.0	1.2	1.4	1.7	1.9	2.1	2.5	2.6	2.9	3.3	3.8	4.8	5.9	7.2
	75'	0.2	0.3	0.4	0.5	0.6	0.7	0.8	1.0	1.2	1.4	1.6	1.8	2.0	2.3	2.5	2.9	3.3	4.1	5.1	6.1
	100'	0.2	0.3	0.4	0.5	0.6	0.7	0.8	0.9	1.1	1.3	1.5	1.7	1.9	2.1	2.3	2.6	3.0	3.8	4.7	5.7
	150'	0.2	0.3	0.3	0.4	0.5	0.6	0.7	0.9	1.0	1.2	1.4	1.6	1.7	1.9	2.1	2.4	2.8	3.5	4.3	5.2
	200'	0.2	0.2	0.3	0.4	0.5	0.6	0.7	0.8	1.0	1.1	1.3	1.5	1.6	1.8	2.0	2.3	2.6	3.3	4.1	4.9

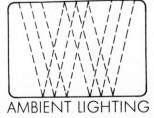

AMBIENT LIGHTING 61

Table 4: Room Cavity Ratios (Continued)

Room Dimensions Width	Length	1.0'	1.5'	2.0'	2.5'	3.0'	3.5'	4.0'	5.0'	6.0'	7.0'	8'	9'	10'	11'	12'	14'	16'	20'	25'	30'
42'	42'	0.2	0.4	0.5	0.6	0.7	0.8	1.0	1.2	1.4	1.6	1.9	2.1	2.4	2.6	2.8	3.3	3.8	4.7	5.9	7.1
	60'	0.2	0.3	0.4	0.5	0.6	0.7	0.8	1.0	1.2	1.4	1.6	1.8	2.0	2.2	2.4	2.8	3.2	4.0	5.0	6.0
	90'	0.2	0.3	0.3	0.4	0.5	0.6	0.7	0.9	1.0	1.2	1.4	1.6	1.7	1.9	2.1	2.4	2.8	3.5	4.4	5.2
	140'	0.2	0.2	0.3	0.4	0.5	0.5	0.6	0.8	0.9	1.1	1.2	1.4	1.5	1.7	1.9	2.2	2.5	3.1	3.9	4.6
	200'	0.1	0.2	0.3	0.4	0.4	0.5	0.6	0.7	0.9	1.0	1.1	1.3	1.4	1.6	1.7	2.0	2.3	2.9	3.6	4.3
	300'	0.1	0.2	0.3	0.3	0.4	0.5	0.5	0.7	0.8	0.9	1.1	1.3	1.4	1.5	1.7	1.9	2.2	2.8	3.5	4.2
50'	50'	0.2	0.3	0.4	0.5	0.6	0.7	0.8	1.0	1.2	1.4	1.6	1.8	2.0	2.2	2.4	2.8	3.2	4.0	5.0	6.0
	70'	0.2	0.3	0.3	0.4	0.5	0.6	0.7	0.9	1.0	1.2	1.4	1.5	1.7	1.9	2.0	2.4	2.7	3.4	4.3	5.1
	100'	0.1	0.2	0.3	0.4	0.4	0.5	0.6	0.7	0.9	1.0	1.2	1.3	1.5	1.6	1.8	2.1	2.4	3.0	3.7	4.5
	150'	0.1	0.2	0.3	0.3	0.4	0.5	0.5	0.7	0.8	0.9	1.1	1.2	1.3	1.5	1.6	1.9	2.1	2.7	3.3	4.0
	300'	0.1	0.2	0.2	0.3	0.3	0.4	0.5	0.6	0.7	0.8	0.9	1.0	1.1	1.3	1.4	1.6	1.9	2.3	2.9	3.5
60'	60'	0.2	0.2	0.3	0.4	0.5	0.6	0.7	0.8	1.0	1.2	1.3	1.5	1.7	1.8	2.0	2.3	2.7	3.3	4.2	5.0
	100'	0.1	0.2	0.3	0.3	0.4	0.5	0.5	0.7	0.8	0.9	1.1	1.2	1.3	1.5	1.6	1.9	2.1	2.7	3.3	4.0
	150'	0.1	0.2	0.2	0.3	0.3	0.4	0.5	0.6	0.7	0.8	0.9	1.0	1.2	1.3	1.4	1.6	1.9	2.3	2.9	3.5
	300'	0.1	0.1	0.2	0.2	0.3	0.3	0.4	0.5	0.6	0.7	0.8	0.9	1.0	1.1	1.2	1.4	1.6	2.0	2.5	3.0
75'	75'	0.1	0.2	0.3	0.3	0.4	0.5	0.5	0.7	0.8	0.9	1.1	1.2	1.3	1.5	1.6	1.9	2.1	2.7	3.3	4.0
	120'	0.1	0.2	0.2	0.3	0.3	0.4	0.4	0.5	0.6	0.8	0.9	1.0	1.1	1.2	1.3	1.5	1.7	2.2	2.7	3.3
	200'	0.1	0.1	0.2	0.2	0.3	0.3	0.4	0.5	0.5	0.6	0.7	0.8	0.9	1.0	1.1	1.3	1.5	1.8	2.3	2.7
	300'	0.1	0.1	0.2	0.2	0.2	0.3	0.3	0.4	0.5	0.6	0.7	0.7	0.8	0.9	1.0	1.2	1.3	1.7	2.1	2.5
100'	100'	0.1	0.1	0.2	0.2	0.3	0.3	0.4	0.5	0.6	0.7	0.8	0.9	1.0	1.1	1.2	1.4	1.6	2.0	2.5	3.0
	200'	0.1	0.1	0.1	0.2	0.2	0.3	0.3	0.4	0.4	0.5	0.6	0.7	0.7	0.8	0.9	1.0	1.2	1.5	1.9	2.2
	300'	0.1	0.1	0.1	0.2	0.2	0.2	0.3	0.3	0.4	0.5	0.5	0.6	0.7	0.7	0.8	0.9	1.1	1.3	1.7	2.0
150'	150'	0.1	0.1	0.1	0.2	0.2	0.2	0.3	0.3	0.4	0.5	0.5	0.6	0.7	0.7	0.8	0.9	1.1	1.3	1.7	2.0
	300'	—	0.1	0.1	0.1	0.1	0.2	0.2	0.2	0.3	0.3	0.4	0.5	0.5	0.6	0.6	0.7	0.8	1.0	1.2	1.5
200'	200'	—	0.1	0.1	0.1	0.1	0.2	0.2	0.2	0.3	0.3	0.4	0.5	0.5	0.6	0.6	0.7	0.8	1.0	1.2	1.5
	300'	—	0.1	0.1	0.1	0.1	0.1	0.2	0.2	0.2	0.3	0.3	0.4	0.4	0.5	0.5	0.6	0.7	0.8	1.0	1.2
300'	300'	—	—	0.1	0.1	0.1	0.1	0.1	0.2	0.2	0.2	0.3	0.3	0.3	0.4	0.4	0.5	0.5	0.6	0.7	0.8
500'	500'	—	—	—	—	0.1	0.1	0.1	0.1	0.1	0.1	0.2	0.2	0.2	0.2	0.2	0.3	0.3	0.4	0.5	0.6

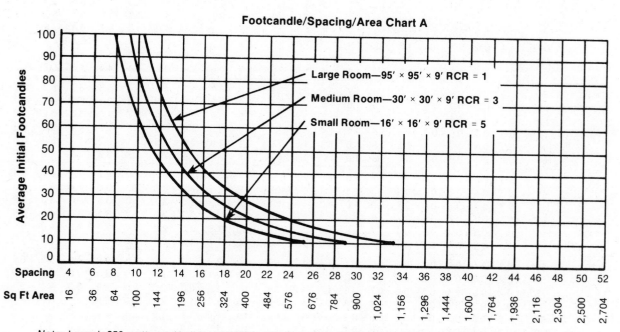

Footcandle/Spacing/Area Chart A

Large Room—95' × 95' × 9' RCR = 1

Medium Room—30' × 30' × 9' RCR = 3

Small Room—16' × 16' × 9' RCR = 5

Note: Lamp is 250-watt metal halide at 19,500 total initial lumens. Assumptions: 80/50/20 reflectances. All footcandles are initial horizontal at work plane height of 2'6".

For super metal halide 250-watt lamp at 23,000 lumens, multiply all footcandles by 1.18.

For super metal halide 175-watt lamp at 15,000 lumens, multiply all footcandles by 0.77.

All lamps are coated.

Footcandle/Spacing/Area Chart B

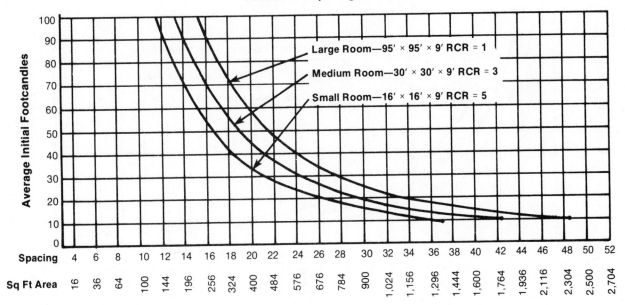

Note: Lamp is 400-watt metal halide at 40,000 total initial lumens. Assumptions: 80/50/20 reflectances. All footcandles are initial horizontal at work plane height of 2'6".

For 250-watt super metal halide lamp at 23,000 lumens, multiply all footcandles by 0.58.

For 250-watt standard metal halide lamp at 19,500 lumens, multiply all footcandles by 0.49.

All lamps are coated.

Footcandle/Spacing/Area Chart C

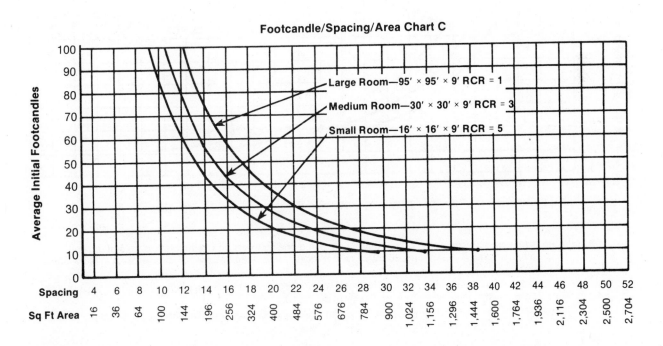

Note: Lamp is 250-watt high pressure sodium at 26,000 total initial lumens. Assumptions: 80/50/20 reflectances. All footcandles are initial horizontal at work plane height of 2'6".

All lamps are diffuse.

63

Footcandle/Spacing/Area Chart D

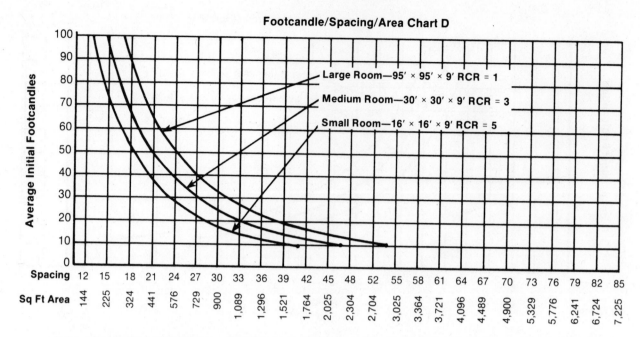

Large Room—95' × 95' × 9' RCR = 1
Medium Room—30' × 30' × 9' RCR = 3
Small Room—16' × 16' × 9' RCR = 5

Note: Lamp is 400-watt high pressure sodium at 47,500 total initial lumens. Assumptions: 80/50/20 reflectances. All footcandles are initial horizontal at work plane height of 2'6".

For 250-watt high pressure sodium lamp at 26,000 lumens, multiply all footcandles by 0.55.

All lamps are diffuse.

Footcandle/Spacing/Area Chart E1

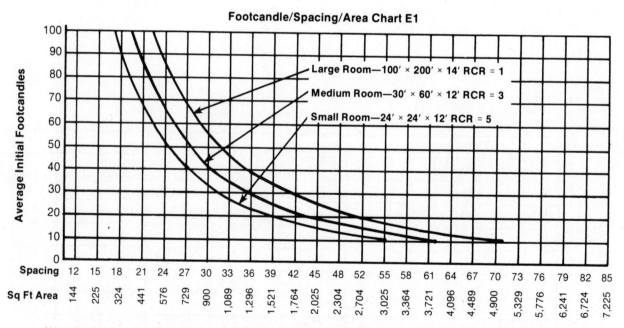

Large Room—100' × 200' × 14' RCR = 1
Medium Room—30' × 60' × 12' RCR = 3
Small Room—24' × 24' × 12' RCR = 5

Note: Lamps are one 400-watt coated super metal halide and one 400-watt diffuse high pressure sodium at 87,500 total initial lumens. Assumptions: 80/50/20 reflectances. All footcandles are initial horizontal at work plane height of 2'6".

For one 250-watt coated super metal halide lamp and one 250-watt diffuse high pressure sodium lamp at 49,000 total initial lumens, multiply all footcandles by 0.56.

For one 250-watt coated standard metal halide lamp and one 250-watt diffuse high pressure sodium lamp at 45,500 lamp initial lumens, multiply all footcandles by 0.52.

Footcandle/Spacing/Area Chart E2

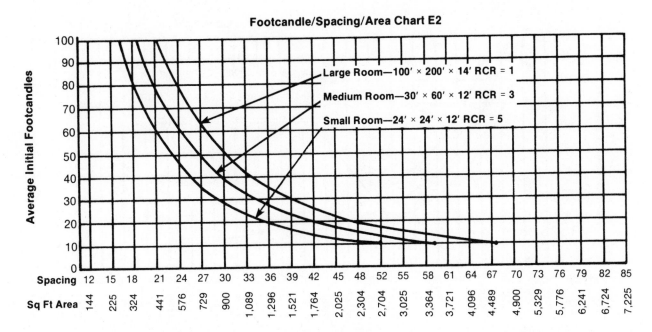

Average Initial Footcandles

Large Room—100′ × 200′ × 14′ RCR = 1
Medium Room—30′ × 60′ × 12′ RCR = 3
Small Room—24′ × 24′ × 12′ RCR = 5

Spacing	12	15	18	21	24	27	30	33	36	39	42	45	48	52	55	58	61	64	67	70	73	76	79	82	85
Sq Ft Area	144	225	324	441	576	729	900	1,089	1,296	1,521	1,764	2,025	2,304	2,704	3,025	3,364	3,721	4,096	4,489	4,900	5,329	5,776	6,241	6,724	7,225

Note: Lamps are two 400-watt metal halide at 80,000 total initial lumens. Assumptions: 80/50/20 reflectances. All footcandles are initial horizontal at work plane height of 2′6″.

For two 250-watt super metal halide lamps at 46,000 total initial lumens, multiply all footcandles by 0.58.

For two 250-watt standard metal halide lamps at 39,000 total initial lumens, multiply all footcandles by 0.49.

All lamps are coated.

Footcandle/Spacing/Area Chart E3

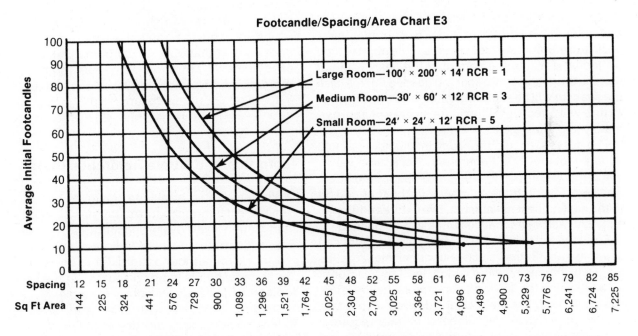

Average Initial Footcandles

Large Room—100′ × 200′ × 14′ RCR = 1
Medium Room—30′ × 60′ × 12′ RCR = 3
Small Room—24′ × 24′ × 12′ RCR = 5

Spacing	12	15	18	21	24	27	30	33	36	39	42	45	48	52	55	58	61	64	67	70	73	76	79	82	85
Sq Ft Area	144	225	324	441	576	729	900	1,089	1,296	1,521	1,764	2,025	2,304	2,704	3,025	3,364	3,721	4,096	4,489	4,900	5,329	5,776	6,241	6,724	7,225

Note: Lamps are two 400-watt diffuse high pressure sodium at 95,000 total initial lumens. Assumptions: 80/50/20 reflectances. All footcandles are initial horizontal at work plane height of 2′6″.

For two 250-watt diffuse high pressure sodium lamps at 52,000 total initial lumens, multiply all footcandles by 0.55.

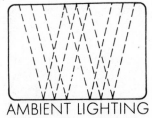

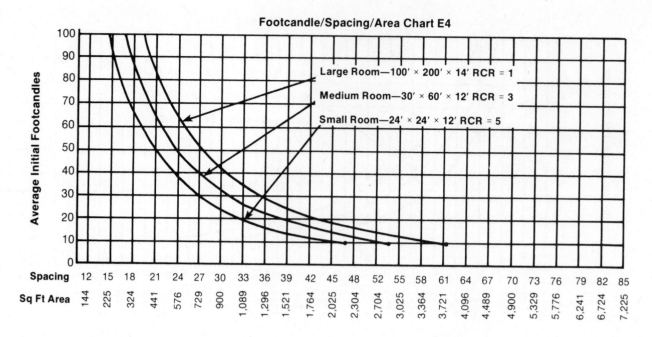

Footcandle/Spacing/Area Chart E4

Large Room—100' × 200' × 14' RCR = 1

Medium Room—30' × 60' × 12' RCR = 3

Small Room—24' × 24' × 12' RCR = 5

Spacing	12	15	18	21	24	27	30	33	36	39	42	45	48	52	55	58	61	64	67	70	73	76	79	82	85
Sq Ft Area	144	225	324	441	576	729	900	1,089	1,296	1,521	1,764	2,025	2,304	2,704	3,025	3,364	3,721	4,096	4,489	4,900	5,329	5,776	6,241	6,724	7,225

Note: Lamps are one 400-watt coated metal halide and one 250-watt diffuse high pressure sodium at 66,000 total initial lumens. Assumptions: 80/50/20 reflectances. All footcandles are initial horizontal at work plane height of 2'6".

medium size, 30' × 30' × 9', room. The system must generate an initial illuminance level of 40 footcandles, and 250-watt metal halide lamps are the designer's first choice as a light source.

The first step in the process is to locate the 40 footcandle level at the left side of Chart A (page 62) and extend this point over to the right until it intersects the medium size room curve. This point is then projected down to the bottom of the chart where it locates the exact fixture spacing needed. In this case the spacing will be slightly greater than 14', and each fixture will effectively illuminate an area of approximately 196 square feet.

The total area of the room in question is 900 square feet (30' × 30'); therefore, 900 square feet ÷ 196 square feet per fixture = 4.59 fixtures needed. Because any fractional number must be rounded off to the next highest full number, five fixtures equipped with 250-watt metal halide lamps will be needed.

From the notes beneath Chart A, the designer can see that substituting a 250-watt super metal halide lamp will increase the footcandle level by a factor of 1.18. By using the 250-watt super metal halide lamp, it is also possible to maintain the desired 40 footcandle level and reduce the number of fixtures required. The new fixture count is found by dividing the old fixture number by the given proration factor. So in this example, 4.59 fixtures ÷ 1.18 = 3.89 or four 250-watt, super metal halide-equipped fixtures will be

required. This is obviously the superior system since it reduces the number of fixtures needed and lends itself to a more even and uniform layout, as shown in Fig. 19. Remember, fixtures must not be located more than 14' apart.

If for some reason super metal halide, 175-watt lamps are used, the original five fixtures would produce an illumination level of approximately 40 footcandles × 0.77 proration factor = 31 footcandles. If the desired 40 footcandle level is maintained, six fixtures (4.59 original fixtures ÷ 0.77 proration factor = 5.96 substitute fixtures) will be required.

Isofootcandle Curve Reference Plots

When mounted or placed at a given height, each SPI indirect lighting fixture generates a unique set of illumination levels over a specific area. For example, Fig. 19 illustrates the footcandle levels generated by the four symmetrical optic fixtures equipped with super metal halide lamps discussed in the previous footcandle/spacing/area chart example.

Lighting levels and distributions for given lamp-fixture combinations are graphically expressed in computer tabulated isofootcandle curve reference plots. Table 5 (page 68) lists the isofootcandle curve reference plot data for various HID light fixtures used in indirect interior lighting applications. Reproductions of the actual reference plots can be found in Appendix B in the back of this handbook.

For example, Table 5 lists reference plot A as that of a metal halide, MS250/C/HOR lamp which pro-

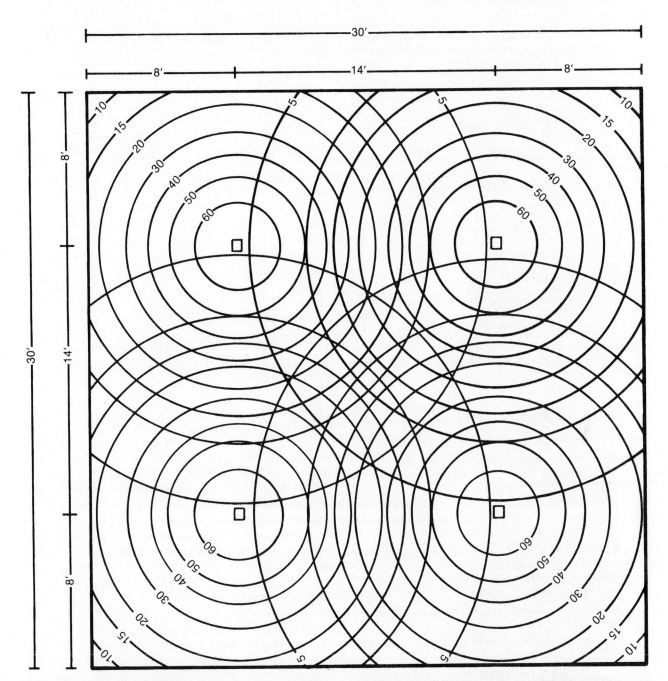

Fig. 19: Equally spaced fixtures create a uniform footcandle level throughout the 30′ x 30′ room. Note the footcandle contributions from each light fixture.

duces 23,000 initial lumens. The lamp is placed in a fixture equipped with a wide, symmetrical, single lamp optical system. The recommended fixture mounting height above the finished floor is 7′ for either fixed single fixtures or portable fixtures or 5′6″ for freestanding units or portable fixtures. The ceiling height in both cases is 9′, and the ceiling height factor is 1.0 for 7′ mounting heights and 0.80 for 5′6″ mounting heights. All footcandle levels on the reference plot must be multiplied by this ceiling height factor. Because the computer tabulation of plot A is based on a 7′ mounting height, the illumination values will not change and the ceiling factor is 1.0.

However, if a metal halide, MS250/C/HOR lamp is placed in a wide, symmetrical, single lamp fixture and mounted at 5′6″, all footcandle values on plot A must be lowered by a factor of 0.80.

The recommended usage section of Table 5 lists the SPI Lighting Luminaire or Fixture Series according to fixture type (freestanding, portable, fixed single, and fixed dual) and series letter designation (SPA, SPQ, SPB, etc.). In this way, the lighting de-

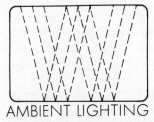

AMBIENT LIGHTING 67

Table 5: Isofootcandle Curve Reference Plot Data for Interior HID Lighting

Plot	Lamp Description[1] Type	Lamp Description[1] Designation	Lamp Description[1] Lumens	Optical Description	Luminaire Height[2]	Ceiling Height[3]
A	MH	MS250/C/HOR	23,000	Wide, Symmetrical, Single Lamp	7' 5'6"	9' 9'
B	MH	MS400/C/HOR	40,000	Wide, Symmetrical, Single Lamp	6' 5'6"	9' 9'
C	HPS	LU250/D	26,000	Wide, Symmetrical, Single Lamp	7' 5'6"	9' 9'
D	HPS	LU400/D	47,500	Wide, Symmetrical, Single Lamp	7' 5'6"	10' 10'
E	MH/HPS	MS400/C/HOR LU400/D	87,500	Wide, Symmetrical, Dual Lamp	7'	12'
F	MH	MS250/C/HOR	23,000	Wide, Symmetrical with Drop-In Asymmetrical Kit, Single Lamp	7' 5'6"	9' 9'
G	MH	MS400/C/HOR	40,000	Wide, Symmetrical with Drop-In Asymmetrical Kit, Single Lamp	6' 5'6"	9' 9'
H	HPS	LU250/D	26,000	Wide, Symmetrical with Drop-In Asymmetrical Kit, Single Lamp	7' 5'6"	9' 9'
I	HPS	LU400/D	47,500	Wide, Symmetrical with Drop-In Asymmetrical Kit, Single Lamp	6' 5'6"	10' 10'
J	MH/HPS	MS250/C/HOR LU250/D	49,000	Forward Throw, Asymmetrical, Dual Lamp	8'	12'
K	MH/HPS	MS250/C/HOR LU250/D	49,000	Forward Throw, Asymmetrical, Dual Lamp with Backlight Deflector	8'	12'
L	MH/HPS	MS400/C/HOR LU400/D	87,500	Forward Throw, Asymmetrical, Dual Lamp	7'	12'
M	MH/HPS	MS400/C/HOR LU400/D	87,500	Forward Throw, Asymmetrical, Dual Lamp with Backlight Deflector	7'	12'

Notes: In all cases ceiling brightness is less than 500 footlamberts.
1. Refer to **Table 7: Lamp Proration Factors for Indirect Indoor HID Lighting** (page 72) for information concerning the use of lower wattage lamps or different lamp combinations in the same optical assembly.
2. Luminaire height is the height the luminaire is located above the finished floor.
3. Ceiling height is the height the ceiling is located above the finished floor.

Table 5: Isofootcandle Curve Reference Plot Data for Interior HID Lighting (Continued)

Height Factor[4]	Freestanding					Portable				Fixed Single				Dual	
	SPA	SPQ	SPB	SPR	SPE	SPF	SPC	SPJ	SPD	SFB	SFD	SFF	SFG	SDD	SDE
1.0						•	•	•	•	•	•	•	•		
.80	•	•	•	•	•	•	•	•	•						
1.0						•	•	•	•	•	•	•	•		
.90	•	•	•	•	•	•	•	•	•						
1.0						•	•	•	•	•	•	•	•		
.80	•	•	•	•	•	•	•	•	•						
1.0						•	•	•	•	•	•	•	•		
.77	•	•	•	•	•	•	•	•	•						
1.0															•
1.0						•	•	•	•	•	•	•	•		
.80	•	•	•	•	•	•	•	•	•						
1.0						•	•	•	•	•	•	•	•		
.90	•	•	•	•	•	•	•	•	•						
1.0						•	•	•	•	•	•	•	•		
.80	•	•	•	•	•	•	•	•	•						
1.0						•	•	•	•	•	•	•	•		
.90	•	•	•	•	•	•	•	•	•						
1.0														•	
1.0														•	
1.0															•
1.0															•

Notes: 4. Height Factor: 1.0 is the height factor for the isofootcandle curve reference plots A through M. To find the exact illumination levels when luminaires are placed at heights lower than those used for the computer tabulation, multiply all illumination values found on the curve by the listed height factor. For example, as shown in the table, if a wide, symmetrical, single lamp luminaire equipped with a MS250/C/HOR lamp was set at a height of 5'6", all illumination values found on plot A should be multiplied by a factor of 0.80.

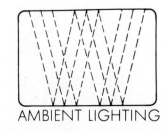

AMBIENT LIGHTING 69

signer knows the exact classification of the SPI fixture that he or she is considering for a particular application.

As Fig. 20 illustrates, the actual isofootcandle curve reference plot computer printout is produced on paper divided into 2' grid increments. The dark square represents the location of the fixture, and the curved lines represent points of equal illumination. The curve closest to the fixture represents points of 60 footcandle illumination, the next closest line represents 50 footcandles, etc. Because the patterns produced are symmetrical, only portions of the total light pattern are reproduced. The total symmetrical or asymmetrical pattern can then be reproduced from this partial information.

Plots A through E coincide with the lamp-fixture combinations used in the Footcandle/Spacing/Area Charts A (super metal halide), B, C, D, and E1. Plots F through M illustrate other popular lamp-fixture combinations for both symmetrical and asymmetrical or forward throw optic systems.

Isofootcandle Curve Design Method

The computer printout plots A through M can be a great aid in solving many unique lighting problems in odd-shaped rooms or in rooms with irregular or special desk or work station spacings. It is possible to locate a freestanding or portable unit adjacent to a special work station location and predict the exact footcandle levels in the area by referring to the proper isofootcandle curve reference plot. As shown in Fig. 19 (page 67) and Fig. 21, the printout curves can be transferred to the actual layout drawing so that precise footcandle levels can be found at given points.

Figure 21 illustrates a 30' × 30' room illuminated with two wall mounted luminaires positioned at the midpoint of opposite walls. The fixtures are mounted at a height of 8' and equipped with forward throw, asymmetrical, dual lamp optical systems. Each luminaire contains one 250-watt metal halide lamp and one 250-watt high pressure sodium lamp for a combined initial lumen output of 49,000 lumens. Isofootcandle curve reference plot J illustrates the illumination pattern generated.

Each point in the 30' × 30' room receives footcandle contributions from each of the fixtures. For example, a point approximately 6' in front of the fixture receives 60 footcandles from the nearest fixture and about 5 footcandles from the fixture on the opposite wall, providing a total illumination level of 65 footcandles—the highest footcandle level occurring in the room. A minimum footcandle level of about 10 footcandles exists in the corners of the room. This results in an absolute maximum/minimum remote area brightness ratio of 6.5:1, an excellent uniformity indicator.

If a desk were located in the room as shown, the maximum illumination on the desk area would be 65 footcandles. The minimum illumination on the desk would be about 35 footcandles for an immediate area brightness ratio of better than 2:1, also quite acceptable by today's lighting standards. Moderate area brightness ratios are well within the 5:1 standard set in Table 1 (page 49).

By using this grid system and the isofootcandle curve reference plots, a lighting designer can place fixtures at any desired spacing and quickly calculate the illumination levels and brightness uniformity ratios which exist in any area of the room. Remember, because SPI fixtures are indirect lighting fixtures, minimum fixture to ceiling distances must be maintained. For easy reference, these minimum distances are summarized in Table 6 (page 72).

Lamp Proration Factors. Table 5 does not list all of the possible lamp-fixture combinations usable in SPI indirect luminaires. It is possible to reduce or increase the illumination level of a given system by simply substituting other high intensity discharge lamps. All illumination values occurring on the original isofootcandle curve reference plot are then prorated up or down by multiplying them by the proper lamp proration factor listed in Table 7 (page 72).

For example, if the 250-watt metal halide, MS250/C/HOR lamp used to produce plot A in Table 5 were replaced by a 175-watt metal halide, MS175/C/HOR listed in Table 7, all footcandle levels found on the isofootcandle curve reference plot A would be multiplied by a factor of 0.652. This means that the isofootcandle line nearest the fixture in Fig. 20 would now designate 60 footcandles × 0.652 proration factor = 39 footcandles, etc.

By using the footcandle/spacing/area charts for regularly shaped areas and the isofootcandle curve reference plots found in Appendix B for irregular or unusually shaped or spaced areas, you will be able to design interior, ambient lighting systems in very short periods of time.

HALO HIGH INTENSITY DISCHARGE DOWNLIGHTS

No discussion of indoor HID ambient lighting would be complete without a discussion of the mer-

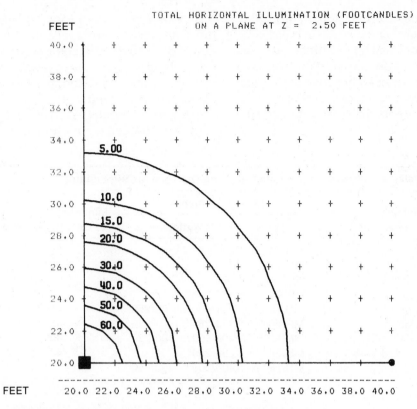

TOTAL HORIZONTAL ILLUMINATION (FOOTCANDLES)
ON A PLANE AT Z = 2.50 FEET

Fig. 20: The computer tabulated isofootcandle curve reference plot A.

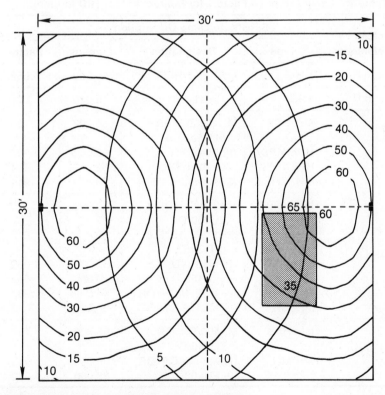

Fig. 21: A two fixture design layout based on information found on isofootcandle curve reference plot J. Because the illumination levels and uniformity ratios can be precisely predicted, fixtures and/or furniture can be positioned to create the finest visibility possible.

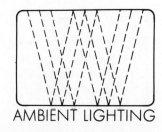

AMBIENT LIGHTING 71

its and uses of HID recessed downlight fixtures (Fig. 22). Halo HID downlights can be used in areas such as alcoves, hallways, or small private offices in cases where HID indirect freestanding, portable, or fixed SPI luminaires cannot be used because of physical or dimensional restrictions. Because of their aesthetic appeal, many clients may prefer to use HID downlights in several applications.

An extremely wide variety of HID downlight fixtures and styles are available. When choosing a downlight design, the color rendering characteristics of the HID lamp must always match the color scheme of the room and any SPI indirect lighting equipment contained in it.

Also, the recessed HID downlight must provide an extremely low ceiling brightness. Table 8 lists some

Table 6: Minimum Luminaire to Ceiling Distance for SPI Lighting

Luminaire Optics	Lamp Information		Minimum Luminaire to Ceiling Distance
	Type	Wattage	
Wide	MH	250	22″
Wide	MH	400	28″
Wide	HPS	250	24″
Wide	HPS	400	30″
Dual Lamp Wide	MH/HPS	400/400 or 400/250	48″
Dual Lamp Wide	MH/HPS	250/250	48″
Dual Lamp Forward Throw	MH/HPS	400/400 or 400/250	48″
Dual Lamp Forward Throw	MH/HPS	250/250	48″
Dual Housing, Separate Optics	MH/HPS	400/400 or 400/250	72″

Table 7: Lamp Proration Factors for Indirect Indoor HID Lighting

Isofootcandle Plot Reference*	Substitute Lamp Description			Proration Factor
	Type	Designation	Lumens	
A and F	MH	MS175/C/HOR	15,000	.652
C and H	HPS	LU150/D	15,000	.577
E	MH/HPS	MS400/C/HOR & LU250/D	66,000	.754
	HPS/HPS	(2) LU400/D	95,000	1.090
	HPS/HPS	(2) LU250/D	52,000	.594
	MH/MH	(2) MS400/C/HOR	80,000	.914
J and K	MH/HPS	MS250/C/HOR & LU150/D	38,000	.776
	MH/HPS	MS175/C/HOR & LU150/D	30,000	.612
	HPS/HPS	(2) LU250/D	52,000	1.060
	HPS/HPS	(2) LU150/D	30,000	.612
	MH/MH	(2) MS250/C/HOR	46,000	.939
	MH/MH	(2) MS175/C/HOR	30,000	.612
L and M	MH/HPS	MS400/C/HOR & LU250/D	66,000	.754
	MH/MH	(2) MS400/C/HOR	80,000	.914
	HPS/HPS	(2) LU400/D	95,000	1.090

*Found in Appendix B.

of the common types of HID downlights which provide this low surface brightness. The table lists the fixture type, the optical system contained in it, and various wattages of metal halide and high pressure sodium lamps which can be successfully installed in the fixture.

Calculating "Cones of Light"

Under each wattage listing for metal halide and high pressure sodium lamps, Table 8 lists the Halo Lighting catalog number of the fixture (M1400, M1401, etc.) and a specification reference number (A5, A6, etc.). Specification reference numbers refer to the specific cones of light that these recessed downlights produce (Fig. 23). The cones of light printouts for all of the fixtures given in Table 8 can be found in Appendix C of this handbook.

As shown in Fig. 23, footcandle readings are given directly under the fixture at various possible work

Fig. 22: A Halo HID downlight fixture.

Table 8: Recessed HID Downlights "Cones of Light" Reference Data

Fixture Type	Optical Type	HPS Lamps				MH Lamps		
		70W	100W	150W	250W	175W	250W	400W
Recessed Open Reflector Downlights	Multiplier Cone	M1400 A5	M1401 A6	M1402 A7	—	M1702 A8	M1703 A9	M1704 A10
	Coilex Baffle	M1420 A16	M1421 A17	M1422 A18	—	M1732 A19	M1733 A20	—
Small Aperture Open Reflector Downlights	Specular Cone	M1440 B5	M1441 B6	M1442 B7	—	M1742 B8	M1743 B9	M1744 B10
	Coilex Baffle	M1450 B15	M1451 B16	M1452 B17	—	M1752 B18	M1753 B19	M1754 B20
Round Lens Downlight	Fresnel	M1460 C5	M1461 C6	M1462 C7	—	M1772 C8	M1773 C9	—
	Concave Prismatic	M1480 C14	M1481 C15	M1482 C16	—	M1792 C17	M1793 C18	—
2 × 2 Squares	Surface Prismatic	—	M1601 E4	M1602 E5	M1603 E6	M1902 E7	M1903 E8	M1904 E9
	Regressed Prismatic	—	M1611 E13	M1612 E14	M1613 E15	M1912 E16	M1913 E17	M1914 E18
	Aluminum Louver	—	M1621 E22	M1622 E23	M1623 E24	M1922 E25	M1923 E26	M1924 E27
Wall Washers	Coilex Baffle Offset Reflector	M1450WW G6	M1451WW G7	M1452WW G8	—	M1752WW G9	M1753WW G10	M1754WW G11

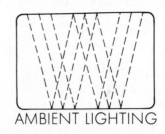

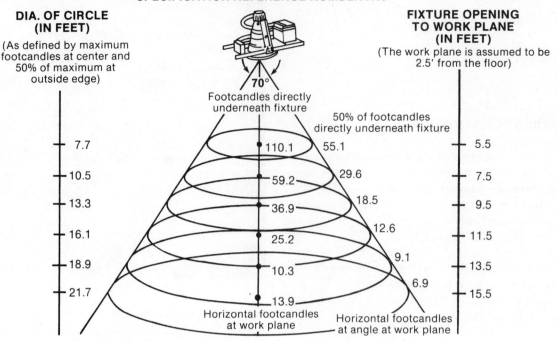

DIA. OF CIRCLE
(IN FEET)

(As defined by maximum
footcandles at center and
50% of maximum at
outside edge)

FIXTURE OPENING
TO WORK PLANE
(IN FEET)

(The work plane is assumed to be
2.5' from the floor)

70°

Footcandles directly
underneath fixture

50% of footcandles
directly underneath fixture

Dia.	Fc center	Fc 50%	Opening
7.7	110.1	55.1	5.5
10.5	59.2	29.6	7.5
13.3	36.9	18.5	9.5
16.1	25.2	12.6	11.5
18.9	10.3	9.1	13.5
21.7	13.9	6.9	15.5

Horizontal footcandles
at work plane

Horizontal footcandles
at angle at work plane

Fig. 23: "Cones of Light" simplify layout of fixtures and fixture comparison.

planes which are always assumed to be located 2'6" from the floor surface. The outer edge of the light cone is defined as the point at which the footcandle readings are 50% of the maximum footcandle readings occurring directly under the fixture. The beam angle of the fixture is determined from the size of the circle produced and is stated directly under the fixture. The diameter of this circle is given in the left-hand margin. Efficiency ratings and spacing to mounting height ratios are also shown beneath each cone.

As shown in Fig. 24, these cones of light are extremely useful in determining fixture spacing and for making fast light level calculations and comparisons. In this example, fixtures are recessed into a 12' ceiling so that the fixture to work plane distance is 12' – 2.5' = 9.5'. From Fig. 23 you can see that at this fixture opening to work plane distance, an illumination level of 36.9 footcandles exists at a point directly under the fixture opening. The diameter of the circle of light is 13.3', and the footcandle level at the edge of this "cone of light" is 18.5 footcandles.

HALO INCANDESCENT DOWNLIGHTS

Recessed incandescent downlights can also be used in a wide number of downlighting and accent lighting applications. These fixtures are often used

74 INTERIOR LIGHTING

EXAMPLE:
For quick calculation of fixture installation in 12' ceiling (fixture opening to work plane = 9.5').

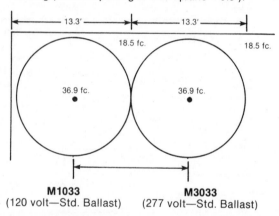

13.3' 13.3'

18.5 fc. 18.5 fc.

36.9 fc. 36.9 fc.

M1033
(120 volt—Std. Ballast)

M3033
(277 volt—Std. Ballast)

Fig. 24: Typical layout utilizing the information found in the "cones of light" data sheets found in Appendix C.

to provide auxiliary lighting for Halo High Intensity Discharge installations because their general styling and ceiling appearance complements the HID units. When used in this capacity, the incandescent downlights can be either wired to an emergency lighting wiring system or installed to operate when the HID units are in their starting mode.

As indicated in Table 9, regular incandescent downlights are equipped with standard "A" or "PS" bulb shape tungsten or tungsten halogen incandescent lamps. Under each lamp type the table lists the various wattages, the Halo Lighting catalog numbers of the fixtures (H4530, etc.), and a specific ref-

Table 9: Recessed Incandescent Downlights "Cones of Light" Reference Data

Fixture Type	Optical Type	Standard Tungsten Filament						Tungsten Halogen
		100W	150W	100W	150W	100W	150W	Q250W I.F.
Recessed Open Reflector Downlights	Multiplier Cone	H4530		H4531		H4532		H4501
		F3	F3A	F4	F4A	F5	F5A	—
	Coilex Baffle	H4540		H4541		H4542		H4511
		F6	F6A	F7	F7A	F8	F8A	—

erence number (F3, F3A, etc.) referring to the specific cones of light produced by these fixtures. "Cones of Light" printouts for Halo incandescent downlights can be found in Appendix D. Refer to the previous section **Calculating "Cones of Light"** (pages 73–74) for information on interpreting and using Halo "Cones of Light."

Accent Lighting Applications.   In addition to standard lamp incandescent downlights, the Halo H1499 or H7 Fit-all recessed fixture can be equipped with low voltage MR–16 tungsten halogen or low voltage PAR36 lamps. These fixtures can be used for direct downlighting, adjustable downlighting, wall washing, highlighting, and other accent lighting applications which do not require a great deal of design

flexibilty. (Refer to the detailed accent lighting information found later in Section II for a more complete understanding of accent lighting application principles and design methods.) Table 10 lists the pertinent data pertaining to low voltage incandescent downlighting. The isofootcandle plot reference numbers for the various fixture-lamp combinations refer to the actual computer generated isofootcandle curve reference plots found in Appendix E. These isofootcandle curve reference plots graphically illustrate the light distribution pattern and actual footcandle levels produced by a given lamp and fixture combination. They allow designers to work up lighting layouts quickly and accurately. Refer to Appendix E for additional design information.

Table 10:   Low Voltage Incandescent Lamp Downlighting Data

Fixture Type	Housing Type	Optical Type	Lamp		Fixture Number	Isofootcandle Plot Reference
			Type	Watts		
Reflector Lamp Recessed Downlight	Universal H7	Coilex Baffle Pinhole	MR–16	20	1479P	42A, 43A
				42		44A, 45A
	H1499 Miniature	Coilex Baffle Pinhole		20	1419P	42A, 43A
				42		44A, 45A
		Coilex Baffle Square		20	991P	42A, 43A
				42		44A, 45A
		Coilex Baffle Round		20	993P	42A, 43A
				42		44A, 45A
Reflector Lamp Adjustable	Universal H7	Coilex Spot		20	1410P	42 & 43, A through D
				42		44 & 45, A through D
		Slot Aperture		20	1450P	42, A through D
				42		44, A through D
	H1499 Miniature	Slot Aperture		20	1420P	42, A through D
				42		44, A through D
	Universal H7	Coilex Accent	PAR36	25	1475P	2 through 4, A & B
				50		6 through 9, A & B

75

Task Lighting

Task lighting is not new. The light from a fire, candle, oil burning lamp, or the sunlight through a window are all forms of task lighting which had been in use long before the electric lamp. Visual tasks, such as reading, writing, sewing, and other artisan work were performed near these light sources which varied greatly in the quantity and quality of the illumination they provided.

Edison's first lamp was essentially a task light, and until very recently the concept of what a task light is and the function it should perform had remained unchanged. The conventional task lighting fixture consists of the well-known adjustable arm design equipped with either an incandescent or fluorescent lamp. Fixed linear fluorescent fixtures, usually located directly in front of the worker, are another popular conventional design.

Such fixtures are used to illuminate a highly localized area or work station. Unfortunately, the conventional fixtures described above were not designed to provide light in the proper quantities or from the proper direction. These design flaws can produce a number of serious seeing problems, including veiling reflections, poor brightness ratios, and high levels of fixture generated glare. Conventional task lights provide substantial light with little regard for light quality. As a result, the raw footcandle levels they generate may exceed the IES requirements. However, the true indicator of how well an object can be seen, the Equivalent Spherical Illuminance footcandle levels, can be much lower than the raw footcandle levels.

Problems With Direct Light Systems

For many years the lighting industry's answer to the problems associated with localized task lighting was to design direct lighting systems which supposedly eliminated the need for task lighting fixtures. By adhering to the philosophy of providing more light everywhere, it was assumed that visual tasks could be performed anywhere in a room blanketed with a uniform level of light. In many commercial and industrial applications, this high level direct lighting system became the entire lighting system, and little research was conducted to find better ways of utilizing task lighting.

An end to energy abundance has forced the lighting industry to closely evaluate its energy inefficient direct lighting philosophy, and a number of serious flaws have been discovered in accepted direct lighting practices. Not only were many direct systems providing **too much** light on work surfaces, but they also were providing "bad footcandles" or light which detracted from the ability to see. It was discovered that light quantity and light quality are not synonymous and that systems must provide **light for people to see by** rather than merely a given footcandle level on a given work surface. The major problems found in direct lighting systems were:

1. Poor brightness ratios.
2. Poor visibility levels.
3. Poor visual comfort (as a result of direct glare from the lamp or lens of the fixture).
4. High energy consumption.
5. High initial cost.
6. Limited flexibility (systems not able to respond to the needs of the dynamic worker).

The HID Indirect/SPI Task Lighting Solution

In recent years, lighting researchers and lighting designers have found that localized HID, indirect ambient lighting systems employing advanced optic technology can solve most of the ambient light related problems previously listed. Use of such luminaires increases system flexibility, lowers initial and energy consumption costs, and improves visual comfort and seeability. (Refer to the beginning of **Section II: Lighting for Interiors** for a full discussion of indirect ambient lighting practices.)

Yet a condition may have existed when HID cabinet type indirect luminaires were used to illuminate contemporary modular office spaces. The partitions used to create the personal privacy that workers desired also created many shadowed areas within the work space. To eliminate these shadows, some form of highly localized task lighting was needed which did not create the light direction and veiling reflection problems associated with conventional task lighting fixtures.

The SPI Task Lighting Concept

A properly designed and balanced ambient/task lighting system is one in which over 50% of the light is provided by the ambient lighting fixtures. The remaining light, which functions to fill in shadowed areas and even out high brightness ratios, is generated by complementary task lights.

SPI task lights are specifically designed to complement ambient HID indirect lighting systems. They are not intended to be the sole source of light at a work station or desk and should be used in conjunction with a properly designed ambient lighting system at all times. As a lighting designer, you must remember that no task light, regardless of its design, can fulfill all the lighting needs of any work space.

STC 30 Task Light. This task light design (Fig. 1) is fitted with a 14-watt U-shaped fluorescent lamp and an asymmetrical reflector which together help distribute more than 70% of the lamp's output onto the work surface. Ideally, two fixtures are mounted at opposite ends of the work surface (Fig. 3A). Because light is directed at right angles to the worker, there are no veiling reflections, brightness ratios are improved, and there is better contrast. This dual fixture arrangement provides far more useful illumination than a single 40-watt fluorescent lamp at substantially lower energy consumption levels.

STA 20 Task Light. The STA 20 design (Fig. 2) is fitted with an 8-watt fluorescent lamp, and as with the STC 30, it is recommended that two STA fixtures be mounted in tandem, one at each end of the work surface. This setup provides far more useful light than a 40-watt fluorescent lamp while offering a 60% reduction in energy consumption. The fixture's unique optics distribute well over 80% of the lamp's output smoothly and evenly over the work surface, and since light is reflected at right angles to the worker, there are no veiling reflections, brightness ratios are lower, and contrast improves.

Task Light Comparison

Figure 3 illustrates the dramatic difference in the Equivalent Spherical Illuminance (ESI) levels attained with SPI task lighting and those attained with a conventional 40-watt fluorescent fixture. Figure 3A shows two STC 30 task lights mounted in the recommended positions 18″ above the work plane. The precision optics of the fixture direct light to the major work area where ESI seeability footcandle levels of 76 and 58 are attained. This translates into a Lighting Effectiveness Factor (LEF) of greater than 1.5 in the major work area.

Fig. 1: The STC 30 Task Light.

Fig. 2: The STA 20 Task Light.

An arrangement using two STA 20 task lights (Fig. 3B) generates ESI footcandle levels of 35 and 28 within the major work area for an LEF of greater than 1. When combined with a properly designed ambient lighting system, 70 ESI footcandles can easily be attained in the major work area.

Figure 3C illustrates the ESI seeability levels generated by a conventional linear fluorescent fixture containing a single 40-watt lamp. The ESI footcandle levels of 30 and 17 are lower than the actual raw

footcandle levels produced due to the presence of veiling reflections. This low level of seeability is the result of light coming from the wrong direction (i.e. parallel with the worker). When compared to the SPI Task Light systems, this conventional setup attains an LEF of only 0.5. The system produces a high quantity of low quality light which translates into energy waste, worker eyestrain, and reduced worker productivity. The following sections summarize the advantages of SPI Task Lighting systems.

Brightness Ratios. SPI Task Lights provide lower quantities of high quality light. Shadows are eliminated. Brightness ratios are lowered, reducing the eye's need to adapt to changing illumination levels within the work space. This results in less eyestrain, less fatigue, and better worker productivity.

Increased Visibility. Unlike conventional task lights, SPI designs are located at right angles to the major work surface. Providing light from this direction eliminates veiling reflections. Since all footcandles generated are "usable footcandles," ESI seeability levels are higher than those produced by conventional fixtures.

Visual Comfort. SPI Task Lights employ a cutoff reflector design which eliminates any direct source of fixture brightness or glare. The result is a more comfortable seeing environment.

Energy Consumption. SPI Task Light systems utilize either two 8-watt or 14-watt lamps as opposed to the single 40-watt lamp used in most conventional task light fixtures. Based on present electrical rates, this wattage reduction can translate into a $5.00 savings per work station per year, a sum which can become quite significant as the density of work stations increases.

Initial Cost. Most conventional task lighting fixtures are quite expensive due to costly lenses or cumbersome mounting techniques. SPI's simple, efficient design lowers costs, and a number of mounting accessories are available to economically adapt SPI Task Lights to any type of work station situation.

System Flexibility. A common complaint of conventional systems is that they cannot provide the flexibility necessary in today's dynamic work situations. SPI Task Lighting systems can be designed for base or wall mounting, arm mounting, or under shelf or cabinet mounting. Especially designed to integrate easily into today's modular office settings, SPI Task Lighting supplies good illumination over a wide area to meet the needs of the dynamic worker. Always remember, however, that any task lighting system serves to complement a properly designed ambient lighting system.

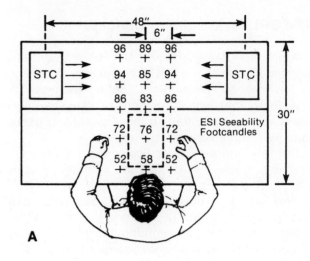

A

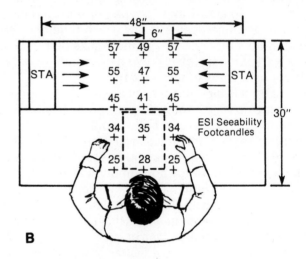

B

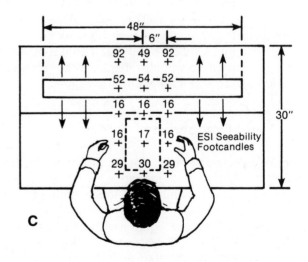

C

Fig. 3: Comparison between the ESI footcandle levels generated by (A) two STC 30 task lights, (B) two STA 20 task lights, and (C) a conventional linear fluorescent light system. In all cases the distance between the work plane and the task light is 18".

Accent Lighting

While ambient and task lighting serve our general visual needs, the role of accent lighting is infinitely more diverse. No other form of lighting has the power to direct a viewer's attention; define form, space, and texture; highlight a visual setting; or create an overall mood or atmosphere.

System Flexibility

The Illuminating Engineering Society defines accent lighting as, "directional lighting used to emphasize a particular object or to draw attention to a part of the field of view." Directional lighting is further defined as, "light provided on an object predominantly from a preferred direction."

This need for precise directional control requires that an element of flexibility be designed into accent lighting systems. When it is also considered that most accent lighting systems are employed in dynamic situations where the relative position, size, and shape of the objects continually change, the need for design flexibility becomes even more apparent. The finest method of achieving a wide range of directional control for accent lighting is through the use of adjustable fixtures mounted on a "Power-Trac" system. The unlimited flexibility of a Power-Trac system enables a lighting designer or owner to employ any of the accent lighting techniques described on the following pages to achieve the visual balance needed in residential, commercial, merchandising, and museum display settings.

Visual Balance

As stated in the introduction to Section II, three types of lighting—ambient, task, and accent—can be used to produce visual balance in indoor areas. Visual balance in a given area is attained by providing not only the correct illumination quantity, but also the correct illumination quality in terms of light control and directional aiming.

The human eye requires sufficient levels of uniform illumination to accurately and comfortably view objects. Such uniform lighting is most often the role of ambient or task lighting. Yet, it is known that the eye performs better when there is a somewhat higher level of illumination on the object or area upon which the eye is focused. The eye is also unconsciously drawn to areas of somewhat higher illumination.

These often subtle differences in illumination levels create visual contrast, an element necessary for comfortable seeing. Indiscriminate use or disregard for excessively high or low lighting contrasts can result in major visual difficulties and undue eyestrain. In this respect, accent lighting becomes extremely important. **Accent lighting can be used to create a needed contrast or to diminish an existing contrast.**

For example, the ambient levels in merchandising areas must be sufficiently high to assure safe customer circulation. Salespersons and checkout attendants also often rely on ambient light to perform their clerical duties. This high and often very uniform level of light imparts a flat, uniform appearance to merchandise. The light does nothing to distinguish the merchandise from other objects in the area. The customers can certainly see the merchandise, but they are not drawn to it.

In this case, absence of contrast is detrimental to the light balance of the area. The best solution would be select use of accent lighting to raise the level of illumination on certain articles of merchandise, such as the flowers shown in the photo on page 43. This contrast will highlight the quality of the merchandise, distinguish it from the surrounding area, and generate customer attention.

The opposite extreme, excessive contrast, can be equally unacceptable. Such situations often occur in offices or work areas where lighting is used only to illuminate specific work surfaces. Perimeter areas appear dark and formless under these conditions. Boundaries are not defined, and a "cave effect" exists. In addition to these aesthetic problems, constant strain is placed on the eyes as they are forced to continually adapt to both high and low illumination levels.

A viable solution to this problem would be to illuminate vertical wall surfaces and certain horizontal areas with wall washing units and spotlight fixtures mounted on a Power-Trac system. As shown in the photo on pages 38 and 39, use of these techniques add dimension and depth to the room, eliminating the "cave effect" and defining boundaries. The added illumination, although not particularly high in terms of footcandles, also effectively reduces the extreme brightness contrast. Eyes are subject to less transient adaptation, resulting in less eyestrain and fatigue.

ILLUMINATION REQUIREMENTS

The majority of accent lighting applications fall into one of two major categories, merchandise lighting or museum lighting. Almost all other applications can be based on the lighting principles used in these two areas. For example, you would light a portrait in a residential home in much the same way you would light a museum portrait.

Table 1 lists the illumination requirements for specific types of merchandise or merchandise display areas. Close attention should be paid to the color scheme of merchandise displays due to the fact that different colors may possess different apparent brightnesses when viewed under the same lighting system. Obviously, darker colors will absorb more light than lighter colors and they may need increased illumination over the requirements listed to achieve the desired effect.

Table 1:   Merchandise Lighting Illumination Requirements

Areas or Tasks	Description	Type of Activity Area[2]	Illumination Levels[3] (footcandles)	Maximum to Minimum Illumination Uniformity Ratios
Circulation[1]	Areas not used for display, appraisal of merchandise, or sales transactions.	High Medium Low	30 20 10	Illumination levels must be at least one-third of those provided in areas where merchandise is displayed and readily accessible for customer evaluation and appraisal.
Sales Transactions[1]	Cashier booths, counters, checkout lines, etc.	—	Category E 50/75/100	Illumination levels must not exceed a maximum/minimum uniformity ratio of 5:1.
General merchandising areas, such as showcases, wall displays, clothing racks, freestanding gondolas, etc.	The vertical or horizontal plane or area in which merchandise is displayed and readily accessible for customer evaluation and appraisal.	High Medium Low	100 75 30	The maximum/minimum uniformity ratio between illumination levels in these areas and general circulation areas must not exceed 3:1. This ratio is also required when merchandise is displayed in one area and appraised in another area. *Example*: When merchandise is taken from a showcase and appraised on the countertop, the countertop illuminance must be at least one-third the showcase illuminance.
Feature displays, including freestanding vertical mannequins, glass encased or open front wall-mounted displays, and glass encased or open front free-standing displays.	Single item, or items, which requires special highlighting to set it apart from the surroundings and attract prospective customers.	High Medium Low	100 75 30	The maximum/minimum uniformity ratio between illumination levels in these areas and the ambient lighting level in general merchandise areas must not exceed 3:1.
Show Windows	Daytime and nighttime displays in highly competitive main business districts. Nighttime displays in secondary districts or small towns.	General Feature General Feature	200 1,000 100 500	The maximum/minimum uniformity ratio between the illumination provided on any show window feature display and the general ambient illumination in the show window must not exceed 5:1.

Notes: 1. Illumination levels as provided by the ambient lighting system. (Refer to the preceding section on interior ambient lighting and Appendix A.)
   2. Activity area types:
      High—Areas where the merchandise displayed has a readily recognizable usage. Evaluation and viewing time is rapid, and the merchandise is displayed in such a way to stimulate the impulse buying decision.
      Medium—Areas where the merchandise displayed has a familiar usage. The customer may require time and/or help in evaluating the quality, usage, and decision to purchase.
      Low—Areas where the merchandise displayed is purchased less frequently. Customers may be unfamiliar with the inherent quality, design, value, and usage of the merchandise and normally require time and salesperson assistance before a buying decision is made.
   3. Listed illumination levels and uniformity ratios are to be the maintained minimum levels present on the task or throughout the area at any time. Illumination levels should be measured in the plane of the merchandise.
      Luminance or brightness level ratios (measured in footlamberts): **General merchandise areas**—To assure correct visibility anywhere in the merchandise space, the maximum/minimum apparent brightness ratio should not exceed 5:1. **Customer attraction areas**—To attract customers to a specific area, the apparent maximum/minimum brightness ratio should not be less than 3:1.

Table 2: Museum Lighting Data

Area or Task	Illumination Levels
Lobbies, general gallery areas, corridors. Displays of nonsensitive materials. Restoration or conservation shops and laboratories.	Category "C": 10/15/20 footcandles[1] Category "D": 20/30/50 footcandles[1] Category "E": 50/75/100 footcandles[1]
Displays of Sensitive Materials[2]	**Maximum Footcandles per Annum[3]**
Highly susceptible materials—silk, nylon, art on paper, antique documents, lace, and fugitive dyes.	12,000[4]
Moderately susceptible materials—cotton, wool, other textiles where the dye is stable, certain wood finishes, and leather.	18,000[5]

Notes:
1. Illumination levels as provided by the ambient lighting system. These levels are expressed in maintained average footcandles. (Refer to the preceding section on interior ambient lighting and Appendix A.)
2. Materials of organic origin that will change or fade due to the absorption of light as its ultraviolet component, particularly materials treated with vegetable dyes and writing inks.
3. These levels, if properly applied, will not result in worse than just perceptible fading in the stated materials in ten years of exposure.
4. Multiply 5 footcandles × 8 hours per day × 300 days per year = 12,000 footcandles/annum.
5. Multiply 7.5 footcandles × 8 hours per day × 300 days per year = 18,000 footcandles/annum.

Table 2 lists illumination requirements and guidelines for museum lighting. Strict attention must be paid to the maximum footcandle exposure allowed per annum for light-sensitive materials. Serious color fading and other damage will occur if these guidelines are disregarded.

Unlike ambient and task lighting which create a certain required illumination level over a given area, accent lighting relies on creating contrasts. For this reason, the exact illumination levels listed in Tables 1 and 2 can be raised or lowered as the situation dictates as long as the stated uniformity ratios are not changed. For example, many residential and commercial accent lighting applications do not require the high illumination levels listed for merchandise lighting. If the lighting levels are lowered and the uniformities do not change, the balance of the lighting system will not change.

LAMPS FOR ACCENT LIGHTING

Due to the extreme control which can be exercised in terms of beam size, direction, shape, and intensity, the incandescent lamp group is the primary lamp group used in accent lighting applications. Although complete design and performance data for suggested incandescent lamps can be found in **Section I: Lamps and Ballasts**, a brief summary of the lamps used in accent applications is given in the following paragraphs.

General Service, S-11, and Tungsten "T." These incandescent lamps emit light in all directions and require reflectors and/or lenses to give their light direction and control. They are most commonly used to provide ambient lighting or wash lighting for specific areas.

Reflector Lamps (Standard Voltage). Reflector lamps have a self-contained optical system employing an internal reflector and either a plain or prismatic lens face. Manufactured in separate designs to produce either very wide, medium, or spotlight type beams suitable for ambient lighting, wall washing, or highlighting applications, their measurably longer lamp life gives reflector lamps an added advantage over general service designs.

Reflector Lamps (Low Voltage). The low voltage reflector lamp employs the same type of optical system as the standard voltage reflector lamp, but due to the uniqueness of this lamp's filament design, the beam size, shape, and concentration are extremely controllable. For this reason, low voltage reflector lamps, particularly PAR 36 and MR-16 models, have virtually replaced all other types of lamps in highlighting applications. The small size of the MR-16 lamp allows it to be used in trac-mounted fixtures of extremely small dimensions. As their name implies, low voltage reflector lamps produce more usable light per watt of electricity consumed than do standard voltage models.

Flood Lamps. Flood lamps produce a wide light beam resulting in rather uniform diffuse light with no visual "hot spots." These incandescent lamps are used for general and ambient lighting purposes.

ACCENT LIGHTING · 81

Spot Lamps. Spot lamps produce intense, concentrated, narrow light beams which are brightest at the beam's center. The most common application for this lamp is in highlighting or accenting particular objects or areas.

FIXTURES FOR ACCENT LIGHTING

There is almost no limit to the variety of Power-Trac fixture style, shape, and finish combinations available for accent lighting (Figs. 1 and 2). The relative size of track lighting fixtures is dependent upon the size of the lamp required, but in most cases equipment selection is largely based on aesthetic preferences. Table 3 lists the general fixture styles and lamps required to produce the accent lighting effects discussed in the following sections.

Fig. 1: Halo (A) Vienti Pinchback and (B) Micro Style Power-Trac Fixtures.

Fig. 2: Halo (A) Antique Brass Pendant and (B) Cylinder Flatback Power-Trac Fixtures.

LIGHTING VARIABLES

The intensity and beam shape of the light emitted from any point source lamp will change as the lamp's aiming angle and projection distance change. The light intensity or footcandle level falling on a particular point or area is reduced by the square of the distance that the light is projected. The incident angle at which the light strikes the surface will also affect the light intensity.

For example the fixture shown in Fig. 3 (page 84) is aimed at 0° in relation to the surface being illuminated (in this particular case the floor). In other words, a center line bisecting the beam emitted from the track fixture would be at a right angle to the surface being illuminated. The concentric rings represent the beam shape of the light pattern produced at this distance and angle, and the numerical values assigned to the rings state the horizontal footcandle level at various points on the surface. These horizontal footcandle levels are based on the particular lamp candlepower and beam spread when the fixture is mounted at a specific distance from the surface being illuminated.

Table 3: Halo Power-Trac Fixture Data

Fixture Style	Fixture Series	Lamp Type	Lighting Effect
Early American, Traditional, and Contemporary (with brass and glass reflectors and diffusers)	L1524, L1522, L1534, and L1536	A	General diffuse
Traditional (with glass or metal reflectors)	L1524, L1526, L1528, L1530, and L1532	A	General diffuse
	L710 and L711	R	Highlighting or diffuse
Classics	L1510 through L1512	R	Highlighting/diffuse
Classic (low voltage)	L2510	MR-16	Highlighting/spot
Cylinders—roundback	L725 and L728	R	Highlighting/diffuse
Cylinders—Vienti roundback	L1541 and L1543	R	Highlighting/diffuse
Cylinders—flatback	L761 through L764 and L1767 and L1769	R and PAR	Highlighting/diffuse
Continentals—two-step contemporary	L731 through L734	R	Highlighting/diffuse
Economy Continental—contemporary	L704	R	Highlighting/diffuse
Vienti Step Cylinder—contemporary	L726	R	Highlighting/diffuse
Vienti Pinchback	L720 and L721	R	Highlighting/diffuse
Euro-Vienti Midi-Modern	L1710 through L1713	R and PAR	Highlighting/diffuse
Euro-Vienti Maxi-Modern	L1722 and L1724	R and PAR	Highlighting/diffuse
Spheres	L780, L781, and L784	R and PAR	Highlighting/diffuse
Vienti Sphere	L791 and L792	R	Highlighting/diffuse
Squares—contemporary	L771 through L773	R	Highlighting/diffuse
Universals—utility	L700 and L1700	R and PAR	Highlighting/diffuse
Projector (framing)—square	L756	Tungsten Halogen	Accent/framing
Projector (adjustable)—cylinder	L757	A	Accent/framing
Commercial Display (standard voltage)	L739 and L778	PAR	High Intensity Spot
Gimbal Ring (standard voltage)	L2738	PAR	High Intensity Spot
Commercial Display Pin Spot (low voltage)	L777	PAR	High Intensity Spot
Gimbal Ring (low voltage)	L2736	PAR	High Intensity Spot
Micro Style and Cylinder (low voltage)	L1760, L1762 L2760 and L2761	MR-16	Highlighting and Spot
Gimbal Ring (low voltage)	L2716	MR-16	Highlighting and Spot
Cylinder Flatback (low voltage)	L1765, L1766, and L2765	PAR	High Intensity Spot
Wall Wash Flood	L752	Tungsten Halogen	Diffuse/flood
Cylinder Economy Wall Wash Flood	L1769	R and PAR	Diffuse/flood

ACCENT LIGHTING

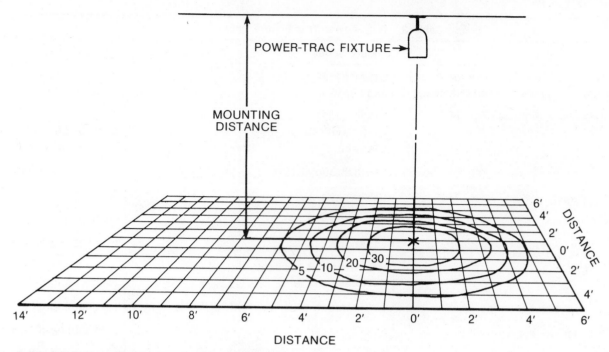

POWER-TRAC FIXTURE →

MOUNTING
DISTANCE

DISTANCE

6'
4'
2'
0'
2'
4'
6'

5 10 20 30

14' 12' 10' 8' 6' 4' 2' 0' 2' 4' 6'

DISTANCE

Fig. 3: Typical light pattern and intensity produced when fixtures are aimed at 0° (at a right angle to the illuminated surface). Note the concentric pattern of the rings.

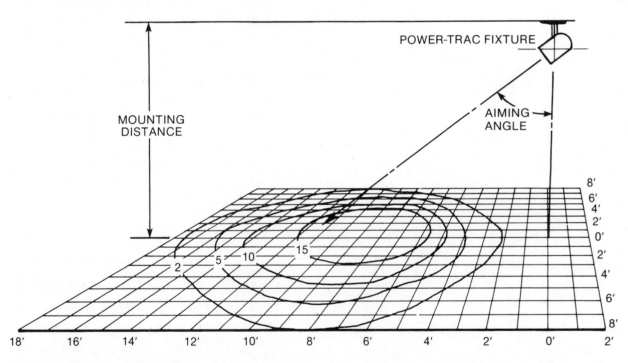

POWER-TRAC FIXTURE

MOUNTING
DISTANCE

AIMING
ANGLE →

8'
6'
4'
2'
0'
2'
4'
6'
8'

2 5 10 15

18' 16' 14' 12' 10' 8' 6' 4' 2' 0' 2'

Fig. 4: Typical light pattern and intensity produced when fixtures are aimed at angles other than 0°. Note how the light distribution has become elongated and intensities reduced as compared to those in Fig. 3.

The aiming angle is expressed in degrees away from the line which forms a right (90°) angle *between the fixture and the illuminated surface* (Fig. 4). For example, a fixture aimed at a 30° angle in rela-

tion to the room's floor is also aimed at a 60° angle in relation to the room wall at which it points. As the aiming angle increases, the light pattern generated becomes larger and elongated in the direction in which the fixture is aimed. Since the light from the fixture must now serve a larger area, the resulting footcandle levels on the illuminated surface must decrease.

84 INTERIOR LIGHTING

Typical aiming angles for flood projector and reflector lamps are 0°, 30°, and 45°. The basic aiming angles for spot projector and reflector lamps are 0°, 30°, 45°, and 60°. The Data Key Table given in Appendix E lists the most popular lamps used in accent lighting and downlighting. Appendix E also illustrates the isofootcandle curve reference plots generated when these lamps are mounted at a specific fixture to surface distance and aiming angle. This appendix includes a method for modifying these isofootcandle curves to fit virtually any fixture to surface distance, and the Data Key Table lists the proper fixture spacing required to guarantee uniform lighting for typical downlighting and wall washing applications. Detailed information and examples using the isofootcandle curve reference plots and the Data Key Table are given in Appendix E.

LIGHT QUALITY

Quality accent lighting is dependent upon numerous factors including predictable control of the light beam's size, shape, and intensity; wise directional and aiming alignment; proper fixture concealment and location; and reflectance factor considerations. All of these factors contribute to the elimination or reduction of direct and indirect glare and increase the visibility of the object or area lighted.

Most light control is provided by the lamp itself and is largely a function of the lamp's beam spread and illumination intensity. Added accessories, such as louvers, visors, or adjustable "barn door" shutters, can also be attached to the fixture to increase light control.

In every accent lighting application, the object or surface illuminated should be seen, not the light source. Proper light source concealment is accomplished by choosing a mounting location away from the normal field of view. At no time should the viewer observe the object with a frontal view of the fixture in the background. The lighting designer should also realize that the amount of lamp face area exposed to a viewer's eyes may increase dramatically when the fixture is viewed at increasingly oblique angles.

Care should be taken to ensure that the light emitted from the fixture does not reflect off the surface being lighted. This reflectance is a particular problem when lighting specular and semi-specular surface materials and mirrors. If reflections cannot be avoided, the fixtures should be set up in such a way that any reflected light is directed at angles away from the viewer's eyes. Light source concealment and reflectance considerations are major reasons why a thorough study of probable viewing angles should be conducted prior to the installation of fixtures.

ACCENT LIGHTING TECHNIQUES

Light is used to illuminate three elements in the human environment: objects, surfaces, and spaces. Numerous accent lighting techniques can be employed to attain the proper effect, balance, and depth for each of these elements.

Lighting Objects

Any object, be it a piece of sculpture, a simple sphere, or a human being, is three-dimensional; it has certain definite height, width, and depth characteristics. A three-dimensional object has a unique shape, size, and mass. Properly directed and controlled beams of light can accentuate these characteristics by creating shadows, highlights, and contrasts which intensify the object's natural depth and character.

Four separate lighting techniques can be used individually or in various combinations in the illumination of three-dimensional objects.

Diffuse Lighting. Diffuse lighting provides uniform object illumination without emphasis on particular points (Fig. 5). Wide beam floodlights are the finest means of generating diffuse light.

Backlighting. Backlighting produces a silhouetting effect which gives an object definition of form without revealing surface detail, finish, color, or other shape detail (Fig. 6). Backlighting adds depth to an object and is best provided by employing wide beam flood lamps in wall washing light fixtures. Light can be directed from either above or below the object, but the fixtures must always be placed behind the object.

Highlighting. Highlighting reveals surface and color detail but fails to separate an object from its surroundings (Fig. 7). When used alone, highlighting also tends to produce unwanted harsh shadows. Medium beam floodlights or spotlights mounted above or to the sides of the object will provide adequate highlighting.

When using medium beam floodlights or spotlights for highlighting purposes, care must be taken to provide the proper luminance or brightness ratios on the surface of the object being lighted. Luminance ratios of between 2:1 and 6:1 usually provide for good transparent shadowing effects and three-dimensional rendering. If the ratio between the brightest and darkest areas on an object falls below 2:1, the lighting becomes "flat" and the object appears to be two-dimensional. When the ratio be-

ACCENT LIGHTING

Fig. 5: Diffuse lighting creates an even level of illumination.

Fig. 7: Highlighting reveals surface detail and color, but when used alone may produce unwanted shadowing.

Fig. 6: Backlighting silhouettes an object against its background.

Fig. 8: Diffuse lighting, backlighting, and highlighting can all be combined to obtain lighting balance.

tween light and dark areas exceeds 6:1, however, light contrast tends to become severe and unpleasant to view. Surface details can also be obscured in shadow areas or highlighted areas.

Figure 8 illustrates how all three types of lighting can be combined to create balanced lighting.

Shadowing. Shadowing enhances the detail of objects by creating contrasting light and dark areas on the object's surface. The distance between the object lighted and the lighting fixture has a direct bearing on the amount of shadowing effect. As the distance between fixture and object increases, the angle at which the light strikes the object decreases or becomes flatter (Fig. 9A). Light striking at these flat angles produces less shadowing and a more uniform, flat appearance. As the distance between object and fixture decreases, the angles at which the light strikes the object increase, resulting in more intense shadowing (Fig. 9B).

A

B

Fig. 9: **(A) Light striking an irregular surface at essentially "flat" angles washes out much of the contrasting shadows. (B) Directing light so it strikes an irregular surface at a sharp or increased angle creates shadowing and contrast.**

Shadowing is best accomplished through the use of multi-directional lighting (lighting from several different directions, locations, and angles). Use of multi-directional lighting results in the generation of a certain amount of fill light which softens the sharp contrast between the extremely dark and light areas. As a result, all details of the given object become more pronounced and visible.

Other Methods. Variations in the light intensity and the beam spread pattern can also enhance the depth and detail of an object. But since few accent lighting applications can be standardized, it is the job of the lighting designer to determine the finest combination of beam angle, beam shape, and light intensity needed to illuminate a particular object. When this combination is found, lighting balance is achieved; the size, shape, and form of the object are revealed to the viewer.

Lighting Surfaces

Horizontal and vertical surfaces such as ceilings, floors, and walls are **essentially** two-dimensional in nature. But in addition to having a specific area, these surfaces can also possess a certain texture. Wall washing with light from floor to ceiling, scallop lighting, or spotlighting designated areas can accent these surface textures and add a certain dimensional depth to walls and ceilings.

As is the case in the shadowing of objects, the distance between the lighting fixture and the vertical or horizontal surface lighted has a marked effect on the texturing created. Again, as the distance from fixture to wall surface increases, the amount of texture brought out on the surface decreases (Fig. 10A). Close-mounted fixtures which create a sharp angle between the light beam and the wall surface increase the texturing effects (Fig. 10B).

As illustrated earlier in this section, wash lighting of walls and ceilings is also an effective means of defining the boundaries of a room or space. While such boundary lighting may also increase the overall ambient lighting level of the room, its main benefit in most cases is to create a better light balance in the area.

A

B

Fig. 10: Accent lighting can solve lighting problems. (A) Diffuse lighting imparts a flat appearance to vertical surfaces. (B) Wall washing with light brings out the surface texture.

Special Vertical Surfaces

When floodlighting or spotlighting highly-defined vertical surfaces or flat vertical displays, such as paintings, prints, or documents, special attention must be paid to fixture aiming angles and the critical lines of sight of potential viewers. A preliminary study should be conducted to determine all angles from which the object will be viewed by people either sitting or standing in the area. The installation should then be planned to assure no unshielded light sources will be visible from these angles.

The actual light fixtures should be aimed so that the center of the light beam strikes the center of the vertical surface at a 30° angle. As illustrated in Fig. 11, this translates into a 60° fixture aiming angle.

The model illustrated in Fig. 11 is based on the following factors:

1. The primary diffuse component of vertical illumination is approximately 40% of the horizontal illuminance at the sight line point.
2. The top to bottom dimension of the display.
3. The ideal utilization of spot or flood lamp beam cones.
4. The minimum effective viewing distance relative to the nominal top to bottom dimension of the displayed object. In this case: A to B = 52" for a 30° cone spot lamp and A to C = 65" for a 60° cone flood lamp.

To calculate viewing zones for vertically larger objects, increase the viewer minimum and maximum viewing distances by 1.5" for each 1" increase in the vertical height of the display object.

5. Use the following formula to determine the setback distance of fixtures:
(Fixture mounting height – Eye height) × (Tangent of 30°) = Setback distance. *Note*: Tangent of 30° = 0.5774. For example: Mounting height = 9' or 108"
Eye height = 5'5" or 65"
(108" – 65") = (43") × (.5774) = 24.8" or approximately 24-3/4" Setback distance.
6. If the display has considerable relief or heavy frames, the aiming angle can be decreased and the fixture setback distance increased.
7. If the display is mounted high and has substantial glossy areas, the reverse of point number 6 is appropriate. The aiming angle can be increased and the setback distance decreased.
8. Normal eye height is assumed to be 65" above the finished floor.

Excessive brightness differences between the featured object and the area surrounding it are highly undesirable. This problem most often occurs when framing projector fixtures are **misused** in the lighting of portraits, artwork, etc.

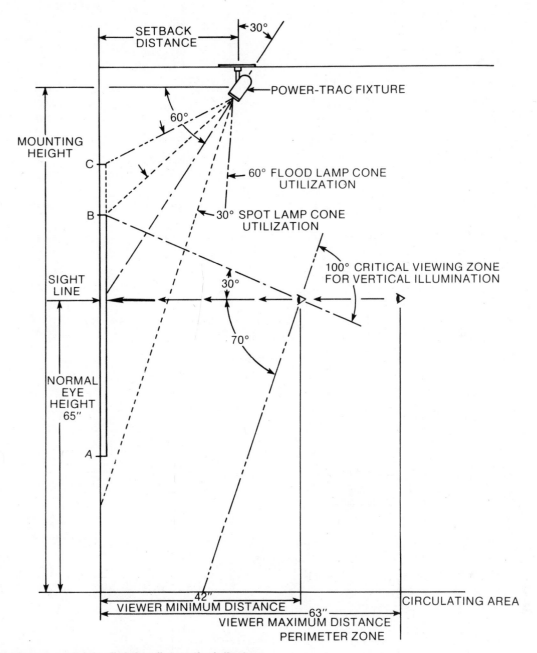

SETBACK DISTANCE
30°
POWER-TRAC FIXTURE
60°
60° FLOOD LAMP CONE UTILIZATION
30° SPOT LAMP CONE UTILIZATION
MOUNTING HEIGHT
C
B
100° CRITICAL VIEWING ZONE FOR VERTICAL ILLUMINATION
SIGHT LINE
30°
70°
NORMAL EYE HEIGHT 65"
A
42"
VIEWER MINIMUM DISTANCE
63"
VIEWER MAXIMUM DISTANCE
PERIMETER ZONE
CIRCULATING AREA

Fig. 11: Preferred angles for lighting flat vertical displays.

A framing projector should never be the sole piece of equipment used to illuminate a featured vertical display. To create the optimum lighting effect, additional fixtures should be employed to illuminate the wall surrounding the painting or display to a general diffuse level of illumination. The framing projector is then used to accent or augment this general level of illumination by providing additional light on the object. This additional light will draw attention to the display as well as accentuate and highlight important details.

In cases where other units cannot be used in conjunction with the framing projector, the shutter of the framing projector should be opened sufficiently to provide light on the surrounding wall as well as the vertical display (Fig. 12).

Lighting Spaces

By its own definition, accent lighting is not intended to be the sole means of lighting a given space, such as a business office, department store, or museum gallery. Accent lighting can, however,

ACCENT LIGHTING 89

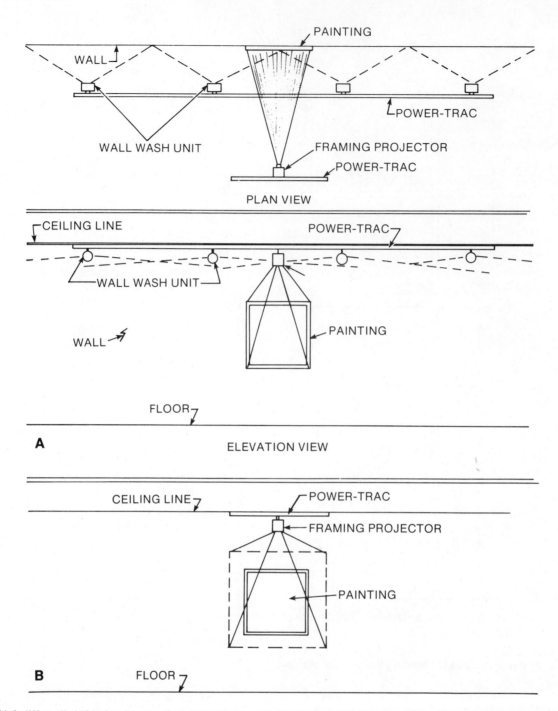

PAINTING

WALL

WALL WASH UNIT

POWER-TRAC

FRAMING PROJECTOR

POWER-TRAC

PLAN VIEW

CEILING LINE

POWER-TRAC

WALL WASH UNIT

WALL

PAINTING

FLOOR

A   ELEVATION VIEW

CEILING LINE

POWER-TRAC

FRAMING PROJECTOR

PAINTING

B   FLOOR

Fig. 12: (A) A diffuse lighting background, such as that created by wall washing units, will enhance the effect created by framing projectors used to light flat vertical displays. (B) If a framing projector must be used alone, it should be adjusted to overlap the boundaries of the flat vertical display.

increase the effectiveness of the ambient and/or task lighting used to illuminate a given space. In certain instances the light from accent lighting fixtures will make a noticeable contribution to the ambient lighting level.

Lighting Mirrors

The lighting of mirrored areas in merchandising, residential, and commercial areas presents a set of rather unique problems. The following list of suggested guidelines will help assure the finest overall results.

1. The face should be softly lighted with light sources which flatter natural skin tones. Light should

90 INTERIOR LIGHTING

be directed at angles which do not produce harsh facial lines or shadows.

2. The light should be of a quality consistent with the illumination under which the merchandise will be viewed when worn or in use.

3. Light sources can be aimed to direct light into the mirror so it can be reflected back onto the merchandise, provided the light is not redirected into the viewer's eyes. Extreme care should be taken when using this method in the lighting of triplicate mirrors since light becomes extremely difficult to control when more than one mirror is present.

4. Directional fixtures should be mounted outside of the 60° visual cone of the viewer. The center line of this visual cone coincides with the viewer's line of sight.

5. The sales item or article of clothing should be adequately lighted over its entirety. In general, clothing has a reflectance value of between 30% and 70%; illumination levels in the D category, 20/30/50 footcandles, are sufficient for general arrangement and assessment when viewing speed is not important. Light-colored clothing in the 50% to 70% reflectance range requires between 20 to 30 footcandles for adequate appraisal. Darker clothing in the 30% to 50% reflectance range requires 30 to 50 footcandles of illumination. However, if the mirrored area is also used as a fitting area, Category F levels, 100/150/200 footcandles, should be provided based on the average clothing reflectances encountered.

6. In the lighting of any mirrored area, approximately one-half of the required illumination should be provided by a diffuse lighting system and one-half provided by a directional system. In any event, the illumination level should meet the standards set for the most difficult seeing task which occurs in that area.

ACCENT LIGHTING EXPERIENCE

A review of accent lighting reveals these major applications:

• Washing vertical and horizontal surfaces with light to define spaces and boundaries and to reveal fine surface textures and details.

• Uni- or multi-directional lighting of objects to create appealing contrasts, expose surface detail, or reveal form and shape.

• Lighting to generate visual and/or customer interest in merchandise, museum, commercial, and residential areas.

• Lighting to offset or complement the ambient and/or task lighting in a given space or area. This often results in increased visual capability and comfort.

Accent lighting can be a great problem solver. It can also be used to "fine-tune" an indoor lighting system to the designer's exact specifications. These are highly desirable characteristics, but by their very nature they make accent lighting a far-from-exact science. The lighting guidelines and general suggestions outlined in the previous section set the basis for sound accent lighting; they are not meant to be a collection of hard and fast rules.

Successful accent lighting stems from control—control of aiming and fixture location, control of beam patterns, control of light intensity. Lighting control eliminates glare, harsh contrasts, and troublesome reflections. The ability to control a lighting situation is a by-product of experience and experimentation. Know the operating characteristics of the equipment most often used in accent lighting. In fact, it is highly recommended that lighting designers acquire the basic lamps and fixtures used for accent lighting and actually practice setting up various lighting effects. This personal experimentation and trial and error method is the best accent lighting teacher. It can benefit the designer on future field installations where unique lighting problems will require a thorough knowledge of lighting possibilities.

In merchandise areas, a single Power-Trac system is flexible enough to illuminate numerous displays. Notice how high-lighting draws attention to the mannequin.

SECTION III
Exterior Lighting

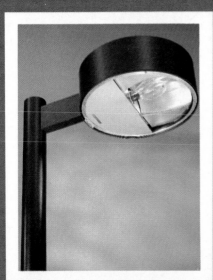

(Above and below) Power Mate Hi-Mast Luminaires provide maximum area coverage with minimum mounting poles.

(Left) Power Drawer Floodlights offer wide, even light coverage. (Opposite page) Power Drawer Concourse Luminaires delivered the pleasing aesthetic appearance and superior light control the developers of the Hickory Hollow Mall in Nashville, Tenn., desired.

(Left) The Resilite Luminaire is specifically designed to produce the lower light levels and good light uniformity needed in residential roadway lighting.

(Right) Power Drawer Concourse Design 20 is a popular, practical choice for roadway lighting.

(Left) Power Mate Hi-Mast Luminaires offer the sharp light cutoff necessary for roadway applications.

(Above) Attractive day-form and night-form appearance is often a high priority when lighting roadways in business districts and urban areas. (Below) Notice how the luminaires are individually aimed to provide the precision lighting for this professional level tennis court installation.

The Sports Lighting design information given in Section III allows layouts for all types of sports, at all levels of competition, to be designed almost instantly.

(Above) The Power Drawer Sign Light Luminaire.

(Right) The Monitor Wall Light used in security lighting systems.

Parking Area Lighting

Society of North America (IES). As each individual situation dictates, illumination levels and uniformity ratios should also coincide with accepted field practices. The lamps and luminaires chosen should combine to form highly-efficient, economically-sound lighting units, and the system should be aesthetically pleasing in both day-form and night-form appearance. Poles should be spaced and luminaires mounted at heights guaranteeing uniform lighting with no dark patches or pockets (Fig. 1).

Fig. 1: The lighting system must provide uniform illumination throughout the parking area.

The lighting design objectives for any outdoor parking area are quite simple. The lighting must provide for the safety, comfort, and convenience of the parking area patrons. Safe nighttime traffic and pedestrian flow must be insured, and illumination levels should be sufficient to afford both users and owners protection against assault, theft, and vandalism. In addition, you may also wish to design the lighting system to act as an attracting force for the business it serves.

Certain fundamental lighting criteria must be met in any parking area. First and utmost, the system must meet the required illumination levels and uniformity ratios set by the Illuminating Engineering

Operating and maintenance costs are the key economic factors.

ILLUMINATION LEVELS

The Illuminating Engineering Society has established a set of illumination guidelines for open area parking based on the activity levels of various parking situations. As shown in Table 1, IES recognizes three activity levels—high, medium, and low—and recommends specific illumination levels and uniformity ratios for each. When specifying an illumination level for a particular parking area, base your decision on these IES standards.

As you can see from Table 1, large or high activity areas constitute facilities for major league athletic events, major cultural and civic centers, regional shopping centers and malls, and other large scale

Table 1: Parking Area Lighting Requirements

High Activity Levels or Large Size Areas	Medium Activity Levels or Medium Size Areas	Low Activity Levels or Small Size Areas
Area Types and Examples		
Major regional shopping centers or malls.	Area shopping centers or strip malls. Fast food franchises.	Local merchant parking and local or neighborhood shopping centers.
Major League athletic stadiums and arenas.	Hospital parking areas. Transportation parking—airports, rail terminals, bus terminals.	Industrial employee parking. Educational facility parking.
Major cultural and civic facilities such as museums, art galleries, etc.	Area cultural, civic, or recreational events. Local sports facilities, residential complex parking, apartment parking, condominium parking.	
Convention centers and parking for major political rallies and concerts.		
Illumination Levels Required by IES		
2.0 average maintained footcandles	1.0 average maintained footcandle	0.5 average maintained footcandle
Uniformity Ratios		
3:1 average/minimum *(.66 footcandle minimum)	3:1 average/minimum *(.33 footcandle minimum)	4:1 average/minimum *(.125 footcandle minimum)
**12:1 maximum/minimum *(8.0 footcandle maximum)	**12:1 maximum/minimum *(4.0 footcandle maximum)	**15:1 maximum/minimum *(2.5 footcandle maximum)

*Maximum or minimum footcandle level at any point in the parking area.
**Considered accepted field practice. Not a current IES recommendation.

enterprises. Medium activity or medium size areas include area shopping centers or strip malls, fast food franchises, as well as parking facilities for hospitals, airport and transportation terminals, and residential housing complexes. Examples of low activity, small area parking include local merchant parking, industrial employee parking, and school area parking.

Exits, entrances, trafficway collector lanes, pedestrian walkways, and loading zones making up portions of the total parking area must be given special consideration. Higher lighting levels are necessary in these areas. As a general rule, the average illumination level of these special areas should not be less than twice the illumination level of the adjacent parking area or adjoining street, whichever is greater.

Uniformity Ratios

As indicated in Table 1, the IES recommends an average/minimum uniformity ratio of 3:1 for parking areas with high and medium activity levels. A ratio of 4:1 is recommended for low activity areas. Notice that **maximum/minimum** uniformity ratios are rec-

ommended. For high and medium levels the ratio is 12:1. A 15:1 maximum/minimum ratio is suggested for low activity areas. While these maximum/minimum ratios are **not** part of the current official IES recommendations, abiding by them is considered good field practice. In many instances, maximum/minimum uniformity ratios are just as important as the average/minimum ratios. It certainly is not reasonable to achieve the average ratio when the maximum ratio is in excess of 12:1 or 15:1. Yet it is entirely feasible, and it often occurs, that the average ratio is 3:1 or 4:1 while the maximum ratio is as high as 25:1 or 30:1. Such a high ratio indicates the presence of undesirable dark pockets or patches.

AESTHETICS

Two types of aesthetics are important in parking area lighting. The first, day-form appearance, relates to the actual physical appearance of the se-

lected luminaire. Is it important that the luminaire design coincide with the overall architectural appearance of the facility it serves? In an industrial complex parking lot this may not be important, but for shopping centers, civic buildings, and sport centers designed to enhance the beauty and value of a community, a complementary luminaire design is often essential. You may also wish to give some special consideration to the mounting height and pole spacing from an aesthetic viewpoint as well. For example, the client may feel that pole heights should be kept below a certain limit, especially if the adjacent building is more horizontal than vertical in design. Another client may disregard pole height in favor of a layout which utilizes as few poles as possible.

In these cases, the job of the lighting designer is to carefully explore all **reasonable** options and decide on the finest overall system. While some slight modifications can be made to the optimum lighting layout for aesthetic reasons, they should not alter the required illumination levels or uniformity ratios. The cost efficiency of the system should never be sacrificed, and any initial or operating cost increases incurred as a result of aesthetic considerations should be fully explained to the client **during the planning stages**.

The second type of aesthetics is known as night-form appearance. Is glare control important? Is it essential that all light be restricted to a specific area and spill light be prevented? Light pollution has become a very serious problem. Zoning laws have become so mixed and complex in many areas that industrial, commercial, and residential districts often overlap or closely adjoin.

Light spilling over into a residential section from the parking area of a fast food franchise or strip mall can be both annoying and disruptive. In fact, many areas in the United States have considered and adopted city, county, and state ordinances specifically designed to eliminate light pollution. So be aware of any ordinances or restrictions before beginning work.

The problems of light control and spill are solved during the equipment selection process. Luminaires can be classified in two groups, cutoff and non-cutoff, with the cutoff designs offering the finest light control characteristics. The characteristics of the various luminaires employed in parking area applications are discussed in the section, **Parking Area Equipment Selection**.

ECONOMICS

Three types of costs must be taken into consideration when designing any lighting system. In order of importance, they are: (1) energy costs, (2) maintenance costs, and (3) initial equipment and installation costs. Twenty years ago these cost factors were reversed in order of importance, but a 10 to 15% annual increase in the cost of electricity has pushed energy considerations to the forefront. Choosing an efficient light source such as high pressure sodium lamps and matching it with the correct ballast and wiring is the key to gaining the most light per energy dollar spent.

The second important economic item is maintenance costs. How much will it cost to relamp the system, and how often will relamping be necessary? How frequently will the luminaires require cleaning, and what will be the maintenance cost for the system's auxiliary equipment, such as ballasts, circuit wiring, and poles?

The third and increasingly least important cost factor is initial equipment and installation costs. While the initial cost of the system can be substantial, operating and maintenance costs can far outdistance these expenditures over the life of the system. Turn to **Section IV: System Maintenance and Economics** for more information dealing with the economic and maintenance factors of outdoor lighting systems.

PARKING AREA EQUIPMENT SELECTION

Satisfying the lighting design needs of any parking area begins with what is fundamentally an equipment selection process. Select the proper luminaire design and aesthetic appearance requirements are resolved, light pollution standards are met, and maintenance costs are reduced. Equip the luminaire with a high-efficiency light source and the required illumination levels are attained at a reasonable operating cost.

LUMINAIRES

The selection options for parking area lighting based on luminaire design are illustrated in the flow diagram in Fig. 2. As the diagram indicates, both cutoff and non-cutoff type luminaires can be used. The advantages and disadvantages of individual luminaire designs are discussed in the following sections. It should be noted here that luminaires designed on the Power Drawer principle have certain added advantages. But because these advantages deal largely with the installation, maintenance, and

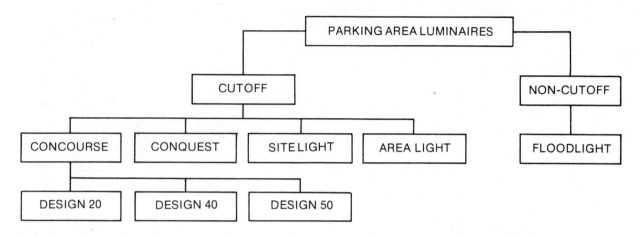

Fig. 2: Luminaire selection options for parking area lighting.

updating of the luminaire, they will be discussed in Section IV. Turn to that section for details.

CUTOFF LUMINAIRES

Cutoff luminaires are defined in several ways. One widely used and essentially accurate definition of a cutoff luminaire is any luminaire that does not emit light at an angle greater than 90° from vertical (Fig. 3). Another widely used and less accurate definition is any luminaire of a square or rectangular shape. (While many cutoff designs are square or rectangular, some are round. Also, many non-cutoff luminaires have basically rectangular housings.)

The best definition of a sharp cutoff luminaire is as follows: A sharp cutoff luminaire is one designed to shield the light source at angles above 72° from vertical (Fig. 4). This shielding angle of 72° was selected since it is generally recognized in the lighting industry that discomforting glare is minimized when light strikes an observer's eye at an angle below 72° from vertical.

Advantages. The main advantages of cutoff luminaires are light control and glare control. Cutoff luminaires generate highly distinct and predictable light patterns, and many designs virtually eliminate spill light from occurring behind the luminaire. Their directional qualities make it easy to place extra light on important parking areas, such as entrances and exits, pedestrian walkways, and loading zones. Perimeter and irregularly shaped areas are more easily lighted, and cutoff luminaires have the added advantage of being among the most architecturally pleasing designs available. Their shielding design also effectively reduces discomforting glare.

Disadvantages. While cutoff luminaires have no true disadvantages, extremely close attention must be paid to both luminaire mounting height and pole spacing. For any type of application using cutoff

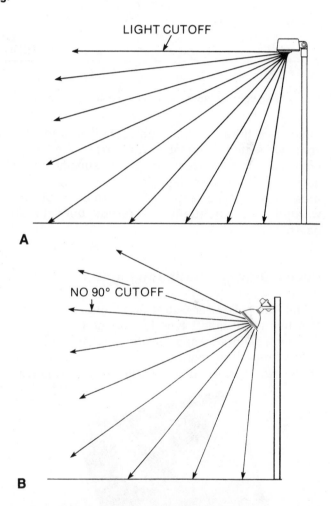

Fig. 3: (A) Cutoff luminaires restrict all light to angles below 90° from vertical. (B) Non-cutoff luminaires do not restrict light to any particular angle.

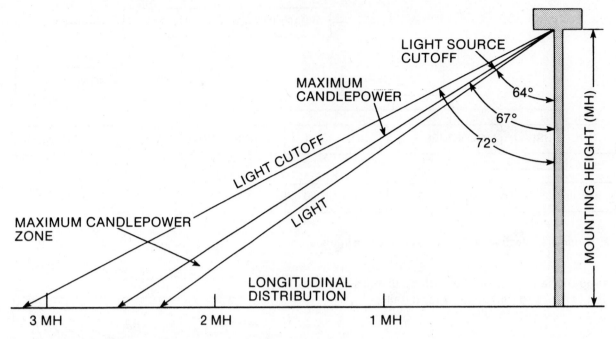

LIGHT SOURCE CUTOFF

MAXIMUM CANDLEPOWER

64°

67°

72°

LIGHT CUTOFF

LIGHT

MOUNTING HEIGHT (MH)

MAXIMUM CANDLEPOWER ZONE

LONGITUDINAL DISTRIBUTION

3 MH   2 MH   1 MH

Fig. 4: The light shielding qualities of a sharp cutoff luminaire.

luminaires, the specified mounting heights and pole spacings stated in the tables and text of this handbook must not be exceeded. These specifications assure even, uniform light levels, and exceeding these limits would result in the formation of unwanted and potentially dangerous pockets of darkness.

Power Drawer Cutoff Site Light

The Power Drawer Cutoff Site Light is the most effective of all cutoff type luminaires (Fig. 5). Its precision calibrated and serrated knuckle and cast marks permit the accurate selection of the aiming angle, resulting in optimum lighting performance.

Fig. 5: The Power Drawer Cutoff Site Light.

The unique optical components allow for the wider spacing of mounting poles at lower mounting heights when compared to other cutoff luminaires. Power Drawer Cutoff Site Lights offer such precise cutoff at both front and rear that light pollution is virtually eliminated (Fig. 6). This luminaire also provides maximum lighting uniformity for maximum visibility, high beam utilization, and overall energy efficiency. They are extremely versatile and are particularly useful in lighting irregularly-shaped parking areas.

Power Drawer Concourse Luminaires

The Power Drawer Concourse luminaire series combines an aesthetically pleasing day-form appearance with the sharp cutoff optics of modern lighting design to produce a lighting unit suitable for a wide range of parking area applications (Fig. 7). The concealed light source creates glareless illumination which facilitates safe pedestrian and vehicular movement throughout the parking area. The absence of glare also increases one's ability to see surrounding areas, such as store displays or entrances.

Design 20. Power Drawer Concourse Design 20 luminaires generate excellent light distribution for the illumination of long rectangular areas perpendicular to the front of the luminaire (Fig. 8). The optics of this luminaire are ideal when wide pole spacings are desired for narrow areas and when sharp cutoff is essential. Two Power Drawer Concourse Design 20 luminaires per pole are used in most parking lot applications.

104 EXTERIOR LIGHTING

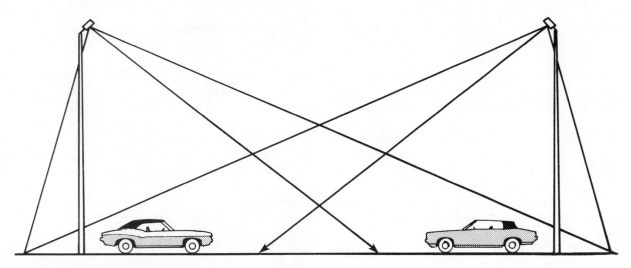

Fig. 6: Power Drawer Cutoff Site Lights offer precise beam cutoff.

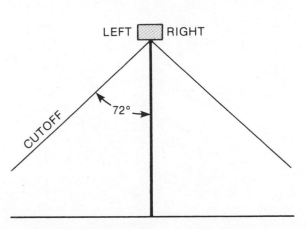

A

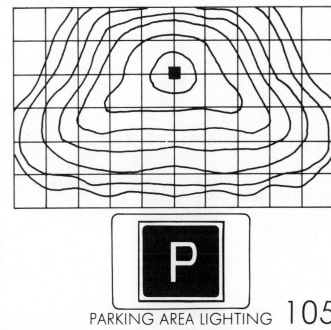

B

Fig. 7: Power Drawer Concourse luminaires: (A) Design 20; (B) Design 50.

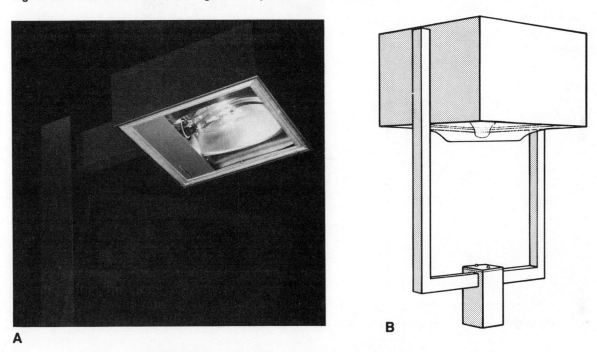

LEFT RIGHT

CUTOFF

72°

Fig. 8: As this light distribution pattern shows, Design 20 is excellent for lighting long rectangular areas perpendicular to the front of the luminaire.

P

PARKING AREA LIGHTING 105

Design 40. As Fig. 9 indicates, Power Drawer Concourse Design 40 luminaires create a light distribution ideally suited for lighting extended areas in front of the luminaire. Use these luminaires when mounting poles must be set back from the area to be lighted and sharp cutoff characteristics are still desired.

For example, Power Drawer Concourse Design 40 luminaires can be used around the perimeter of a parking area since they will throw light into the parking area without generating a backlash of spill light. Pole configurations of four luminaires set 90° apart are commonly used to illuminate the interior of medium to large parking areas.

Design 50. Power Drawer Concourse Design 50 luminaires utilize a single luminaire placed in a pole top mounting configuration. The resulting light distribution pattern is symmetrical in shape and quite useful for lighting many smaller areas (Fig. 10). This luminaire also has great architectural appeal.

Power Mod Conquest Landscape Luminaires

The Power Mod Conquest Landscape luminaire is another aesthetically attractive luminaire. Its chandelier-like qualities are often preferred by architects and other day-form appearance conscious clients (Fig. 11). The visual cutoff of high angle light assures glare-free areas of uniform light, and the correct combination of distributor reflectors within the luminaire assures parking areas will have high visibility, using energy saving lamps on wide pole spacings. Fewer poles and lower mounting heights will result in a bottom line saving in both first costs and operating costs.

Power Drawer Area Light

The Power Drawer Area Light luminaire is quite similar to the Power Drawer Concourse design

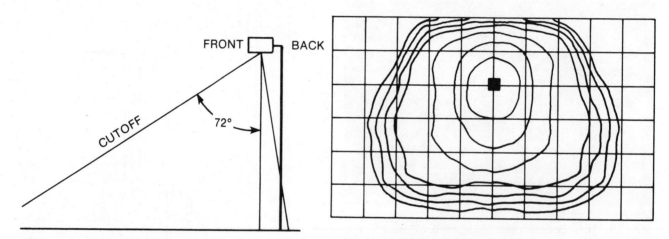

Fig. 9: The light pattern generated by Design 40 optics. Notice the sharp cutoff characteristic.

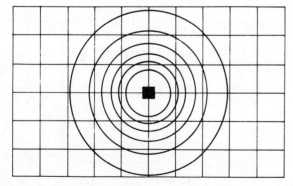

Fig. 10: The symmetrical light pattern developed by Design 50 pole top-mounted luminaires.

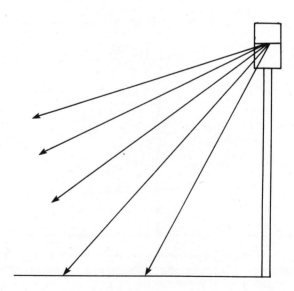

Fig. 11: The highly aesthetic Power Mod Conquest Land-scape luminaire.

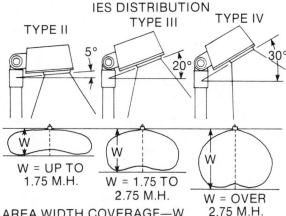

W = UP TO 1.75 M.H.

W = 1.75 TO 2.75 M.H.

W = OVER 2.75 M.H.

AREA WIDTH COVERAGE—W
Expressed in terms of ratios of luminaire mounting heights (M.H.)

Fig. 13: The various IES/ANSI light distribution patterns attainable with the Power Drawer Area Light luminaire.

series described earlier. It contains the same basic optical components as the Power Drawer Concourse, but the Power Drawer Area Light differs in that it employs a ruggedly constructed cast aluminum tapered sidewall housing (Fig. 12).

The main advantage of this luminaire is that it can be set up to produce standard offset IES/ANSI light distribution patterns. Figure 13 demonstrates how a simple aiming angle adjustment can produce various IES/ANSI light distribution patterns. The adjustment aiming angle overcomes the design limitations of conventional luminaires with fixed optics and eliminates the need to change refractors with each aiming angle change. The single reflector system design fits all application requirements and the pre-positioned lamp socket requires no additional adjustment when angle changes are made.

Fig. 12: Power Drawer Area Light luminaires are ruggedly constructed for maximum life.

Single and twin luminaire mounting configurations are commonly used. As shown in Table 7 (page 115), an aiming angle of 20° and an IES/ANSI Type III light distribution pattern are quite popular in parking area applications. Table 7 also lists details for Power Drawer Area Light luminaire tilt angles of 10° and 15°.

NON-CUTOFF LUMINAIRES

Non-cutoff luminaires do not restrict the visible light to any set angles such as 90° or 72° from vertical (see Fig. 3, page 103). This simple fact results in some very important performance characteristics.

Advantages. The main advantage of non-cutoff luminaires versus cutoff luminaires is increased flexibility in choosing mounting heights and pole spacings. When compared to similarly lamped cutoff luminaires, non-cutoff luminaires can produce uniform lighting patterns at usable footcandle levels when set at greater mounting heights and pole spacings. Lighting uniformity is better, and the possibility of extremely dark patches occurring in the parking area is reduced.

Disadvantages. Lack of light control constitutes the main disadvantage of non-cutoff luminaires. With no effective means of regulating spill light or beam control, indiscriminate use of non-cutoff luminaires, especially in perimeter parking areas, could result in substantial light pollution of adjoining areas. Lack of control also results in poor utilization of the generated light. Only a portion of the light produced falls on the desired area. Since these luminaires do not shield light above the recognized

glare angle of 72°, their use, especially at lower mounting heights, could result in some noticeable visual discomfort.

Power Drawer Floodlights

The Power Drawer Floodlight (Fig. 14) is the one type of non-cutoff luminaire utilized in parking area lighting applications. This luminaire employs a single reflector system, providing maximum efficiency with clear or phosphor coated lamps. The housing is high-strength, one-piece cast aluminum; and the modern, lower profile styling complements many architectural styles and environmental surroundings. These luminaires are also equipped with a knuckle-type, serrated, calibrated adjustment for the precision aiming and positioning of the fixture.

Fig. 14: The non-cutoff Power Drawer Floodlight.

LAMP SELECTION

The two light sources recommended for use in parking area lighting applications are high pressure sodium (HPS) lamps and metal halide (MH) lamps— both members of the High Intensity Discharge (HID) lamp group. Capable of producing up to 140 lumens per watt of electrical power consumed, high pressure sodium lamps are the most efficient light sources in the world today. Their overall light producing efficacy is roughly 50% greater than that of mercury vapor, and HPS sources have the finest lumen maintenance characteristics of all HID lamps.

With HPS lamps, an operating life of 12,000 to 20,000 hours can be expected, depending upon starting frequency and the rate of lamp voltage rise. The golden-white color rendering characteristic of high pressure sodium lamps does not pose a problem in the vast majority of parking area applications. Also, the tremendous light producing capabilities of HPS lamps often lowers system costs by reducing the amount of luminaires, poles, and auxiliary equipment needed.

Metal halide lamps are also a viable choice for parking area applications, particularly in cases where more "natural" color rendition is desired, as in automobile display lots. Lumen maintenance of MH lamps is very good, and although metal halide lamp efficacy and life span are not as fine as those of HPS lamps, they are quite adequate by modern standards.

It is highly recommended that you refer to **Section I: Lamps and Ballasts** for more detailed information concerning the selection and use of HID lamps.

DESIGN METHODS

The keys to designing parking area lighting systems are found in the Application Photometric Data Tables 2 through 8 given on the following pages. Each table corresponds to a specific luminaire design previously discussed in the Equipment Selection section, and the table provides all the necessary data for designing a workable lighting system using that luminaire. Each of the tables is arranged in the same manner to ensure easy cross-reference and comparison. Brief descriptions of the table headings and other pertinent facts are given below. Use Table 2 (page 110) as a guide.

Lamp Type. This column lists the two types of HID lamps used in parking area applications. MH denotes metal halide and HPS denotes high pressure sodium.

Lamp Designation. This column states the designation ordering numbers for the specific MH and HPS lamps recommended.

Lamp Lumens. This value refers to initial lumen output. See Sections I and IV of the handbook for information concerning lumen depreciation and lamp maintenance factors pertinent to these lamps.

Catalog Number. This column lists the actual catalog numbers of the given lamp-luminaire combinations. These catalog numbers allow for easy cross-reference to additional information found in other SPI Lighting publications, making it possible to develop a total performance and cost analysis using the most recent information available.

Pole Mounting Height. The luminaire should never be mounted at a height below the minimum

mounting height specified in the table. For example, Power Drawer Site Light luminaires equipped with 250-watt metal halide lamps should never be mounted at heights below 20'. Also, do not exceed the maximum height listed. The double asterisk denotes the finest, most applicable mounting height for that lamp-luminaire combination. This is the height which will provide the best overall illumination in the majority of parking area applications.

Luminaire Tilt Angle. The luminaire must be positioned at this angle to produce the listed illumination specifications (Fig. 15). **Note:** In order to maintain their cutoff classification, adjustable cutoff luminaires must not be aimed at angles exceeding this recommended maximum angle.

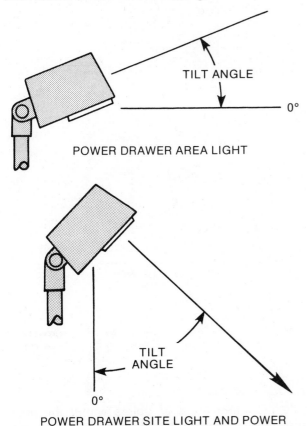

POWER DRAWER AREA LIGHT

POWER DRAWER SITE LIGHT AND POWER DRAWER FLOODLIGHT

Fig. 15: The luminaire tilt angle.

Pole Spacing. Exceeding recommended pole spacings will result in unwanted dark areas, especially when cutoff luminaires are employed.

Average Initial Footcandles. These are the average **initial** footcandle levels generated by a particular lamp-luminaire combination mounted at a specific height, aimed at a specific angle, and spaced at specific intervals. Refer to Sections I and IV for details concerning maintenance and lamp depreciation factors.

Footcandle Plot Reference. The footcandle plot reference letter given to the ideal mounting height

for each lamp wattage corresponds to a computer generated plot printout. Instructions concerning use of the plots are given later in this section.

Mounting Height Ratio. The mounting height ratio is important when designing systems with footcandle levels lower than those listed in the Application Tables. Its function is explained later in this section.

Particular attention should also be given to any footnotes listed under the tables. These footnotes define light distribution types, cutoff designations, illumination levels, and uniformity ratios. For example, the second footnote under the Power Drawer Site Light Table indicates that the above lamp-luminaire combinations have average/minimum uniformity ratios of 3:1 or better. By referring to Table 1 (page 101), you can see that these ratios are acceptable for all types of activity or size levels, high, medium, or low. The maximum/minimum uniformity ratio of 12:1 also falls within the limits set for accepted field practice in all types of parking situations.

Working with the Tables

The Application Tables enable a lighting designer to quickly lay out many types of parking areas, especially those with regular rectangular or square shapes (Fig. 16). The designer simply selects a lamp-luminaire combination, mounting height, and pole spacing from the table and designs a layout to

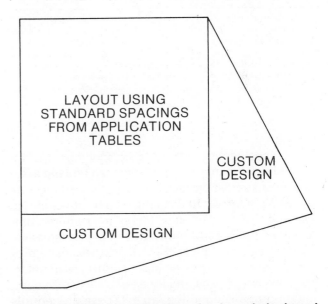

Fig. 16: Treat the largest portion of an irregularly shaped area as a square or rectangle, and use the application tables in the layout. Custom design the remaining perimeter spots.

Table 2: Power Drawer Cutoff Site Light Application Photometric Data

Type	Lamp Designation*	Lumens	Catalog Number	Pole Mounting Height	Luminaire Tilt Angle	Pole Spacing	Average Initial Footcandles	Footcandle Plot Reference	Mounting Height Ratio
MH	MS250/HOR	23,000	FC1158S	20 25** 30	47.5°	96 120 144	6.90 4.42 3.05	— A —	4.0
	MS400/HOR	40,000	FC2168S	30** 35 40	45°	140 164 186	5.68 4.20 3.18	C — 	4.67
	MVR1000/U	107,800	FC3188S	40 45 50** 55 60	40°	184 207 230 253 276	8.02 6.37 5.14 4.27 3.55	— — E — —	4.6
HPS	LU150	16,000	FC1238S	20 25** 30	47.5°	96 120 144	4.95 3.17 2.19	— B —	4.0
	LU250/S	30,000	FC1258S	25 30** 35	45°	117 140 164	5.69 3.95 2.92	— D —	4.0
	LU400	50,000	FC2268S	35 40** 45 50 55	42.5°	158 180 203 225 247	5.25 4.01 3.17 2.57 2.13	— F — — —	4.5
	LU1000	140,000	FC3288S	50 55 60** 65 70 80 100	45°	242 266 290 314 338 386 483	7.13 5.89 4.95 4.21 3.66 2.77 1.78	— — G — — — —	4.83

*Lamp wattages are listed after the initial identifying letters. Example: MS250/HOR = 250-watt metal halide, LU150 = 150-watt high pressure sodium, etc.

**This is the basic mounting height corresponding to the isofootcandle curve reference plots A through G and A-1 through G-1 found in Appendix F.

Notes: 1. Cutoff: All units which cut off all light at 80° above nadir or less.

2. Uniformities: For all applications, maximum/minimum ratio is 12:1 or better. Average/minimum ratio is 3:1 or better.

3. Illumination Levels: These are the average initial horizontal footcandles as plotted in the data area of the plan drawing.

4. Conversion: If levels of illumination lower than those listed above are required, follow the procedure outlined in the text under **Converting to Lower Illumination Levels** (page 113).

5. When substituting lamps of lower wattages in the same housing at the same mounting height and pole spacing, follow the procedure outlined in the text under **Using Lamp Proration Factors** (page 115).

these specifications. If the pole spacings are not altered significantly, the designer can find the average initial footcandle level for the entire parking area by simply referring to the table. The designer is also assured that the layout will meet the required uniformity ratios for all parking areas. No mathematical work is required unless the designer wishes to prorate the system to a lower illumination level or determine a new pole spacing for a lamp-luminaire combination not listed in the table. (These procedures are explained later in this section.)

Perimeter areas pose the greatest problem in the lighting of parking areas, and the designer must locate mounting poles at points within the area which ensure that sufficient light will reach the perimeter areas. Irregularly shaped parking areas pose another problem. However in many cases, the designer can lay out interior sections using standard spacings listed in the tables and then solve for problem perimeter areas by placing several additional poles at appropriate locations.

Scale Considerations. Close examination of the Application Tables reveals the following distinct relationship between lamp wattage, pole mounting height, and pole spacing: The greater the lamp wattage rating, the greater the pole mounting height and pole spacing.

Consider this simple guideline: Smaller areas normally will require lower illumination levels, so it is best to design using lower wattage lamps, lower

Table 3: Power Drawer Concourse Design 20 Roadway Optics Application Photometric Data

Type	Lamp Designation*	Lumens	Catalog Number	Pole Mounting Height	Luminaire Tilt Angle	Pole Spacing	Average Initial Footcandles	Footcandle Plot Reference	Mounting Height Ratio
MH	MS250/HOR	23,000	CS11521 (Design 20)	20 25** 30	0°	64 80 96	15.46 9.91 6.84	— A —	3.2
	MS400/HOR	40,000	CS21621 (Design 20)	30** 35 40	0°	110 128 147	7.98 5.91 4.47	C — —	3.67
	MVR1000/U	107,800	CS31821 (Design 20)	40 45 50** 55 60	0°	160 180 200 220 240	9.70 7.71 6.22 5.16 4.29	— — E — —	4.0
HPS	LU150	16,000	CS18321	20 25** 30	0°	64 80 96	11.53 7.39 5.10	— B —	3.2
	LU250/S	30,000	CS12521	30** 35 40	0°	100 116 132	8.45 6.25 4.73	— D —	3.3
	LU400	50,000	CS22621	35 40** 45 50 55	0°	140 160 180 200 220	6.50 4.96 3.92 3.17 2.63	— F — — —	4.0
	LU1000	140,000	CS32821	50 55 60** 65 70 80 100	0°	210 230 250 273 294 336 420	7.79 6.44 5.41 4.60 4.00 3.03 1.95	— — G — — — —	4.2

*Lamp wattages are listed after the initial identifying letters. Example: MS250/HOR = 250-watt metal halide, LU150 = 150-watt high pressure sodium, etc.

**This is the basic mounting height corresponding to the isofootcandle curve reference plots A through G, A-1 through G-1, and A-2 through G-2 found in Appendix F.

Notes:
1. Distribution Types: Curves A, B, and D are Type II, Medium, Cutoff. Curves C, F, and G are Type III, Medium, Cutoff. Curve E is a Type III, Short, Cutoff.
2. Cutoff: All units which cut off all light at 78° above nadir or less.
3. Uniformities: For all applications, maximum/minimum ratio is 12:1 or better. Average/minimum ratio for curves E, F, and G is 3:1 or better, and the average/minimum ratio for curves A, B, C, and D is 3.7:1 or better.
4. Illumination Levels: These are the average initial horizontal footcandles as plotted in the data area of the plan drawing.
5. Conversion: If levels of illumination lower than those listed above are required, follow the procedure outlined in the text under **Converting to Lower Illumination Levels** (page 113).
6. When substituting lamps of lower wattages in the same housing at the same mounting height and pole spacing, follow the procedure outlined in the text under **Using Lamp Proration Factors** (page 115).

mounting heights, and smaller pole spacings. Medium areas require medium lamp wattages and illumination levels with medium mounting heights and pole spacings. The highest lamp wattages should be reserved for wide pole spacings and high mounting positions.

In addition to categorically breaking lighting design down into small, medium, and large areas, the specific desires of architects or clients may also merit special consideration. As mentioned earlier, in many instances clients do not wish the light pole or luminaire to project above the top of their building. They may restrict the lighting design to lower mounting heights and, consequently, lower wattage lamps and closer pole spacings.

Another guideline to consider is that higher wattage lamps with their subsequent mounting heights and spacings generally create more efficient systems, especially when sharp cutoff luminaires are employed. Due to the nature of their optic control, the mounting height of cutoff luminaires is a very critical factor. The lower the mounting height, the closer the fixtures must be located to one another, regardless of the lamp wattage employed. To increase pole spacing with cutoff luminaires, the mounting height must be increased and an appro-

Table 4:   Power Drawer Concourse Design 40 Extended Area Forward Throw Optics Application Photometric Data

Type	Lamp Designation*	Lumens	Catalog Number	Pole Mounting Height	Luminaire Tilt Angle	Pole Spacing	Average Initial Footcandles	Footcandle Plot Reference	Mounting Height Ratio
MH	MS400/HOR	40,000	CS21641	30**	0°	120	6.46	H	4.0
				35		140	4.78	—	
				40		160	3.62	—	
	MVR1000/U	107,800	CS31841	40	0°	160	8.97	—	4.0
				45		180	7.13	—	
				50**		200	5.75	J	
				55		220	4.77	—	
				60		240	3.97	—	
HPS	LU400	50,000	CS22641	35	0°	123	7.35	—	3.5
				40**		140	5.61	I	
				45		158	4.43	—	
				50		175	3.59	—	
				55		193	2.97	—	
	LU1000	140,000	CS32841	50	0°	142	14.57	—	2.83
				55		156	12.04	—	
				60**		170	10.12	K	
				65		184	8.60	—	
				70		198	7.49	—	
				80		226	5.67	—	
				100		283	3.64	—	

*Lamp wattages are listed after the initial identifying letters. Example: MS400/HOR = 400-watt metal halide, LU400 = 400-watt high pressure sodium, etc.

**This is the basic mounting height corresponding to the isofootcandle curve reference plots H through K, H-1 through K-1, and H-2 through K-2 found in Appendix F.

Notes: 1. Distribution Types: All curves are modified Type IV, Short, Cutoff.
  2. Cutoff: All units which cut off all light at 78° above nadir or less.
  3. Uniformities: For all applications, maximum/minimum ratio is 12:1 or better. Average/minimum is 3.7:1 or better.
  4. Conversion: If levels of illumination lower than those listed above are required, follow the procedure outlined in the text under **Converting to Lower Illumination Levels.**
  5. When substituting lamps of lower wattages in the same housing at the same mounting height and pole spacing, follow the procedure outlined in the text under **Using Lamp Proration Factors** (page 115).

priate lamp wattage installed. The relationship between mounting height and pole spacing is expressed in the mounting height ratios listed in the Application Tables. These ratios should never be exceeded.

Isofootcandle Curve Reference Plots

When placed at a given mounting height and pole spacing, each lamp-luminaire combination generates a unique set of illumination levels over a specific area. These lighting levels are graphically expressed in computer-tabulated isofootcandle curve reference plots which are listed in Appendix F of this handbook. The Application Tables list a letter reference to the type of plots that selected lamp-luminaire combinations produce.

For example, the Power Drawer Cutoff Site Light Application Table indicates that a metal halide MS250/HOR lamp in a Power Drawer Cutoff Site Lite luminaire mounted at 25' and aimed at 47.5° will produce a Power Drawer Cutoff Site Light Type-A photometric curve which is illustrated in Fig. 17.

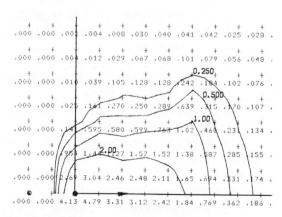

Fig. 17: Example of an isofootcandle curve reference plot. Grid increments are spaced 12.5' apart.

Table 5: Power Drawer Concourse Design 50 Symmetrical Optics Application Photometric Data

Type	Lamp Designation*	Lumens	Catalog Number	Pole Mounting Height	Pole Spacing	Average Initial Footcandles	Footcandle Plot Reference	Mounting Height Ratio
MH	MVR400/VBU	40,000	CT21650	20	120	1.85	—	6.0
				25	150	1.18	—	
				30**	180	.82	C	
				35	210	.61	—	
				40	240	.46	—	
HPS	LU400	50,000	CT22650	20	110	2.40	—	5.5
				25	138	1.54	—	
				30	165	1.07	—	
				35	193	.79	—	
				40**	220	.60	F	
				45	248	.47	—	
				50	275	.38	—	

*Lamp wattages are listed after the initial identifying letters. Example: LU400 = 400-watt high pressure sodium, etc.

**This is the basic mounting height corresponding to the isofootcandle curve reference plots C and F listed in Appendix F.

Notes: 1. Distribution Types: Curves C and F are Type V, Cutoff.
2. Cutoff: All units which cut off all light at 80° above nadir.
3. Uniformities: For all applications, maximum/minimum ratio is 11.5:1 or better. Average/minimum ratio is 3.5:1 or better.
4. Illumination Levels: These are the average initial horizontal footcandles as plotted in the data area of the plan drawing.
5. Conversion: If levels of illumination lower than those listed above are required, follow the procedure outlined in the text under **Converting to Lower Illumination Levels.**
6. When substituting lamps of lower wattages in the same housing at the same mounting height and pole spacing, follow the procedure outlined in the text under **Using Lamp Proration Factors** (page 115).

The printout is produced on paper divided into 12.5′ grid increments. The dark circle represents the location of the luminaire and the arrow represents the aiming direction. The actual footcandle levels generated are printed below each grid cross location, and the curved lines represent points of equal illumination. For example, the outer curve represents points of 0.25 footcandle, the next line 0.5 footcandle, etc.

For each lamp-luminaire combination, isofootcandle curve reference plots are available for one-, four-, and sometimes two-luminaire per pole configurations. Because the light patterns produced are often symmetrical, only portions of the total light pattern need be shown on the printout. The total light pattern can be produced from this partial information.

These computer printouts can be a great aid in solving many unique lighting problems. As you will see in the design sketches on the next few pages, the printout grid can be transferred to the actual layout drawing so that precise footcandle levels can be found at desired points. This is extremely useful in lighting perimeter areas or odd-shaped areas. By using this grid system, the designer can also place mounting poles at spacings other than those listed in the Application Tables and then check the footcandle levels and uniformity ratios using the computer printout information.

As an alternate method to this grid system procedure, the designer can secure the actual isofootcandle curve printout to the drafting board and place a scale drawing of the parking area on top of it. The designer can then pencil in the pole locations and trace certain isofootcandle lines onto the layout, making certain all areas meet the required illumination levels. The one drawback of this alternate method is that the parking area must be drawn to the same scale as the isofootcandle curve plots. More will be said concerning these design methods in later sections of the book.

Converting to Lower Illumination Levels

The Application Tables do not list all the possible lamp-luminaire combinations or illumination levels. If illumination levels lower than those listed in the table are desired, choose a desired mounting height and replace the recommended lamp with a lamp of lower wattage. In this case, a new pole spacing must also be calculated using the given mounting height ratio. The following example is based on the Power Drawer Cutoff Site Light Application Table (page 110).

Table 6: Power Mod Conquest Landscape Symmetrical Optics Application Photometric Data

Type	Designation*	Lumens	Catalog Number	Pole Mounting Height	Pole Spacing	Average Initial Footcandles	Footcandle Plot Reference	Mounting Height Ratio
MH	M250/U	20,500	LS1150 or LS4150	12**	66	2.28	A	5.5
				15	83	1.46	—	
				20	110	.82	—	
				25	138	.52	—	
	MV400/VBD	40,000	LS2160 or LS6160	20	110	1.69	—	5.5
				24**	132	1.17	C	
				30	165	.75	—	
				35	193	.55	—	
	MS1000/BU	125,000	LS3180 or LS6180	30	180	1.92	—	6.0
				35	210	1.41	—	
				40	240	1.08	—	
				45	270	.86	—	
				50**	300	.69	E	
				55	330	.57	—	
				60	360	.48	—	
HPS	LU150	16,000	LS1230 or LS4230	12**	72	1.78	B	5.5
				15	83	1.14	—	
				20	110	.64	—	
				25	138	.41	—	
	LU400	50,000	LS2260 or LS5260	20	120	1.94	—	6.0
				24**	144	1.35	F	
				30	180	.86	—	
				35	210	.64	—	
				40	240	.49	—	

*Lamp wattages are listed after the initial identifying letters. Example: MS250/U = 250-watt metal halide, LU150 = 150-watt high pressure sodium, etc.

**This is the basic mounting height corresponding to the isofootcandle curve reference plots A through F found in Appendix F.

Notes: 1. Distribution Types: All curves are Type V, Cutoff.

2. Cutoff: All units cut off light at 80° above nadir.

3. Uniformities: For all applications maximum/minimum ratio is 11:1 or better. Average/minimum is 3.8:1 or better for curve A, 3.5:1 or better for curves B, C, and E, and 3:1 or better for curve F.

4. Illumination Levels: These are the average initial horizontal footcandles as plotted in the data area of the plan drawing.

5. Conversion: If higher illumination levels are desired, use multiple units on the same mounting pole at the same mounting height. To find the new illumination level, multiply the appropriate illumination level listed in the above table by the total number of luminaires on the pole. Example: 400-watt HPS at a 40' mounting height generates 0.49 initial footcandles. Therefore, 2 units/pole = 2 × .49 = .98 initial footcandles
    3 units/pole = 3 × .49 = 1.47 initial footcandles
    4 units/pole = 4 × .49 = 1.96 initial footcandles
Uniformities do not change.

6. When substituting lamps of lower wattages in the same housing at the same mounting height and pole spacing, follow the procedure outlined in the text under **Using Lamp Proration Factors.**

7. Pole mounting heights are the optimum recommended heights. The mounting height conversion factors found in Table 9 on page 117 are **not applicable** for Power Mod Conquest Landscape luminaires.

As indicated, a **1000-watt metal halide lamp** mounted at a **50' pole height** with poles spaced at 230' produces **5.14 average initial footcandles.** To determine the new average initial footcandle level when using **400-watt metal halide lamps,** proceed as follows:

1. Determine the new maximum allowable pole spacing. As indicated in the table, the **mounting height ratio** for **400-watt metal halide lamps** is **4.67.** Multiply this ratio by the desired mounting height, **50'** in this case: **4.67 × 50' = 233.5' maximum allowable pole spacing.**

2. Obtain a new lamp illumination level based on the footcandle plot reference of the desired lamp. For a **400-watt metal halide lamp,** the **plot reference** is designated as **C,** with a **mounting height** of **30'** and an **average initial footcandle level** of **5.68.**

3. Multiply this new illumination level by the correct mounting height conversion factor listed in Table 9 (page 117). As shown in **Table 9,** for **plot reference C,** the **conversion factor** at a **mounting height**

Table 7: Power Drawer Area Light Application Photometric Data

Type	Lamp Designation*	Lumens	Catalog Number	Pole Mounting Height	Luminaire Tilt Angle	Pole Spacing	Average Initial Footcandles	Footcandle Plot Reference	Mounting Height Ratio
MH	MVR250/U	19,500	FR1155	20 25** 30	20°	72 90 108	10.72 6.87 4.74	— A —	3.6
	MVR400/U	32,000	FR2165	30** 35 40	20°	110 128 146	5.67 4.20 3.18	C — —	3.67
	MVR1000/U	107,800	FR3185	40 45 50** 55 60	15°	144 162 180 312 340	9.25 7.35 5.93 4.92 4.09	— — E — —	3.6
HPS	LU150	16,000	FR1835	20 25** 30	15°	72 90 108	7.54 4.83 3.33	— B —	3.6
	LU250/S	30,000	FR2255	25 30** 35	20°	92 110 128	8.18 5.68 4.20	— D —	3.67
	LU400	50,000	FR2265	35 40** 45 50 55	20°	130 150 168 188 206	6.63 5.06 4.00 3.24 2.68	— F — — —	3.75
	LU1000	140,000	FR3285	50 55 60** 65 70 80 100	10°	192 210 230 250 268 306 383	8.70 7.19 6.04 5.13 4.47 3.38 2.17	— — G — — — —	3.83

*Lamp wattages are listed after the initial identifying letters. Example: MVR250/U = 250-watt metal halide, LU150 = 150-watt high pressure sodium, etc.

**This is the basic mounting height corresponding to the isofootcandle curve reference plots A through G and A-1 through G-1 found in Appendix F.

Notes: 1. Distribution Types: Curves A, B, C, D, and F are Type III, Medium, Semi-cutoff.
Curves E and G are Type III, Medium, Cutoff.

2. Cutoff: All units cut off all light at 87° above nadir or less.

3. Uniformities: For all applications, maximum/minimum ratio is 12:1 or better. Average/minimum ratio is 3.5:1 or better.

4. Illumination Levels: These are the average initial horizontal footcandles as plotted in the data area of the plan drawing.

5. Conversion: If levels of illumination lower than those listed above are required, follow the procedure outlined in the text under **Converting to Lower Illumination Levels** (page 113).

6. When substituting lamps of lower wattages in the same housing at the same mounting height and pole spacing, follow the procedure outlined in the text under **Using Lamp Proration Factors.**

of **30′** is **1.0**. At a **50′ mounting height**, the **conversion factor** equals **0.36**. Therefore, **5.68** footcandles × **.36** conversion factor = **2.05** footcandles. The new data is as follows: **A 400-watt metal halide lamp mounted at a 50′ height with poles spaced 233.5′ apart produces 2.05 average initial footcandles.**

This procedure does not change the uniformity ratios stated in the footnotes of the tables.

Using Lamp Proration Factors

It is also possible to attain lower illumination levels by substituting lower wattage lamps in place of those recommended for a given luminaire at a specified mounting height and spacing. When substituting lamps of lower wattages in the same housing at the same mounting height and pole spacing, multi-ply the average initial footcandle level of the original lamp by the correct Lamp Proration Factor given in Table 10 (page 118).

For example, as listed in the Power Drawer Cutoff Site Application Table, a **150-watt high pressure sodium lamp** at a **25′ mounting height** and **120′ pole spacing** generates **3.17 average initial footcandles.** When replacing this lamp with a **70-watt high pressure sodium lamp**, locate the correct **proration factor (0.363)** in **Table 10** under Power Drawer Cutoff Site Light by using the footcandle reference plot **(B)** and the desired lower lamp wattage **(70)**. Multiply: **.363** proration factor × **3.17** footcandles = **1.15 aver-**

Table 8: Power Drawer Floodlight Application Photometric Data

Type	Lamp Designation*	Lumens	Catalog Number	Pole Mounting Height	Luminaire Tilt Angle	Pole Spacing	Average Initial Footcandles	Footcandle Plot Reference	Mounting Height Ratio
MH	MVR250/U	20,500	FL1151	20 25** 30	60°	120 150 180	2.73 1.75 1.21	— A —	6.0
	MVR400/U	34,000	FL2161	30** 35 40	60°	170 198 227	2.39 1.77 1.34	C — —	5.67
	MVR1000/U	110,000	FL3181	40 45 50** 55 60	60°	216 243 270 297 324	5.41 4.30 3.47 2.88 2.39	— — E — —	5.4
HPS	LU150	16,000	FL1831	20 25** 30	60°	128 160 192	2.01 1.29 .89	— B —	6.4
	LU250/S	30,000	FL1851	25 30** 35	60°	158 190 222	2.32 1.61 1.19	— D —	6.33
	LU400	50,000	FL2261	35 40** 45 50 55	60°	210 240 270 300 330	2.44 1.86 1.47 1.19 .99	— — F — —	6.0
	LU1000	140,000	FL3281	50 55 60** 65 70 80 100	60°	267 293 320 347 373 427 533	3.86 3.19 2.68 2.28 1.98 1.50 .97	— — G — — — —	5.33

*Lamp wattages are listed after the initial identifying letters. Example: MVR250/U = 250-watt metal halide, LU150 = 150-watt high pressure sodium, etc.

**This is the basic mounting height corresponding to the isofootcandle curve reference plots A through G and A-1 through G-1 found in Appendix F.

Notes: 1. Distribution Types: Curves A, B, and D are IES/NEMA 7 × 7.
Curves C, E, F, and G are IES/NEMA 6 × 7.

2. Cutoff: All luminaires are classified as floodlight, non-cutoff.

3. Uniformities: For all applications, maximum/minimum ratio is 12:1 or better. Average/minimum ratio is 3.5:1 or better.

4. Illumination Levels: These are the average initial horizontal footcandles as plotted in the data area of the plan drawing.

5. Conversion: If levels of illumination lower than those listed above are required, follow the procedure outlined in the text under **Converting to Lower Illumination Levels** (page 113).

6. When substituting lamps of lower wattages in the same housing at the same mounting height and pole spacing, follow the procedure outlined in the text under **Using Lamp Proration Factors.**

age initial footcandles for 70-watt high pressure sodium lamps at 25' mounting heights and 100' pole spacings.

APPLICATION SKETCH: MEDIUM SIZE AREA

Figure 18 (page 120) illustrates a partially completed lighting layout for a hospital parking area. The layout is being designed using computer-generated isofootcandle curve reference plots. The designer has broken down the parking area into several segments and is solving the lighting problems of each segment in turn. Because pole spacings other than those listed in the Application Tables are being used, the grid system of design is being employed. A step-by-step description of the process follows.

Design Criteria. As previously shown in Table 1 (page 101), hospital parking areas are classified as medium size or medium activity level areas requiring 1 footcandle of illumination and maximum/minimum and average/minimum uniformity ratios of 12:1 and 3:1 respectively.

Spacial Considerations. The overall physical size and arrangement of the parking area must be reviewed. As in many medium to small size parking

Table 9: Mounting Height Conversion Factors

Mounting Height	New Grid Increment	Footcandle Plot					
		A,B A-1, B-1	C,D C-1, D-1	E E-1	F F-1	G G-1
15	7.5	2.78	—	—	—	—
20	10	1.56	2.25	—	4.00	—
25	12.5	1.00	1.44	4.00	2.56	5.76
30	15	.69	1.00	2.78	1.78	4.00
35	17.5	.51	.74	2.04	1.31	2.94
40	20	.39	.56	1.56	1.00	2.25
45	22.5	—	.44	1.24	.79	1.78
50	25	—	.36	1.00	.64	1.44
55	27.5	—	—	.83	.53	1.19
60	30	—	—	.69	.44	1.00
65	32.5	—	—	.59	.38	.85
70	35	—	—	.51	.33	.74
75	37.5	—	—	.44	—	.64
80	40	—	—	.39	—	.56
85	42.5	—	—	.35	—	.50
90	45	—	—	.31	—	.44
95	47.5	—	—	.28	—	.40
100	50	—	—	.25	—	.36

Note: When working with the footcandle plots given in Appendix F, multiply all footcandle values given on the plots by the conversion factor listed for the desired mounting height.
Do not use for **Power Mod Conquest Landscape** luminaires.

areas, the design shown in Fig. 18 employs what is commonly known as a trafficway parking concept—two adjoining rows of parking space separated by individual trafficways. This type of setup creates a situation which closely resembles roadway lighting. A luminaire capable of producing a long rectangular light pattern parallel to the front of the luminaire would be the finest choice for spacial arrangement.

Equipment Selection. Power Drawer Concourse Design 20 luminaires are the designer's choice because they produce a light pattern similiar to that previously described. Two luminaires per pole set 180° apart are used in most cases, however, some one-luminaire poles are placed in some perimeter locations. As a tentative light source, LU400 high pressure sodium lamps are the designer's selection. A medium mounting height of 40' was selected in keeping with the scale design concept.

Gridding out the Area. The isofootcandle curve reference plots for one- and two-luminaire pole configurations as previously described are illustrated in Figs. 19 and 20 (page 120) respectively. Since both of these plots are produced on the printout using 20' grid increments, the designer also broke down the segment of the parking area being worked on into squares measuring 20' on each side.

Roughing out Pole Locations. As you can see in Fig. 18, the majority of the parking area was roughed-out using pole spacings of 160' to the side and 140' spacings to the front. The designer placed two-luminaire units at points 1, 2, 3, 5, 6, 7, and 10, and one-luminaire units at points 4, 8, 9, 11, and 12 as indicated by the circled numbers. Once tentative pole locations are selected, the actual footcandle levels listed under the grid points on the isofootcandle curve reference plots can be transferred to the corresponding points on the parking area layout.

Since each point will receive light from several pole locations, it is necessary to add these values to find the total illumination at a given point. It is not necessary to determine the illumination level at all the grid points within a given section of the parking area. Obviously, points near the pole locations will easily meet required illumination levels. However, illumination levels should be compiled at a series of points throughout the area to assure that light levels and uniformity ratios meet desired specifications. Select points where the illumination level will be abnormally high or low, such as directly beneath a

Table 10: Lamp Proration Factors

Power Drawer Cutoff Site Light

Footcandle Plot	Lamp				Proration Factor
	Wattage	Type	Designation	Initial Lumens	
A, A-1	175	MH	MVR175/U	12,000	.522
	175	Super MH	MS175/HOR	15,000	.652
B, B-1	70	HPS	LU70	5,800	.363
	100	HPS	LU100	9,500	.594
C, C-1	400	MH	MVR400/U	32,000	.800
E, E-1	1500	MH	MVR1500/HBD	150,000	1.390
F, F-1	200	HPS	LU200	22,000	.440
	250	HPS	LU250	27,500	.550
	250	HPS Superior	LU250/S	30,000	.600
	310	HPS	LU310	37,000	.740

Power Drawer Concourse Design 20 and Design 40

Footcandle Plot	Wattage	Type	Designation	Initial Lumens	Proration Factor
A, A-1, A-2	175	MH	MS175/HOR	15,000	.652
B, B-1, B-2	70	HPS	LU70	5,800	.363
	100	HPS	LU100	9,500	.594
C, C-1, C-2	400	MH	MVR400/U	32,000	.800
H, H-1, H-2					
F, F-1, F-2	200	HPS	LU200	22,000	.440
I, I-1, I-2	250	HPS	LU250	27,500	.550
	250	HPS Superior	LU250/S	30,000	.600
	310	HPS	LU310	37,000	.740

Power Drawer Concourse Design 50

Footcandle Plot	Wattage	Type	Designation	Initial Lumens	Proration Factor
C	400	MH	MVR400/U	34,000	.850
F	200	HPS	LU200	22,000	.440
	250	HPS	LU250	27,000	.550
	250	HPS Superior	LU250/S	30,000	.600
	310	HPS	LU310	37,000	.740

Conquest Landscape

Footcandle Plot	Wattage	Type	Designation	Initial Lumens	Proration Factor
A	175	MH	MVR175/U	14,200	.693
	175	MH	MVR175	14,200	.693
B	70	HPS	LU70	5,800	.363
	100	HPS	LU100	9,500	.594
C	400	MH	MVR400/U	34,000	.850
F	200	HPS	LU200	22,000	.440
	250	HPS	LU250	27,500	.550
	250	HPS Superior	LU250/S	30,000	.600
	310	HPS	LU310	37,000	.740

luminaire or at the area's perimeter. In checking for problem spots in the northwest section of the hospital, the lighting designer compiled footcandle levels at 17 separate points, designated by the numbers in the squares on the drawing layout.

Table 11 (page 121) lists the footcandle level contribution from each pole at these points and gives the total illumination level at each select point. Once such a table is compiled, the designer can then examine that section for problem spots. For example, one problem spot exists at the northwest perimeter. As you can see, the illumination level at point 6 is 10.916 footcandles while the level at point 3 is only 0.733 footcandle. From dividing the maximum reading by the minimum reading, a maximum/minimum uniformity ratio of 14.89:1 is obtained. Since this ratio exceeds the 12:1 recommendation for medium size areas, the illumination level at point 3 must be

Power Drawer Area Light

Footcandle Plot	Lamp				Proration Factor
	Wattage	Type	Designation	Initial Lumens	
A, A-1	175	MH	MVR175/U	12,000	.615
B, B-1	70	HPS	LU70	5,800	.363
	100	HPS	LU100	9,500	.594
D, D-1	200	HPS	LU200	22,000	.440
	250	HPS	LU250	27,500	.917
	310	HPS	LU310	37,000	1.230
	400	HPS	LU400	50,000	1.670
E, E-1	1500	MH	MVR1500/HBD	150,000	1.390
F, F-1	200	HPS	LU200	22,000	.440
	250	HPS	LU250	27,500	.550
	250	HPS Superior	LU250/S	30,000	.600
	310	HPS	LU310	37,000	.740

Power Drawer Floodlight

Footcandle Plot	Lamp				Proration Factor
A, A-1	175	MH	MVR175/U	12,000	.522
	175	Super MH	MS175/HOR	15,000	.652
B, B-1	70	HPS	LU70	5,800	.363
	100	HPS	LU100	9,500	.594
D, D-1	250	HPS	LU250	27,500	.917
E, E-1	1500	MH	MVR1500/HBD	155,000	1.410
F, F-1	200	HPS	LU200	22,000	.440
	250	HPS	LU250	27,500	.550
	250	HPS Superior	LU250/S	30,000	.600
	310	HPS	LU300	37,000	.740

Note: When using the isofootcandle curve reference plots given in Appendix F in conjunction with the lamps listed above, be certain to multiply all footcandle values given on the plot by the correct proration factor.

increased. The designer has added a single-unit pole near point 3 on the northwest perimeter to accomplish this increase. The effect this luminaire has on the light levels in this section of the parking area is also listed in Table 11. The new pole increases the old minimum value of 0.733 footcandle to 3.763 footcandles, and the maximum level is increased to 11.491 footcandles. The new minimum value of 1.231 footcandles now occurs at point 7; therefore, the new maximum/minimum uniformity ratio in this portion of the parking area is 11.491 ÷ 1.231 = 9.33:1, an acceptable ratio.

The **average** illumination level in this portion of the parking area must also be tabulated. This value is found by adding the new footcandle levels found at each test point together and dividing by the number of test points. The average illumination in this section of the parking area is 3.48 initial footcandles, a level which substantially exceeds the 1 footcandle requirement.

At this point in the layout, the designer has solved for **one problem area** along the northwest perimeter. There will definitely be other problem spots in the parking area, such as the low illumination levels at

points 13 and 13A and at other perimeter sections. However, by breaking down the total area into smaller segments, the designer can solve these problems one at a time using the method previously described. As a lighting designer, you must always realize that adding or subtracting luminaires can affect the illumination levels and uniformity ratios over a sizable area. For instance, in the hospital layout, the designer may add additional luminaires to problem areas, which will again alter the light levels in the northwest section. However, one of the "traps" a designer can encounter is a preoccupation with tabulating precise footcandle levels. While precision and accuracy are important in lighting design, some of the footcandle contributions listed in Table 11, such as 0.001, 0.002, and 0.004 are virtually negligible in this case and need not be included in tabulations to produce a sufficiently accurate layout. Channel your efforts into visualizing the total lighting scheme of the parking area.

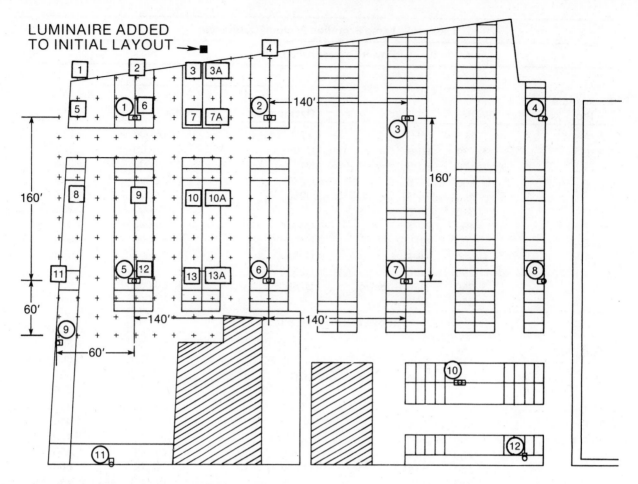

LUMINAIRE ADDED TO INITIAL LAYOUT →

Fig. 18: Medium size parking area application sketch.

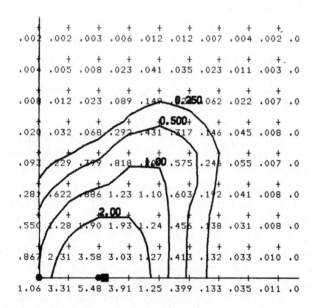

Fig. 19: Power Drawer Concourse Design 20, single luminaire, 400-watt HPS lamp, 40' mounting height. Grid increments are spaced 20' apart.

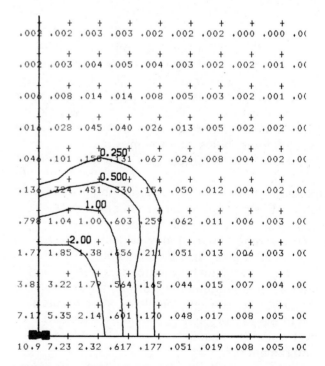

Fig. 20: Power Drawer Concourse Design 20, two luminaire, 400-watt HPS lamp, 40' mounting height. Grid increments are spaced 20' apart.

EXTERIOR LIGHTING

120

Table 11: Illumination Levels (Footcandles)—Medium Size Application Sketch

Test Point	1	2	3	3A	4	5	6	7	7A
Mounting Pole									
1	1.790	3.810	.564	.165	.006	2.320	10.900	.617	.177
2	.003	.007	.165	.564	1.770	.003	.008	.177	.617
3	—	—	.001	.002	.006	—	—	.002	.002
5	.002	.002	.003	.002	—	.014	.006	.014	.008
6	—	—	—	—	—	.001	.002	.008	.014
7	—	—	—	—	—	—	—	—	—
9	—	—	—	—	—	—	—	—	—
Total	1.795	3.819	.733	.733	1.782	2.338	10.916	.818	.818
New Luminaire	.089	.818	3.030	3.030	1.230	.250	.575	.413	.413
New Total	1.884	4.637	3.763	3.763	3.012	2.588	11.491	1.231	1.231

Test Point	8	9	10	10A	11	12	13	13A
Mounting Pole								
1	.603	.798	.603	.259	.014	.006	.008	.014
2	.002	.006	.259	.603	—	.002	.008	.014
3	—	—	—	—	—	—	—	—
5	.603	.798	.603	.259	.177	10.900	.617	.177
6	.002	.006	.259	.603	.002	.008	.177	.617
7	—	—	—	—	—	—	.002	.002
9	.023	.023	.001	.001	.886	.192	.008	.003
Total	1.233	1.631	1.725	1.725	1.079	11.108	.820	.827
New Luminaire	.001	.003	.004	.004	—	—	—	—
New Total	1.234	1.634	1.729	1.729	1.079	11.108	.820	.827

Adjusting Light Levels. As mentioned before, a 3.48 initial footcandle average is quite high for a medium size parking area. If this average holds true in all sections of the parking design, the designer will probably want to reduce this level by replacing the 400-watt high pressure sodium lamp with an HPS design of lower wattage. The lamp proration factors found in Table 10 (page 118) make this process quite simple. For example, if the original lamps were replaced with 200-watt HPS, all illumination levels would be prorated down by a factor of 0.440, and the new average illumination level would be approximately 1.5 footcandles. Also, using the proration factors does not affect the uniformity ratios in any way, so the lighting designer can work up the layout based on the isofootcandle curve reference plots of 400-watt HPS lamp-luminaire combinations. He or she can then prorate the system down to an ideal illumination level in one quick final step.

The Overlay Method

Figure 21 illustrates how the actual isofootcandle reference curves can be traced onto the parking area layout to give the lighting designer a general overview of the illumination levels at different points. The lines are labeled as they appear on a computer printout in 2 footcandle, 1 footcandle, 0.5 footcandle, and 0.25 footcandle designations. Always remember the following when using the overlay method: **The parking area must be drawn to the exact same scale as the actual isofootcandle curves.** For example, if the computer printout of the isofootcandle curve is sized so that 1″ = 40′, the scale drawing of the parking area must be drawn to this size to accurately utilize the curves.

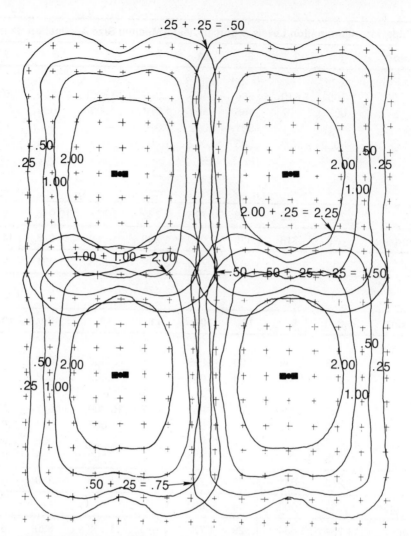

.25 + .25 = .50

.50

.25

2.00

1.00

2.00 + .25 = 2.25

1.00 + 1.00 = 2.00

.50 + .50 + .25 + .25 = 1.50

.50 2.00

.25 1.00

.50 + .25 = .75

.50

2.00

.25

1.00

.50

.25

2.00

1.00

Fig. 21: How the overlay method of layout would be used in the medium-sized area illustrated in Fig. 18.

Determining footcandle levels involves a certain amount of addition or multiplication and some interpolation skills. For example, the exact center point between the four poles in Fig. 21 occurs halfway between the 0.5 isofootcandle line and the 0.25 isofootcandle line, so we can interpolate this value to be 0.375 footcandle. Since four poles contribute 0.375 footcandle, the total illumination level at this point is 4 × .375 = 1.5 footcandles. Several other footcandle levels are given in Fig. 21 where the isofootcandle lines cross. As you can see, this overlay method is not nearly as accurate as the grid method, and the computation of reliable uniformity ratios is particularly difficult.

While this overlay method has been used for many years by many lighting designers, it is strongly recommended that the grid system of layout be used whenever the lighting layout does not fall into the pole spacings listed in the Application Tables. The grid system is highly accurate. Once the designer has become accustomed to working with the computer printouts, he or she can produce a finished layout very quickly.

APPLICATION SKETCH: LARGE AREAS

Figure 22 illustrates an appropriate lighting layout for a large parking area serving a regional shopping mall. The designer has used several different luminaire combinations in this case. In the upper left-hand corner, four-luminaire per pole configurations known as quad luminaires are used; while sections along the area's southern border employ two luminaires per pole. The designer has also placed several one-luminaire units throughout the layout where the need for more light is apparent. A layout such as this can be made using information contained in the Application Tables or by obtaining the appropriate isofootcandle curve reference plots and working with the grid system. Most likely a combination of the two was used.

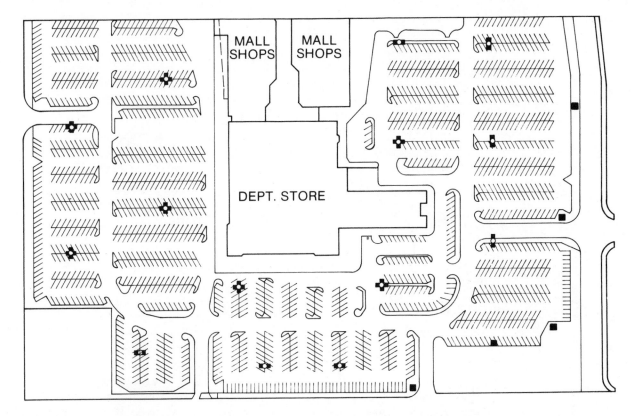

Fig. 22: Large area application sketch. Note the use of several types of luminaire configurations.

Another example of a large parking area lighting system is shown in Fig. 23. This system was designed using 1000-watt high pressure sodium lamps placed in Twin Power Drawer Concourse Design 20 fixtures. The screened sections of the parking area indicate spots where the designer gridded out the area and tabulated actual footcandle levels using computer-generated isofootcandle curve reference plots.

Note the overall shape of the shopping mall. As is often the case in modern developments, a pie-shaped piece of land is utilized. The main tenants, such as large chain department stores, are located in individual quadrants of that pie. The small mall shops are situated in the center of the pie. Parking areas are located in quadrants around the pie's perimeter.

APPLICATION SKETCH: SMALL PARKING AREA

The lighting layout for the small shopping center parking area shown in Fig. 24 (page 125) was designed using both the Application Tables and computer-generated isofootcandle curve reference plots. The procedure is described in the following paragraphs.

Design Criteria. As listed in Table 1 (page 101), small parking areas with low activity levels require a 0.5 footcandle maintained illumination level and 15:1 and 4:1 maximum/minimum and average/minimum uniformity ratios respectively.

Spacial Considerations. The overall size and shape of the area is small and rectangular, a situation which lends itself to work with the application tables. The designer must also consider that there are store buildings located at the lot's east and west perimeters and that the canopy lighting from these store fronts provides 0.1 footcandle of light at the perimeter areas.

Equipment Selection. The designer chose Power Mod Conquest Landscape luminaires due to their great aesthetic appeal. The luminaires were tentatively equipped with LU150 high pressure sodium lamps and in keeping with the scale principle, mounted at a low 12' height.

Setting Pole Spacings. Table 6 (page 114) states that an LU150 HPS lamp mounted at 12' and spaced at 72' intervals will produce 1.78 average initial footcandles having maximum/minimum and average/minimum uniformity ratios of 11:1 and 3.5:1 or better respectively. Even when this value is multiplied by a 0.9 lamp lumen depreciation factor and a 0.86 dirt

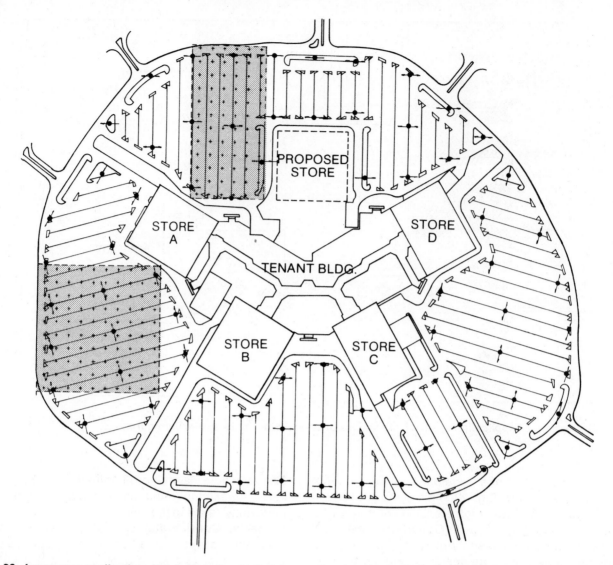

Fig. 23: Large area application sketch. Note the shaded areas where isofootcandle curve reference plots have been fitted into the layout.

depreciation factor (1.78 × .9 × .86 = 1.38), the resulting maintained illuminance of 1.38 footcandles is quite adequate for a small parking area. (See Section IV for more information concerning the computation of maintained footcandle levels.)

Knowing this, the designer placed the poles within the parking area interior at 62' spacings to the front and 65' spacings to the sides. At these intervals, it is certain that the area's interior will meet all illumination and uniformity requirements.

Troubleshooting Perimeter Areas. Two questions must still be answered before the system can be approved for use. These are: (1) What are the lighting levels at the east and west perimeters? (2) Do these levels adversely alter the uniformity ratios?

The information found on the Type-B Power Drawer Conquest Landscape isofootcandle curve computer printout (Fig. 25, page 126) can help answer these questions. By studying the printout, you can see that a maximum lighting level of 3.46 footcandles occurs at a point 12' out from the pole. Because of the 15:1 maximum/minimum uniformity ratio, the minimum acceptable light level at any point in the parking area is 3.46 ÷ 15 = .230 footcandle.

Table 12 (page 126) lists the individual light contributions from various luminaires at key points along the east and west perimeters. The table was compiled using the grid system described earlier in the medium size area application sketch. As you can see, points 1 through 7 on the west perimeter receive light from luminaires 1 through 4. The minimum reading of 0.292 footcandle occurs at points 2, 4, and 6. This light level exceeds the minimum requirement and produces a maximum/minimum uniformity ratio of 11.85:1 (3.46 ÷ .292) which is also acceptable.

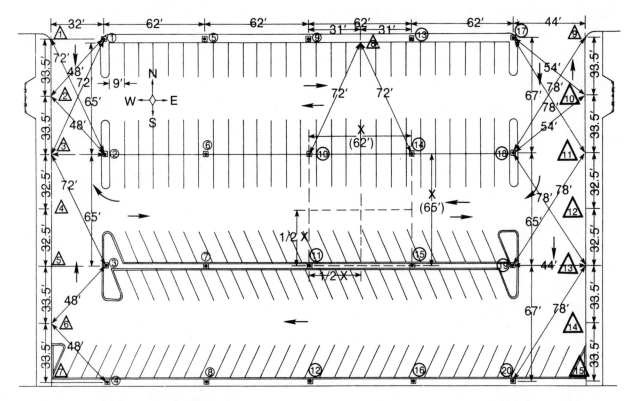

Fig. 24: Small parking area application sketch.

Points 9 through 15 receive light from luminaires 17 through 20, and the minimum reading of 0.176 footcandle occurring at points 10, 12, and 14 does not meet the minimum requirement. It also produces an unsatisfactory maximum/minimum uniformity ratio of 19.65:1 (3.46 ÷ .176). However, the designer must also consider that all points on the east and west perimeters receive an additional 0.1 footcandle from the canopy lighting on the adjacent store fronts. When this 0.1 value is added to the 0.176 footcandle level generated by the luminaires, the total amount of light falling on these points becomes 0.276 footcandle. This level exceeds the minimum requirement and produces a maximum/minimum uniformity ratio of 12.5:1.

Adjusting Light Levels. The average maintained illumination level at all points in the parking area is approximately 1.4 footcandles, quite high for a low activity level area. So the next logical step in the design procedure is to prorate the lighting level down to a more suitable value. By using Table 10 (page 118), you can see that replacing the 150-watt HPS lamps with 100-watt HPS lamps will reduce the light level by a factor of 0.594. The average maintained illumination would then be approximately 0.83 footcandle. The proration factor for a 70-watt HPS lamp would be 0.363, resulting in an average maintained illumination of about 0.508 footcandle, still acceptable for this particular application. Remember, prorating systems does not change the uniformity ratios.

HIGH MAST LIGHTING

High mast lighting systems—those utilizing mounting heights up to 150', Power Drawer Hi-Mast luminaires, and high-wattage HID lamps—are among the most efficient systems available today for the lighting of **large area** parking facilities (Fig. 26). The main advantage of high mast lighting is a drastic reduction in the number of mounting poles required. For example, when mounted at 150', 12 Hi-Mast luminaires equipped with 1000-watt high pressure sodium lamps can illuminate approximately 10 acres to a maintained level of 1 footcandle. By comparison, standard systems mounted at 40' heights normally illuminate an area approximately 1 acre in size.

The overall cost of lighted area per square foot decreases as the mounting height increases. However, since pole costs rise rapidly with increased mounting heights, the initial cost of high mast systems below 100' will be greater than standard 40' pole systems. At heights greater than 100', the initial cost of high mast systems becomes competitive with standard 40' systems. Use of Hi-Mast luminaires below 100' may still be the finest overall choice due to reduced maintenance, increased usable parking area, and fewer pole obstructions.

Table 12: Illumination Levels (Footcandles)—Small Size Application Sketch

Test Point	1	2	3	4	5	6	7
Mounting Pole							
1	1.0	.146	.023	.146	.023	.146	1.0
2	.023	.146	1.0	.146	1.0	.146	.023
3	—	—	.023	—	.023	—	—
4	—	—	—	—	—	—	—
Total	1.023	.292	1.046	.292	1.046	.292	1.023

Test Point	9	10	11	12	13	14	15
Mounting Pole							
17	.25	.088	.088	.088	.088	.088	.25
18	—	.088	.25	.088	.25	.088	—
19	—	—	.088	—	.088	—	—
20	—	—	—	—	—	—	—
Total	.25	.176	.426	.176	.426	.176	.25

Notes: 1. Test point 8 on Fig. 24 receives the following illumination: luminaires 9 and 13, 1.0 foot-candle each; luminaires 10 and 14, 0.023 footcandle each. Total footcandle level at point 8 is 2.046.

2. Add an additional 0.1 footcandle to all illumination levels at test points 1 through 7 and 9 through 15.

The multiple mounting heights and luminaire configurations available for high mast lighting rule out making generalizations concerning these systems. The majority of high mast lighting applications are essentially unique, and such lighting designs must be carefully considered on a job-to-job basis. When considering the use of high mast systems, contact the Lighting Products Division of SPI Lighting for full details concerning design criteria and available equipment options.

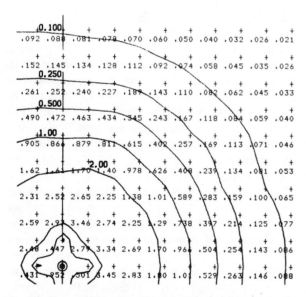

Fig. 25: Type-B Conquest Landscape isofootcandle curve reference plot. Grid increments are spaced 6′ apart.

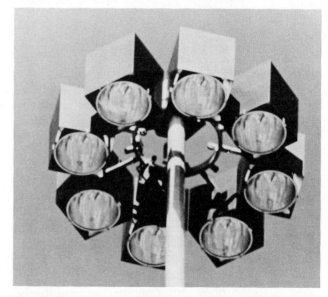

Fig. 26: Example of a high mast luminaire system.

Roadway Lighting

The purpose of roadway lighting is to create an environment conducive to accurate, comfortable seeing which will promote improved traffic safety, effective traffic movement, and adequate pedestrian safety under all types of weather conditions. A number of key factors which directly affect a person's ability to see must be taken into consideration when designing lighting systems for traffic and roadways. These include:

1. The brightness of the roadway background.
2. The ratio of the pavement brightness to the surrounding brightness as seen by either pedestrians or motorists.
3. The size of objects viewed and their detail. Objects viewed can range from a steel bar lying in the roadway, to a dark chuckhole, to a pedestrian walking along the roadside.
4. The brightness of objects viewed on or near the roadway.
5. The brightness contrast between the object viewed and its general surroundings (the roadway and its adjacent areas).
6. The time available to the motorist or pedestrian to view the object.
7. Direct glare from the luminaire.
8. Reflected glare from the pavement surface.
9. The visual capability of the motorist or the pedestrian.

Glare control is of utmost importance in roadway lighting. Most light-related problems occur when the motorist's or pedestrian's view is partially or completely impaired due to direct or reflected glare. Roadway lighting systems must conform to the required illumination levels and uniformity ratios set by the Illuminating Engineering Society of North America (IES) and the American National Standard Institute (ANSI). As each individual situation dictates, the lighting system should also coincide with accepted field practices. The lamp-luminaire combinations used should form highly efficient, economically practical lighting units, and poles should be spaced and luminaires mounted at heights guaranteeing uniform lighting. The system should be aesthetically pleasing in both day-form and night-form appearance. The designer must always be aware of the operating and maintenance costs of the proposed system since they constitute the two major economic factors pertinent to roadway lighting.

ILLUMINATION REQUIREMENTS

The IES and ANSI have established an American National Standard Practice based on the illumination levels and uniformities given in Table 2 (page 129). Illumination levels increase as traffic density, traffic speed, and peripheral areas requiring lighting increase. The illumination levels listed are the **minimum** required levels expressed in maintained average footcandles on the roadway surface. It must be noted that required lighting levels for specific areas or types of roadways are sometimes higher than those listed due to unique situations or local design requirements. Five different roadway classifications recognized by the IES and ANSI are listed in the following paragraphs.

Freeway. A divided major roadway with full control of access and with no crossing at grade. This definition applies to both toll and non-toll roads.

Class A Freeway: These are roadways with greater visual complexity and high traffic volumes. Class A freeways are commonly located in major metropolitan areas and are normally traveled at or near capacity during the early evening hours of darkness.

Class B Freeways: These are all other divided roadways with full control access which require lighting for safe operation.

Expressway. A divided major roadway designed for through traffic with partial control of access. In general, there are interchanges at major crossroads. Expressways for noncommercial traffic within parks and park-like areas are often referred to as parkways.

Major. The part of the roadway system that serves as the principal network for through traffic flow. These routes connect areas of principal traffic generation and important rural highways entering the city.

Collector. These are the distributor and collector roadways serving traffic between major and local roadways. They are used mainly for traffic movement within residential, commercial, and industrial areas.

Local. These are the roadways used primarily for direct access to residential, commercial, industrial, or other abutting properties. Local roadways do not include those which carry through traffic. Long local roadways are often divided into shorter sections by collector roadway systems.

Area Classification

The five types of roadways listed can exist under one of three types of urban or area classifications:

commercial, intermediate, or residential. These area classifications are defined as follows.

Commercial. Commercial areas are those portions of a municipality where ordinarily there are large numbers of pedestrians during business hours. This definition applies to densely-developed business areas outside, as well as within, the central part of a municipality. Such commercial areas also attract relatively heavy volumes of nighttime vehicular and/or pedestrian traffic on a frequent basis.

Intermediate. Intermediate areas are those portions of a municipality often characterized by a moderately heavy nighttime pedestrian activity level such as that found around libraries, community recreation centers, large apartment buildings, and neighborhood retail stores.

Residential. These areas can be strictly residential districts or a combination of residential and commercial establishments. In either case, these areas are characterized by light nighttime pedestrian traffic. This definition includes areas with single family homes, town houses, and/or small apartment buildings.

Roadway Reflectance

The key to successful roadway lighting is the brightness of luminance of the roadway surface. Because accurately determining roadway luminance is a very difficult and time consuming process, IES/ ANSI has established a set of reflectance coefficients and surface classes for various roadway materials (Table 1). Using these coefficients, it is possible to calculate the amount of light needed to produce adequate roadway luminance or surface brightness. Table 2 lists the illumination requirements for various roadway classifications as keyed to the surface classes described in Table 1. These illumination levels are expressed in horizontal footcandles at the road surface.

If, for example, an application calls for the illumination of a Class A freeway constructed of portland cement, proceed as follows. From Table 1 it is found that any roadway constructed of portland cement has a surface class of R1. From Table 2 it is found that a Class A freeway with a surface class of R1 requires 0.56 footcandles of illumination at the roadway surface.

This handbook will only directly address lighting designs for major, collector, and local roadways in commercial, intermediate, and residential areas since these classifications best lend themselves to standardized layouts. Freeways and expressways are highly specific in nature and design. There is little standardization in regard to widths and shapes, and each individual freeway or expressway must be individually assessed before a lighting layout can be designed. Contact SPI Lighting for assistance in the design of specific freeway and expressway applications.

Table 1: Roadway Surface Classifications			
Surface Class	Mean Luminance Coefficient	Description of Roadway Material	Mode of Reflectance
R1	0.10	Portland cement, concrete road surface. Asphalt road surface with a minimum of the aggregates composed of artificial brighteners.	Mostly diffuse
R2	0.07	Asphalt road surface with an aggregate composed of a minimum of 60% gravel. Asphalt road surfaces with aggregate mix composed of 10 to 15% artificial brighteners.	Mixed (Diffuse Specular)
R3	0.07	Asphalt road surface (regular and carpet seal) with dark aggregates and a rough texture after several months of use. This is the surface of most typical highways.	Slightly Specular
R4	0.08	Asphalt road surface with very smooth surface.	Mostly Specular

Vehicular Roadway Classification		Surface Class			Average/Minimum Uniformity*
		R1	R2 and R3	R4	
Table 2: Roadway Lighting Requirements					
Class A Freeway		.56	.84	.74	3:1
Class B Freeway		.37	.56	.47	3:1
Expressway	Commercial	.93	1.30	1.21	3:1
	Intermediate	.74	1.11	.93	3:1
	Residential	—	—	—	—
Major	Commercial	1.11	1.58	1.39	3:1
	Intermediate	.84	1.21	1.02	3:1
	Residential	.56	.84	.74	3:1
Collector	Commercial	.74	1.12	.93	3:1
	Intermediate	.56	.84	.74	3:1
	Residential	.56	.56	.47	3:1
Local	Commercial	.56	.84	.74	6:1
	Intermediate	.47	.65	.56	6:1
	Residential	.28	.37	.37	6:1

*Although maximum/minimum uniformity ratios are not a part of the current IES recommendations, a 12:1 maximum/minimum ratio is considered good field practice for all roadway classifications except Local. A 15:1 maximum/minimum uniformity ratio is recommended for local roadways.

Uniformity Ratios

The illuminance values expressed in Table 2 will only provide effective visibility when combined with the proper average/minimum and maximum/minimum uniformity ratios. With the exception of residential local roadways, the IES recommends an average/minimum uniformity ratio of 3:1. For residential local roadways, the recommended average/minimum uniformity ratio is 6:1. While the IES does not recommend a maximum/minimum uniformity ratio for roadway lighting applications, it is highly recommended that a 12:1 maximum/minimum uniformity ratio be used in all applications but local roadways. A 15:1 maximum/minimum ratio is acceptable for local roadways.

In many instances, maximum/minimum uniformity ratios are just as important as the average/minimum ratios. It is entirely possible to achieve the required 3:1 or 6:1 average/minimum ratio with a maximum/minimum uniformity ratio of 25:1 or poorer. Such a high ratio would indicate the presence of dark patches or pockets within the lighted area.

AESTHETICS

Two types of aesthetics are important in roadway lighting. The first, day-form appearance, relates to the actual physical appearance of the luminaire and pole. When selecting a luminaire type, it is important that the overall architectural design standard of the community is met. Many modern communities and developments have a total planned concept in which essentially all public elements must conform to certain aesthetic guidelines set by an architectural review committee. For example, the "cobra head" or dropped ovate refractor luminaire, once the most popular luminaire for commercial and intermediate applications, has now fallen into disfavor among architects, a fact largely attributable to its industrial appearance. Since many communities consider day-form appearance critical to the acceptance of roadway lighting installations, the lighting designer must clearly define the aesthetic advantages and disadvantages of applicable luminaires at the beginning of the project's planning stage.

The second type of aesthetics, known as night-form appearance, relates to the luminaire's capacity to control glare and unwanted light distribution. In many cases, the luminaire will be required to restrict the light it emits to the actual roadway surface or the area immediately adjacent to it. Many communities are now seriously considering adopting ordinances which will limit the amount of spill light that their roadway luminaires can generate.

Night-form appearance is also closely related to glare control. Many communities have opted to replace older luminaire designs with luminaires providing sharp light cutoff with subsequently less glare.

The problems of light control and spill and the resulting glare are solved during the equipment selection process. Luminaires are classified in two groups: cutoff and non-cutoff, with the cutoff designs offering the finest light control characteristics. More will be said on this subject under **Roadway Equipment Selection.**

ECONOMICS

Three types of costs must be taken into consideration when designing roadway layouts. In order of importance they are : (1) energy costs, (2) maintenance costs, and (3) initial equipment and installation costs. Twenty years ago these cost factors were reversed in order of importance, but a 10% to 15% annual increase in the cost of electricity has made energy costs the most important economic consideration.

The second important economic item is maintenance costs. How much will it cost to relamp the system, and how often will relamping be necessary? How frequently will the luminaires require cleaning, and what will be the maintenance cost for the system's auxiliary equipment, such as ballasts, circuit wiring, and poles?

The third and increasingly least important cost factor is initial equipment and installation costs. While the initial cost of the system can be substantial, operating and maintenance costs can far outdistance these expenditures over the life of the system. Turn to **Section IV: System Maintenance and Economics** for more information dealing with the economic and maintenance factors of outdoor lighting systems.

ROADWAY EQUIPMENT SELECTION

Satisfying the lighting design needs of any roadway application begins with what is fundamentally an equipment selection process. Select the proper luminaire design and aesthetic appearance requirements are resolved, light pollution standards are met, and maintenance costs are reduced. Equip the luminaire with a high-efficiency light source and the required illumination levels are attained at a reasonable operating cost.

LAMP SELECTION

Due to their high efficacy (lumens of light produced per watt of electricity consumed), high pressure sodium lamps are the primary lamps used today for roadway lighting applications. All tables given in the design section on roadway lighting are based on the use of high pressure sodium lamps. An effective lamp life of up to 24,000 hours or five to six years of normal roadway operations can be expected, and HPS lamps also have the finest lumen maintenance characteristics of all high intensity lamp types. Their golden-white light does not pose any color-rendering problems in these applications, and the tremendous light-producing capabilities of HPS lamps assure minimal luminaire, pole, and auxiliary equipment costs.

LUMINAIRES

The luminaire selection options for roadway lighting are illustrated in the flow diagram in Fig. 1. As

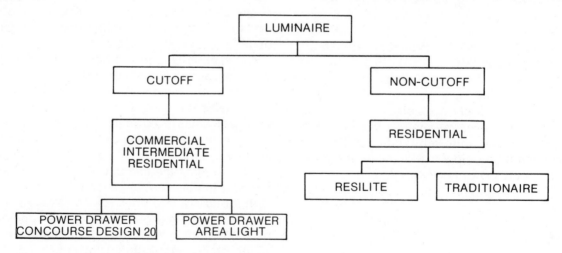

Fig. 1: Flow diagram of the luminaires used in roadway lighting.

shown, both cutoff and non-cutoff luminaires can be used with resulting advantages and disadvantages in each case. Those luminaires designed on the Power Drawer principle have certain added advantages dealing largely with the installation, maintenance, and updating of the luminaire.

CUTOFF LUMINAIRES

A cutoff luminaire is best defined as one which shields light being emitted from the luminaire at angles above 72° from vertical. (See page 103 in **Parking Area Lighting** for a further explanation of cutoff luminaires.) The main advantage of cutoff luminaires is light and glare control. These luminaires produce highly distinctive and predictable light patterns, and many designs virtually eliminate spill light from occurring behind the luminaire. Cutoff luminaires are also quite aesthetically pleasing in day-form appearance.

Because of their shielding and glare-reducing qualities, cutoff luminaires are primarily recommended for use in lighting commercial and intermediate roadways where heavy volumes of traffic and higher rates of speed are common. Cutoff luminaires are also employed in all types of residential roadway applications, particularly when precise control of light spill is desired or when high standards of day-form and night-form appearance must be met (Fig. 2).

While cutoff luminaires have no true disadvantages, extremely close attention must be paid to the recommended luminaire mounting heights and pole spacings given in the roadway lighting application tables listed throughout this section. Do not exceed these specifications since they assure even, uniform light levels along the entire roadway. Exceeding these limits will result in the formation of unwanted and potentially dangerous pockets of darkness.

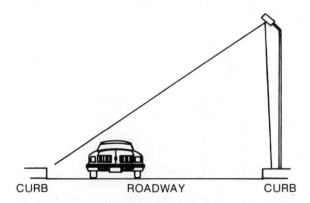

Fig. 2: Cutoff luminaires can restrict the light to the actual roadway areas.

Power Drawer Concourse Luminaires

Power Drawer Concourse luminaires (Fig. 3) combine an aesthetically pleasing day-form appearance with the sharp cutoff optics of modern lighting design. The concealed light source creates glareless illumination which facilitates safe vehicular and pedestrian movement on and near the roadway. The absence of glare is of particular importance when the reaction time of a motorist is short due to high speeds and/or heavy traffic.

Fig. 3: The Power Drawer Concourse luminaire.

The Power Drawer Concourse Design 20 luminaire is the only model of the Concourse series recommended for roadway lighting. Design 20 optics generate excellent light distribution for the illumination of long rectangular areas perpendicular to the front of the luminaire (Fig. 4), a pattern which coincides with the layout of most roadways.

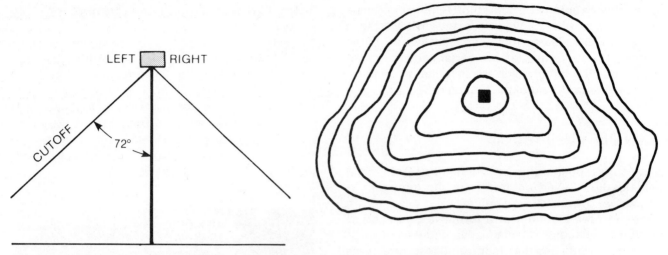

LEFT RIGHT

CUTOFF

72°

Fig. 4: The light pattern generated by Power Drawer Concourse Design 20 luminaires.

Power Drawer Area Light Luminaires

The Power Drawer Area Light luminaire is quite similar to the Power Drawer Concourse design series described. It contains the same basic optical components as the Power Drawer Concourse, but differs in that it employs a ruggedly-constructed, cast aluminum, tapered sidewall housing (Fig. 5). While the aiming angle of the Power Drawer Area Light luminaire is fully adjustable, the luminaire is aimed at a 20° angle for roadway applications. This angle produces an IES/ANSI type III light distribution pattern which is quite suitable for roadway lighting (Fig. 6).

NON-CUTOFF LUMINAIRES

Non-cutoff luminaires do not restrict the visible light emitted from the luminaire to any specific angle away from vertical, such as 72°, a fact resulting in several important performance characteristics.

The main advantage of non-cutoff luminaires versus cutoff luminaires is increased flexibility in mounting heights and pole spacing. When compared to similarly lamped cutoff luminaires, non-cutoff luminaires produce more uniform light patterns when mounted at lower heights on greater pole spacings. This is especially true at lower lighting levels, such as those required for residential roadways. The reason for this increased uniformity and the absence of extremely dark patches is the use of a unique combination of reflector and refractor optics.

The lack of light control constitutes the main disadvantage of non-cutoff luminaires. Standard non-

Fig. 5: The Power Drawer Area Light luminaire.

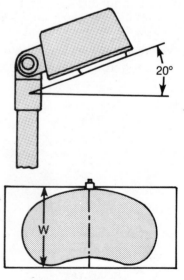

20°

W

W = 1.75 TO 2.75 M.H.

Fig. 6: When aimed at 20°, the Power Drawer Area Light luminaire produces an IES/ANSI type III light pattern suitable for roadway applications.

132 EXTERIOR LIGHTING

cutoff luminaires have no effective means of regulating the beam spread or spill light, and indiscriminate use of these luminaires in secluded residential neighborhoods could result in substantial light pollution of private property. Shielding devices placed in the internal optical compartment can reduce this light pollution.

Also, since these luminaires do not shield light above the recognized glare angle of 72° from vertical, their use, especially at lower mounting heights, must be carefully reviewed so there is no noticeable visual discomfort. Because of their glare producing properties, non-cutoff luminaires are only recommended for use in residential roadway lighting applications where the concentration of traffic is normally light and traffic speeds are reduced. They should not be used in commercial and intermediate applications.

Resilite Luminaires

The Resilite luminaire is specifically designed to meet the lower illumination levels required in the lighting of residential roadways. Its aesthetically pleasing day-form appearance matches many residential landscape schemes (Fig. 7). The luminaire is constructed of a heavy-duty cast aluminum housing containing a specially designed refractor and separate optical and ballast compartments. The Resilite luminaire is intended to be mounted on the end of a street pole arm, and its low profile styling complements low mounting heights.

The Resilite luminaire utilizes an optical reflector and refractor system which allows these luminaires to be mounted at a standard residential height of 23' and spaced up to 195' apart. Even at these distances, a Resilite system will still meet the maximum/minimum and average/minimum uniformity ratios set by

Fig. 7: The Resilite luminaire used for residential roadway applications.

IES and ANSI for roadway lighting. These uniformities are generally 6 to 10 times superior to those achieved by conventional horizontal lamp "cobra head" luminaires spaced at 195'.

Due to the wide spacings possible with Resilite luminaires, fewer fixtures and poles are required, thus reducing the initial costs of the roadway lighting system. Generally, only three Resilite luminaires are needed to light a 600' long residential street block. Layouts using conventional luminaires require four units for the same length of roadway.

Traditionaire Luminaires

The Traditionaire luminaire may be mounted in either the pendant position or top mounted position (Fig. 8). Constructed of very heavy-duty cast aluminum in a traditional coach lantern styling, the main advantage of this luminaire is its day-form aesthetic appeal. The Traditionaire luminaire was originally designed for parking area lighting, but by placing prismatic refractors into the sides of the luminaire, the correct asymmetrical light distribution patterns for roadway lighting can be achieved.

Fig. 8: The post top mounted position used for the Traditionaire luminaire.

Both the lamp and ballast are integrated into a design known as the power module ballast system which can be quickly and easily replaced to assure low cost maintenance. The main lighting advantage of the Traditionaire is that due to its refractor panel design these luminaires can be mounted as low as 15' above ground level and still provide adequate illumination for residential roadways. Also, because the Traditionaire is a non-cutoff luminaire, the pole

spacings can exceed those normally used for cutoff luminaires. An internal shield can be added to obtain more light control and prevent excessive spill light on the house side of the luminaire.

ROADWAY LIGHTING DESIGN

The keys to designing sound roadway lighting systems are found in the Roadway Lighting Data Tables 3, 4, and 5 (pages 134 to 138). Each table corresponds to a specific luminaire or luminaires discussed under **Roadway Equipment Selection** (page 130). All tables are based on the use of high pressure sodium lamps, and specific lamp wattages are listed in the tables or stated in the table headings. Refer to **Section I: Lamps and Ballasts** to obtain the lumen maintenance and lamp life characteristics of these HPS models. The catalog numbers given in Tables 3 and 4 refer to the given lamp-luminaire combinations and allow for easy cross-reference to additional information found in other SPI Lighting publications. This makes it possible to develop a total performance and cost analysis using the most recent information available.

The stated luminaire mounting heights must be followed exactly. Changing the stated mounting height will seriously affect the illumination levels generated and the maximum/minimum and average/minimum uniformity ratios produced. Disabling glare is also another unwanted possibility. It has been found that the mounting heights listed in the tables are the optimum heights for roadway lighting with these luminaires. These heights will produce the finest overall illumination when all other given specifications are followed. The average initial footcandle level listed is the illumination level which will exist at the roadway surface as expressed in horizontal footcandles.

Strict adherence to the stated mounting pole spacings is also essential since exceeding these spacings will result in unwanted dark areas, especially when cutoff luminaires are used. In addition to affecting uniformities, altering pole spacing will also drastically change the stated average illumination levels. In cases where the designer considers employing pole spacing and/or mounting heights different than those listed in the tables, he or she should contact SPI Lighting for consultation.

WORKING WITH THE TABLES

The roadway lighting data tables enable the designer to quickly lay out any type of basic roadway lighting application based on the specific roadway widths and illumination requirements of the various roadway classifications. The designer needs only to select a lamp-luminaire combination, luminaire mounting height, mounting pole spacing, and mounting pole arrangement (staggered or one-side-only) from the information given in the tables. If the layout is made to these exact specifications, the average initial footcandle level listed in the table will be that generated on the roadway surface. The designer is also assured that the layout will meet the

Table 3: Roadway Lighting Data—Power Drawer Concourse Design 20 High Pressure Sodium Lamps

Staggered Pole Spacing

Commercial Areas

Roadway Classification	Width	Mounting Height	Lamp Wattage	Catalog Number	Pole Spacing	Avg. Initial Footcandles
Major	72'	40'	400	CS22621	81'	3.04
	60'	40'	250	CS12521	88'	2.22
	48'	35'	250	CS12521	96'	2.46
Collector	60'	40'	250	CS12521	105'	1.86
	48'	35'	150	CS18321	90'	1.56
	36'	30'	100	CS18221	81'	1.32
Local	48'	35'	100	CS18221	84'	1.00
	36'	30'	100	CS18221	81'	1.32
	24'	25'	100	CS18221	137'	1.05

Note: All luminaires are mounted in a horizontal position for an effective tilt angle of 0°.

**Table 3: Roadway Lighting Data—Power Drawer Concourse Design 20
High Pressure Sodium Lamps (Continued)**

Roadway Classification	Width	Mounting Height	Lamp Wattage	Catalog Number	Pole Spacing	Avg. Initial Footcandles
Intermediate Areas						
Major	72'	40'	250	CS12521	104'	1.63
	60'	40'	250	CS12521	105'	1.86
	48'	35'	250	CS12521	66'	2.4
Collector	60'	40'	250	CS12521	102'	1.14
	48'	35'	150	CS18321	90'	1.56
	36'	30'	100	CS18221	81'	1.32
Local	48'	35'	100	CS18221	90'	.93
	36'	30'	70	CS18221	81'	.81
	24'	25'	70	CS18221	126'	.70
Residential Areas						
Major	72'	40'	250	CS12521	104'	1.63
	60'	40'	250	CS12521	105'	1.86
	48'	35'	150	CS18321	90'	1.56
Collector	60'	40'	150	CS18321	102'	1.14
	48'	35'	100	CS18221	90'	.93
	36'	30'	70	CS18121	81'	.81
Local	48'	35'	100	CS18221	133'	.63
	36'	30'	100	CS18221	135'	.48
	24'	25'	70	CS18221	147'	.60
One-Side-Only Pole Spacing						
Commercial Areas						
Major	72'	40'	400	CS22621	105'	2.19
	60'	40'	400	CS22621	120'	2.22
	48'	35'	400	CS22621	145'	2.19
Collector	60'	40'	250	CS12521	145'	1.31
	48'	35'	250	CS12521	175'	1.31
	36'	30'	150	CS18321	130'	1.31
Local	48'	35'	250	CS12521	205'	1.12
	36'	30'	150	CS18321	170'	1.00
	24'	25'	100	CS18221	123'	1.17
Intermediate Areas						
Major	72'	40'	400	CS22621	135'	1.70
	60'	40'	400	CS22621	135'	1.97
	48'	35'	400	CS22621	172'	1.85
Collector	60'	40'	250	CS12521	156'	1.21
	48'	35'	250	CS12521	205'	1.12
	36'	30'	150	CS18321	170'	1.00
Local	48'	35'	250	CS12521	205'	1.12
	36'	30'	150	CS18321	170'	1.00
	24'	25'	70	CS18321	123'	.71

Note: All luminaires are mounted in a horizontal position for an effective tilt angle of 0°.

Table 3: Roadway Lighting Data—Power Drawer Concourse Design 20 High Pressure Sodium Lamps (Continued)

Residential Areas

Roadway Classification	Width	Mounting Height	Lamp Wattage	Catalog Number	Pole Spacing	Avg. Initial Footcandles
Major	72'	40'	400	CS22621	135'	1.70
	60'	40'	250	CS12521	156'	1.21
	48'	35'	250	CS12521	205'	1.12
Collector	60'	40'	250	CS12521	156'	1.21
	48'	35'	250	CS12521	205'	1.12
	36'	30'	150	CS18321	170'	1.00
Local	48'	35'	150	CS18321	200'	.69
	36'	30'	100	CS18221	190'	.53
	24'	25'	70	CS18121	137'	.64

Note: All luminaires are mounted in a horizontal position for an effective tilt angle of 0°.

Table 4: Roadway Lighting Data—Power Drawer Area Light Luminaire High Pressure Sodium Lamps

Staggered Pole Spacing

Commercial Areas

Roadway Classification	Width	Mounting Height	Lamp Wattage	Catalog Number	Pole Spacing	Luminaire Tilt Angle	Avg. Initial Footcandles
Major	72'	40'	400	FR2265	90'	20°	2.53
	60'	40'	400	FR2265	100'	20°	2.56
	48'	35'	400	FR2265	100'	20°	2.55
Collector	60'	40'	400	FR2265	130'	20°	1.97
	48'	35'	250	FR2255	120'	20°	1.52
	36'	30'	250	FR2255	150'	20°	1.52
Local	48'	35'	250	FR2255	144'	20°	1.27
	36'	30'	150	FR1835	115'	15°	1.14
	24'	25'	150	FR1835	120'	5°	1.49

Intermediate Areas

Roadway Classification	Width	Mounting Height	Lamp Wattage	Catalog Number	Pole Spacing	Luminaire Tilt Angle	Avg. Initial Footcandles
Major	72'	40'	400	FR2265	105'	20°	2.17
	60'	40'	400	FR2265	130'	20°	1.97
	48'	35'	400	FR2265	160'	20°	1.91
Collector	60'	40'	250	FR2255	100'	20°	1.53
	48'	35'	250	FR2255	144'	20°	1.27
	36'	30'	150	FR1835	115'	15°	1.14
Local	48'	35'	150	FR1835	135'	15°	.78
	36'	30'	150	FR1835	145'	15°	.91
	24'	25'	150	FR1835	120'	5°	1.49

Residential Areas

Roadway Classification	Width	Mounting Height	Lamp Wattage	Catalog Number	Pole Spacing	Luminaire Tilt Angle	Avg. Initial Footcandles
Major	72'	40'	250	FR2255	84'	20°	1.62
	60'	40'	250	FR2255	104'	20°	1.47
	48'	35'	250	FR2255	143'	20°	1.27
Collector	60'	40'	150	FR1835	94'	15°	.94
	48'	35'	150	FR1835	135'	15°	.78
	36'	30'	150	FR1835	145'	15°	.91
Local	48'	35'	150	FR1835	203'	5°	.53
	36'	30'	150	FR1835	176'	5°	.78
	24'	25'	150	FR1835	144'	5°	1.24

One-Side-Only Pole Spacing

Commercial Areas

Roadway Classification	Width	Mounting Height	Lamp Wattage	Catalog Number	Pole Spacing	Luminaire Tilt Angle	Avg. Initial Footcandles
Major	72'	40'	400	FR2265	85'	30°	2.54
	60'	40'	400	FR2265	100'	20°	2.56
	48'	35'	400	FR2265	120'	20°	2.55
Collector	60'	40'	400	FR2265	170'	20°	1.51
	48'	35'	250	FR2255	120'	20°	1.52
	36'	30'	250	FR2255	138'	5°	1.50
Local	48'	35'	250	FR2255	145'	20°	1.25
	36'	30'	150	FR1835	120'	5°	1.14
	24'	25'	150	FR1835	100'	5°	1.79

Intermediate Areas

Roadway Classification	Width	Mounting Height	Lamp Wattage	Catalog Number	Pole Spacing	Luminaire Tilt Angle	Avg. Initial Footcandles
Major	72'	40'	400	FR2265	123'	30°	1.75
	60'	40'	400	FR2265	145'	20°	1.77
	48'	35'	400	FR2265	170'	20°	1.80
Collector	60'	40'	250	FR2255	135'	20°	1.13
	48'	35'	250	FR2255	146'	20°	1.25
	36'	30'	150	FR1835	120'	25°	1.14
Local	48'	35'	150	FR1835	140'	15°	.75
	36'	30'	150	FR1835	110'	15°	1.29
	24'	25'	150	FR1835	100'	5°	1.79

Residential Areas

Roadway Classification	Width	Mounting Height	Lamp Wattage	Catalog Number	Pole Spacing	Luminaire Tilt Angle	Avg. Initial Footcandles
Major	72'	40'	250	FR2255	105'	30°	1.28
	60'	40'	250	FR2255	120'	20°	1.27
	48'	35'	250	FR2255	146'	20°	1.25
Collector	60'	40'	150	FR1835	110'	15°	.80
	48'	35'	150	FR1835	140'	15°	.75
	36'	30'	150	FR1835	120'	5°	1.14
Local	48'	35'	150	FR1835	179'	5°	.60
	36'	30'	150	FR1835	151'	5°	.90
	24'	25'	150	FR1835	123'	5°	1.14

Table 5:   Roadway Lighting Data—30' Width (Residential)

Resilite Luminaire—150-watt High Pressure Sodium Lamp

Spacing	23' Mounting Height—One Side			23' Mounting Height—Staggered		
	Average Footcandles	Avg./Min. Uniformity	Max./Min. Uniformity	Average Footcandles	Avg./Min. Uniformity	Max./Min. Uniformity
150'	.97	2.2:1	3.4:1	.97	1.8:1	2.7:1
160'	.91	2.6:1	4.1:1	.91	2.0:1	3.3:1
170'	.86	3.1:1	5.2:1	.86	2.3:1	3.9:1
180'	.81	3.6:1	6.2:1	.81	2.6:1	4.6:1
190'	.77	4.1:1	7.5:1	.77	3.0:1	5.6:1
200'	.73	4.9:1	9.2:1	.73	3.5:1	6.6:1
210'	.70	5.8:1	11.2:1	.70	3.9:1	7.5:1
220'	—	—	—	.66	4.4:1	8.6:1
230'	—	—	—	.63	5.0:1	10.2:1
240'	—	—	—	.61	5.6:1	11.9:1

Traditionaire Luminaire—150-watt High Pressure Sodium Lamp

Spacing	15' Mounting Height—One Side			15' Mounting Height—Staggered		
120'	1.11	4.2:1	8.3:1	1.11	2.9:1	5.7:1
130'	1.03	5.4:1	11.0:1	1.03	3.6:1	7.4:1
140'	—	—	—	.95	5.0:1	10.8:1
	20' Mounting Height—One Side			**20' Mounting Height—Staggered**		
120'	.94	1.8:1	2.9:1	.94	1.8:1	2.8:1
130'	.87	2.0:1	3.2:1	.87	1.9:1	3.0:1
140'	.81	2.2:1	3.6:1	.81	1.9:1	3.1:1
150'	.76	2.5:1	4.5:1	.76	2.2:1	3.9:1
160'	.71	2.9:1	5.5:1	.71	2.6:1	5.0:1
170'	.67	3.7:1	7.4:1	.67	3.3:1	6.6:1
180'	.63	4.5:1	9.5:1	.63	4.2:1	8.8:1
190'	.60	5.6:1	12.4:1	.60	5.3:1	11.7:1

Resilite Luminaire (6' Arm)—150-watt High Pressure Sodium Lamp

Spacing	23' Mounting Height—One Side			23' Mounting Height—Staggered		
150'	.97	2.2:1	3.4:1	.97	1.8:1	2.7:1
160'	.91	2.6:1	4.1:1	.91	2.0:1	3.3:1
170'	.86	3.1:1	5.2:1	.86	2.3:1	3.9:1
180'	.81	3.6:1	6.2:1	.81	2.6:1	4.6:1
190'	.77	4.1:1	7.5:1	.77	3.0:1	5.6:1
200'	.73	4.9:1	9.2:1	.73	3.5:1	6.6:1
210'	.70	5.8:1	11.2:1	.70	3.9:1	7.5:1
220'	.66	6.4:1	12.7:1	.66	4.4:1	8.6:1
230'	.63	7.3:1	14.8:1	.63	5.0:1	10.2:1
240'	.61	8.4:1	17.4:1	.61	5.6:1	11.9:1
250'	.58	10.1:1	21.2:1	.58	6.3:1	13.9:1

required uniformity ratios for the roadway classification being lighted. No mathematical work is required unless the designer wishes to prorate the system to a lower illumination level. When this is done, a lower wattage lamp is substituted for the basic lamp rec-ommended in the table; no other variables change. The new illumination level is found by multiplying the original footcandle level by the appropriate pro-ration factor as listed in Table 6. Uniformities do not change. It is not recommended that lamps with wat-tages higher than those specified be substituted for the basic lamps since the resulting higher illumina-tion levels may cause disabling glare at these mount-ing heights and pole spacings.

138   EXTERIOR LIGHTING

Traditionaire Luminaire (6′ Arm)—150-watt High Pressure Sodium Lamp

Spacing	23′ Mounting Height—One Side			23′ Mounting Height—Staggered		
	Average Footcandles	Avg./Min. Uniformity	Max./Min. Uniformity	Average Footcandles	Avg./Min. Uniformity	Max./Min. Uniformity
	23′ Mounting Height—One Side			23′ Mounting Height—Staggered		
150′	.70	2.2:1	3.4:1	.70	1.7:1	2.7:1
160′	.66	2.5:1	4.1:1	.66	2.0:1	3.3:1
170′	.62	3.0:1	5.0:1	.62	2.4:1	4.0:1
180′	.59	3.5:1	6.1:1	.59	2.8:1	4.8:1
190′	.56	4.3:1	7.7:1	.56	3.5:1	6.3:1
200′	.53	5.4:1	10.3:1	.53	4.4:1	8.5:1
210′	—	—	—	.50	5.5:1	11.0:1

Notes:
1. Resilite Luminaire: All Resilite luminaires utilize 150-watt high pressure sodium (LU150) lamps in these residential applications. The lamp generates 16,000 initial lumens.
   Mast arm mounted Resilite design: Catalog number UR3614
   Top mounted (pendant) Resilite design: Catalog number UR4614
2. Traditionaire Luminaire: All Traditionaire luminaires utilize 150-watt high pressure sodium (LU150) lamps in these residential applications. The lamp generates 16,000 initial lumens.
   Pendant mounted Traditionaire design: Catalog number TT2283
   Post top mounted Traditionaire design: Catalog number TT1283
3. Roadway Information: All information is based on 30′ roadway widths which are applicable for the vast majority of residential applications.
4. Luminaire Location: Mast arm Resilite, Pendant Resilite, and Traditionaire designs are located 4′ out beyond the curb edge. They are hung from 6′ mast arms, so the actual distance from mounting pole to roadway curb is 2′. Post top Traditionaire designs are mounted directly to the mounting pole which is located 2′ back from the curb edge.

Table 6: Roadway Lighting Proration Factors

Power Drawer Concourse Design 20 (CS22621) and Power Drawer Area Light (FR2265)

Basic Lamp	Substitute Lamp	Proration Factor
HPS 400-watt LU400 50,000 lumens	HPS 310-watt LU310, 37,000 lumens	.740
	HPS 250-watt LU250/S, 30,000 lumens	.600
	HPS 250-watt LU250/S, 27,500 lumens	.550
	HPS 200-watt LU200, 22,000 lumens	.440

Power Drawer Concourse Design 20 (CS12521) and Power Drawer Area Light (FR2255)

HPS 250-watt LU250/S 30,000 lumens	HPS 250-watt LU250, 27,500 lumens	.917
	HPS 200-watt LU200, 22,000 lumens	.733

Power Drawer Concourse Design 20 (CS18323), Power Drawer Area Light (FR1835), Resilite (UR3614 and UR4614), and Traditionaire (TT2283 and TT1283)

HPS 150-watt LU150 16,000 lumens	HPS 100-watt LU100, 9,500 lumens	.594
	HPS 70-watt LU70, 5,800 lumens	.363

ROADWAY LIGHTING 139

The designer must also decide if the system will employ staggered pole spacings or one-side-only pole spacings (Fig. 9). Staggered pole arrangements produce better light uniformity than one-side-only designs, and in some cases their increased pole spacing as compared to similar one-side-only arrangements gives staggered settings an economic advantage. One-side-only pole arrangements are applicable when there are physical obstructions on one side of the roadway. They are also commonly used to upgrade systems which were originally designed as one-side-only layouts. The need for a single electrical wiring system is another advantage of one-side-only design; staggered systems require electrical wiring on both sides of the roadway.

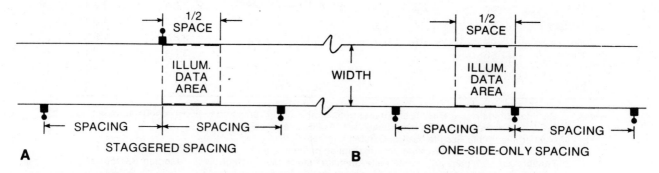

A   STAGGERED SPACING   B   ONE-SIDE-ONLY SPACING

Fig. 9: (A) Staggered and (B) one-side-only mounting pole configurations used in roadway lighting.

Sports Lighting

The lighting of any outdoor nighttime sporting activity or event presents a very difficult problem to the lighting designer. The primary objective of any sports lighting design is to provide adequate visibility for both participants and spectators. Good visibility is obtained by controlling the brightness of the playing object or ball and the background it is viewed against. Regardless of its size, location, trajectory, or travel speed, the playing object must be visible from any normal viewing position. In most cases, this visibility is achieved through the illumination of vertical as well as horizontal surfaces.

The viewing background of a playing object is made up of all surfaces or spaces above, below, and on all sides of the player positions. Sudden changes in the viewing background can cause visibility problems, a situation compounded by the fact that in many sports the ball or object of play moves quite rapidly. Consider a baseball in flight. At one moment the white ball may be viewed against the night sky, a situation which produces high viewing contrast. But in the next instant, the ball may be viewed against a background of multi-colored spectator clothing, and the green of the playing field grass or surface may constitute the viewing background a moment later. In perhaps the most sudden contrast change of all, the ball may be viewed against the dark sky at one moment and then be intercepted by the high brightness of a large bank of floodlights.

Changes in the brightness contrast between playing object and viewing background can occur in a time span of less than a few seconds. In fact, the brightness contrast between the **light source and the viewing background** creates the major problem in outdoor sports lighting—glare. As you will see, controlling glare is the key to good sports lighting.

ILLUMINATION LEVELS

The illumination level or quantity of light required is solely dependent upon the type and classification of sport that the lighting layout will serve. The Illuminating Engineering Society of North America (IES) has broken down modern sporting events into approximately 50 different general categories with numerous subcategories. Each of these categories has its own set of illumination requirements. This handbook cannot possibly discuss all sports and will cover only the major sports popular in the United States and Canada today. Among the sports covered will be base sports such as baseball and softball; foot sports including football, soccer, and rugby; racquet sports such as tennis, squash, and racquetball. Layouts for the stick sport of outdoor ice hockey are also given. Other major sports included in the lighting design discussions will be basketball, badminton, volleyball, golf, and target shooting.

Lighting data tables for each of the major sports discussed are found under **Design Methods and Layouts** (page 154). As you will see, each table is related to a specific seeing task which is different and unique for each sport. Regardless of the sport, the lighting level must be sufficient to allow the participants to comfortably and accurately perform their tasks and to allow the spectator to follow the course of play. Often times, the skill level of the player or the classification of play must be taken into consideration. For example, in Table 2 (page 155) you can see that each classification of baseball—major league, semi-pro, little league, recreational, etc.—requires a different illumination level to ensure safe playing conditions. Notice that illumination levels for little league fields are higher than those required for semi-professional diamonds. Since the pace of play is certainly faster at semi-professional levels, the logic behind the reduced lighting levels may not be evident. However, the decision was based on the reaction time of the participants. Because the reaction time of young children is considerably longer than that of adults, increased illumination is needed to ensure that young players can see and react to thrown or struck balls fast enough to permit safe play.

The visual needs of the spectator also affect illumination requirements. In many professional and major college level sports, such as football and baseball, spectators are seated a considerable distance from the playing field. Illumination levels must be such that spectators seated farthest from the playing field can still view the sport comfortably and accurately. To ensure this, illumination levels on the field of play may have to exceed those actually required by the participants. The lighting levels needed for clear television broadcasting may also affect the lighting design of larger stadiums and playing fields.

Illumination levels in sports lighting are most often stated in horizontal footcandles maintained in service. In aerial sports, such as baseball, football,

and tennis, the proper illumination level should occur on a theoretical horizontal plane located 36" above the playing surface. Ground or low level sports, such as ice hockey or field hockey, require that illumination be placed at the actual playing surface or in the area of concentrated activity (Fig. 1A). The only time vertical footcandles are of major significance is in sports such as archery, target shooting, and golf ball driving. In these cases, a vertical area (such as the target) or the back of the playing object (such as the golf ball) must be illuminated to significant levels (Fig. 1B).

It is extremely important to remember that all aerial sports require illumination in the open space at the 36" level above the playing surface. It is also important to note that the horizontal illumination levels given in the tables throughout this section will normally provide adequate vertical illumination when lighting equipment of the proper type is positioned at mounting heights and locations conforming to accepted field practices.

LIGHT QUALITY

In any lighting system, the ability to see is dependent not only on the quantity of light, but its quality as well. Light quality in sports applications can be broken down into three distinct areas: glare control, light uniformity, and light direction.

Glare Control

Glare occurs when the luminance within a particular visual field is sufficiently greater than the illuminates to which the viewer's eyes have become accustomed. Glare can cause physical annoyance and discomfort with a resulting loss of visual performance and visibility. Because floodlights are designed primarily for lighting efficiency and not lighting control, the floodlight luminaires employed in many sports lighting designs are inherently glare sources. Therefore, one of the primary tasks of the lighting designer is to reduce the objectionable effects of this glare to a minimum. This task involves consideration of four factors:

1. Proper beam spread
2. Adequate mounting height
3. Proper luminaire location
4. Proper floodlight aiming techniques

Beam Spread. A joint committee of the Illuminating Engineering Society and the National Electrical Manufacturers Association (IES/NEMA) has set standards for beam spread classifications. Of the seven original beam spread classes, six remain applicable in modern lighting design (Fig. 2). (Class 1 for beam spreads of less than 18° was designated strictly for incandescent floodlight sources and is not practical in floodlighting applications.) The IES determines beam spread classification by locating the point away from the beam center where 10% of the maximum candlepower occurs.

Figure 2 lists the beam spread degree range and the effective projection distances of the six classifications. The effective projection distance is measured in a straight line from the base of the mounting pole to the area requiring illumination. Locating mounting poles so that beam spread ranges or effective projection distances are exceeded will result in dimly lighted areas or dark patches. Beam spread patterns must also overlap to ensure uniform lighting.

VERTICAL FOOTCANDLES

B

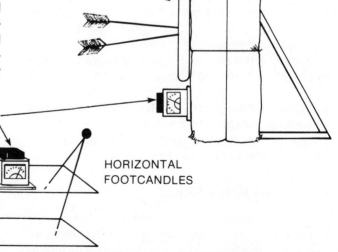

HORIZONTAL FOOTCANDLES

COLOR AND COSINE CORRECTED LIGHT METER

A

AERIAL SPORTS

36"

GROUND LEVEL SPORTS

Fig. 1: (A) Most sports require a specific level of horizontal maintained footcandles either at ground level or at a theoretical plane located 36" above ground level. **(B)** Certain sports require a higher than average level of vertical maintained footcandles.

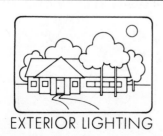

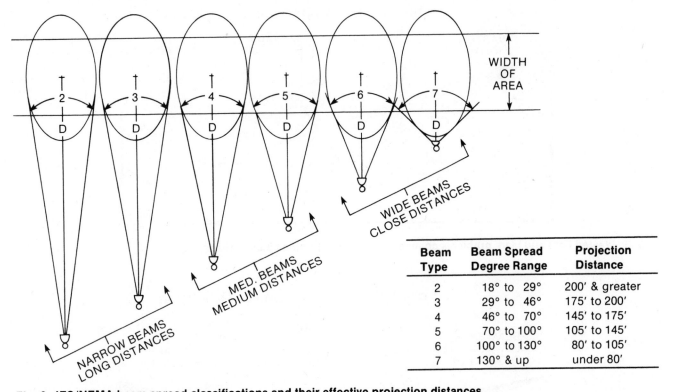

Beam Type	Beam Spread Degree Range	Projection Distance
2	18° to 29°	200' & greater
3	29° to 46°	175' to 200'
4	46° to 70°	145' to 175'
5	70° to 100°	105' to 145'
6	100° to 130°	80' to 105'
7	130° & up	under 80'

Fig. 2: IES/NEMA beam spread classifications and their effective projection distances.

Floodlights produce a light pattern having both a vertical and horizontal axis. Floodlights can be categorized as either symmetrical or asymmetrical, with symmetrical designs having equal beam spread angles in both the vertical and horizontal axes. Asymmetrical floodlights do not have equal vertical and horizontal beam widths. For example, a particular floodlight used in sports lighting may have a type 4 IES/NEMA beam spread in its vertical axis and a type 7 IES/NEMA beam spread in its horizontal axis. In general, as the distance from the floodlight to the areas lighted increases, the beam spread of the floodlight must decrease. Figure 3 illustrates a common problem associated with improper beam spread. The floodlight shown in this case generates too great of a vertical beam spread for this particular application, resulting in glare and wasted light. A floodlight luminaire with less vertical beam width would reduce this glare problem.

Mounting Height. Determining the optimum floodlight mounting height is a crucial step in sports lighting design. Mounting luminaires at lower than optimum levels can cause severe problems, such as generating glare in the eyes of spectators seated facing the lights (Fig. 4). Tilting down the luminaire to create a lower aiming angle can reduce this glare, but this practice also results in another serious lighting problem—a substantially reduced lighting ceiling. The lighting ceiling is the highest plane above the playing field adequately illuminated for comfortable night viewing. If the trajectory of the ball or playing object carries it above this lighting ceiling, the ball will momentarily disappear from view, causing obvious problems for both participants and spectators.

For these reasons, the IES has established recommended minimum mounting heights for various sports applications. The mounting heights listed in application tables throughout this section meet these minimum requirements. If for any physical or economical reason it is necessary to utilize mounting heights lower than these recommended minimums, the possibility of objectionable glare must be addressed.

It is possible to determine the minimum glare-producing mounting height for any sports lighting application by employing a simple formula. This formula is based on the tested principle that the angle created by the horizontal playing surface and a line drawn through the lowest mounted floodlight and a point one-third the distance across the playing field should not be less than 30° (Fig. 5). This translates into the following formula: H = (D + 1/3W) (tangent 30°), where H is the minimum mounting height, D is the distance from the mounting pole to the edge of the playing field, and W is the width of the playing field. The tangent of 30° equals 0.57735. This formula is essential when it becomes necessary to modify the dimensions of

SPORTS LIGHTING 143

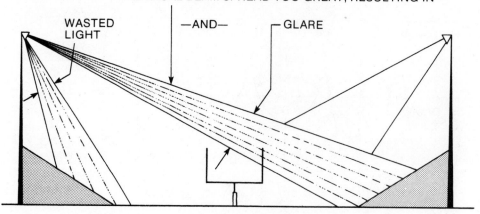

Fig. 3: **Wasted light and glare problems common to excessively wide beam spreads.**

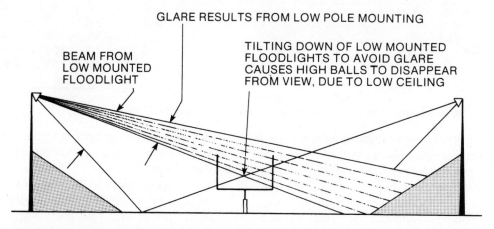

Fig. 4: **Glare is a common problem with low mounting heights. Note: Tilting down of luminaires to reduce this glare may result in a lighting ceiling too low for successful play.**

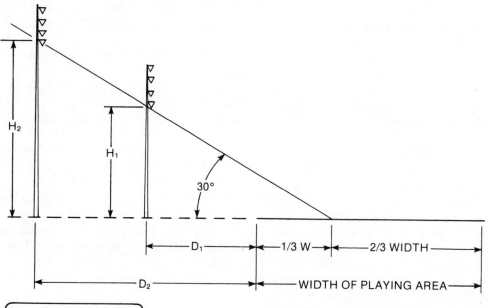

Fig. 5: **For any sports lighting application, the angle created by the ground and a straight line passing through the luminaire and a point one-third across the playing field should not be less than 30°.**

EXTERIOR LIGHTING

standard layouts or to design one-of-a-kind applications.

By studying this formula, it is evident that as the value of D increases, the minimum mounting height increases dramatically. In addition, it must be noted that an **absolute minimum mounting height** of 20′ is recommended for any ground sports layout. The absolute minimum mounting height for aerial sports is 30′. No layout should employ mounting heights less than these absolute minimums.

Luminaire Location. Improper positioning of luminaires can also generate disabling glare. Maximum glare is experienced when the participant or spectator must face directly into the luminaire. The brightness and glare of floodlights, particularly narrow beam designs, appears to decrease as the luminaires are viewed at angles increasingly away from the axis of the beam (Fig. 6). This means that the effects of glare can be diminished by removing luminaires from the normal lines of sight of viewers and players (Figs. 7, 8, and 9).

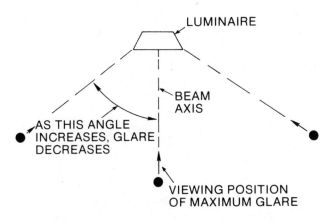

Fig. 6: Viewing at angles away from the beam axis decreases glare.

Positioning luminaires out of the normal lines of sight or critical viewing angles of participants and spectators is accomplished through proper mounting pole location and actual luminaire aiming. The angle between the normal lines of sight of a player or viewer and a particular luminaire is dependent upon three factors: the distance from the observer to the luminaire, the luminaire's mounting height, and the luminaire's aiming angle. Changing one of these factors will affect the others. For example, pole positions B1 and B2 in the baseball layout shown in Fig. 7 will vary as follows. As the distance between the mounting pole and the first or third base line increases, the luminaire mounting height must increase and the poles must be moved farther

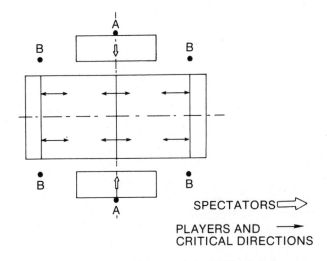

Fig. 8: The critical viewing angles for football and soccer.

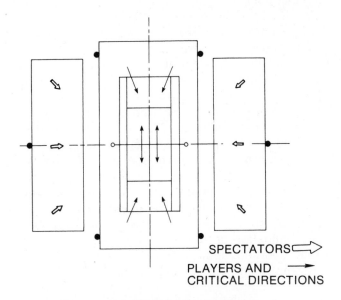

Fig. 9: The critical viewing angles for tennis.

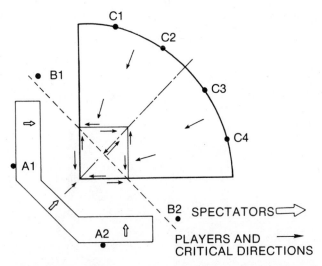

Fig. 7: The critical viewing angles for baseball and softball.

down the base lines toward the outfield. Once a pole location and mounting height have been determined, the luminaires should be mounted and aimed in such a way that a line from the axis of the luminaire beam should cross normal lines of sight at angles between 45° and 90°. This angle should not be less than 45° if at all possible.

In some cases, removal of luminaires from critical lines of sight may adversely affect light direction and lower overall lighting quality. In general, the recommended layouts illustrated in this section show luminaire locations which reflect a balance in judgment between ideal directional locations and minimum glare producing locations.

Shielding Glare. At times physical obstructions or economic considerations may limit the location of mounting poles to sites that are less than ideal. In such situations, the alternate pole positions must be carefully evaluated in terms of vital lines of sight or critical viewing angles. A number of glare-reducing procedures can be followed in instances when the luminaire must be positioned along a critical viewing angle. Shielding, in the form of top or side mounted visors, and louvers mounted on the luminaire face are the two most popular glare reduction methods used in these cases.

Of the two, shields are the most common (Fig. 10A). Shields or visors reduce glare by redirecting the light emitted from the luminaire to change the beam spread pattern. The main disadvantage of shields is that they add to the total projected wind load factor of the unit which in turn can increase the cost of the pole, its supporting structure, and the luminaire itself.

Louvers (Fig. 10B) reduce glare and brightness by reducing the actual viewing angle of the luminaire's lamp. The main disadvantage of louvers is that they reduce the amount of usable light emitted from the luminaire by as much as 50%. In any sports lighting system employing louvers to control glare, the quantity of floodlights must be increased to compensate for this light loss. This equipment increase will add to initial luminaire, pole, and support structure costs and also increase operating and maintenance expenses.

Reducing Brightness Contrasts. Perhaps the most effective means of reducing discomforting glare or brightness is to increase the brightness or illumination of the surrounding areas. For outdoor sporting applications, this can be readily accomplished by providing additional illumination in the spectator seating area, by using light-colored fences in the perimeter areas, and by providing

some form of illumination on the ground immediately around the playing area.

Floodlight Aiming. Even with proper mounting pole locations and mounting heights, the proper aiming of floodlights determines to a large extent whether lighting uniformity, lighting direction, and illumination levels will be satisfactory. Figure 5 (page 144), used in the discussion on minimum mounting height, can also be used to draw an important generalization concerning the luminaire aiming angle. As previously stated, the angle formed by the center of the light beam and the playing surface should not be less than 30°. As you can see, a 30° angle between beam and playing surface sets up a 30°-60°-90° triangle with apexes at the intersection points of the pole and playing surface, the light beam and pole, and the light beam and the playing field.

The fact that the three angles of any triangle will always add up to 180° allows us to draw an important conclusion concerning the aiming angle. Since the angle formed by the pole and playing surface is always 90° and the angle between the beam spread and playing surface must not be less than 30°, **the angle between the beam spread and the mounting pole should not be greater than 60°.** Because the point directly below the luminaire is referred

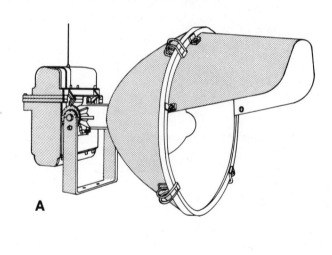

A

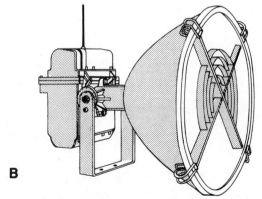

B

Fig. 10: (A) Example of a properly designed glare shield, and (B) example of properly designed louvers.

to as nadir, this general rule is more often stated as follows: The angle created between nadir and the center of the luminaire's beam spread should not exceed 60°.

Lighting Uniformity

Reasonable uniformity of illumination is also a prime design consideration. Expressed in terms of horizontal illumination, acceptable uniformity occurs when the ratio of maximum/minimum illumination within the specified playing area does not exceed IES standards. For example the recommended maximum/minimum uniformity ratio for tennis is 2:1. A maximum/minimum ratio for other sports in which the play is fast-paced or requires great hand-eye coordination is 3:1. A 3:1 ratio is also recommended for any sports application which includes spectators. Exact IES uniformity ratios are listed in the illumination requirement tables given in this section. Sharp changes in the illumination levels over a playing field can result in an interesting but potentially dangerous phenomenon. When the ball or object of play travels through areas of increased and decreased illumination, it will appear to accelerate as it passes from light to dark areas and decelerate as it passes from dark to light areas.

Problems in light uniformity generally occur when there is an inadequate overlap of beam spreads. To help alleviate potential uniformity problems, the beam spreads of floodlights should overlap by no less than 50% as shown in Fig. 11. Figure 11 illustrates another important design point concerning selection of beam spreads. As you can see, Figs. 11A and 11B show identical 100' × 100' areas. In Fig. 11A this area is illuminated by eight luminaires each containing a 1000-watt lamp generating type 6 × 7 beam spread. The overall light utilization is 60% and the illumination level throughout the area is 8.0 footcandles. In Fig. 11B, this same area is illuminated using six luminaires with 1000-watt lamps generating type 5 × 5 beam spreads. In this case, total light utilization is 85% and the illumination level is 7.8 footcandles.

Although both examples produce acceptable results, the system shown in Fig. 11B is superior to that shown in Fig. 11A since it results in better light utilization and lower costs without sacrificing acceptable beam overlap, uniformity, or footcandle levels. Of course, correct floodlight aiming is essential to ensure maximum light utilization.

Light Direction

Adequate light direction is closely related to light uniformity and proper aiming. In order for the

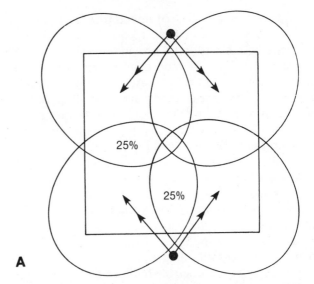

A

EIGHT 1000-WATT FLOODLIGHTS—TYPE 6 x 7 BEAM SPREAD COVER 100' x 100' AREA.
UTILIZATION = 60%
Fc. LEVEL = 8.0

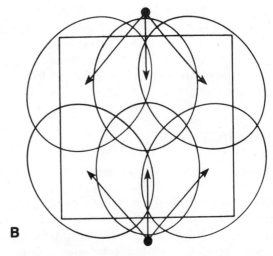

B

SIX 1000-WATT FLOODLIGHTS—TYPE 5 × 5 BEAM SPREAD COVER 100' × 100' AREA.
UTILIZATION = 85%
Fc LEVEL = 7.8

Fig. 11: Floodlight beams must overlap by no less than 50%. Selecting the proper beam spread for specific applications results in better light utilization, lower overall costs, and acceptable beam overlap and uniformity.

eye to see, there must be a difference in the illuminance of an object and its surroundings. There must also be a difference in the illumination of various surfaces on the object itself. In all cases, some type of lighting contrast is necessary for the eye to see clearly.

Since the visual task of spectators and participants involves viewing both vertical and horizontal surfaces, it is essential to provide adequate illumination on both the horizontal and vertical surfaces of the ball or object of play. Adequate illumination does not necessarily mean uniform illumination on all surfaces of the playing object. In fact semi-directional illumination provides the shading and modeling necessary for clear seeing.

To eliminate harsh shadows and permit good visibility at all points on the playing surface, it is generally necessary to provide each point on the playing surface with light from several different directions. Since the very nature of floodlighting tends to produce shadows, good directional quality in outdoor sports lighting application is not characterized by an absence of shadows but by a reduction in the number and severity of the shadows produced.

For unidirectional sports, such as archery and driving golf balls, it is permissible and desirable to provide a much higher footcandle level in one direction or plane (in these cases, the vertical plane) than in the other. In unidirectional sports, it is often possible to locate luminaires so that they are completely removed or shielded from the normal lines of sight.

ECONOMICS

The major economic factors pertinent to outdoor sports lighting are energy costs, maintenance costs, and initial equipment and installation costs. Much of the control a lighting designer has over the cost of a particular lighting system stems from decisions he or she makes concerning luminaire-lamp combinations, desired operating voltages, wiring methods, and mounting heights. In successful sports lighting systems, a balance exists between these cost factors and other key considerations, such as aesthetics or outward appearance, safety, and overall system reliability.

Overall system comparisons based on these three major economic factors can be made through the use of a detailed cost analysis. A true and fair comparison should only involve systems providing illumination of comparable quantity and quality. See **Section IV: System Maintenance and Economics** for the details of system cost analysis.

EQUIPMENT SELECTION

There is an ever increasing variety of lamp-luminaire combinations available for outdoor sports lighting. Choosing an efficient lamp and luminaire team can meet economic demands and provide desired aesthetics and light quality.

LAMP SELECTION

Two types of high intensity discharge lamps, metal halide and high pressure sodium, are used in modern sports applications. These two lamp types provide an efficacy (lumens of light produced per watt of energy consumed) that no incandescent or mercury lamp system can match. Lamps in the 1000 to 1500-watt range provide optimum results.

The superior color rendering qualities of metal halide lamps make them the logical choice over high pressure sodium lamps in major sports installations where video broadcasting is common; however, high pressure sodium lamps are steadily gaining popularity in all types of sporting applications where maximum lighting efficacy is desired and color rendering is of secondary importance.

A more complete comparison of metal halide and high pressure sodium lamps can be obtained by reviewing **Section I: Lamps and Ballasts.** Tables 20, 21, and 22 (pages 25 and 26) of Section I are particularly useful in this regard. They compare lamp efficacy, system cost factors, and color rendering characteristics.

LUMINAIRES FOR SPORTS LIGHTING

Luminaires used in sports lighting can be broken down into four major classifications: round spun floodlights of general purpose design, cast heavy-duty floodlights, architectural sharp-cutoff luminaires, and a new entry into the sports lighting field—sharp cutoff floodlight luminaires.

Round Spun Floodlights

The Power Mate Floodlight (Figs. 12 and 13) is the most popular of all luminaires used for sports lighting, a fact primarily attributed to the luminaire's low initial cost. Round spun floodlights consist of three major components: a single piece spun aluminum reflector, a separate modular ballast assembly containing all electrical components, and a separate optical support assembly. These luminaires are available in designs which produce each of the six modern beam spread configurations.

Fig. 12: The Power Mate Floodlight.

VERTICAL BEAM COMPONENT

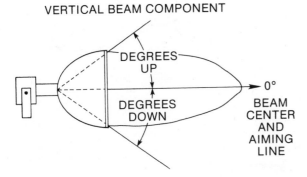

DEGREES UP

DEGREES DOWN

0°

BEAM CENTER AND AIMING LINE

HORIZONTAL BEAM COMPONENT

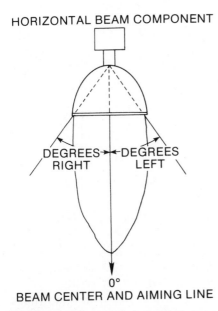

DEGREES RIGHT — DEGREES LEFT

0°

BEAM CENTER AND AIMING LINE

Fig. 13: The horizontal and vertical beam components of the Power Mate Floodlight. This luminaire generates a light pattern that is always symmetrical (up, down, right, and left) from the beam center.

All of the round spun designs employ hinged glass lenses to facilitate easy servicing. While some round spun models offer no outer protection for the reflec-

tor, shrouded or heavy-duty units have a second aluminum spinning which encases the reflector and protects it from hail and other weather related damage. The shroud is not designed to protect the reflector from vandal damage such as that caused by thrown rocks or pellets fired from air rifles.

Cast Heavy-Duty Floodlights

The cast Power Drawer Sports Light luminaire (Figs. 14 and 15) consists of a rectangular cast aluminum shell which houses a separate aluminum reflector and a separate built-in ballast drawer assembly containing all necessary electrical components.

Like the round spun luminaire, cast heavy-duty units are available in specific designs to produce all six beam spread classifications. Of the six, wide beam (Type 7) units are the most broadly used because they give the lighting designer an effective means of lighting a large area when pole locations are restricted to points very close to the playing surface perimeter. Power Drawer Sports Light luminaires generating narrower beam spreads of both symmetrical and asymmetrical types are commonly used when increased projection distance is required.

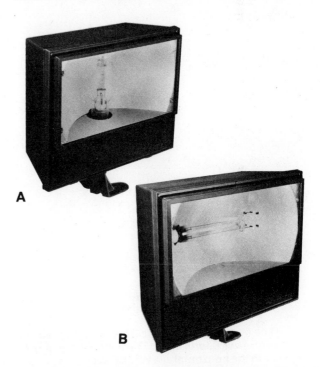

A

B

Fig. 14: The cast Power Drawer Sports Light luminaire: (A) vertical optics and (B) horizontal optics.

SPORTS LIGHTING 149

Due to their increased initial cost, cast designs are not as widely used as round spun varieties. However, in terms of usable light generated, cast heavy-duty luminaires are more than 15% more efficient than round spun units, a fact which can offset this initial cost difference. For example, in larger installations, fewer cast luminaires will be required to produce desired illumination levels. The rising trend in operating and maintenance costs has also made the more efficient cast heavy-duty luminaire more economically appealing, and there has been a rapid upsurge in the use of this particular floodlight for many sports applications.

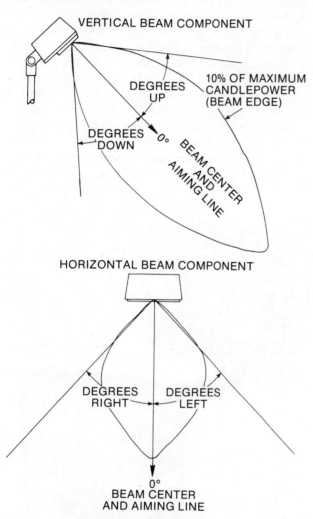

Fig. 15: **The horizontal and vertical beam components of the Power Drawer Sports Light. The light pattern may be either in both the horizontal and vertical axes or asymmetrical (different in the vertical and horizontal axes). In either case, the vertical component is always symmetrical above and below the main axis, and the horizontal component is always symmetrical to the right and left of the main axis.**

EXTERIOR LIGHTING

Architectural Cutoff Luminaires

Architectural cutoff luminaires (Fig. 16), so named for their pleasing aesthetic appearance, were originally designed for use in parking area and roadway lighting applications. These units, also known as Power Drawer Concourse Design 40 luminaires, are constructed of a formed or cast aluminum housing which contains all electrical and optical equipment.

Due to the very nature of the luminaire's design, the light emitted is restricted to specific angles below horizontal (Fig. 17), thus minimizing discomforting glare. The cutoff luminaire's second great advantage is its ability to restrict light to highly specific areas, thereby reducing light spill or light pollution.

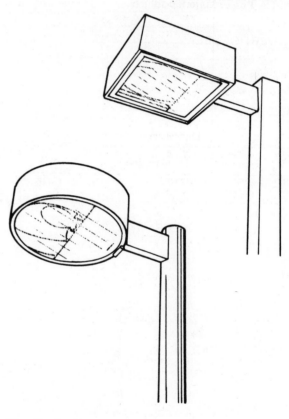

Fig. 16: **Architectural sharp cutoff luminaires.**

For these reasons, cutoff luminaires work extremely well in certain types of sports lighting such as in the illumination of tennis courts or other smaller areas where light spill into adjacent areas could cause problems. Two types of optics are used. One type generates a standard asymmetrical light pattern such as those used for roadway, area, and site lighting. The second type of optical design, known as extended area optics, was developed to create a light pattern in an extended area in front of the luminaire. Such a pattern is extremely useful in the lighting of tennis courts.

Fig. 17: The sharp cutoff and glare control possible through the use of sharp cutoff luminaires.

Although aesthetically pleasing in day-form appearance, architectural cutoff luminaires are the most expensive and least efficient of all sports lighting luminaires. They are also the least flexible of all sports lighting luminaires in terms of mounting heights and pole spacings. When working with any type of cutoff luminaire, the manufacturer's recommended ratio between pole spacing and mounting height, known as the luminaire's mounting height ratio, must never be exceeded. As shown in Fig. 18, spacing cutoff luminaires too far apart to the front or side will result in poor beam overlap, nonuniform lighting, and dangerous dark patches. For more detailed information on working with cutoff luminaires, refer to the sections in this book concerning the illumination of parking areas and roadways.

Power Drawer Cutoff Site Light Floodlight

Figure 19 (page 153) illustrates the newest entry into the field of sports floodlighting—the Power Drawer Cutoff Site Light floodlight. Although it closely resembles the cast heavy-duty luminaire in outer housing design and ballast drawer arrangement, this floodlight's unique optical arrangement gives it distinct advantages over other floodlight luminaires.

As shown in Figs. 13 and 15 (pages 149 and 150), the beam of a typical floodlight is basically symmetrical around both the vertical and horizontal beam axes, a fact that creates ineffective utilization of much of the light in the vertical beam component. This wasted light, found in the angles above the vertical beam center line, is a result of the luminaire's inability to direct most of the beam onto the surface or vertical plane requiring illumination. Also, standard floodlight designs expose the lamp to the viewer's eye, a fact which restricts the possible aiming angles.

The Power Drawer Cutoff Site Light floodlight solves both of these problems through the use of an optical arrangement employing a horizontally mounted lamp. This design shifts the main beam of maximum candlepower up to 23° above the aiming line, a line generally regarded as one running perpendicular to the axis of the floodlight's lens (Fig. 20, page 153). From Fig. 20 we can also see that the light from the maximum candlepower line to the top edge of the beam spread is highly restricted to a compact area. When metal halide lamps are used, this angle is about 17°; with high pressure sodium lamps, the angle can be as narrow as 10°. The angle down from the aiming line is also quite restrictive, permitting sharp beam cutoff to the rear of the floodlight.

The end result of these design modifications is a luminaire which can be aimed directly at the area requiring maximum illumination. The maximum beam projection distance is increased, and since light cutoff at both the top and bottom beam edges is extremely sharp, glare is reduced, beam control is increased, and light waste and spill are decreased. The fact that the luminaire's design conceals the lamp from the viewer's eye also decreases glare problems. Because the lamp always rests in a horizontal position regardless of the aiming angle, the lamp lumen depreciation problem which occurs when metal halide lamps are operated at angles away from horizontal is no longer of concern.

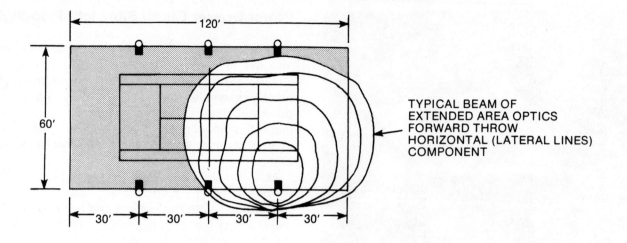

TYPICAL BEAM OF
EXTENDED AREA OPTICS
FORWARD THROW
HORIZONTAL (LATERAL LINES)
COMPONENT

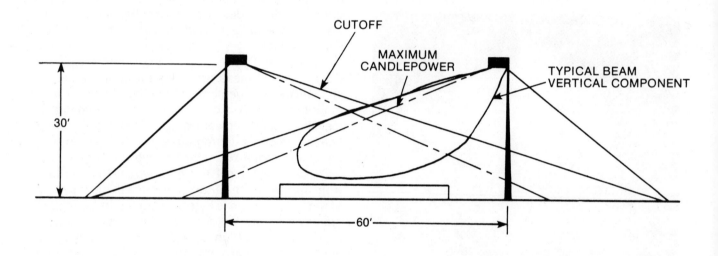

CUTOFF

MAXIMUM
CANDLEPOWER

TYPICAL BEAM
VERTICAL COMPONENT

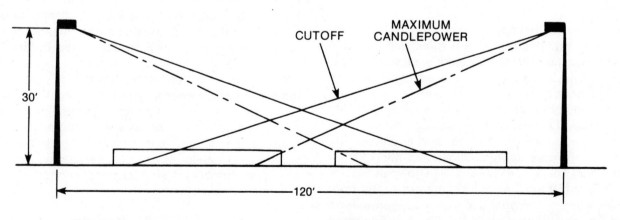

MAXIMUM
CANDLEPOWER

CUTOFF

Fig. 18: Spacing cutoff luminaires too far apart to the
front and sides results in poor beam overlap and non-
uniform lighting. Remember that the proper spacing of
cutoff luminaires is based on luminaire mounting height.

152 EXTERIOR LIGHTING

Fig. 19: The Power Drawer Cutoff Site Light Floodlight luminaire.

The sharp cutoff floodlight is housed in what is basically a standard heavy-duty cast floodlight housing. The one disadvantage of the sharp cutoff floodlight luminaire is that it cannot be used to project great distances such as the luminaires which produce types 2, 3, and 4 beam spread. The sharp cutoff floodlight is a type 5, 6, or 7 luminaire and should only be used to project light to medium and close distances. A typical example of a medium distance would be a football field where the mounting poles are located no further away than 50' from the edge of the playing field. Tennis and racquet sport court lighting would be a fine example of close projection lighting suitable for this luminaire. To restate: The main advantages of sharp cutoff floodlights are reduced glare and a decrease of light spill or light pollution into adjoining areas you do not wish to illuminate.

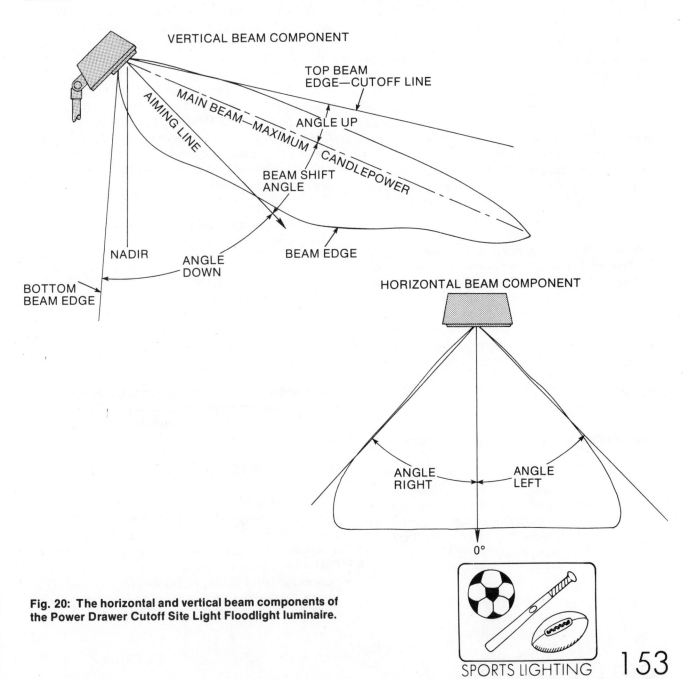

Fig. 20: The horizontal and vertical beam components of the Power Drawer Cutoff Site Light Floodlight luminaire.

SPORTS LIGHTING

DESIGN METHODS AND LAYOUTS

The following pages contain all the tables and layout sketches needed to design successful lighting systems for outdoor sports installations. Regardless of the sport involved, the initial steps in the design of any system are the same—the required illumination level and uniformity ratio should be found in the appropriate lighting requirement table, and the actual playing area should be carefully analyzed. In some sports, such as baseball, the actual dimensions of the playing field will change according to the classification or level of competition; in others, such as football, the playing field dimensions will remain constant throughout all levels of play.

Layout Sketches and Application Tables

Under each major sports heading, you will find a number of layout sketches of approved lighting designs for that particular sport. These layout sketches indicate actual mounting pole locations and precise field dimensions. Accompanying these layouts will be varying numbers of highly specific luminaire application tables. These luminaire application tables list the data needed to fill out the framework presented in the layout sketches and complete the lighting design. Each luminaire application table lists a specific lamp-luminaire combination and specifies lamp wattage, pole location, minimum mounting height, number of luminaires per pole, beam spreads, and the SPI Lighting catalog numbers. The total kilowatt load is also tabulated. A detailed description of how to combine the tables and layout sketches to produce a finished lighting design is presented in the following section on base sports. It is recommended that you read this section carefully because the working principles presented hold true for all subsequent layouts for foot, racquet, stick, combination, and miscellaneous sports installations.

Metal Halide Lamp Proration Factors

Many of the floodlight luminaire application tables found on the following pages list 1500-watt metal halide high intensity discharge lamps as possible light sources. Although 1500-watt metal halide lamps are the preferred metal halide choice, 1000-watt metal halide lamps can also be used for these appli-

Table 1: 1000-Watt Metal Halide Lamp Proration Factors

Luminaire Type	Proration Factor	
	Fixture	Footcandle
Cast Heavy-Duty Floodlight (vertical lamp)	1.41	.71
Cast Heavy-Duty Floodlight (horizontal lamp)	1.39	.72
Round Spun Floodlight	1.41	.71

cations. When 1000-watt lamps are used in place of 1500-watt lamps, the number of luminaires used must be increased to maintain the same footcandle level. If the same number of luminaires is used, the overall footcandle level will decrease. The proration factors found in Table 1 can be used to find the new number of luminaires required or the new footcandle level. For example: If 10 cast heavy-duty floodlight luminaires, equipped with vertically mounted 1500-watt metal halide lamps are to be replaced with cast heavy-duty floodlight luminaires, equipped with vertically mounted 1000-watt metal halide lamps, the new number of luminaires needed to maintain the desired footcandle level is found by multiplying the original number of luminaires by the proper fixture proration factor.

10 luminaires × 1.41 fixture proration factor = 14.1 luminaires, equipped with 1000-watt metal halide lamps now needed. (Round off to the nearest number—14.)

If the same number of luminaires are used when the 1000-watt substitution is made, the new footcandle level is found by multiplying the old footcandle level by the proper footcandle proration factor.

20 footcandles × .71 footcandle proration factor = 14.2 footcandles now generated.

Consult SPI Lighting for the correct lamp-luminaire catalog numbers when substituting 1000-watt metal halide lamps for 1500-watt metal halide lamps.

BASE SPORTS

The two major base sports, baseball and softball, present a difficult seeing task. The ball is small in size, often moves rapidly, and is commonly viewed at varying distances against varying backgrounds. Fortunately base sports do not present a particularly prolonged seeing task and the need for high levels of concentration is intermittent. The large number of spectator and player positions also present some

154 EXTERIOR LIGHTING

Class of Play or League	Illumination Level*		Dimensions (feet)								Area (square feet)		Application Reference	Minimum Mounting Height (feet)		
	Infield	Outfield	R	S	T	U	W	X	Y	Z	Infield	Outfield		A	B	C
Baseball																
Major League	150	100	Will vary. Consult SPI Lighting.								22,500	110,000*	—	Will vary.		
Pro AAA, AA	70	50	400	30	90	150	90—120	110—140	20—30	130—180	22,500	110,000	A-1	110	110	110
Pro A, B, and College level	50	30	400	30	90	150	60—90	80—110	20—30	130—180	22,500	110,000	A-2	90	90	90
Pro C, D	30	20	400	30	90	150	30—60	40—80	20—30	130—180	22,500	110,000	A-3	70	70	70
Semi-Pro and Municipal League	20	15	400	30	90	150	30—60	40—80	20—30	130—180	22,500	110,000	A-4	70	70	70
High School	30	20	350	30	90	150	30—60	40—80	20—30	130—180	22,500	90,000	B-1	70	70	70
Babe Ruth	30	20	330	30	90	150	30—60	40—80	20—30	130—180	22,500	72,000	B-2	70	70	70
Little League																
Senior Division	30	20	300	30	90	150	30—60	40—80	20—30	130—180	22,500	67,100	B-3	70	70	70
Junior Division II	30	20	250	25	75	125	24—45	35—65	10—25	110—145	15,625	46,600	B-4	50	50	60
Junior Division I	30	20	200	20	60	100	20—30	25—50	5—15	90—110	10,000	29,800	B-5 or C-1	40	40	50
Softball																
Pro, Amateur Championship, and College	50	30	300	20	60	100	20—60	35—80	10—25	110—145	10,000	72,725	B-6	70	70	70
			280	20	60	100	20—60	35—80	10—25	110—145	10,000	63,200	B-7	50	50	60
			240	20	60	100	20—60	35—80	10—25	110—145	10,000	45,260	B-8 or C-2	50	50	60
Semi-Pro and High School	30	20	280	20	60	100	20—30	25—50	5—15	110—145	10,000	63,200	B-9	40	40	55
			240	20	60	100	20—30	25—50	5—15	110—145	10,000	45,260	C-3	40	40	50
Industrial League	20	15	280	20	60	100	20—30	25—50	5—15	90—110	10,000	63,200	B-10	35	35	50
			240	20	60	100	20—30	25—50	5—15	90—110	10,000	45,260	C-4	35	35	45
			200	20	60	100	20—30	25—50	5—15	90—110	10,000	29,800	C-5 or D-1	35	35	40=C-5 / 50=D-1
Bobbie Sox and Junior League	30	20	200	20	60	100	20—30	25—50	5—15	90—110	10,000	29,800	C-6 or D-2	35	35	40=C-6 / 50=D-2

* Uniformities: For any given area, infield or outfield, a maximum/minimum uniformity ratio of 3:1 should not be exceeded.

Notes: 1. For Major League Baseball, the outfield distances and possible pole locations will vary from installation to installation. Also, the lighting must be suitable for television broadcasting. Consult SPI Lighting when designing these layouts.

2. Professional AAA, AA, A, B, and college level baseball; and professional, amateur championship, and college level softball may require lighting satisfactory for television broadcasting.

3. Illumination levels are measured in horizontal maintained footcandles at a theoretical plane 36" above the playing surface.

lighting problems. For all base sports applications, floodlights should be aimed so that the beam spread overlap will provide lighting from two different directions at almost all outfield points and from four directions at almost all infield points.

Table 2 lists the vital data needed for designing lighting systems for base sports. This includes illumination and uniformity requirements, the various playing field dimensions and areas, suggested application references, and minimum pole mounting heights. These suggested dimensions and application references correspond to the layout sketches and luminaire application tables listed under base sports.

For example, as listed in Table 2, the information on Professional AAA and AA baseball reads as follows: The illumination requirements are 70 and 50 footcandles for the respective infield and outfield areas, and a 3:1 maximum/minimum uniformity ratio is needed. Dimensions include the center field radius (R = 400'), the base path distance (T = 90'), the foul line to mounting pole A1 distance range (X = 110' to 140'), etc. The respective areas

of the infield and outfield are 22,500 and 110,000 square feet. The application reference is A-1. This letter-number combination refers the designer to two separate pieces of information, the baseball layout sketch labeled A and the luminaire application table, **Layout A-1: Baseball—Professional AAA and AA Classifications** (page 157). The final three columns of the line indicate the minimum pole mounting height for the three types of poles (A, B, and C) found on layout sketch A.

The luminaire application table contains the following information. It suggests two possible layouts. The first employs Power Mate Floodlight Luminaires (end pierced optics), equipped with 1500-watt metal halide lamps. The second layout option uses Power Drawer Sports Light Luminaires (vertical lamp optics) equipped with 1500-watt metal halide lamps. For each of the listed pole locations, A1 through C4, the exact number of luminaires to be mounted on

SPORTS LIGHTING 155

each pole and the minimum luminaire mounting height are given. The IES/NEMA beam spread classification is also listed, and the SPI Lighting catalog numbers are included to facilitate easy cross-reference to other SPI Lighting materials. Finally, the total number of luminaires and the total kilowatt load is calculated.

By using the exact dimensions and materials listed, a lighting designer can produce a satisfactory lighting system for baseball fields used at the Professional AAA and AA levels of competition. However, it must be pointed out that there is seldom a truly standard baseball field layout, especially at the higher levels of competition. Factors such as spectator need, space limitations, overall stadium design, and the project's monetary budget can have a strong effect on the final lighting system design. Yet, the suggested layouts given here for the various classifications of baseball and softball make ideal points from which to initiate any design. Moreover, in many cases, especially at lower levels of competition where spectator and land use problems are often minimal, these suggested layouts can be employed almost exactly as presented.

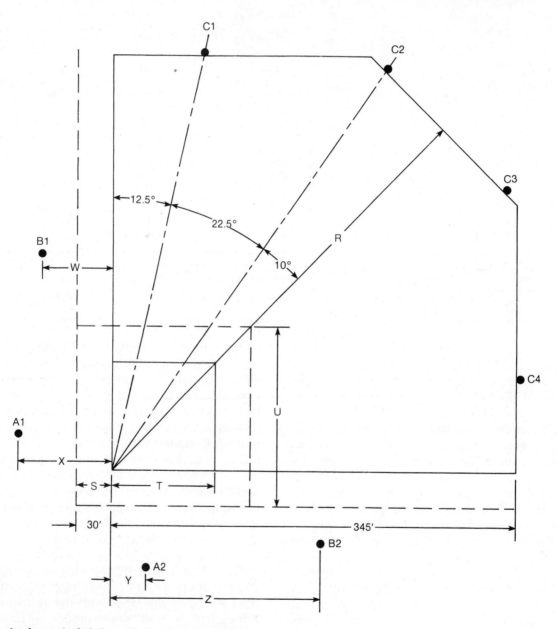

Base Sports: Layouts A-1 through A-4 field dimensions and pole locations.

Layout A-1: Baseball—Professional AAA and AA Classifications

		Power Mate Floodlight End Pierced Optics 1500-watt Metal Halide				Power Drawer Sports Light Vertical Lamp Optics 1500-watt Metal Halide			
Mounting Poles		Catalog Number MS3195 MS3194 MS3193				Catalog Number FL3194 FL3193 FL3192			
	Minimum	Beam Spread				Beam Spread			
Location	Height	2 × 2	3 × 3	5 × 5		1 × 3	3 × 3	4 × 4	
		Luminaires per Pole			Total	Luminaires per Pole			Total
A1	110'	12	—	—	12	10	—	—	10
A2	110'	12	—	—	12	10	—	—	10
B1	110'	17	8	—	25	14	5	—	19
B2	110'	17	8	—	25	14	5	—	19
C1	110'	—	4	12	16	—	3	11	14
C2	110'	—	4	12	16	—	3	11	14
C3	110'	—	4	12	16	—	3	11	14
C4	110'	—	4	12	16	—	3	11	14
Totals		58	32	48	138	48	22	44	114
		Kilowatt load @ 1.61 each =			222.18	Kilowatt load @ 1.61 each =			183.54

	Avg. Hor. Fc	Avg./Min. Unif.	Max./Min. Unif.	Avg. Hor. Fc	Avg./Min. Unif.	Max./Min. Unif.
Infield	71.99	1.62:1	2.02:1	70.16	1.28:1	1.47:1
Outfield	50.13	1.84:1	2.51:1	51.02	1.53:1	1.90:1

Layout A-2: Baseball—Professional A-B Leagues and College

		Power Mate Floodlight End Pierced Optics 1500-watt Metal Halide				Power Drawer Sports Light Vertical Lamp Optics 1500-watt Metal Halide			
Mounting Poles		Catalog Number MS3195 MS3194 MS3193				Catalog Number FL3194 FL3193 FL3192			
	Minimum	Beam Spread				Beam Spread			
Location	Height	2 × 2	3 × 3	5 × 5		1 × 3	3 × 3	4 × 4	
		Luminaires per Pole			Total	Luminaires per Pole			Total
A1	90'	5	5	—	10	4	4	—	8
A2	90'	5	5	—	10	4	4	—	8
B1	90'	8	8	—	16	6	6	—	12
B2	90'	8	8	—	16	6	6	—	12
C1	90'	—	2	6	8	—	2	5	7
C2	90'	—	2	6	8	—	2	5	7
C3	90'	—	2	6	8	—	2	5	7
C4	90'	—	2	6	8	—	2	5	7
Totals		26	34	24	84	20	28	20	68
		Kilowatt load @ 1.61 each =			135.24	Kilowatt load @ 1.61 each =			109.48

	Avg. Hor. Fc	Avg./Min. Unif.	Max./Min. Unif.	Avg. Hor. Fc	Avg./Min. Unif.	Max./Min. Unif.
Infield	50.40	1.49:1	2.25:1	51.57	1.27:1	1.75:1
Outfield	29.55	1.66:1	2.55:1	30.80	1.82:1	2.54:1

Layout A-3: Baseball—Professional C-D Leagues

		Power Mate Floodlight End Pierced Optics 1500-watt Metal Halide				Power Drawer Sports Light Vertical Lamp Optics 1500-watt Metal Halide				Power Drawer Sports Light Horizontal Lamp Optics 1000-watt High Pressure Sodium			
Mounting Poles		Catalog Number MS3194 MS3193 MS3192				Catalog Number FL3193 FL3192 FL3191				Catalog Number FL6284 FL6283 FL6282			
	Minimum	Beam Spread				Beam Spread				Beam Spread			
Location	Height	3 × 3	5 × 5	6 × 6		3 × 3	4 × 4	6 × 7		5 × 3	5 × 3	6 × 7	
		Luminaires per Pole			Total	Luminaires per Pole			Total	Luminaires per Pole			Total
A1	70'	5	1	—	6	4	1	—	5	4	2	—	6
A2	70'	5	1	—	6	4	1	—	5	4	2	—	6
B1	70'	6	4	—	10	4	3	—	7	7	4	—	11
B2	70'	6	4	—	10	4	3	—	7	7	4	—	11
C1	70'	—	2	4	6	—	2	4	6	4	1	2	7
C2	70'	—	2	4	6	—	2	4	6	4	1	2	7
C3	70'	—	2	4	6	—	2	4	6	4	1	2	7
C4	70'	—	2	4	6	—	2	4	6	4	1	2	7
Totals		22	18	16	56	16	16	16	48	38	16	8	62
		Kilowatt load @ 1.61 each =			90.16	Kilowatt load @ 1.61 each =			77.28	Kilowatt load @ 1.09 each =			67.58

	Avg. Hor. Fc	Avg./Min. Unif.	Max./Min. Unif.	Avg. Hor. Fc	Avg./Min. Unif.	Max./Min. Unif.	Avg. Hor. Fc	Avg./Min. Unif.	Max./Min. Unif.
Infield	30.72	1.34:1	2.22:1	31.97	1.27:1	1.52:1	29.93	1.19:1	1.46:1
Outfield	20.21	1.73:1	2.33:1	20.09	1.69:1	2.47:1	20.67	1.59:1	2.03:1

Layout A-4: Baseball—Semi-Professional and Municipal Leagues													
		Power Mate Floodlight End Pierced Optics 1500-watt Metal Halide				Power Drawer Sports Light Vertical Lamp Optics 1500-watt Metal Halide				Power Drawer Sports Light Horizontal Lamp Optics 1000-watt High Pressure Sodium			
Mounting Poles		Catalog Number MS3194 MS3193 MS3192				Catalog Number FL3193 FL3192 FL3191				Catalog Number FL6284 FL6283 FL6282			
	Minimum	Beam Spread				Beam Spread				Beam Spread			
Location	Height	3 × 3	5 × 5	6 × 6		3 × 3	4 × 4	6 × 7		5 × 3	5 × 3	6 × 7	
		Luminaires per Pole			Total	Luminaires per Pole			Total	Luminaires per Pole			Total
A1	70'	3	1	—	4	1	3	—	4	1	4	—	5
A2	70'	3	1	—	4	1	3	—	4	1	4	—	5
B1	70'	5	2	—	7	3	2	—	5	2	5	—	7
B2	70'	5	2	—	7	3	2	—	5	2	5	—	7
C1	70'	2	—	2	4	2	—	2	4	1	2	2	5
C2	70'	2	—	2	4	2	—	2	4	1	2	2	5
C3	70'	2	—	2	4	2	—	2	4	1	2	2	5
C4	70'	2	—	2	4	2	—	2	4	1	2	2	5
Totals		24	6	8	38	16	10	8	34	10	26	8	44
		Kilowatt load @ 1.61 each =			61.18	Kilowatt load @ 1.61 each =			54.74	Kilowatt load @ 1.09 each =			47.96
		Avg. Hor. Fc	Avg./Min. Unif.	Max./Min. Unif.		Avg. Hor. Fc	Avg./Min. Unif.	Max./Min. Unif.		Avg. Hor. Fc	Avg./Min. Unif.	Max./Min. Unif.	
Infield		19.89	1.38:1	1.88:1		20.90	1.30:1	1.62:1		20.69	1.17:1	1.36:1	
Outfield		14.71	2.01:1	2.72:1		15.08	1.84:1	2.97:1		15.42	1.59:1	1.94:1	

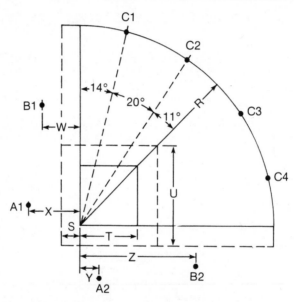

Base Sports: Layouts B-1 through B-10 field dimensions and pole locations.

Layout B-1: Baseball—High School													
		Power Mate Floodlight End Pierced Optics 1500-watt Metal Halide				Power Drawer Sports Light Vertical Lamp Optics 1500-watt Metal Halide				Power Drawer Sports Light Horizontal Lamp Optics 1000-watt High Pressure Sodium			
Mounting Poles		Catalog Number MS3194 MS3193 MS3192				Catalog Number MS3193 MS3192 MS3191				Catalog Number FL6284 FL6283 FL6282			
	Minimum	Beam Spread				Beam Spread				Beam Spread			
Location	Height	3 × 3	5 × 5	6 × 6		3 × 3	4 × 4	6 × 7		5 × 3	5 × 3	6 × 7	
		Luminaires per Pole			Total	Luminaires per Pole			Total	Luminaires per Pole			Total
A1	70'	4	2	—	6	3	2	—	5	5	2	—	7
A2	70'	4	2	—	6	3	2	—	5	5	2	—	7
B1	70'	5	3	1	9	5	3	1	9	5	6	—	11
B2	70'	5	3	1	9	5	3	1	9	5	6	—	11
C1	70'	2	—	4	6	1	—	4	5	—	4	2	6
C2	70'	2	—	4	6	1	—	4	5	—	4	2	6
C3	70'	2	—	4	6	1	—	4	5	—	4	2	6
C4	70'	2	—	4	6	1	—	4	5	—	4	2	6
Totals		26	10	18	54	20	10	18	48	20	32	8	60
		Kilowatt load @ 1.61 each =			86.94	Kilowatt load @ 1.61 each =			77.28	Kilowatt load @ 1.09 each =			65.4
		Avg. Hor. Fc	Avg./Min. Unif.	Max./Min. Unif.		Avg. Hor. Fc	Avg./Min. Unif.	Max./Min. Unif.		Avg. Hor. Fc	Avg./Min. Unif.	Max./Min. Unif.	
Infield		29.94	1.30:1	2.09:1		30.69	1.30:1	1.53:1		30.07	1.19:1	1.66:1	
Outfield		19.78	2.22:1	3.03:1		20.16	2.19:1	3.02:1		20.64	2.29:1	3.04:1	

Layout B-2: Baseball—Babe Ruth

		Power Mate Floodlight End Pierced Optics 1500-watt Metal Halide				Power Drawer Sports Light Vertical Lamp Optics 1500-watt Metal Halide				Power Drawer Sports Light Horizontal Lamp Optics 1000-watt High Pressure Sodium			
Mounting Poles		Catalog Number MS3194 MS3193 MS3192				Catalog Number FL3193 FL3192 FL3191				Catalog Number FL6284 FL6283 FL6282			
	Minimum	Beam Spread				Beam Spread				Beam Spread			
Location	Height	3 × 3	5 × 5	6 × 6		3 × 3	4 × 4	6 × 7		5 × 3	5 × 3	6 × 7	
		Luminaires per Pole			Total	Luminaires per Pole			Total	Luminaires per Pole			Total
A1	70'	4	2	—	6	3	2	—	5	3	5	—	8
A2	70'	4	2	—	6	3	2	—	5	3	5	—	8
B1	70'	5	2	1	8	1	5	—	6	2	7	—	9
B2	70'	5	2	1	8	1	5	—	6	2	7	—	9
C1	70'	2	1	2	5	2	1	2	5	2	1	2	5
C2	70'	2	1	2	5	2	1	2	5	2	1	2	5
C3	70'	2	1	2	5	2	1	2	5	2	1	2	5
C4	70'	2	1	2	5	2	1	2	5	2	1	2	5
Totals		26	12	10	48	16	18	8	42	18	28	8	54
		Kilowatt load @ 1.61 each =			77.28	Kilowatt load @ 1.61 each =			67.62	Kilowatt load @ 1.09 each =			58.86
		Avg. Hor. Fc	Avg./Min. Unif.	Max./Min. Unif.		Avg. Hor. Fc	Avg./Min. Unif.	Max./Min. Unif.		Avg. Hor. Fc	Avg./Min. Unif.	Max./Min. Unif.	
Infield		30.29	1.38:1	2.21:1		29.93	1.36:1	1.75:1		30.90	1.36:1	1.90:1	
Outfield		20.14	1.50:1	2.01:1		20.41	2.04:1	2.99:1		20.19	1.65:1	2.22:1	

Layout B-3: Baseball—Senior Division Little League and Colt League

		Power Mate Floodlight End Pierced Optics 1500-watt Metal Halide				Power Drawer Sports Light Vertical Lamp Optics 1500-watt Metal Halide				Power Drawer Sports Light Horizontal Lamp Optics 1000-watt High Pressure Sodium			
Mounting Poles		Catalog Number MS3194 MS3193 MS3192				Catalog Number FL3193 FL3192 FL3191				Catalog Number FL6284 FL6283 FL6282			
	Minimum	Beam Spread				Beam Spread				Beam Spread			
Location	Height	3 × 3	5 × 5	6 × 6		3 × 3	4 × 4	6 × 7		5 × 3	5 × 3	6 × 7	
		Luminaires per Pole			Total	Luminaires per Pole			Total	Luminaires per Pole			Total
A1	70'	4	2	—	6	3	2	—	5	2	5	—	7
A2	70'	4	2	—	6	3	2	—	5	2	5	—	7
B1	70'	5	1	1	7	—	5	2	7	1	8	—	9
B2	70'	5	1	1	7	—	5	2	7	1	8	—	9
C1	70'	2	—	2	4	—	2	2	4	—	2	2	4
C2	70'	2	—	2	4	—	2	2	4	—	2	2	4
C3	70'	2	—	2	4	—	2	2	4	—	2	2	4
C4	70'	2	—	2	4	—	2	2	4	—	2	2	4
Totals		26	6	10	42	6	22	12	40	6	34	8	48
		Kilowatt load @ 1.61 each =			67.62	Kilowatt load @ 1.61 each =			64.40	Kilowatt load @ 1.09 each =			52.32
		Avg. Hor. Fc	Avg./Min. Unif.	Max./Min. Unif.		Avg. Hor. Fc	Avg./Min. Unif.	Max./Min. Unif.		Avg. Hor. Fc	Avg./Min. Unif.	Max./Min. Unif.	
Infield		30.58	1.34:1	2.12:1		30.38	1.24:1	1.54:1		30.54	1.29:1	1.77:1	
Outfield		20.02	1.71:1	2.32:1		20.26	1.97:1	2.46:1		20.91	1.74:1	2.14:1	

Layout B-4: Baseball—Junior Division II Pony League

		Power Mate Floodlight End Pierced Optics 1500-watt Metal Halide			Power Drawer Sports Light Vertical Lamp Optics 1500-watt Metal Halide			Power Drawer Sports Light Horizontal Lamp Optics 1000-watt High Pressure Sodium		
Mounting Poles		Catalog Number MS3193 MS3192			Catalog Number FL3192 FL3191			Catalog Number FL6283 FL6282		
	Minimum	Beam Spread			Beam Spread			Beam Spread		
Location	Height	5 × 5	6 × 6		4 × 4	6 × 7		5 × 3	6 × 7	
		Luminaires per Pole		Total	Luminaires per Pole		Total	Luminaires per Pole		Total
A1	50'	3	2	5	2	2	4	3	1	4
A2	50'	3	2	5	2	2	4	3	1	4
B1	50'	4	1	5	4	1	5	5	1	6
B2	50'	4	1	5	4	1	5	5	1	6
C1	60'	1	2	3	1	2	3	1	2	3
C2	60'	1	2	3	1	2	3	1	2	3
C3	60'	1	2	3	1	2	3	1	2	3
C4	60'	1	2	3	1	2	3	1	2	3
Totals		18	14	32	16	14	30	20	12	32
		Kilowatt load @ 1.61 each =		51.52	Kilowatt load @ 1.61 each =		48.30	Kilowatt load @ 1.09 each =		34.88
		Avg. Hor. Fc	Avg./Min. Unif.	Max./Min. Unif.	Avg. Hor. Fc	Avg./Min. Unif.	Max./Min. Unif.	Avg. Hor. Fc	Avg./Min. Unif.	Max./Min. Unif.
Infield		30.74	1.23:1	1.58:1	30.85	1.35:1	1.66:1	30.11	1.16:1	1.41:1
Outfield		20.03	1.73:1	2.16:1	20.41	1.69:1	2.45:1	20.00	1.44:1	1.86:1

Layout B-5: Baseball—Junior Division I Little League, Bronco League

		Power Mate Floodlight End Pierced Optics 1500-watt Metal Halide			Power Drawer Sports Light Vertical Lamp Optics 1500-watt Metal Halide			Power Drawer Sports Light Horizontal Lamp Optics 1000-watt High Pressure Sodium		
Mounting Poles		Catalog Number MS3193 / MS3192			Catalog Number FL3192 / FL3191			Catalog Number FL6283 / FL6282		
		Beam Spread			Beam Spread			Beam Spread		
Location	Minimum Height	5×5	6×6		4×4	6×7		5×3	6×7	
		Luminaires per Pole		Total	Luminaires per Pole		Total	Luminaires per Pole		Total
A1	40'	1	2	3	1	2	3	2	1	3
A2	40'	1	2	3	1	2	3	2	1	3
B1	40'	2	1	3	1	2	3	1	2	3
B2	40'	2	1	3	1	2	3	1	2	3
C1	50'	—	2	2	1	1	2	2	—	2
C2	50'	—	2	2	—	2	2	2	—	2
C3	50'	—	2	2	—	2	2	2	—	2
C4	50'	—	2	2	1	1	2	2	—	2
Totals		6	14	20	6	14	20	14	6	20
		Kilowatt load @ 1.61 each = 32.20			Kilowatt load @ 1.61 each = 32.20			Kilowatt load @ 1.09 each = 21.80		
		Avg. Hor. Fc	Avg./Min. Unif.	Max./Min. Unif.	Avg. Hor. Fc	Avg./Min. Unif.	Max./Min. Unif.	Avg. Hor. Fc	Avg./Min. Unif.	Max./Min. Unif.
Infield		30.10	1.46:1	2.01:1	31.06	1.30:1	1.61:1	31.08	1.27:1	1.58:1
Outfield		21.01	2.35:1	3.00:1	20.83	1.44:1	2.13:1	20.73	1.56:1	2.17:1

Layout B-6: Softball—300' Professional, Amateur Championship, and College

		Power Mate Floodlight End Pierced Optics 1500-watt Metal Halide				Power Drawer Sports Light Vertical Lamp Optics 1500-watt Metal Halide			Power Drawer Sports Light Horizontal Lamp Optics 1000-watt High Pressure Sodium		
Mounting Poles		Catalog Number MS3194 / MS3193 / MS3192				Catalog Number FL3192 / FL3191			Catalog Number FL6283 / FL6282		
		Beam Spread				Beam Spread			Beam Spread		
Location	Minimum Height	3×3	5×5	6×6		4×4	6×7		5×3	6×7	
		Luminaires per Pole			Total	Luminaires per Pole		Total	Luminaires per Pole		Total
A1	70'	3	4	—	7	7	—	7	9	—	9
A2	70'	3	4	—	7	7	—	7	9	—	9
B1	70'	1	3	3	7	5	2	7	8	1	9
B2	70'	1	3	3	7	5	2	7	8	1	9
C1	70'	1	3	3	7	4	2	6	4	2	6
C2	70'	1	2	4	7	3	3	6	3	3	6
C3	70'	1	2	4	7	3	3	6	3	3	6
C4	70'	1	3	3	7	4	2	6	4	2	6
Totals		12	24	20	56	38	14	52	48	12	60
		Kilowatt load @ 1.61 each = 90.16				Kilowatt load @ 1.61 each = 83.72			Kilowatt load @ 1.09 each = 65.40		
		Avg. Hor. Fc	Avg./Min. Unif.	Max./Min. Unif.		Avg. Hor. Fc	Avg./Min. Unif.	Max./Min. Unif.	Avg. Hor. Fc	Avg./Min. Unif.	Max./Min. Unif.
Infield		50.32	1.56:1	2.05:1		50.14	1.27:1	1.41:1	50.36	1.19:1	1.35:1
Outfield		29.82	1.47:1	2.04:1		30.11	1.46:1	2.23:1	30.79	1.75:1	2.82:1

Layout B-7: Softball—280' Professional, Amateur Championship, and College

		Power Mate Floodlight End Pierced Optics 1500-watt Metal Halide				Power Drawer Sports Light Vertical Lamp Optics 1500-watt Metal Halide			Power Drawer Sports Light Horizontal Lamp Optics 1000-watt High Pressure Sodium		
Mounting Poles		Catalog Number MS3194 / MS3193 / MS3192				Catalog Number FL3192 / FL3191			Catalog Number FL6283 / FL6282		
		Beam Spread				Beam Spread			Beam Spread		
Location	Minimum Height	3×3	5×5	6×6		4×4	6×7		5×3	6×7	
		Luminaires per Pole			Total	Luminaires per Pole		Total	Luminaires per Pole		Total
A1	50'	4	3	—	7	7	—	7	7	—	7
A2	50'	4	3	—	7	7	—	7	7	—	7
B1	50'	4	3	—	7	5	2	7	6	2	8
B2	50'	4	3	—	7	5	2	7	6	2	8
C1	60'	2	2	2	6	3	2	5	4	2	6
C2	60'	2	2	2	6	3	2	5	4	2	6
C3	60'	2	2	2	6	3	2	5	4	2	6
C4	60'	2	2	2	6	3	2	5	4	2	6
Totals		24	20	8	52	36	12	48	42	12	54
		Kilowatt load @ 1.61 each = 83.72				Kilowatt load @ 1.61 each = 77.28			Kilowatt load @ 1.09 each = 58.86		
		Avg. Hor. Fc	Avg./Min. Unif.	Max./Min. Unif.		Avg. Hor. Fc	Avg./Min. Unif.	Max./Min. Unif.	Avg. Hor. Fc	Avg./Min. Unif.	Max./Min. Unif.
Infield		51.53	2.10:1	2.60:1		51.33	1.46:1	1.82:1	50.17	1.30:1	1.67:1
Outfield		30.33	1.68:1	2.99:1		30.07	1.28:1	1.93:1	30.98	1.45:1	2.21:1

Layout B-8: Softball—240' Professional, Amateur-Championship, and College

Mounting Poles		Power Mate Floodlight End Pierced Optics 1500-watt Metal Halide				Power Drawer Sports Light Vertical Lamp Optics 1500-watt Metal Halide			Power Drawer Sports Light Horizontal Lamp Optics 1000-watt High Pressure Sodium		
		Catalog Number MS3194 MS3193 MS3192				**Catalog Number** FL3192 FL3191			**Catalog Number** FL6283 FL6282		
	Minimum	**Beam Spread**				**Beam Spread**			**Beam Spread**		
Location	Height	3 × 3	5 × 5	6 × 6		4 × 4	6 × 7		5 × 3	6 × 7	
		Luminaires per Pole			Total	Luminaires per Pole		Total	Luminaires per Pole		Total
A1	50'	3	4	—	7	6	—	6	7	—.	7
A2	50'	3	4	—	7	6	—	6	7	—	7
B1	50'	2	3	1	6	5	—	5	7	—	7
B2	50'	2	3	1	6	5	—	5	7	—	7
C1	60'	—	2	2	4	2	2	4	2	2	4
C2	60'	—	2	2	4	2	2	4	2	2	4
C3	60'	—	2	2	4	2	2	4	2	2	4
C4	60'	—	2	2	4	2	2	4	2	2	4
Totals		10	22	10	42	30	8	38	36	8	44
		Kilowatt load @ 1.61 each = 67.62				Kilowatt load @ 1.61 each = 61.18			Kilowatt load @ 1.09 each = 47.96		
		Avg. Hor. Fc	Avg./Min. Unif.	Max./Min. Unif.		Avg. Hor. Fc	Avg./Min. Unif.	Max./Min. Unif.	Avg. Hor. Fc	Avg./Min. Unif.	Max./Min. Unif.
Infield		49.99	1.69:1	1.97:1		50.03	1.38:1	1.79:1	50.71	1.42:1	1.86:1
Outfield		30.43	1.68:1	2.75:1		30.55	1.43:1	2.00:1	31.50	1.71:1	2.80:1

Layout B-9: Softball—280' Semi-Pro, High School, and Bobbie Sox Senior

Mounting Poles		Power Mate Floodlight End Pierced Optics 1500-watt Metal Halide			Power Drawer Sports Light Vertical Lamp Optics 1500-watt Metal Halide			Power Drawer Sports Light Horizontal Lamp Optics 1000-watt High Pressure Sodium		
		Catalog Number MS3193 MS3192			**Catalog Number** FL3192 FL3191			**Catalog Number** FL6283 FL6282		
	Minimum	**Beam Spread**			**Beam Spread**			**Beam Spread**		
Location	Height	5 × 5	6 × 6		4 × 4	6 × 7		5 × 3	6 × 7	
		Luminaires per Pole		Total	Luminaires per Pole		Total	Luminaires per Pole		Total
A1	40'	2	2	4	2	1	3	2	2	4
A2	40'	2	2	4	2	1	3	2	2	4
B1	40'	3	1	4	2	2	4	3	1	4
B2	40'	3	1	4	2	2	4	3	1	4
C1	55'	2	2	4	2	2	4	2	2	4
C2	55'	2	2	4	1	2	3	2	2	4
C3	55'	2	2	4	1	2	3	2	2	4
C4	55'	2	2	4	2	2	4	2	2	4
Totals		18	14	32	14	14	28	18	14	32
		Kilowatt load @ 1.61 each = 51.52			Kilowatt load @ 1.61 each = 45.08			Kilowatt load @ 1.09 each = 34.88		
		Avg. Hor. Fc	Avg./Min. Unif.	Max./Min. Unif.	Avg. Hor. Fc	Avg./Min. Unif.	Max./Min. Unif.	Avg. Hor. Fc	Avg./Min. Unif.	Max./Min. Unif.
Infield		30.27	1.56:1	2.46:1	30.12	1.54:1	2.25:1	30.99	1.43:1	1.72:1
Outfield		20.59	1.72:1	2.30:1	19.90	1.76:1	2.51:1	20.48	1.55:1	1.92:1

		Power Mate Floodlight End Pierced Optics 1500-watt Metal Halide			Power Drawer Sports Light Vertical Lamp Optics 1500-watt Metal Halide			Power Drawer Sports Light Horizontal Lamp Optics 1000-watt High Pressure Sodium		
Mounting Poles		Catalog Number MS3193 MS3192			Catalog Number FL3192 FL3191			Catalog Number FL6283 FL6282		
Location	Minimum Height	Beam Spread 5 × 5	6 × 6		Beam Spread 4 × 4	6 × 7		Beam Spread 5 × 3	6 × 7	
		Luminaires per Pole		Total	Luminaires per Pole		Total	Luminaires per Pole		Total
A1	35′	1	1	2	1	1	2	1	1	2
A2	35′	1	1	2	1	1	2	1	1	2
B1	35′	3	—	3	2	1	3	3	1	4
B2	35′	3	—	3	2	1	3	3	1	4
C1	50′	3	1	4	2	1	3	2	1	3
C2	50′	1	2	3	1	2	3	1	2	3
C3	50′	1	2	3	1	2	3	1	2	3
C4	50′	3	1	4	2	1	3	2	1	3
Totals		16	8	24	12	10	22	14	10	24
		Kilowatt load @ 1.61 each =		38.64	Kilowatt load @ 1.61 each =		35.42	Kilowatt load @ 1.09 each =		26.16
		Avg. Hor. Fc	Avg./Min. Unif.	Max./Min. Unif.	Avg. Hor. Fc	Avg./Min. Unif.	Max./Min. Unif.	Avg. Hor. Fc	Avg./Min. Unif.	Max./Min. Unif.
Infield		20.36	1.48:1	2.06:1	21.18	1.32:1	2.17:1	21.92	1.27:1	1.59:1
Outfield		15.49	1.64:1	2.61:1	15.43	1.57:1	2.61:1	16.11	1.71:1	2.81:1

Layout B-10:   Softball—280′ Industrial League

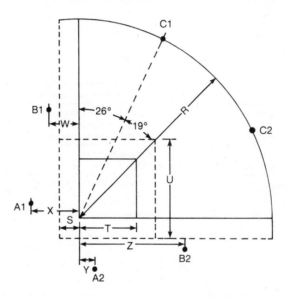

Base Sports: Layouts C-1 through C-6 field dimensions and pole locations.

Layout C-1:   Junior Division I Little League, Bronco League

		Power Mate Floodlight End Pierced Optics 1500-watt Metal Halide			Power Drawer Sports Light Vertical Lamp Optics 1500-watt Metal Halide			Power Drawer Sports Light Horizontal Lamp Optics 1000-watt High Pressure Sodium		
Mounting Poles		Catalog Number MS3193 MS3192			Catalog Number FL3192 FL3191			Catalog Number FL6283 FL6282		
Location	Minimum Height	Beam Spread 5 × 5	6 × 6		Beam Spread 4 × 4	6 × 7		Beam Spread 5 × 3	6 × 7	
		Luminaires per Pole		Total	Luminaires per Pole		Total	Luminaires per Pole		Total
A1	40′	1	2	3	1	2	3	1	2	3
A2	40′	1	2	3	1	2	3	1	2	3
B1	40′	3	1	4	1	2	3	1	2	3
B2	40′	3	1	4	1	2	3	1	2	3
C1	50′	3	1	4	3	1	4	3	2	5
C2	50′	3	1	4	3	1	4	3	2	5
Totals		14	8	22	10	10	20	10	12	22
		Kilowatt load @ 1.61 each =		35.42	Kilowatt load @ 1.61 each =		32.20	Kilowatt load @ 1.09 each =		23.98
		Avg. Hor. Fc	Avg./Min. Unif.	Max./Min. Unif.	Avg. Hor. Fc	Avg./Min. Unif.	Max./Min. Unif.	Avg. Hor. Fc	Avg./Min. Unif.	Max./Min. Unif.
Infield		31.06	1.60:1	2.16:1	31.85	1.52:1	1.89:1	30.66	1.30:1	1.59:1
Outfield		20.82	2.17:1	3.00:1	20.55	1.87:1	2.76:1	20.57	1.87:1	2.78:1

Layout C-2: Softball—240' Professional Amateur Championship and College

		Power Mate Floodlight * End Pierced Optics 1500-watt Metal Halide				Power Drawer Sports Light Vertical Lamp Optics 1500-watt Metal Halide			Power Drawer Sports Light Horizontal Lamp Optics 1000-watt High Pressure Sodium		
Mounting Poles		Catalog Number MS3194 MS3193 MS3192				Catalog Number FL3192 FL3191			Catalog Number FL6283 FL6282		
Location	Minimum Height	Beam Spread 3×3	5×5	6×6		Beam Spread 4×4	6×7		Beam Spread 5×3	6×7	
		Luminaires per Pole			Total	Luminaires per Pole		Total	Luminaires per Pole		Total
A1	50'	4	2	—	6	6	—	6	7	—	7
A2	50'	4	2	—	6	6	—	6	7	—	7
B1	60'	2	4	2	8	4	3	7	7	—	7
B2	60'	2	4	2	8	4	3	7	7	—	7
C1	60'	2	3	3	8	4	4	8	4	4	8
C2	60'	2	3	3	8	4	4	8	4	4	8
Totals		16	18	10	44	28	14	42	36	8	44
		Kilowatt load @ 1.61 each =			70.84	Kilowatt load @ 1.61 each =		67.62	Kilowatt load @ 1.09 each =		47.96
		Avg. Hor. Fc	Avg./Min. Unif.	Max./Min. Unif.		Avg. Hor. Fc	Avg./Min. Unif.	Max./Min. Unif.	Avg. Hor. Fc	Avg./Min. Unif.	Max./Min. Unif.
Infield		49.60	1.98:1	2.33:1		51.05	1.40:1	1.65:1	50.67	1.38:1	1.82:1
Outfield		29.99	1.75:1	2.91:1		30.53	1.66:1	2.83:1	29.64	1.68:1	2.84:1

Layout C-3: Softball—240' Semi-Pro, High School, and Bobbie Sox Senior

		Power Mate Floodlight End Pierced Optics 1500-watt Metal Halide			Power Drawer Sports Light Vertical Lamp Optics 1500-watt Metal Halide			Power Drawer Sports Light Horizontal Lamp Optics 1000-watt High Pressure Sodium		
Mounting Poles		Catalog Number MS3193 MS3192			Catalog Number FL3192 FL3191			Catalog Number FL6283 FL6282		
Location	Minimum Height	Beam Spread 5×5	6×6		Beam Spread 4×4	6×7		Beam Spread 5×3	6×7	
		Luminaires per Pole		Total	Luminaires per Pole		Total	Luminaires per Pole		Total
A1	40'	2	2	4	2	1	3	2	2	4
A2	40'	2	2	4	2	1	3	2	2	4
B1	40'	3	2	5	3	2	5	4	1	5
B2	40'	3	2	5	3	2	5	4	1	5
C1	50'	1	3	4	2	2	4	2	2	4
C2	50'	1	3	4	2	2	4	2	2	4
Totals		12	14	26	14	10	24	16	10	26
		Kilowatt load @ 1.61 each =		41.86	Kilowatt load @ 1.61 each =		38.64	Kilowatt load @ 1.09 each =		28.34
		Avg. Hor. Fc	Avg./Min. Unif.	Max./Min. Unif.	Avg. Hor. Fc	Avg./Min. Unif.	Max./Min. Unif.	Avg. Hor. Fc	Avg./Min. Unif.	Max./Min. Unif.
Infield		29.87	1.70:1	2.70:1	30.82	1.47:1	2.09:1	30.19	1.40:1	1.69:1
Outfield		20.10	1.66:1	2.75:1	21.00	1.71:1	2.73:1	19.67	1.50:1	1.86:1

Layout C-4: Softball—240' Industrial League

		Power Mate Floodlight End Pierced Optics 1500-watt Metal Halide			Power Drawer Sports Light Vertical Lamp Optics 1500-watt Metal Halide			Power Drawer Sports Light Horizontal Lamp Optics 1000-watt High Pressure Sodium		
Mounting Poles		Catalog Number MS3193 MS3192			Catalog Number FL3192 FL3191			Catalog Number FL6283 FL6282		
Location	Minimum Height	Beam Spread 5×5	6×6		Beam Spread 4×4	6×7		Beam Spread 5×3	6×7	
		Luminaires per Pole		Total	Luminaires per Pole		Total	Luminaires per Pole		Total
A1	35'	1	1	2	1	1	2	1	1	2
A2	35'	1	1	2	1	1	2	1	1	2
B1	35'	3	1	4	2	1	3	3	1	4
B2	35'	3	1	4	2	1	3	3	1	4
C1	45'	2	2	4	2	2	4	2	2	4
C2	45'	2	2	4	2	2	4	2	2	4
Totals		12	8	20	10	8	18	12	8	20
		Kilowatt load @ 1.61 each =		32.20	Kilowatt load @ 1.61 each =		28.98	Kilowatt load @ 1.09 each =		21.80
		Avg. Hor. Fc	Avg./Min. Unif.	Max./Min. Unif.	Avg. Hor. Fc	Avg./Min. Unif.	Max./Min. Unif.	Avg. Hor. Fc	Avg./Min. Unif.	Max./Min. Unif.
Infield		20.45	1.44:1	2.08:1	21.31	1.29:1	2.13:1	22.72	1.32:1	1.62:1
Outfield		15.82	1.78:1	2.76:1	15.50	1.85:1	2.95:1	16.40	1.90:1	2.88:1

Layout C-5: Softball—200' Industrial League

		Power Mate Floodlight End Pierced Optics 1500-watt Metal Halide			Power Drawer Sports Light Vertical Lamp Optics 1500-watt Metal Halide			Power Drawer Sports Light Horizontal Lamp Optics 1000-watt High Pressure Sodium		
Mounting Poles		Catalog Number MS3193 MS3192			Catalog Number FL3192 FL3191			Catalog Number FL6283 FL6282		
Location	**Minimum Height**	Beam Spread 5 × 5	6 × 6		Beam Spread 4 × 4	6 × 7		Beam Spread 5 × 3	6 × 7	
		Luminaires per Pole		Total	Luminaires per Pole		Total	Luminaires per Pole		Total
A1	35'	1	1	2	1	1	2	1	1	2
A2	35'	1	1	2	1	1	2	1	1	2
B1	35'	2	1	3	1	1	2	1	2	3
B2	35'	2	1	3	1	1	2	1	2	3
C1	40'	1	2	3	1	2	3	1	2	3
C2	40'	1	2	3	1	2	3	1	2	3
Totals		8	8	16	6	8	14	6	10	16
		Kilowatt load @ 1.61 each = 25.76			Kilowatt load @ 1.61 each = 22.54			Kilowatt load @ 1.09 each = 17.44		
		Avg. Hor. Fc	Avg./Min. Unif.	Max./Min. Unif.	Avg. Hor. Fc	Avg./Min. Unif.	Max./Min. Unif.	Avg. Hor. Fc	Avg./Min. Unif.	Max./Min. Unif.
Infield		21.26	1.41:1	2.03:1	22.23	1.29:1	2.05:1	20.99	1.52:1	1.97:1
Outfield		18.05	1.74:1	2.96:1	16.56	1.64:1	2.55:1	17.01	1.93:1	2.77:1

Layout C-6: Softball—200' Bobbie Sox Junior

		Power Mate Floodlight End Pierced Optics 1500-watt Metal Halide			Power Drawer Sports Light Vertical Lamp Optics 1500-watt Metal Halide			Power Drawer Sports Light Horizontal Lamp Optics 1000-watt High Pressure Sodium		
Mounting Poles		Catalog Number MS3193 MS3192			Catalog Number FL3192 FL3191			Catalog Number FL6283 FL6282		
Location	**Minimum Height**	Beam Spread 5 × 5	6 × 6		Beam Spread 4 × 4	6 × 7		Beam Spread 5 × 3	6 × 7	
		Luminaires per Pole		Total	Luminaires per Pole		Total	Luminaires per Pole		Total
A1	35'	2	1	3	2	1	3	2	1	3
A2	35'	2	1	3	2	1	3	2	1	3
B1	35'	2	2	4	2	1	3	2	1	3
B2	35'	2	2	4	2	1	3	2	1	3
C1	40'	1	2	3	1	2	3	1	3	4
C2	40'	1	2	3	1	2	3	1	3	4
Totals		10	10	20	10	8	18	10	10	20
		Kilowatt load @ 1.61 each = 32.20			Kilowatt load @ 1.61 each = 28.98			Kilowatt load @ 1.09 each = 21.80		
		Avg. Hor. Fc	Avg./Min. Unif.	Max./Min. Unif.	Avg. Hor. Fc	Avg./Min. Unif.	Max./Min. Unif.	Avg. Hor. Fc	Avg./Min. Unif.	Max./Min. Unif.
Infield		29.70	1.59:1	2.32:1	30.86	1.57:1	2.63:1	31.30	1.48:1	1.91:1
Outfield		20.14	1.72:1	2.83:1	20.38	1.76:1	2.49:1	20.22	1.77:1	2.58:1

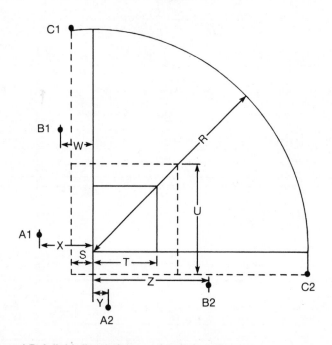

Base Sports: Layouts D-1 and D-2 field dimensions and pole locations.

Layout D-1: Softball—200' Industrial League

Mounting Poles		Power Mate Floodlight End Pierced Optics 1500-watt Metal Halide				Power Drawer Sports Light Vertical Lamp Optics 1500-watt Metal Halide				Power Drawer Sports Light Horizontal Lamp Optics 1000-watt High Pressure Sodium		
		Catalog Number MS3194 MS3193 MS3192				Catalog Number FL3193 FL3192 FL3191				Catalog Number FL6283 FL6282		
		Beam Spread				Beam Spread				Beam Spread		
Location	Minimum Height	3 × 3	5 × 5	6 × 6		3 × 3	4 × 4	6 × 7		5 × 3	6 × 7	
		Luminaires per Pole			Total	Luminaires per Pole			Total	Luminaires per Pole		Total
A1	35'	—	1	1	2	—	1	1	2	1	1	2
A2	35'	—	1	1	2	—	1	1	2	1	1	2
B1	35'	—	2	1	3	—	1	1	2	1	1	2
B2	35'	—	2	1	3	—	1	1	2	1	1	2
C1	50'	1	1	1	3	1	1	1	3	3	1	4
C2	50'	1	1	1	3	1	1	1	3	3	1	4
Totals		2	8	6	16	2	6	6	14	10	6	16
		Kilowatt load @ 1.61 each = 25.76				Kilowatt load @ 1.61 each = 22.54				Kilowatt load @ 1.09 each = 17.44		
		Avg. Hor. Fc	Avg./Min. Unif.	Max./Min. Unif.		Avg. Hor. Fc	Avg./Min. Unif.	Max./Min. Unif.		Avg. Hor. Fc	Avg./Min. Unif.	Max./Min. Unif.
Infield		20.74	1.45:1	2.06:1		22.04	1.27:1	2.05:1		21.04	1.36:1	1.76:1
Outfield		16.48	1.83:1	2.97:1		15.59	1.48:1	2.12:1		15.44	1.62:1	2.17:1

Layout D-2: Softball—200' Bobbie Sox Junior

Mounting Poles		Power Mate Floodlight End Pierced Optics 1500-watt Metal Halide				Power Drawer Sports Light Vertical Lamp Optics 1500-watt Metal Halide			Power Drawer Sports Light Horizontal Lamp Optics 1000-watt High Pressure Sodium		
		Catalog Number MS3194 MS3193 MS3192				Catalog Number FL3192 FL3191			Catalog Number FL6283 FL6282		
		Beam Spread				Beam Spread			Beam Spread		
Location	Minimum Height	3 × 3	5 × 5	6 × 6		4 × 4	6 × 7		5 × 3	6 × 7	
		Luminaires per Pole			Total	Luminaires per Pole		Total	Luminaires per Pole		Total
A1	35'	—	2	1	3	2	1	3	2	1	3
A2	35'	—	2	1	3	2	1	3	2	1	3
B1	35'	—	2	1	3	2	1	3	2	1	3
B2	35'	—	2	1	3	2	1	3	2	1	3
C1	50'	4	—	1	5	2	2	4	3	2	5
C2	50'	4	—	1	5	2	2	4	3	2	5
Totals		8	8	6	22	12	8	20	14	8	22
		Kilowatt load @ 1.61 each = 35.42				Kilowatt load @ 1.61 each = 32.2			Kilowatt load @ 1.09 each = 23.98		
		Avg. Hor. Fc	Avg./Min. Unif.	Max./Min. Unif.		Avg. Hor. Fc	Avg./Min. Unif.	Max./Min. Unif.	Avg. Hor. Fc	Avg./Min. Unif.	Max./Min. Unif.
Infield		30.01	1.34:1	1.92:1		31.15	1.56:1	2.59:1	31.74	1.47:1	1.87:1
Outfield		20.35	1.80:1	2.83:1		20.70	1.80:1	2.76:1	20.08	1.73:1	2.55:1

FOOT SPORTS

Today, football and soccer (European football) are the two major foot sports (Table 3) played in the United States and Canada. Because these sports involve both aerial and ground level play, they require adequate lighting from ground level to approximately 50' above ground level. Unlike base sports, the field dimensions for foot sports are more standardized, and the symmetrical shape of the playing field lends itself to good lighting. As with base sports, however, unique construction, land use, and spectator situations may alter the designs presented, especially at the higher levels of competition.

Table 3: Foot Sports Data

American Football

Class of Play	Class I	Class II	Class III	Class IV	Class V
Illumination Level*	**100 Fc**	**50 Fc**	**30 Fc**	**20 Fc**	**10 Fc**
Recommended Layouts					
Level of Competition					
Professional	1 to 14				
Semi-Pro Championship	1 to 14				
College	1 to 14	15 to 31			
Semi-Pro		15 to 31	32 to 41		
Junior College		15 to 31	32 to 41		
High School			32 to 41	42 to 51	52 to 56
Junior High School**				42 to 51	52 to 56
Flag, Touch, Recreational					57 to 61
Setback Distance (sideline to farthest row of spectators)	100'+	50' to 100'	30' to 50'	up to 30'	no fixed seating
Number of Spectators	30,000+	10,000 to 30,000	5,000 to 10,000	up to 5,000	—

European (Soccer) Football

Class of Play	Class I	Class II	Class III	Class IV	Class V
Illumination Level*	**100 Fc**	**50 Fc**	**30 Fc**	**20 Fc**	**10 Fc**
Recommended Layouts					
Level of Competition					
Professional	1 to 6				
College	1 to 6	1 to 6			
Junior College		1 to 6	7 to 14		
High School			7 to 14	15 to 19	
Junior High School **					20 to 24
Setback Distance (sideline to farthest row of spectators)	100'	75' to 100'	50' to 75'	30'	30'
Number of Spectators	30,000+	10,000 to 30,000	5,000 to 10,000	up to 5,000	—

* Uniformities: A maximum/minimum uniformity ratio of 3:1 within the playing area boundaries should not be exceeded. Illumination levels are measured in horizontal maintained footcandles at a theoretical plane 36" above the playing surface.

** Includes Junior High School, Junior All-American, Pop Warner, Vince Lombardi football leagues etc.

Note: Professional, Semi-Pro, and college level foot sports may require lighting for television broadcasting. Consult SPI Lighting for details and information.

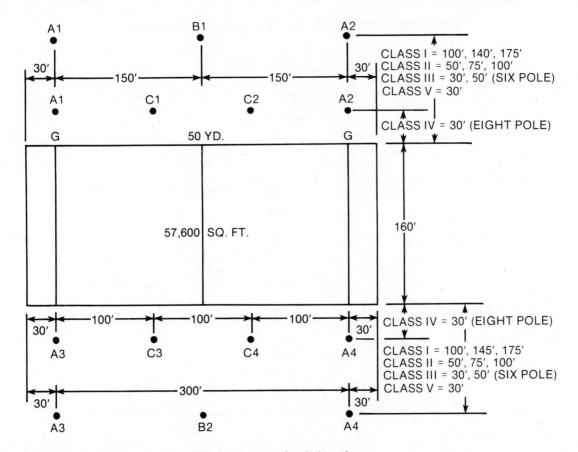

American Football: Competitive level field dimensions and pole locations.

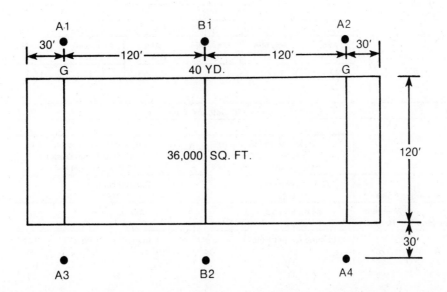

American Football: Recreational level (flag, touch, and Class V) field dimensions and pole locations.

SPORTS LIGHTING   167

AMERICAN FOOTBALL CLASS I: Layouts 1 through 6

Football Class I—175' Setback, Four Poles

		1		2	
		Power Mate Floodlight **End Pierced Optics** **1500-watt Metal Halide**		**Power Drawer Sports Light** **Vertical Lamp Optics** **1500-watt Metal Halide**	
Mounting Poles		**Catalog Number** **MS3195**		**Catalog Number** **FL3194**	
Location	**Minimum Height**	**Beam Spread** **2 × 2**		**Beam Spread** **1 × 3**	
		Luminaires per Pole	**Total**	**Luminaires per Pole**	**Total**
A1	140'	38	38	40	40
A2	140'	38	38	40	40
A3	140'	38	38	40	40
A4	140'	38	38	40	40
Totals		152	152	160	160
		Kilowatt load @ 1.61 each =	244.72	Kilowatt load @ 1.61 each =	257.6
		Avg. Hor. Fc	**Avg./Min. Unif.**	**Max./Min. Unif.**	**Avg. Hor. Fc**	**Avg./Min. Unif.**	**Max./Min. Unif.**
		101.58	1.93:1	2.36:1	99.96	1.32:1	1.49:1

Football Class I—175' Setback, Six Poles

		3		4	
		Power Mate Floodlight **End Pierced Optics** **1500-watt Metal Halide**		**Power Drawer Sports Light** **Vertical Lamp Optics** **1500-watt Metal Halide**	
Mounting Poles		**Catalog Number** **MS3195**		**Catalog Number** **FL3194**	
Location	**Minimum Height**	**Beam Spread** **2 × 2**		**Beam Spread** **1 × 3**	
		Luminaires per Pole	**Total**	**Luminaires per Pole**	**Total**
A1	130'	26	26	27	27
A2	130'	26	26	27	27
A3	130'	26	26	27	27
A4	130'	26	26	27	27
B1	130'	27	27	27	27
B2	130'	27	27	27	27
Totals		158	158	162	162
		Kilowatt load @ 1.61 each =	254.38	Kilowatt load @ 1.61 each =	260.82
		Avg. Hor. Fc	**Avg./Min. Unif.**	**Max./Min. Unif.**	**Avg. Hor. Fc**	**Avg./Min. Unif.**	**Max./Min. Unif.**
		99.96	1.77:1	2.15:1	100.58	1.34:1	1.50:1

Football Class I—140' Setback, Four Poles

		5		6	
		Power Mate Floodlight **End Pierced Optics** **1500-watt Metal Halide**		**Power Drawer Sports Light** **Vertical Lamp Optics** **1500-watt Metal Halide**	
Mounting Poles		**Catalog Number** **MS3192**		**Catalog Number** **FL3194**	
Location	**Minimum Height**	**Beam Spread** **2 × 2**		**Beam Spread** **1 × 3**	
		Luminaires per Pole	**Total**	**Luminaires per Pole**	**Total**
A1	120'	34	34	35	35
A2	120'	34	34	35	35
A3	120'	34	34	35	35
A4	120'	34	34	35	35
Totals		136	136	140	140
		Kilowatt load @ 1.61 each =	218.96	Kilowatt load @ 1.61 each =	225.40
		Avg. Hor. Fc	**Avg./Min. Unif.**	**Max./Min. Unif.**	**Avg. Hor. Fc**	**Avg./Min. Unif.**	**Max./Min. Unif.**
		99.50	2.26:1	2.89:1	100.18	1.34:1	1.52:1

AMERICAN FOOTBALL CLASS I: Layouts 7 through 14

Football Class I—140' Setback, Six Poles					
		7		**8**	
		Power Mate Floodlight End Pierced Optics 1500-watt Metal Halide		Power Drawer Sports Light Vertical Lamp Optics 1500-watt Metal Halide	
Mounting Poles		Catalog Number MS3195		Catalog Number FL3194	
	Minimum	Beam Spread 2 × 2		Beam Spread 1 × 3	
Location	Height	Luminaires per Pole	Total	Luminaires per Pole	Total
A1	110'	24	24	23	23
A2	110'	24	24	23	23
A3	110'	24	24	23	23
A4	110'	24	24	23	23
B1	110'	25	25	24	24
B2	110'	25	25	24	24
Totals		146	146	140	140
		Kilowatt load @ 1.61 each =	235.06	Kilowatt load @ 1.61 each =	225.40
		Avg. Hor. Fc	Avg./Min. Unif.	Max./Min. Unif.	Avg. Hor. Fc	Avg./Min. Unif.	Max./Min. Unif.
		100.68	1.95:1	2.55:1	100.09	1.45:1	1.71:1

Football Class I—100' Setback, Four Poles						
		9		**10**		**11**
		Power Mate Floodlight End Pierced Optics 1500-watt Metal Halide		Power Drawer Sports Light Vertical Lamp Optics 1500-watt Metal Halide		Power Drawer Sports Light Horizontal Lamp Optics 1000-watt High Pressure Sodium
Mounting Poles		Catalog Number MS3195		Catalog Number FL3194		Catalog Number FL6283
	Minimum	Beam Spread 2 × 2		Beam Spread 1 × 3		Beam Spread 5 × 3
Location	Height	Luminaires per Pole	Total	Luminaires per Pole	Total	Luminaires per Pole	Total
A1	100'	32	32	40	40	54	54
A2	100'	32	32	40	40	54	54
A3	100'	32	32	40	40	54	54
A4	100'	32	32	40	40	54	54
Totals		128	128	160	160	216	216
		Kilowatt load @ 1.61 each =	206.08	Kilowatt load @ 1.61 each =	257.60	Kilowatt load @ 1.09 each =	235.44
		Avg. Hor. Fc	Avg./Min. Unif.	Max./Min. Unif.	Avg. Hor. Fc	Avg./Min. Unif.	Max./Min. Unif.	Avg. Hor. Fc	Avg./Min. Unif.	Max./Min. Unif.
		100.13	2.00:1	2.91:1	102.20	1.56:1	1.84:1	100.23	1.75:1	2.08:1

Football Class I—100' Setback, Six Poles						
		12		**13**		**14**
		Power Mate Floodlight End Pierced Optics 1500-watt Metal Halide		Power Drawer Sports Light Vertical Lamp Optics 1500-watt Metal Halide		Power Drawer Sports Light Horizontal Lamp Optics 1000-watt High Pressure Sodium
Mounting Poles		Catalog Number MS3195		Catalog Number FL3194		Catalog Number FL6283
	Minimum	Beam Spread 2 × 2		Beam Spread 1 × 3		Beam Spread 5 × 3
Location	Height	Luminaires per Pole	Total	Luminaires per Pole	Total	Luminaires per Pole	Total
A1	90'	21	21	20	20	34	34
A2	90'	21	21	20	20	34	34
A3	90'	21	21	20	20	34	34
A4	90'	21	21	20	20	34	34
B1	90'	21	21	18	18	33	33
B2	90'	21	21	18	18	33	33
Totals		126	126	116	116	202	202
		Kilowatt load @ 1.61 each =	202.86	Kilowatt load @ 1.61 each =	186.76	Kilowatt load @ 1.09 each =	220.18
		Avg. Hor. Fc	Avg./Min. Unif.	Max./Min. Unif.	Avg. Hor. Fc	Avg./Min. Unif.	Max./Min. Unif.	Avg. Hor. Fc	Avg./Min. Unif.	Max./Min. Unif.
		100.88	1.68:1	2.45:1	99.92	1.54:1	1.90:1	100.65	1.62:1	1.95:1

AMERICAN FOOTBALL CLASS II: Layouts 15 through 23

Football Class II—100' Setback, Four Poles

		15		16		17	
		Power Mate Floodlight **End Pierced Optics** **1500-watt Metal Halide**		**Power Drawer Sports Light** **Vertical Lamp Optics** **1500-watt Metal Halide**		**Power Drawer Sports Light** **Horizontal Lamp Optics** **1000-watt High Pressure Sodium**	
Mounting Poles		**Catalog Number** **MS3195**		**Catalog Number** **FL3194**		**Catalog Number** **FL6283**	
Location	Minimum Height	**Beam Spread** **2 × 2**		**Beam Spread** **1 × 3**		**Beam Spread** **5 × 3**	
		Luminaires per Pole	Total	Luminaires per Pole	Total	Luminaires per Pole	Total
A1	90'	16	16	15	15	27	27
A2	90'	16	16	15	15	27	27
A3	90'	16	16	15	15	27	27
A4	90'	16	16	15	15	27	27
Totals		64	64	60	60	108	108
		Kilowatt load @ 1.61 each = 103.04		Kilowatt load @ 1.61 each = 96.60		Kilowatt load @ 1.09 each = 117.72	
		Avg. Hor. Fc	**Avg./Min. Unif.** **Max./Min. Unif.**	**Avg. Hor. Fc**	**Avg./Min. Unif.** **Max./Min. Unif.**	**Avg. Hor. Fc**	**Avg./Min. Unif.** **Max./Min. Unif.**
		50.86	1.72:1 2.62:1	51.10	1.56:1 1.84:1	50.12	1.75:1 2.08:1

Football Class II—100' Setback, Six Poles

		18		19		20	
		Power Mate Floodlight **End Pierced Optics** **1500-watt Metal Halide**		**Power Drawer Sports Light** **Vertical Lamp Optics** **1500-watt Metal Halide**		**Power Drawer Sports Light** **Horizontal Lamp Optics** **1000-watt Metal Halide**	
Mounting Poles		**Catalog Number** **MS3195**		**Catalog Number** **FL3194**		**Catalog Number** **FL6283**	
Location	Minimum Height	**Beam Spread** **2 × 2**		**Beam Spread** **1 × 3**		**Beam Spread** **5 × 3**	
		Luminaires per Pole	Total	Luminaires per Pole	Total	Luminaires per Pole	Total
A1	90'	10	10	10	10	17	17
A2	90'	10	10	10	10	17	17
A3	90'	10	10	10	10	17	17
A4	90'	10	10	10	10	17	17
B1	90'	11	11	9	9	16	16
B2	90'	11	11	9	9	16	16
Totals		62	62	58	58	100	100
		Kilowatt load @ 1.61 each = 99.82		Kilowatt load @ 1.61 each = 93.38		Kilowatt load @ 1.09 each = 109.00	
		Avg. Hor. Fc	**Avg./Min. Unif.** **Max./Min. Unif.**	**Avg. Hor. Fc**	**Avg./Min. Unif.** **Max./Min. Unif.**	**Avg. Hor. Fc**	**Avg./Min. Unif.** **Max./Min. Unif.**
		49.92	1.84:1 2.60:1	49.81	1.40:1 1.65:1	49.69	1.60:1 1.92:1

Football Class II—75' Setback, Four Poles

		21			22			23	
		Power Mate Floodlight **End Pierced Optics** **1500-watt Metal Halide**			**Power Drawer Sports Light** **Vertical Lamp Optics** **1500-watt Metal Halide**			**Power Drawer Sports Light** **Horizontal Lamp Optics** **1000-watt High Pressure Sodium**	
Mounting Poles		**Catalog Number** MS3195 MS3194			**Catalog Number** FL3194 FL3193			**Catalog Number** FL6283	
Location	Minimum Height	**Beam Spread** 2 × 2 3 × 3			**Beam Spread** 1 × 3 3 × 3			**Beam Spread** 5 × 7	
		Luminaires per Pole		Total	Luminaires per Pole		Total	Luminaires per Pole	Total
A1	85'	5	12	17	4	10	14	24	24
A2	85'	5	12	17	4	10	14	24	24
A3	85'	5	12	17	4	10	14	24	24
A4	85'	5	12	17	4	10	14	24	24
Totals		20	48	68	16	40	56	96	96
		Kilowatt load @ 1.61 each = 109.48			Kilowatt load @ 1.61 each = 90.16			Kilowatt load @ 1.09 each = 104.64	
		Avg. Hor. Fc	**Avg./Min. Unif.**	**Max./Min. Unif.**	**Avg. Hor. Fc**	**Avg./Min. Unif.**	**Max./Min. Unif.**	**Avg. Hor. Fc**	**Avg./Min. Unif.** **Max./Min. Unif.**
		50.74	1.93:1	2.47:1	50.38	1.75:1	2.28:1	50.49	1.56:1 1.93:1

AMERICAN FOOTBALL CLASS II: Layouts 24 through 31

Football Class II—75' Setback, Six Poles

		24		25		26	
		Power Mate Floodlight **End Pierced Optics** **1500-watt Metal Halide**		**Power Drawer Sports Light** **Vertical Lamp Optics** **1500-watt Metal Halide**		**Power Drawer Sports Light** **Horizontal Lamp Optics** **1000-watt High Pressure Sodium**	
Mounting Poles		**Catalog Number** **MS3194**		**Catalog Number** **FL3193**		**Catalog Number** **FL6283**	
Location	Minimum Height	**Beam Spread** 3 × 3		**Beam Spread** 3 × 3		**Beam Spread** 5 × 3	
		Luminaires per Pole	Total	Luminaires per Pole	Total	Luminaires per Pole	Total
A1	75'	11	11	9	9	15	15
A2	75'	11	11	9	9	15	15
A3	75'	11	11	9	9	15	15
A4	75'	11	11	9	9	15	15
B1	75'	11	11	10	10	14	14
B2	75'	11	11	10	10	14	14
Totals		66	66	56	56	88	88
		Kilowatt load @ 1.61 each =	106.26	Kilowatt load @ 1.61 each =	90.16	Kilowatt load @ 1.09 each =	95.92
		Avg. Hor. Fc	Avg./Min. Unif.	Max./Min. Unif.	Avg. Hor. Fc	Avg./Min. Unif.	Max./Min. Unif.

Avg. Hor. Fc	Avg./Min. Unif.	Max./Min. Unif.	Avg. Hor. Fc	Avg./Min. Unif.	Max./Min. Unif.	Avg. Hor. Fc	Avg./Min. Unif.	Max./Min. Unif.
49.76	1.70:1	2.18:1	49.91	1.62:1	1.92:1	49.83	1.82:1	2.27:1

Football Class II—50' Setback, Six Poles

		27		28		29	
		Power Mate Floodlight **End Pierced Optics** **1500-watt Metal Halide**		**Power Drawer Sports Light** **Vertical Lamp Optics** **1500-watt Metal Halide**		**Power Drawer Sports Light** **Horizontal Lamp Optics** **1000-watt High Pressure Sodium**	
Mounting Poles		**Catalog Number** **MS3194**		**Catalog Number** **FL3193**		**Catalog Number** **FL6283**	
Location	Minimum Height	**Beam Spread** 3 × 3		**Beam Spread** 3 × 3		**Beam Spread** 5 × 3	
		Luminaires per Pole	Total	Luminaires per Pole	Total	Luminaires per Pole	Total
A1	60'	12	12	9	9	13	13
A2	60'	12	12	9	9	13	13
A3	60'	12	12	9	9	13	13
A4	60'	12	12	9	9	13	13
B1	60'	11	11	8	8	13	13
B2	60'	11	11	8	8	13	13
Totals		70	70	52	52	78	78
		Kilowatt load @ 1.61 each =	112.70	Kilowatt load @ 1.61 each =	83.72	Kilowatt load @ 1.09 each =	85.02

Avg. Hor. Fc	Avg./Min. Unif.	Max./Min. Unif.	Avg. Hor. Fc	Avg./Min. Unif.	Max./Min. Unif.	Avg. Hor. Fc	Avg./Min. Unif.	Max./Min. Unif.
50.16	2.06:1	2.65:1	51.53	1.79:1	2.27:1	50.21	1.74:1	2.33:1

Football Class II—50' Setback, Six Poles

		30		31	
		Power Drawer Cutoff Site Light **Horizontal Lamp Sharp Cutoff** **1500-watt Metal Halide**		**Power Drawer Cutoff Site Light** **Horizontal Lamp Sharp Cutoff** **1500-watt Metal Halide**	
Mounting Poles		**Catalog Number** **FL3198**		**Catalog Number** **FL3288**	
Location	Minimum Height	**Beam Spread** 6 × 5		**Beam Spread** 6 × 5	
		Luminaires per Pole	Total	Luminaires per Pole	Total
A1	55'	13	13	12	12
A2	55'	13	13	12	12
A3	55'	13	13	12	12
A4	55'	13	13	12	12
B1	55'	13	13	12	12
B2	55'	13	13	12	12
Totals		78	78	72	72
		Kilowatt load @ 1.61 each =	125.58	Kilowatt load @ 1.09 each =	78.48

Avg. Hor. Fc	Avg./Min. Unif.	Max./Min. Unif.	Avg. Hor. Fc	Avg./Min. Unif.	Max./Min. Unif.
49.60	1.56:1	2.16:1	49.94	1.61:1	2.18:1

AMERICAN FOOTBALL CLASS III: Layouts 32 through 39

Football Class III—50' Setback, Six Poles

		32		33		34	
		Power Mate Floodlight **End Pierced Optics** **1500-watt Metal Halide**		**Power Drawer Sports Light** **Vertical Lamp Optics** **1500-watt Metal Halide**		**Power Drawer Sports Light** **Horizontal Lamp Optics** **1000-watt High Pressure Sodium**	
Mounting Poles		Catalog Number MS3194		Catalog Number FL3193		Catalog Number FL6283	
Location	Minimum Height	Beam Spread 3 × 3		Beam Spread 3 × 3		Beam Spread 5 × 3	
		Luminaires per Pole	Total	Luminaires per Pole	Total	Luminaires per Pole	Total
A1	60'	7	7	5	5	8	8
A2	60'	7	7	5	5	8	8
A3	60'	7	7	5	5	8	8
A4	60'	7	7	5	5	8	8
B1	60'	7	7	6	6	8	8
B2	60'	7	7	6	6	8	8
Totals		42	42	32	32	48	48
		Kilowatt load @ 1.61 each =	67.62	Kilowatt load @ 1.61 each =	51.52	Kilowatt load @ 1.09 each =	52.32
		Avg. Hor. Fc	Avg./Min. Unif.	Max./Min. Unif.	Avg. Hor. Fc	Avg./Min. Unif.	Max./Min. Unif.

Avg. Hor. Fc	Avg./Min. Unif.	Max./Min. Unif.	Avg. Hor. Fc	Avg./Min. Unif.	Max./Min. Unif.	Avg. Hor. Fc	Avg./Min. Unif.	Max./Min. Unif.
30.32	2.06:1	2.85:1	31.81	1.77:1	2.34:1	30.91	1.74:1	2.29:1

Football Class III—50' Setback, Six Poles (Continued)

		35		36	
		Power Drawer Cutoff Site Light **Horizontal Lamp Sharp Cutoff** **1500-watt Metal Halide**		**Power Drawer Cutoff Site Light** **Horizontal Lamp Sharp Cutoff** **1000-watt High Pressure Sodium**	
Mounting Poles		Catalog Number FL3198		Catalog Number FL3288	
Location	Minimum Height	Beam Spread 6 × 5		Beam Spread 6 × 5	
		Luminaires per Pole	Total	Luminaires per Pole	Total
A1	55'	8	8	7	7
A2	55'	8	8	7	7
A3	55'	8	8	7	7
A4	55'	8	8	7	7
B1	55'	8	8	8	8
B2	55'	8	8	8	8
Totals		48	48	44	44
		Kilowatt load @ 1.61 each =	77.28	Kilowatt load @ 1.09 each =	47.96

Avg. Hor. Fc	Avg./Min. Unif.	Max./Min. Unif.	Avg. Hor. Fc	Avg./Min. Unif.	Max./Min. Unif.
30.60	1.58:1	2.16:1	30.52	1.61:1	2.28:1

Football Class III—30' Setback, Six Poles

		37				38			39	
		Power Mate Floodlight **End Pierced Optics** **1500-watt Metal Halide**				**Power Drawer Sports Light** **Vertical Lamp Optics** **1500-watt Metal Halide**			**Power Drawer Sports Light** **Horizontal Lamp Optics** **1000-watt High Pressure Sodium**	
Mounting Poles		Catalog Number MS3194 MS3193 MS3192				Catalog Number FL3193 FL3192			Catalog Number FL6283	
Location	Minimum Height	Beam Spread 3 × 3	5 × 5	6 × 6	Total	Beam Spread 3 × 3	4 × 4	Total	Beam Spread 5 × 3	Total
		Luminaires per Pole			Total	Luminaires per Pole		Total	Luminaires per Pole	Total
A1	50'	5	1	1	7	3	2	5	7	7
A2	50'	5	1	1	7	3	2	5	7	7
A3	50'	5	1	1	7	3	2	5	7	7
A4	50'	5	1	1	7	3	2	5	7	7
B1	50'	4	—	2	6	4	1	5	7	7
B2	50'	4	—	2	6	4	1	5	7	7
Totals		28	4	8	40	20	10	30	42	42
		Kilowatt load @ 1.61 each =			64.4	Kilowatt load @ 1.61 each =		48.30	Kilowatt load @ 1.09 each =	45.78

Avg. Hor. Fc	Avg./Min. Unif.	Max./Min. Unif.	Avg. Hor. Fc	Avg./Min. Unif.	Max./Min. Unif.	Avg. Hor. Fc	Avg./Min. Unif.	Max./Min. Unif.
29.73	1.71:1	2.42:1	30.43	2.14:1	2.98:1	30.57	1.75:1	2.26:1

AMERICAN FOOTBALL CLASSES III and IV: Layouts 40 through 46

Football Class III—30' Setback, Six Poles (Continued)

		40		41	
		Power Drawer Cutoff Site Light Horizontal Lamp Sharp Cutoff 1500-watt Metal Halide		**Power Drawer Cutoff Site Light** Horizontal Lamp Sharp Cutoff 1000-watt High Pressure Sodium	
Mounting Poles		Catalog Number FL3198		Catalog Number FL3288	
		Beam Spread 6 × 5		Beam Spread 6 × 5	
Location	Minimum Height	Luminaires per Pole	Total	Luminaires per Pole	Total
A1	45'	7	7	6	6
A2	45'	7	7	6	6
A3	45'	7	7	6	6
A4	45'	7	7	6	6
B1	45'	6	6	6	6
B2	45'	6	6	6	6
Totals		40	40	36	36
		Kilowatt load @ 1.61 each =	64.40	Kilowatt load @ 1.09 each =	39.24
		Avg. Hor. Fc	Avg./Min. Unif.	Max./Min. Unif.	Avg. Hor. Fc	Avg./Min. Unif.	Max./Min. Unif.
		29.87	1.58:1	2.50:1	29.61	1.54:1	2.44:1

Football Class IV—30' Setback, Six Poles

		42			43		44	
		Power Mate Floodlight End Pierced Optics 1500-watt Metal Halide			**Power Drawer Sports Light** Vertical Lamp Optics 1500-watt Metal Halide		**Power Drawer Sports Light** Horizontal Lamp Optics 1000-watt High Pressure Sodium	
Mounting Poles		Catalog Number MS3193 MS3192			Catalog Number FL3192		Catalog Number FL6283	
		Beam Spread 5 × 5 6 × 6			Beam Spread 4 × 4		Beam Spread 5 × 3	
Location	Minimum Height	Luminaires per Pole		Total	Luminaires per Pole	Total	Luminaires per Pole	Total
A1	50'	2	3	5	4	4	5	5
A2	50'	2	3	5	4	4	5	5
A3	50'	2	3	5	4	4	5	5
A4	50'	2	3	5	4	4	5	5
B1	50'	2	3	5	4	4	4	4
B2	50'	2	3	5	4	4	4	4
Totals		12	18	30	24	24	28	28
		Kilowatt load @ 1.61 each =		48.30	Kilowatt load @ 1.61 each =	38.64	Kilowatt load @ 1.09 each =	30.52
		Avg. Hor. Fc	Avg./Min. Unif.	Max./Min. Unif.	Avg. Hor. Fc	Avg./Min. Unif.	Max./Min. Unif.	Avg. Hor. Fc	Avg./Min. Unif.	Max./Min. Unif.
		19.60	1.39:1	2.46:1	20.41	1.71:1	2.37:1	20.31	1.67:1	2.15:1

Football Class IV—30' Setback, Six Poles (Continued)

		45		46	
		Power Drawer Cutoff Site Light Horizontal Lamp Sharp Cutoff 1500-watt Metal Halide		**Power Drawer Cutoff Site Light** Horizontal Lamp Sharp Cutoff 1000-watt High Pressure Sodium	
Mounting Poles		Catalog Number FL3198		Catalog Number FL3288	
		Beam Spread 6 × 5		Beam Spread 6 × 5	
Location	Minimum Height	Luminaires per Pole	Total	Luminaires per Pole	Total
A1	45'	4	4	4	4
A2	45'	4	4	4	4
A3	45'	4	4	4	4
A4	45'	4	4	4	4
B1	45'	5	5	4	4
B2	45'	5	5	4	4
Totals		26	26	24	24
		Kilowatt load @ 1.61 each =	41.86	Kilowatt load @ 1.09 each =	26.16
		Avg. Hor. Fc	Avg./Min. Unif.	Max./Min. Unif.	Avg. Hor. Fc	Avg./Min. Unif.	Max./Min. Unif.
		19.92	1.65:1	2.87:1	19.92	1.64:1	2.64:1

AMERICAN FOOTBALL CLASSES IV and V: Layouts 47 through 54

Football Class IV—30' Setback, Eight Poles

Mounting Poles		47			48		49	
		Power Mate Floodlight End Pierced Optics 1500-watt Metal Halide			Power Drawer Sports Light Vertical Lamp Optics 1500-watt Metal Halide		Power Drawer Sports Light Horizontal Lamp Optics 1000-watt High Pressure Sodium	
		Catalog Number MS3192 MS3193			Catalog Number FL6192		Catalog Number FL6283	
	Minimum	Beam Spread			Beam Spread		Beam Spread	
Location	Height	6 × 6	5 × 5		5 × 5		5 × 3	
		Luminaires per Pole		Total	Luminaires per Pole	Total	Luminaires per Pole	Total
A1	50'	3	1	4	3	3	4	4
A2	50'	3	1	4	3	3	4	4
A3	50'	3	1	4	3	3	4	4
A4	50'	3	1	4	3	3	4	4
C1	50'	3	—	3	3	3	3	3
C2	50'	3	—	3	3	3	3	3
C3	50'	3	—	3	3	3	3	3
C4	50'	3	—	3	3	3	3	3
Totals		24	4	28	24	24	28	28
		Kilowatt load @ 1.61 each = 45.08			Kilowatt load @ 1.61 each = 38.64		Kilowatt load @ 1.09 each = 30.52	
		Avg. Hor. Fc	Avg./Min. Unif.	Max./Min. Unif.	Avg. Hor. Fc / Avg./Min. Unif. / Max./Min. Unif.		Avg. Hor. Fc / Avg./Min. Unif. / Max./Min. Unif.	
		19.56	1.44:1	2.47:1	20.91 1.47:1 1.90:1		21.08 1.78:1 2.51:1	

Football Class IV—30' Setback, Eight Poles (Continued)

Mounting Poles		50		51	
		Power Drawer Cutoff Site Light Horizontal Lamp Sharp Cutoff 1500-watt Metal Halide		Power Drawer Cutoff Site Light Horizontal Lamp Sharp Cutoff 1000-watt High Pressure Sodium	
		Catalog Number FL3198		Catalog Number FL3288	
	Minimum	Beam Spread 6 × 5		Beam Spread 6 × 5	
Location	Height	Luminaires per Pole	Total	Luminaires per Pole	Total
A1	45'	3	3	3	3
A2	45'	3	3	3	3
A3	45'	3	3	3	3
A4	45'	3	3	3	3
C1	45'	3	3	3	3
C2	45'	3	3	3	3
C3	45'	3	3	3	3
C4	45'	3	3	3	3
Totals		24	24	24	24
		Kilowatt load @ 1.61 each = 38.64		Kilowatt load @ 1.09 each = 26.16	
		Avg. Hor. Fc	Avg./Min. Unif.	Max./Min. Unif.	Avg. Hor. Fc / Avg./Min. Unif. / Max./Min. Unif.
		19.56 1.47:1 1.92:1		20.97 1.55:1 2.11:1	

Football Class V—30' Setback, Six Poles

Mounting Poles		52			53		54	
		Power Mate Floodlight End Pierced Optics 1500-watt Metal Halide			Power Drawer Sports Light Vertical Lamp Optics 1500-watt Metal Halide		Power Drawer Sports Light Horizontal Lamp Optics 1000-watt High Pressure Sodium	
		Catalog Number MS3192 MS3193			Catalog Number FL3192		Catalog Number FL6283	
	Minimum	Beam Spread			Beam Spread		Beam Spread	
Location	Height	6 × 6	5 × 5		4 × 4		5 × 3	
		Luminaires per Pole		Total	Luminaires per Pole	Total	Luminaires per Pole	Total
A1	50'	2	1	3	2	2	2	2
A2	50'	2	1	3	2	2	2	2
A3	50'	2	1	3	2	2	2	2
A4	50'	2	1	3	2	2	2	2
B1	50'	—	2	2	2	2	2	2
B2	50'	—	2	2	2	2	2	2
Totals		8	8	16	12	12	12	12
		Kilowatt load @ 1.61 each = 25.76			Kilowatt load @ 1.61 each = 19.32		Kilowatt load @ 1.09 each = 13.08	
		Avg. Hor. Fc	Avg./Min. Unif.	Max./Min. Unif.	Avg. Hor. Fc / Avg./Min. Unif. / Max./Min. Unif.		Avg. Hor. Fc / Avg./Min. Unif. / Max./Min. Unif.	
		10.67	1.45:1	2.49:1	10.02 1.72:1 2.78:1		9.52 1.59:1 2.83:1	

AMERICAN FOOTBALL CLASS V: Layouts 55 through 61

Football Class V—30' Setback, Six Poles (Continued)

Mounting Poles		55			56		
		Power Drawer Cutoff Site Light Horizontal Lamp Sharp Cutoff 1500-watt Metal Halide			Power Drawer Cutoff Site Light Horizontal Lamp Sharp Cutoff 1000-watt High Pressure Sodium		
		Catalog Number FL3198			Catalog Number FL3288		
		Beam Spread 6 × 5			Beam Spread 6 × 5		
Location	Minimum Height	Luminaires per Pole	Total		Luminaires per Pole	Total	
A1	45'	2	2		2	2	
A2	45'	2	2		2	2	
A3	45'	2	2		2	2	
A4	45'	2	2		2	2	
B1	45'	2	2		2	2	
B2	45'	2	2		2	2	
Totals		12	12		12	12	
		Kilowatt load @ 1.61 each =	19.32		Kilowatt load @ 1.09 each =	13.08	
		Avg. Hor. Fc	Avg./Min. Unif.	Max./Min. Unif.	Avg. Hor. Fc	Avg./Min. Unif.	Max./Min. Unif.
		9.62	1.81:1	2.79:1	10.21	1.66:1	2.69:1

Football Class V Junior—30' Setback, Six Poles

Mounting Poles		57			58		59		
		Power Mate Floodlight End Pierced Optics 1500-watt Metal Halide			Power Drawer Sports Light Horizontal Lamp Optics 1000-watt Metal Halide		Power Drawer Sports Light Vertical Lamp Optics 400-watt High Pressure Sodium		
		Catalog Number MS3192 MS3193			Catalog Number FL6182		Catalog Number FL2262 FL2263		
		Beam Spread 6 × 6	5 × 5		Beam Spread 5 × 5		Beam Spread 6 × 5	3 × 4	
Location	Minimum Height	Luminaires per Pole		Total	Luminaires per Pole	Total	Luminaires per Pole		Total
A1	40'	1	1	2	2	2	2	2	4
A2	40'	1	1	2	2	2	2	2	4
A3	40'	1	1	2	2	2	2	2	4
A4	40'	1	1	2	2	2	2	2	4
B1	40'	2	—	2	2	2	2	2	4
B2	40'	2	—	2	2	2	2	2	4
Totals		8	4	12	12	12	12	12	24
		Kilowatt load @ 1.61 each =		19.32	Kilowatt load @ 1.08 each =	12.96	Kilowatt load @ .465 each =		11.16
		Avg. Hor. Fc	Avg./Min. Unif.	Max./Min. Unif.	Avg. Hor. Fc	Avg./Min. Unif.	Max./Min. Unif.	Avg. Hor. Fc	Avg./Min. Unif.	Max./Min. Unif.
		10.39	1.59:1	2.76:1	10.06	1.84:1	2.46:1	9.70	1.65:1	2.82:1

Football Class V Junior—30' Setback, Six Poles (Continued)

Mounting Poles		60			61		
		Power Drawer Cutoff Site Light Horizontal Lamp Sharp Cutoff 1000-watt Metal Halide			Power Drawer Cutoff Site Light Horizontal Lamp Sharp Cutoff 400-watt High Pressure Sodium		
		Catalog Number FL3188			Catalog Number FL2268		
		Beam Spread 6 × 5			Beam Spread 5 × 5		
Location	Minimum Height	Luminaires per Pole	Total		Luminaires per Pole	Total	
A1	35'	2	2		4	4	
A2	35'	2	2		4	4	
A3	35'	2	2		4	4	
A4	35'	2	2		4	4	
B1	35'	2	2		4	4	
B2	35'	2	2		4	4	
Totals		12	12		24	24	
		Kilowatt load @ 1.08 each =	12.96		Kilowatt load @ .465 each =	11.16	
		Avg. Hor. Fc	Avg./Min. Unif.	Max./Min. Unif.	Avg. Hor. Fc	Avg./Min. Unif.	Max./Min. Unif.
		10.03	1.63:1	2.71:1	9.85	1.74:1	2.83:1

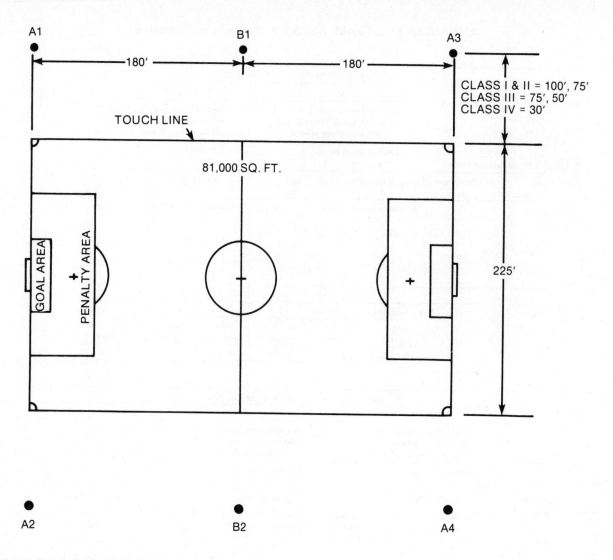

European Football (Soccer): Field layout and pole locations.

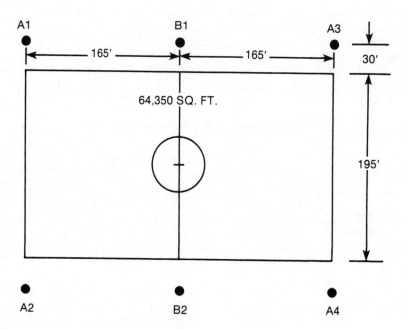

Junior or Youth Soccer: Field layout and pole locations.

EUROPEAN FOOTBALL CLASSES I, II, and III: Layouts 1 through 9

European Football (Soccer) Class I (see note) and Class II—100' Setback, Six Poles

		1		2		3	
		Power Mate Floodlight End Pierced Optics 1500-watt Metal Halide		Power Drawer Sports Light Vertical Lamp Optics 1500-watt Metal Halide		Power Drawer Sports Light Horizontal Lamp Optics 1000-watt High Pressure Sodium	
Mounting Poles		Catalog Number MS3195		Catalog Number FL3194		Catalog Number FL6283	
	Minimum	Beam Spread 2 × 2		Beam Spread 1 × 3		Beam Spread 5 × 3	
Location	Height	Luminaires per Pole	Total	Luminaires per Pole	Total	Luminaires per Pole	Total
A1	100'	16	16	13	13	22	22
A2	100'	16	16	13	13	22	22
A3	100'	16	16	13	13	22	22
A4	100'	16	16	13	13	22	22
B1	100'	16	16	13	13	23	23
B2	100'	16	16	13	13	23	23
Totals		96	96	78	78	134	134
		Kilowatt load @ 1.61 each = 154.56		Kilowatt load @ 1.61 each = 125.58		Kilowatt load @ 1.09 each = 146.06	
		Avg. Hor. Fc	Avg./Min. Unif.	Max./Min. Unif.	Avg. Hor. Fc	Avg./Min. Unif.	Max./Min. Unif.
		50.37	1.86:1	2.72:1	50.30	1.49:1	1.86:1

(Layout 3 footcandle values: Avg. Hor. Fc 50.27, Avg./Min. Unif. 1.73:1, Max./Min. Unif. 2.06:1)

Note: For Class I play, use same pole locations and double all floodlight quantities.

European Football (Soccer) Class I (see note) and Class II—75' Setback, Six Poles

		4			5		6	
		Power Mate Floodlight End Pierced Optics 1500-watt Metal Halide			Power Drawer Sports Light Vertical Lamp Optics 1500-watt Metal Halide		Power Drawer Sports Light Horizontal Lamp Optics 1000-watt High Pressure Sodium	
Mounting Poles		Catalog Number MS3194 MS3195			Catalog Number FL3194		Catalog Number FL6283	
	Minimum	Beam Spread 3 × 3	2 × 2		Beam Spread 1 × 3		Beam Spread 5 × 3	
Location	Height	Luminaires per Pole		Total	Luminaires per Pole	Total	Luminaires per Pole	Total
A1	90'	7	8	15	12	12	20	20
A2	90'	7	8	15	12	12	20	20
A3	90'	7	8	15	12	12	20	20
A4	90'	7	8	15	12	12	20	20
B1	90'	8	9	17	11	11	20	20
B2	90'	8	9	17	11	11	20	20
Totals		44	50	94	70	70	120	120
		Kilowatt load @ 1.61 each = 151.34			Kilowatt load @ 1.61 each = 112.70		Kilowatt load @ 1.09 each = 130.80	
		Avg. Hor. Fc	Avg./Min. Unif.	Max./Min. Unif.	Avg. Hor. Fc	Avg./Min. Unif.	Max./Min. Unif.
		50.47	1.85:1	2.72:1	50.36	2.08:1	2.75:1

(Layout 6 footcandle values: Avg. Hor. Fc 50.17, Avg./Min. Unif. 1.78:1, Max./Min. Unif. 2.18:1)

Note: For Class I play, use same pole locations and double all floodlight quantities.

European Football (Soccer) Class III—75' Setback, Six Poles

		7		8		9	
		Power Mate Floodlight End Pierced Optics 1500-watt Metal Halide		Power Drawer Sports Light Vertical Lamp Optics 1500-watt Metal Halide		Power Drawer Sports Light Horizontal Lamp Optics 1000-watt High Pressure Sodium	
Mounting Poles		Catalog Number MS3194		Catalog Number FL3194		Catalog Number FL6283	
	Minimum	Beam Spread 3 × 3		Beam Spread 1 × 3		Beam Spread 5 × 3	
Location	Height	Luminaires per Pole	Total	Luminaires per Pole	Total	Luminaires per Pole	Total
A1	90'	9	9	7	7	12	12
A2	90'	9	9	7	7	12	12
A3	90'	9	9	7	7	12	12
A4	90'	9	9	7	7	12	12
B1	90'	10	10	7	7	12	12
B2	90'	10	10	7	7	12	12
Totals		56	56	42	42	72	72
		Kilowatt load @ 1.61 each = 90.16		Kilowatt load @ 1.61 each = 67.62		Kilowatt load @ 1.09 each = 78.48	
		Avg. Hor. Fc	Avg./Min. Unif.	Max./Min. Unif.	Avg. Hor. Fc	Avg./Min. Unif.	Max./Min. Unif.
		31.50	1.56:1	2.10:1	30.65	1.84:1	2.55:1

(Layout 9 footcandle values: Avg. Hor. Fc 30.13, Avg./Min. Unif. 1.79:1, Max./Min. Unif. 2.18:1)

EUROPEAN FOOTBALL CLASSES III and IV: Layouts 10 through 17

European Football (Soccer) Class III—50' Setback, Six Poles

		10			11		12	
		Power Mate Floodlight End Pierced Optics 1500-watt Metal Halide			Power Drawer Sports Light Vertical Lamp Optics 1500-watt Metal Halide		Power Drawer Sports Light Horizontal Lamp Optics 1000-watt High Pressure Sodium	
Mounting Poles		Catalog Number MS3194 MS3193			Catalog Number FL3193		Catalog Number FL6283	
		Beam Spread			Beam Spread 3 × 3		Beam Spread 5 × 3	
Location	Minimum Height	3 × 3	5 × 5					
		Luminaires per Pole		Total	Luminaires per Pole	Total	Luminaires per Pole	Total
A1	75'	6	4	10	7	7	11	11
A2	75'	6	4	10	7	7	11	11
A3	75'	6	4	10	7	7	11	11
A4	75'	6	4	10	7	7	11	11
B1	75'	5	4	9	6	6	10	10
B2	75'	5	4	9	6	6	10	10
Totals		34	24	58	40	40	64	64
		Kilowatt load @ 1.61 each = 93.38			Kilowatt load @ 1.61 each = 64.40		Kilowatt load @ 1.09 each = 69.76	

Avg. Hor. Fc	Avg./Min. Unif.	Max./Min. Unif.	Avg. Hor. Fc	Avg./Min. Unif.	Max./Min. Unif.	Avg. Hor. Fc	Avg./Min. Unif.	Max./Min. Unif.
29.50	1.71:1	2.28:1	30.03	1.60:1	2.03:1	30.11	1.54:1	1.94:1

European Football (Soccer) Class III—50' Setback, Six Poles (Continued)

		13		14	
		Power Drawer Cutoff Site Light Horizontal Lamp Sharp Cutoff 1500-watt Metal Halide		Power Drawer Cutoff Site Light Horizontal Lamp Sharp Cutoff 1000-watt High Pressure Sodium	
Mounting Poles		Catalog Number FC3198		Catalog Number FC3288	
		Beam Spread 6 × 5		Beam Spread 6 × 5	
Location	Minimum Height	Luminaires per Pole	Total	Luminaires per Pole	Total
A1	70'	11	11	10	10
A2	70'	11	11	10	10
A3	70'	11	11	10	10
A4	70'	11	11	10	10
B1	70'	11	11	10	10
B2	70'	11	11	10	10
Totals		66	66	60	60
		Kilowatt load @ 1.61 each = 106.26		Kilowatt load @ 1.09 each = 65.40	

Avg. Hor. Fc	Avg./Min. Unif.	Max./Min. Unif.	Avg. Hor. Fc	Avg./Min. Unif.	Max./Min. Unif.
30.30	1.34:1	1.75:1	30.31	1.25:1	1.62:1

European Football (Soccer) Class IV—30' Setback, Six Poles

		15			16		17	
		Power Mate Floodlight End Pierced Optics 1500-watt Metal Halide			Power Drawer Sports Light Vertical Lamp Optics 1500-watt Metal Halide		Power Drawer Sports Light Horizontal Lamp Optics 1000-watt High Pressure Sodium	
Mounting Poles		Catalog Number MS3192 MS3193			Catalog Number FL3192		Catalog Number FL6283	
		Beam Spread			Beam Spread 4 × 4		Beam Spread 5 × 3	
Location	Minimum Height	6 × 6	5 × 5					
		Luminaires per Pole		Total	Luminaires per Pole	Total	Luminaires per Pole	Total
A1	60'	3	4	7	5	5	7	7
A2	60'	3	4	7	5	5	7	7
A3	60'	3	4	7	5	5	7	7
A4	60'	3	4	7	5	5	7	7
B1	60'	3	4	7	6	6	6	6
B2	60'	3	4	7	6	6	6	6
Totals		18	24	42	32	32	40	40
		Kilowatt load @ 1.61 each = 67.62			Kilowatt load @ 1.61 each = 51.52		Kilowatt load @ 1.09 each = 43.60	

Avg. Hor. Fc	Avg./Min. Unif.	Max./Min. Unif.	Avg. Hor. Fc	Avg./Min. Unif.	Max./Min. Unif.	Avg. Hor. Fc	Avg./Min. Unif.	Max./Min. Unif.
20.30	1.57:1	2.69:1	19.88	1.76:1	2.41:1	20.02	1.41:1	1.80:1

EUROPEAN FOOTBALL CLASSES IV and V: Layouts 18 through 24

European Football (Soccer) Class IV—30' Setback, Six Poles (Continued)

		18		19	
		Power Drawer Cutoff Site Light Horizontal Lamp Sharp Cutoff 1500-watt Metal Halide		Power Drawer Cutoff Site Light Horizontal Lamp Sharp Cutoff 1000-watt High Pressure Sodium	
Mounting Poles		Catalog Number FC3198		Catalog Number FC3288	
		Beam Spread 6 × 5		Beam Spread 6 × 5	
Location	Minimum Height	Luminaires per Pole	Total	Luminaires per Pole	Total
A1	55'	6	6	6	6
A2	55'	6	6	6	6
A3	55'	6	6	6	6
A4	55'	6	6	6	6
B1	55'	6	6	6	6
B2	55'	6	6	6	6
Totals		36	36	36	36
		Kilowatt load @ 1.61 each =	57.96	Kilowatt load @ 1.09 each =	39.24
		Avg. Hor. Fc	Avg./Min. Unif.	Max./Min. Unif.	Avg. Hor. Fc	Avg./Min. Unif.	Max./Min. Unif.

Avg. Hor. Fc	Avg./Min. Unif.	Max./Min. Unif.	Avg. Hor. Fc	Avg./Min. Unif.	Max./Min. Unif.
19.50	1.54:1	2.67:1	20.82	1.57:1	2.74:1

Junior European Football (Soccer) Class V—30' Setback, Six Poles

		20		21		22	
		Power Mate Floodlight End Pierced Optics 1500-watt Metal Halide		Power Drawer Sports Light Horizontal Lamp Optics 1500-watt Metal Halide		Power Drawer Sports Light Horizontal Lamp Optics 1000-watt High Pressure Sodium	
Mounting Poles		Catalog Number MS3193		Catalog Number FL6192		Catalog Number FL6283	
		Beam Spread 5 × 5		Beam Spread 5 × 5		Beam Spread 5 × 3	
Location	Minimum Height	Luminaires per Pole	Total	Luminaires per Pole	Total	Luminaires per Pole	Total
A1	55'	3	3	2	2	3	3
A2	55'	3	3	2	2	3	3
A3	55'	3	3	2	2	3	3
A4	55'	3	3	2	2	2	2
B1	55'	3	3	3	3	2	2
B2	55'	3	3	3	3	2	2
Totals		18	18	14	14	16	16
		Kilowatt load @ 1.61 each =	28.98	Kilowatt load @ 1.61 each =	22.54	Kilowatt load @ 1.09 each =	17.44

Avg. Hor. Fc	Avg./Min. Unif.	Max./Min. Unif.	Avg. Hor. Fc	Avg./Min. Unif.	Max./Min. Unif.	Avg. Hor. Fc	Avg./Min. Unif.	Max./Min. Unif.
10.12	1.78:1	2.30:1	9.72	1.87:1	2.62:1	9.91	1.42:1	1.91:1

Junior European Football (Soccer) Class V—30' Setback, Six Poles (Continued)

		23		24	
		Power Drawer Cutoff Site Light Horizontal Lamp Sharp Cutoff 1500-watt Metal Halide		Power Drawer Cutoff Site Light Horizontal Lamp Sharp Cutoff 1000-watt High Pressure Sodium	
Mounting Poles		Catalog Number FC3198		Catalog Number FC3288	
		Beam Spread 6 × 5		Beam Spread 6 × 5	
Location	Minimum Height	Luminaires per Pole	Total	Luminaires per Pole	Total
A1	50'	3	3	2	2
A2	50'	3	3	2	2
A3	50'	3	3	2	2
A4	50'	3	3	2	2
B1	50'	2	2	3	3
B2	50'	2	2	3	3
Totals		16	16	14	14
		Kilowatt load @ 1.61 each =	25.76	Kilowatt load @ 1.09 each =	15.26

Avg. Hor. Fc	Avg./Min. Unif.	Max./Min. Unif.	Avg. Hor. Fc	Avg./Min. Unif.	Max./Min. Unif.
10.38	1.48:1	2.72:1	9.95	1.49:1	3.00:1

RACQUET SPORTS

Racquet sports (Table 4) such as tennis, racquet-ball, and handball are fast aerial sports, played on a relatively small playing surface. Light quality is the major consideration in racquet sport lighting installations, and as you can see in the following luminaire application tables, luminaires used for these sports must have fine light control, sharp cutoff, and minimal glare producing qualities. Some form of supplemental glare control, such as shields or louvers, may be necessary to further ensure comfortable viewing conditions. Standardized court sizes facilitate standard lighting layouts in many cases, a situation which reduces the problems faced by the lighting designer.

Tennis Court Layouts

All of the tennis court layouts and luminaire application tables given here employ 1000-watt metal halide lamps which generate 107,800 lumens. A number of lamp substitutions can be successfully made in these layouts with a subsequent change in the footcandle levels produced. These new footcandle levels can easily be found by multiplying the existing footcandle level by the proper proration factor as follows:

When replacing 1000-watt metal halide lamps with 1000-watt high pressure sodium lamps (LU1000) generating 140,000 lumens each, multiply the footcandle level by a proration factor of 1.30.

Table 4: Racquet Sports Data

Class of Play or Level of Competition	Illumination Levels and Suggested Layouts					
	100 Fc	75 Fc	50 Fc	30 Fc	20 Fc	10 Fc
Tennis						
Major Pro Tournament	*					
Major Pro Practice		*				
Minor Pro Tournament		*				
Minor Pro Practice			B,C,D,I			
College			B,C,D,I			
Club Tournament				A,G,H,K,L		
Club Non-Tournament				A,G,H,K,L	F,J,N,O	
High School				A,G,H,K,L	F,J,N,O	
Municipal Tournament				A,G,H,K,L	F,J,N,O	
Municipal Non-Tournament					F,J,N,O	
Recreational**						E,M
Handball, Racquetball, and Squash						
Four-wall Tournament		A,B				
Four-wall Club			A,B	B		
Three-wall Club			D,E	E		
Four-wall Recreational					C	
Three-wall Recreational**					F	
One-wall Recreational**						G,H
Badminton						
Tournament				A,B		
Club					C,D	
Recreational						G,H

* May require lighting for television broadcasting. Consult SPI Lighting for information. Due to the varying physical layouts of the facilities, no suggested layouts are shown. Each layout must be custom designed.
** Uniformities: A maximum/minimum uniformity ratio of 3:1 is recommended in these three cases. All of the other layouts listed require a maximum/minimum uniformity ratio of 2:1. Illumination levels are measured in horizontal maintained footcandles at a theoretical plane 36″ above the playing surface.

When replacing 1000-watt metal halide lamps with 400-watt metal halide lamps (MS400/HOR) generating 40,000 lumens each, multiply the footcandle level by a proration factor of 0.37.

When replacing 1000-watt metal halide lamps with 400-watt high pressure sodium lamps (LU400) generating 50,000 lumens each, multiply the footcandle level by a proration factor of 0.46.

The SPI Lighting catalog numbers for these substitutions are given here.

Listed Number
1000-watt MH
FC3188
CS31841

Substitute Number

1000-watt HPS	400-watt MH	400-watt HPS
FC3288	FC2168	FC2268
CS32841	CS21841	CS22841

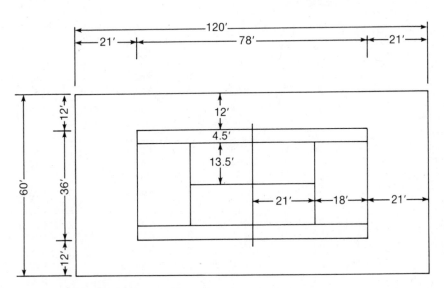

Tennis: Standard single-court dimensions.

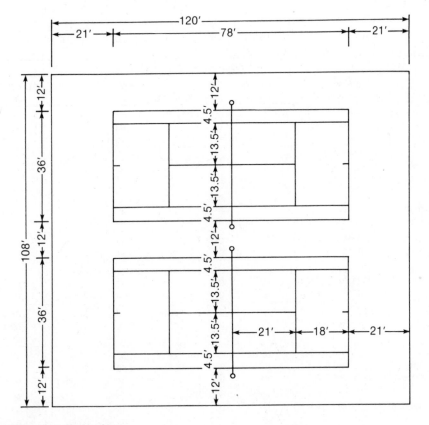

Tennis: Standard double-court dimensions.

Table 4A: Tennis Court Layout Data (1000-watt Metal Halide Lamps)

Power Drawer Cutoff Site Light

Tennis Classification	Catalog Number	Type	Mounting Height	Tilt Angle	Quantity	KW Total	Footcandle Level	Max./Min. Unif.	Layout
Minor Pro Practice 50 footcandles	FC3188S	6 × 5	25'	32.5°	6	6.48	49.51	1.50:1	B
	FC3187S	6 × 5	25'	27.5°	8	8.64	50.03	1.66:1	C
	FC3187S	6 × 5	25'	32.5°	8	8.64	61.92	1.45:1	D
	FC3188S	6 × 5	30'	37.5°	12	12.96	51.49	1.43:1	I
College 50 footcandles	FC3188S	6 × 5	25'	32.5°	6	6.48	49.51	1.50:1	B
	FC3187S	6 × 5	25'	27.5°	8	8.64	50.03	1.66:1	C
	FC3187S	6 × 5	25'	32.5°	8	8.64	61.92	1.45:1	D
	FC3188S	6 × 5	30'	37.5°	12	12.96	51.49	1.43:1	I
Club Tournament 30 footcandles	FC3188S	6 × 5	25'	37.5°	4	4.32	35.74	1.58:1	A
	FC3188S	6 × 5	30'	37.5°	8	8.64	34.99	1.36:1	G
	FC3188S	6 × 5	30'	37.5°	8	8.64	33.99	1.53:1	H
Club Non-Tournament 30 footcandles	FC3188S	6 × 5	25'	37.5°	4	4.32	35.74	1.58:1	A
	FC3188S	6 × 5	30'	37.5°	8	8.64	34.99	1.36:1	G
	FC3188S	6 × 5	30'	37.5°	8	8.64	33.99	1.53:1	H
Club Non-Tournament 20 footcandles	FC3188S	6 × 5	30'	37.5°	6	6.48	26.17	1.79:1	F
High School 30 footcandles	FC3188S	6 × 5	25'	37.5°	4	4.32	35.74	1.58:1	A
	FC3188S	6 × 5	30'	37.5°	8	8.64	34.99	1.36:1	G
	FC3188S	6 × 5	30'	37.5°	8	8.64	33.99	1.53:1	H
High School 20 footcandles	FC3188S	6 × 5	30'	37.5°	6	6.48	26.17	1.79:1	F
Municipal Tournament 30 footcandles	FC3188S	6 × 5	25'	37.5°	4	4.32	35.74	1.58:1	A
	FC3188S	6 × 5	30'	37.5°	8	8.64	34.99	1.36:1	G
	FC3188S	6 × 5	30'	37.5°	8	8.64	33.99	1.53:1	H
Municipal Tournament 20 footcandles	FC3188S	6 × 5	30'	37.5°	6	6.48	26.17	1.79:1	F
Municipal Non-Tournament 20 footcandles	FC3188S	6 × 5	30'	37.5°	6	6.48	26.17	1.79:1	F
Recreational 10 footcandles	FC3188S	6 × 5	30'	37.5°	4	4.32	18.24	1.64:1	E

Power Drawer Concourse Design 40 Cutoff

Tennis Classification	Catalog Number	Type	Mounting Height	Tilt Angle	Quantity	KW Total	Footcandle Level	Max./Min. Unif.	Layout
Club Tournament 30 footcandles	CS31841	F.T.*	25'	0°	6	6.48	37.60	1.65:1	K
	CS31841	F.T.*	25'	0°	8	8.64	45.30	1.52:1	L
Club Tournament 20 footcandles	CS31841	F.T.*	25'	0°	6	6.48	37.60	1.65:1	K
	CS31841	F.T.*	25'	0°	8	8.64	45.30	1.52:1	L
Club Non-Tournament 20 footcandles	CS31841	F.T.*	25'	0°	4	4.32	25.63	1.47:1	J
	CS31841	F.T.*	35'	0°	6	6.48	20.14	1.94:1	N
	CS31841	F.T.*	30'	0°	8	8.64	25.66	1.91:1	O
High School 30 footcandles	CS31841	F.T.*	25'	0°	6	6.48	37.60	1.65:1	K
	CS31841	F.T.*	25'	0°	8	8.64	45.30	1.52:1	L
High School 20 footcandles	CS31841	F.T.*	25'	0°	4	4.32	25.63	1.47:1	J
	CS31841	F.T.*	35'	0°	6	6.48	20.14	1.94:1	N
	CS31841	F.T.*	30'	0°	8	8.64	25.66	1.91:1	O
Municipal Tournament 30 footcandles	CS31841	F.T.*	25'	0°	6	6.48	37.60	1.65:1	K
	CS31841	F.T.*	25'	0°	8	8.64	45.30	1.52:1	L
Municipal Tournament 20 footcandles	CS31841	F.T.*	25'	0°	4	4.32	25.63	1.47:1	J
	CS31841	F.T.*	35'	0°	6	6.48	20.14	1.94:1	N
	CS31841	F.T.*	30'	0°	8	8.64	25.66	1.91:1	O
Municipal Non-Tournament 20 footcandles	CS31841	F.T.*	25'	0°	4	4.32	25.63	1.47:1	J
	CS31841	F.T.*	35'	0°	6	6.48	20.14	1.94:1	N
	CS31841	F.T.*	30'	0°	8	8.64	25.66	1.91:1	O
Recreational 10 footcandles	CS31841	F.T.*	35'	0°	4	4.32	13.33	1.89:1	M

*Forward Throw Optics

Notes:
1. All lamps are Metal Halide 1000-watt, MVR1000/U which produce 107,800 initial footcandles.
2. Footcandle levels are expressed in average initial horizontal footcandles on the actual court area 36" above the playing surface.
3. Maximum/minimum uniformity ratios are those which exist on the actual court area.

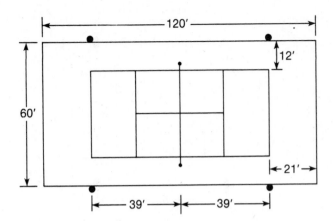

Tennis: Layout A pole locations.

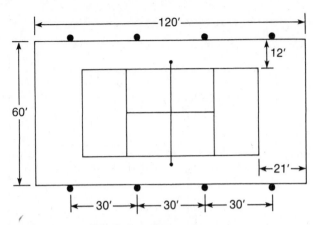

Tennis: Layout D pole locations.

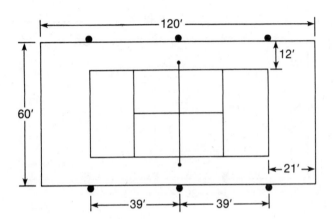

Tennis: Layout B pole locations.

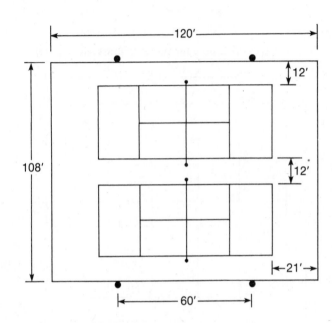

Tennis: Layout E pole locations.

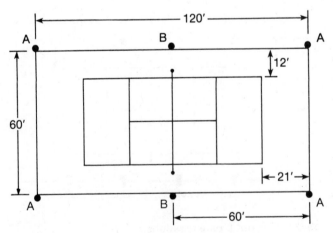

Tennis: Layout C pole locations. (Note: B poles have 2 luminaires/pole.)

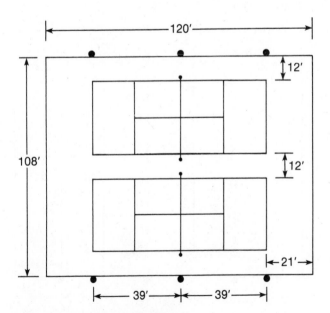

Tennis: Layout F pole locations.

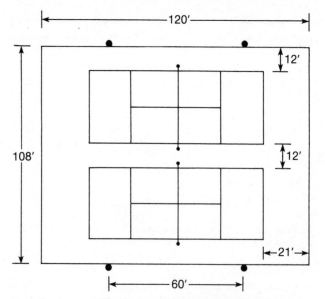

Tennis: Layout G pole locations (2 luminaires/pole).

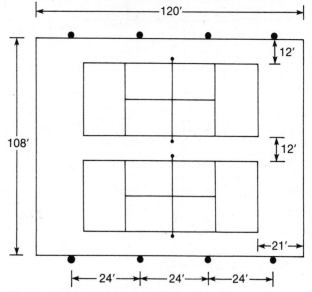

Tennis: Layout H pole locations.

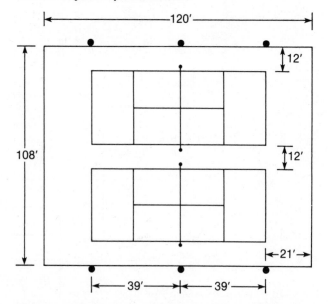

Tennis: Layout I pole locations (2 luminaires/pole).

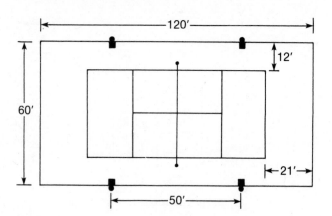

Tennis: Layout J pole locations.

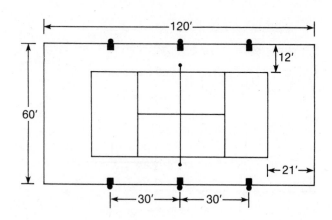

Tennis: Layout K pole locations.

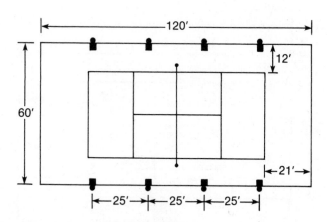

Tennis: Layout L pole locations.

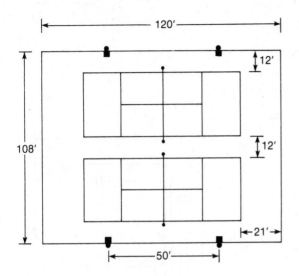

Tennis: Layout M pole locations.

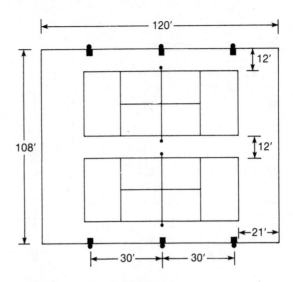

Tennis: Layout N pole locations.

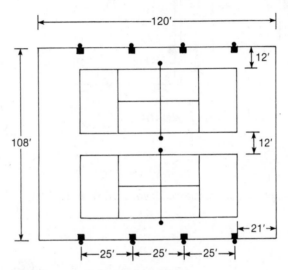

Tennis: Layout O pole locations.

	Class and Foot-candle Level	Type	Lamp Data Designation	Lumens	Catalog No.	Type	Mounting Height	Tilt Angle	Quantity	KW Total	Layout
					Power Drawer Concourse Design 20 Cutoff Luminaire						
Four Wall	Tournament 75 footcandles	MH HPS	MS250/HOR LU250/S	23,000 30,000	CT11521 CT12521	II Med II Med	21' 21'	0° 0°	12 9	3.52 2.70	A B
	Club 50 footcandles	MH HPS	MS250/HOR LU150	23,000 16,000	CT11521 CT18321	II Med II Med	21' 21'	0° 0°	9 12	2.64 2.25	B A
	Club 30 footcandles	MH HPS	MS175/HOR LU150	15,000 16,000	CT11421 CT18321	II Med II Med	21' 21'	0° 0°	9 9	1.89 1.69	B B
	Recreational 20 footcandles	MH HPS	MS175/HOR LU150	15,000 16,000	CT11421 CT18321	II Med II Med	21' 21'	0° 0°	7 7	1.47 1.31	C C
Three Wall	Club 50 footcandles	MH HPS	MS250/HOR LU250/S	23,000 30,000	CT11521 CT12521	II Med II Med	21' 21'	0° 0°	9 13	2.64 3.90	E D
	Club 30 footcandles	MH HPS	MS175/HOR LU150	15,000 16,000	CT11421 CT18321	II Med II Med	21' 21'	0° 0°	9 9	1.89 1.69	E E
	Recreational 20 footcandles	MH HPS	MS175/HOR LU150	15,000 16,000	CT11421 CT18321	II Med II Med	21' 21'	0° 0°	7 7	1.47 1.31	F F
					Power Drawer Cutoff Site Light Luminaire						
One Wall	Recreational 20 footcandles	MH HPS	MVR1000/U LU1000	107,800 140,000	FC3187 FC3287	6 x 5 6 x 5	26' 26'	50° 50°	4 4	4.32 4.36	G
	Recreational 10 footcandles	MH HPS	MVR1000/U LU1000	107,800 140,000	FC3187 FC3287	6 x 5 6 x 5	26' 26'	50° 50°	2 2	2.16 2.18	H

Table 4B: Outdoor Handball, Racquetball, and Squash Application Table

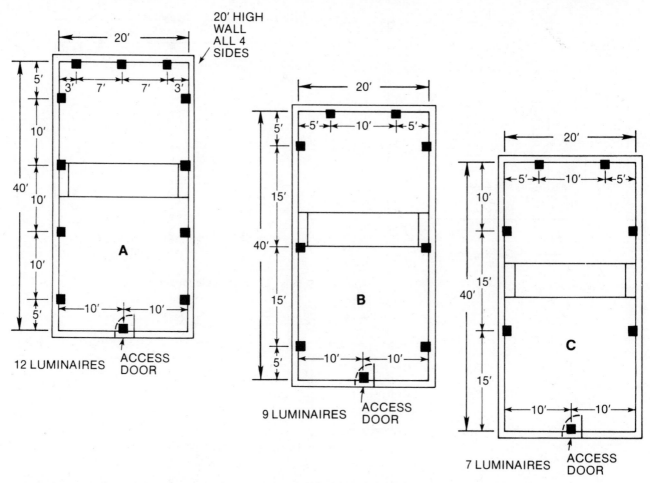

Outdoor Four-Wall Handball, Racquetball, and Squash: Layouts A, B, and C.

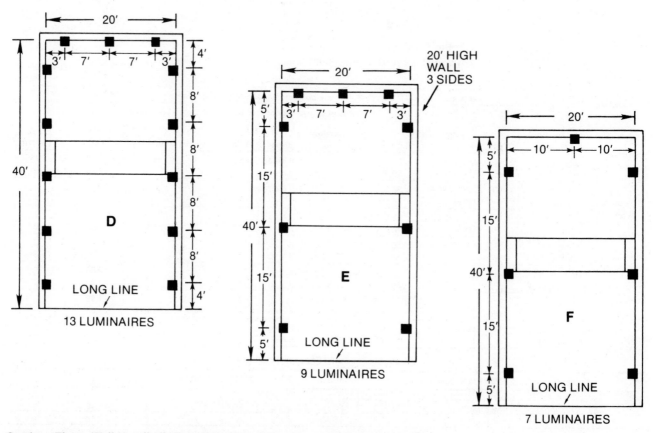

Outdoor Three-Wall Handball, Racquetball, and Squash: Layouts D, E, and F.

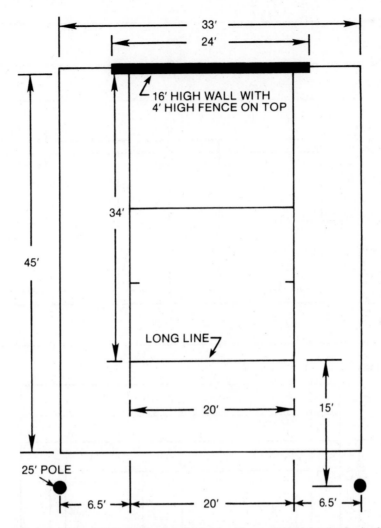

16' HIGH WALL WITH
4' HIGH FENCE ON TOP

LONG LINE

25' POLE

Outdoor One-Wall Recreational: Layout G (2 luminaires/pole) and Layout H (1 luminaire/pole).

Table 4C: Badminton Application Table											
	Pole Data		Power Drawer Cutoff Site Light				Lamp Data				
Classification Footcandle Level	Location Type	Min. Mounting Height	Catalog Number	Type	Number per Pole	Total Quantity	Type	Designation	Lumens	KW Total	Layout
Tournament 30 footcandles	A	20'	FC3187	6 x 5	2	4	MH	MVR1000/U	107,800	4.32	A
			FC3287	6 x 5	2	4	HPS	LU1000	140,000	4.36	A
Club 20 footcandles	A	20'	FC2167	6 x 5	3	6	MH	M5400/HOR	40,000	2.73	C
			FC2267	6 x 5	3	6	HPS	LU400	50,000	2.79	C
Recreational 10 footcandles	A	20'	FC2167	6 x 5	2	4	MH	MS400/HOR	40,000	1.82	E
			FC2267	6 x 5	2	4	HPS	LU400	50,000	1.86	E
Power Drawer Floodlight											
Tournament 30 footcandles	A	25'	FL3181	6 x 7	2	4	MH	MVR1000/U	110,000	4.32	B
			FL3281	6 x 7	2	4	HPS	LU1000	140,000	4.36	B
Club 20 footcandles	A	25'	FL2161	6 x 7	3	6	MH	MVR400/U	34,000	2.73	D
			FL2261	6 x 7	3	6	HPS	LU400	50,000	2.79	D
Recreational 10 footcandles	A	25'	FL2161	6 x 7	2	4	MH	MVR400/U	34,000	1.82	F
			FL2261	6 x 7	2	4	HPS	LU400	50,000	1.86	F

SPORTS LIGHTING

187

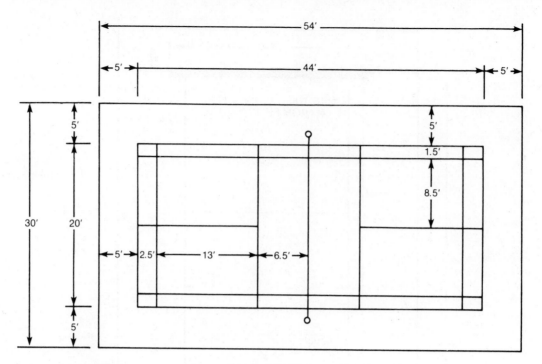

Badminton: Court dimensions.

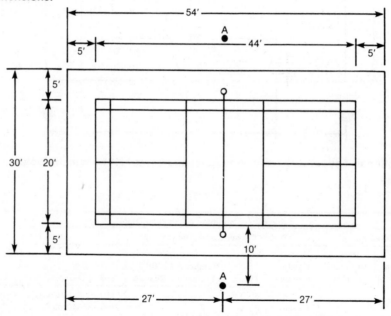

Badminton: Layouts A, B, C, D, E, and F.

STICK SPORTS

Ice hockey is the one major stick sport played on a surface and layout unique from all others (Table 5). Ice hockey is a sport in which the participants and spectators do not normally look upward because play is conducted on a low plane. All illumination levels are expressed in horizontal maintained footcandles at a plane 36″ above ice level. The possible loss of visibility due to reflected glare from the ice surface, as well as potential glare from the luminaires themselves, necessitates careful pole location and luminaire aiming.

Other stick sports, such as field hockey and lacrosse, are normally played on fields originally designed for foot sports or a combination of sports. Refer to those particular sections for design details.

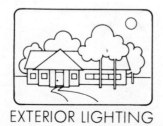

Table 5: Stick Sports Data

Class of Play or Level of Competition	Illumination Level (footcandles)		
	50	20	10
Ice Hockey			
Professional	X		
College	X		
Adult Amateur and High School		X	
Recreational and Junior Instructional			X

Uniformities: A maximum/minimum uniformity ratio of 3:1 is required within the playing area. Illumination levels are measured in horizontal maintained footcandles at a theoretical plane 36" above the playing surface.

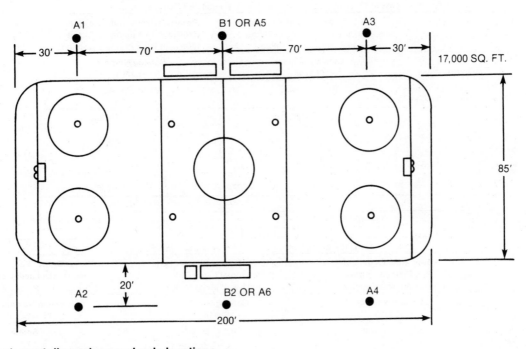

Ice Hockey: Layout dimensions and pole locations.

Layout A:	Outdoor Ice Hockey—Professional and College		
		Power Mate Floodlight **End Pierced Optics** **1500-watt Metal Halide**	
Mounting Poles		**Catalog Number** **MS3192**	
Location	**Minimum Height**	**Beam Spread** **6 × 6**	
		Luminaires per Pole	
A1	40'	3	
A2	40'	3	
A3	40'	3	
A4	40'	3	
B1	40'	4	
B2	40'	4	
Totals		20	
		Kilowatt load @ 1.61 each =	32.2

Layout B: Outdoor Ice Hockey—Professional and College

Mounting Poles		Power Drawer Sports Light Horizontal Lamp Optics 1500-watt Metal Halide	Power Drawer Sports Light Horizontal Lamp Optics 1000-watt High Pressure Sodium
		Catalog Number FL6192	Catalog Number FL6282
Location	Minimum Height	Beam Spread 5 × 5	Beam Spread 6 × 7
		Luminaires per Pole	Luminaires per Pole
A1	40'	3	3
A2	40'	3	3
A3	40'	3	3
A4	40'	3	3
A5	40'	3	3
A6	40'	3	3
Totals		18	18
		Kilowatt load @ 1.61 each = 28.98	Kilowatt load @ 1.09 each = 19.62

Layout C: Outdoor Ice Hockey—Professional and College

Mounting Poles		Power Drawer Cutoff Site Light Horizontal Lamp Sharp Cutoff 1500-watt Metal Halide	Power Drawer Cutoff Site Light Horizontal Lamp Sharp Cutoff 1000-watt High Pressure Sodium
		Catalog Number FL3198	Catalog Number FL3288
Location	Minimum Height	Beam Spread 6 × 5	Beam Spread 6 × 5
		Luminaires per Pole	Luminaires per Pole
A1	35'	3	3
A2	35'	3	3
A3	35'	3	3
A4	35'	3	3
A5	35'	3	3
A6	35'	3	3
Totals		18	18
		Kilowatt load @ 1.61 each = 28.98	Kilowatt load @ 1.09 each = 19.62

Layout A: Outdoor Ice Hockey—Adult Amateur and High School

Mounting Poles		Power Mate Floodlight End Pierced Optics 1000-watt Metal Halide	Power Drawer Sports Light Horizontal Lamp Optics 1000-watt Metal Halide	Power Drawer Sports Light Horizontal Lamp Optics 1000-watt High Pressure Sodium
		Catalog Number MS3182	Catalog Number FL6182	Catalog Number FL6282
Location	Minimum Height	Beam Spread 6 × 6	Beam Spread 5 × 5	Beam Spread 6 × 7
		Luminaires per Pole	Luminaires per Pole	Luminaires per Pole
A1	40'	2	2	1
A2	40'	2	2	1
A3	40'	2	2	1
A4	40'	2	2	1
B1	40'	3	2	2
B2	40'	3	2	2
Totals		14	12	8
		Kilowatt load @ 1.08 each = 15.12	Kilowatt load @ 1.08 each = 12.96	Kilowatt load @ 1.09 each = 8.72

Layout B: Outdoor Ice Hockey—Adult Amateur and High School

Mounting Poles		Power Drawer Cutoff Site Light Horizontal Lamp Sharp Cutoff 1000-watt Metal Halide	Power Drawer Cutoff Site Light Horizontal Lamp Sharp Cutoff 1000-watt High Pressure Sodium
		Catalog Number FL3188	Catalog Number FL3288
Location	Minimum Height	Beam Spread 6 × 5	Beam Spread 6 × 5
		Luminaires per Pole	Luminaires per Pole
A1	35'	2	1
A2	35'	2	1
A3	35'	2	1
A4	35'	2	1
B1	35'	2	2
B2	35'	2	2
Totals		12	8
		Kilowatt load @ 1.08 each = 12.96	Kilowatt load @ 1.09 each = 8.72

Layout A:	Outdoor Ice Hockey—Recreational and Junior Instructional			
Mounting Poles		Power Drawer Sports Light Horizontal Lamp Sharp Cutoff 400-watt Metal Halide		Power Drawer Sports Light Horizontal Lamp Sharp Cutoff 400-watt High Pressure Sodium
		Catalog Number FL2168		Catalog Number FL2268
Location	Minimum Height	Beam Spread 6 × 5		Beam Spread 5 × 5
		Luminaires per Pole		Luminaires per Pole
A1	35'	2		2
A2	35'	2		2
A3	35'	2		2
A4	35'	2		2
B1	35'	2		1
B2	35'	2		1
Totals		12		10
		Kilowatt load @ .455 each =	5.46	Kilowatt load @ .465 each = 4.65

Layout B:	Outdoor Ice Hockey—Recreational and Junior Instructional			
Mounting Poles		Power Drawer Sports Light Vertical Lamp Optics 400-watt Metal Halide		Power Drawer Sports Light Vertical Lamp Optics 400-watt High Pressure Sodium
		Catalog Number FL2162		Catalog Number FL2262
Location	Minimum Height	Beam Spread 5 × 5		Beam Spread 6 × 5
		Luminaires per Pole		Luminaires per Pole
A1	40'	2		2
A2	40'	2		2
A3	40'	2		2
A4	40'	2		2
B1	40'	3		2
B2	40'	3		2
Totals		14		12
		Kilowatt load @ .455 each =	6.37	Kilowatt load @ .465 each = 5.58

COMBINATION FIELDS

Lighting systems designed to allow the playing of several sports on the same field or playing surface are never as satisfactory as individual sports lighting systems, but many schools and institutions find combination fields the only solution to land space and monetary limitations. Most fields are designed to accommodate a two- or three-game combination (Table 6) which may include such sports as baseball, softball, football, soccer, field hockey, and lacrosse. While the specific lighting requirements of the individual sports involved must be taken into consideration, many compromises will inevitably be necessary. For example, the relative position of the various fields and their boundaries will have a decided effect on the mounting pole locations. If an ideal pole position for lighting the softball field falls within the boundaries of the proposed football playing area, a new pole position will have to be decided upon that is best for both sports. Minimizing glare for all sports is the main design criterion when working with combination field systems.

Table 6: Combination Field Data				
Field Type	**Illumination Level**		**Area (square feet)***	
	Infield	Outfield	Infield	Outfield
Baseball—Football	20 Fc	15 Fc	22,500	110,000
Softball—Football	20 Fc	15 Fc	10,000	63,200

* The football field is included in the outfield area.
Uniformities: For any given area (infield, outfield, or football area) a maximum/minimum uniformity ratio of 3:1 should not be exceeded. Illumination levels are measured in horizontal maintained footcandles at a theoretical plane 36" above the playing surface.

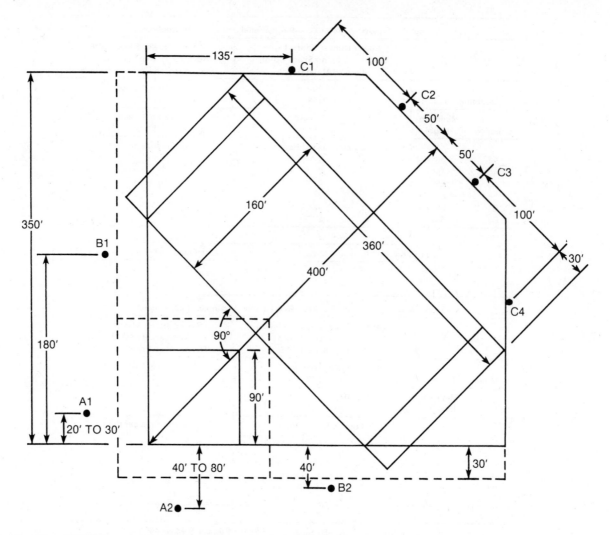

Combination Baseball-American Football: Layout A field dimensions and pole locations.

Layout A: Combination Baseball/American Football										
		Power Mate Floodlight **End Pierced Optics** **1500-watt Metal Halide**				**Power Drawer Sports Light** **Vertical Lamp Optics** **1500-watt Metal Halide**				**Power Drawer Sports Light** **Horizontal Lamp Optics** **1000-watt High Pressure Sodium**		
Mounting Poles		**Catalog Number** MS3194 MS3193 MS3192				**Catalog Number** FL3193 FL3192 FL3191				**Catalog Number** FL6284 FL6283 FL6282		
Location	**Minimum Height**	**Beam Spread** 3 × 3	5 × 5	6 × 6		**Beam Spread** 3 × 3	4 × 4	6 × 7		**Beam Spread** 5 × 5	5 × 3	6 × 5
		Luminaires per Pole			Total	Luminaires per Pole			Total	Luminaires per Pole			Total
A1	70′	3	1	—	4	1	3	—	4	1	4	—	5
A2	70′	3	1	—	4	1	3	—	4	1	4	—	5
B1	70′	2	4	2	8	2	2	2	6	2	3	2	7
B2	70′	2	4	2	8	2	2	2	6	2	3	2	7
C1	70′	1	1	3	5	1	2	2	5	2	2	2	6
C2	90′	2	1	3	6	1	2	2	5	2	2	2	6
C3	90′	2	1	3	6	1	2	2	5	2	2	2	6
C4	90′	1	1	3	5	1	2	2	5	2	2	2	6
Totals		16	14	16	46	10	18	12	40	14	22	12	48
		Kilowatt load @ 1.61 each =		74.06		Kilowatt load @ 1.61 each =		64.40		Kilowatt load @ 1.09 each =		52.32
		Avg. **Hor. Fc**	**Avg./Min.** **Unif.**	**Max./Min.** **Unif.**		**Avg.** **Hor. Fc**	**Avg./Min.** **Unif.**	**Max./Min.** **Unif.**		**Avg.** **Hor. Fc**	**Avg./Min.** **Unif.**	**Max./Min.** **Unif.**
Infield		19.92	1.48:1	2.16:1		20.69	1.41:1	1.68:1		19.55	1.23:1	1.46:1
Outfield		14.84	1.65:1	2.31:1		15.11	1.86:1	2.36:1		14.59	2.06:1	3.01:1
Football		14.73	1.32:1	1.60:1		15.15	1.33:1	1.62:1		15.60	1.50:1	1.98:1

Note: Operate all floodlights for baseball. Do not operate floodlights on poles A1 and A2 for football.

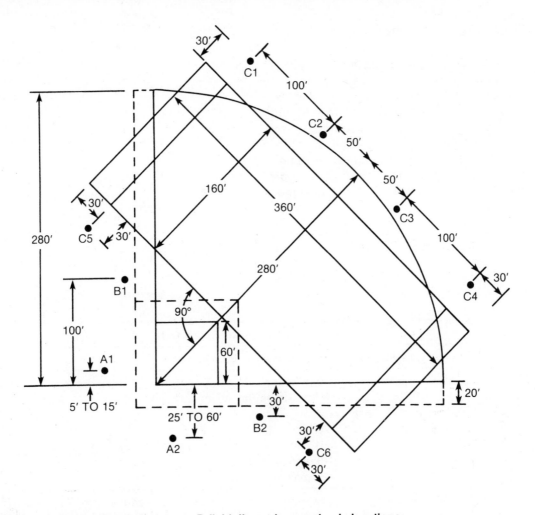

Combination Softball-American Football: Layout B field dimensions and pole locations.

		Layout B: Combination Softball/American Football									
		Power Mate Floodlight End Pierced Optics 1500-watt Metal Halide			**Power Drawer Sports Light Vertical Lamp Optics 1500-watt Metal Halide**			**Power Drawer Sports Light Horizontal Lamp Optics 1000-watt High Pressure Sodium**			
Mounting Poles		**Catalog Number** MS3193 MS3192			**Catalog Number** FL3192 FL3191			**Catalog Number** FL6283 FL6282			
Location	**Minimum Height**	**Beam Spread** 5 × 5	6 × 6		**Beam Spread** 4 × 4	6 × 7		**Beam Spread** 5 × 3	6 × 7		
		Luminaires per Pole		Total	Luminaires per Pole		Total	Luminaires per Pole		Total	
A1	50'	1	1	2	1	1	2	1	1	2	
A2	50'	1	1	2	1	1	2	1	1	2	
B1	50'	2	2	4	3	1	4	2	2	4	
B2	50'	2	2	4	3	1	4	2	2	4	
C1	50'	3	1	4	2	1	3	2	1	3	
C2	50'	1	2	3	1	2	3	2	1	3	
C3	50'	1	2	3	1	2	3	2	1	3	
C4	50'	3	1	4	2	1	3	2	1	3	
C5	50'	2	1	3	1	1	2	1	1	2	
C6	50'	2	1	3	1	1	2	1	1	2	
Totals		18	14	32	16	12	28	16	12	28	
		Kilowatt load @ 1.61 each =		51.52	Kilowatt load @ 1.61 each =		45.08	Kilowatt load @ 1.09 each =		30.52	
		Avg. Hor. Fc	**Avg./Min. Unif.**	**Max./Min. Unif.**	**Avg. Hor. Fc**	**Avg./Min. Unif.**	**Max./Min. Unif.**	**Avg. Hor. Fc**	**Avg./Min. Unif.**	**Max./Min. Unif.**	
Infield		20.61	1.41:1	1.93:1	20.51	1.16:1	1.37:1	20.05	1.38:1	1.65:1	
Outfield		15.26	1.70:1	2.69:1	15.69	1.59:1	2.29:1	14.54	1.60:1	2.30:1	
Football		15.47	1.47:1	2.33:1	16.03	1.91:1	2.93:1	14.61	2.00:1	2.53:1	

Note: For softball operation—operate all floodlights on all poles except C5 and C6.
  For football operation—operate all floodlights on all poles except A1 and A2.

MISCELLANEOUS SPORTS

Lighting requirements and suggested layouts for other popular sports are given in Table 7. As in the previous sports lighting sections, these exact layouts can be used to produce satisfactory lighting results or to serve as a basis for custom designing a unique system to solve unique problems. In these and all other sports lighting systems, always remember that the elimination of glare for both the participants and spectators is the lighting designer's main concern.

Table 7: Miscellaneous Sports Data	
Sport and Classification	**Lighting System Information**
Basketball (recreational)	10 footcandles 3:1 maximum/minimum uniformity ratio
Volleyball	
Tournament	20 footcandles 3:1 maximum/minimum uniformity ratio
Recreational	10 footcandles 3:1 maximum/minimum uniformity ratio
Note: The following sports require vertical illumination in addition to horizontal illumination.	
Shooting	
Skeet (60' to 100')	30 footcandles vertical (60' to 100') on target area 5 footcandles at firing area
Trap (100' to 120')	30 footcandles vertical (100' to 120') on target area 5 footcandles at firing area
Golf	
Driving Range	10 footcandles at each tee 5 vertical footcandles on the back of the ball up to 50' elevation 300' down range and at grade 600' down range. 1 footcandle average at ground level. Do not exceed 10:1 maximum/minimum uniformity ratio in the area from the tee to 300' down range.
Practice Green*	10 footcandles Illuminate all points from a minimum of two directions to eliminate harsh shadows.
Miniature*	10 footcandles

* No standard layouts. Must be designed for each specific shape or size. Use the same system employed when lighting the perimeter areas of parking areas. See **Parking Area Lighting** for details.

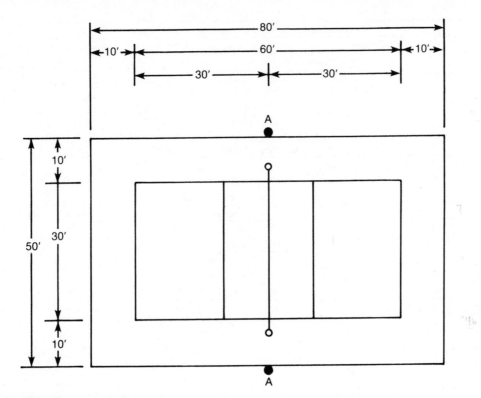

Volleyball: Court dimensions and pole locations.

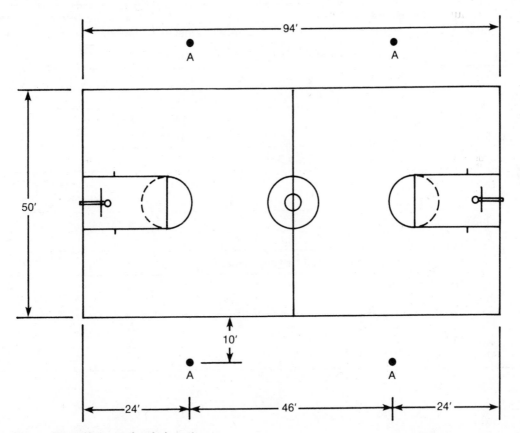

Basketball: Court dimensions and pole locations.

SPORTS LIGHTING 195

Table 7A: Basketball and Volleyball Application Table

Class and Footcandle Level	Pole Data			Lamp Data			Power Drawer Cutoff Site Light				
	Location	Quantity	Min. Mounting Height	Type	Designation	Lumens	Catalog Number	Type	Number/ Pole	Total Quantity	KW Total
Basketball Recreational (10 fc)	A	4	25'	MH	MS250/HOR	23,000	FC1158S	6 x 5	2	8	2.36
	A	4	25'	HPS	LU250/S	30,000	FC1258S	6 x 5	2	8	2.40
Volleyball Tournament (20 fc)	A	2	25'	MH	MS400/HOR	40,000	FC2168S FC2167S	6 x 5 6 x 5	2 1	6	2.73
	A	2	30'	HPS	LU400	50,000	FC2268S	6 x 5	3	6	2.79
Volleyball Recreational (10 fc)	A	2	25'	MH	MS250	30,000	FC1158S	6 x 5	3	6	1.77
	A	2	25'	MH	MS400	40,000	FC2168S	6 x 5	2	4	1.82
	A	2	25'	HPS	LU250/S	30,000	FC1258S	6 x 5	2	4	1.20

	Pole Data			Lamp Data			Power Drawer Floodlight				
Basketball Recreational (10 fc)	A	4	30'	MH	MS250	20,500	FL1151	7 x 7	3	12	3.54
	A	4	30'	MH	MS400/BD	34,000	FL2161	6 x 7	2	8	3.64
	A	4	30'	HPS	LU250/S	30,000	FL1251	7 x 7	2	8	2.40
Volleyball Tournament (20 fc)	A	2	30'	MH	MS/1000	110,000	FL3181	6 x 7	2	4	4.32
	A	2	30'	HPS	LU1000	140,000	FL3281	6 x 7	2	4	4.36
Volleyball Recreational (10 fc)	A	2	30'	MH	MS4000	40,000	FL2161	6 x 7	3	6	2.73
	A	2	30'	HPS	LU400	50,000	FL2261	6 x 7	2	4	1.86

Table 7B: Shooting and Golf Application Table

Luminaire Type	Catalog Number	Min. Mounting Height	Number/ Pole	Total Number	KW Total	Pole Location	Pole Quantity	Lamp Designation
Skeet and Skeet/Trap Combination								
Power Drawer Floodlight	FL3183	20'	2	4	4.32	A	2	Metal Halide MVR1000/U
Power Mate Floodlight	MS3182	20'	2	4	4.32	A	2	Metal Halide MVR1000/U
Trap Shooting								
Power Drawer Floodlight	FL3183	20'	3	3	3.24	A	1	Metal Halide MVR1000/U
Power Mate Floodlight	MS3182	20'	3	3	3.24	A	1	Metal Halide MVR1000/U
Golf Driving Range								
Power Drawer Floodlight	FL3181 FL3184	25'	1 2	12	12.96	A	4	Metal Halide MVR1000/U
Power Mate Floodlight	MS3182 MS3183 MS3185	25'	1 1 2	16	17.28	A	4	Metal Halide MVR1000/U

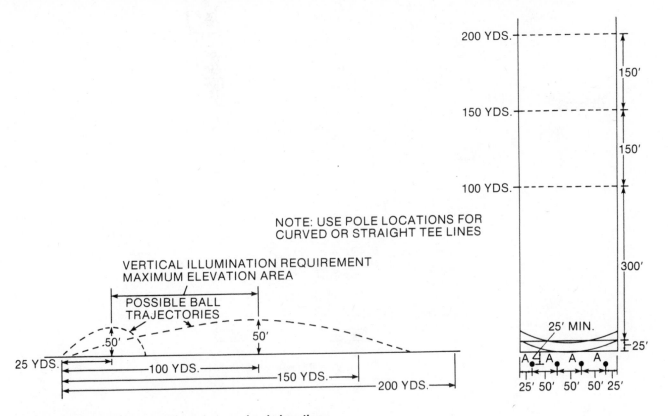

Golf Driving Ranges: Range dimensions and pole locations.

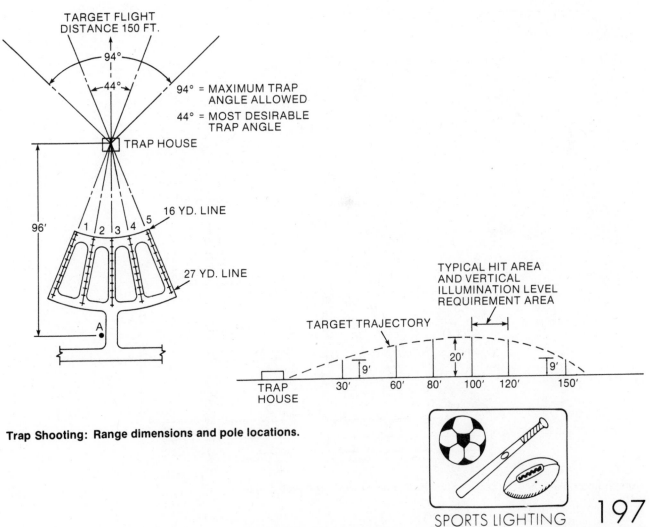

Trap Shooting: Range dimensions and pole locations.

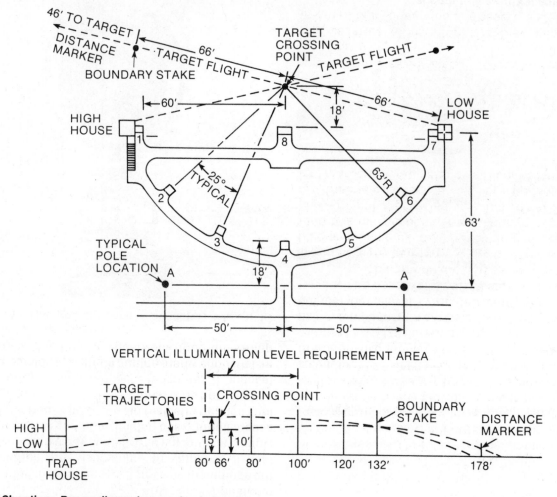

Skeet Shooting: Range dimensions and pole locations.

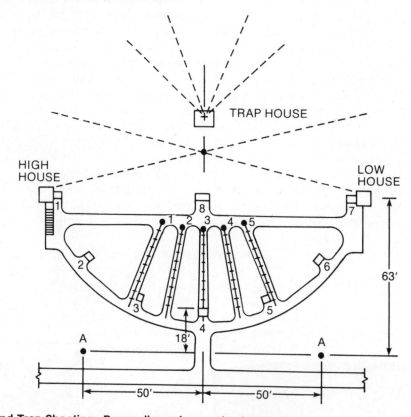

Combination Skeet and Trap Shooting: Range dimensions and pole locations.

Sign & Building Lighting

The purpose of lighting a sign or building for nighttime visual display may be to give viewers information or direction, advertise a product or service, or create a striking light-produced visual effect. Since they both involve the lighting of vertical surfaces, building and sign floodlighting are best discussed together. As you will see later in this section, the design techniques used for lighting these vertical surfaces are among the simplest and most accurate of all outdoor lighting methods.

ILLUMINATION REQUIREMENTS

Illumination levels, uniformities, and surrounding brightness contrasts will vary according to the type of sign or building, its function, and the conditions in which it is viewed. Illumination data for roadway signs, advertising signs, and exterior building walls is given in Tables 1 through 3 (pages 200 and 201). For any application, the illumination level must be sufficient for the observer to view the sign or vertical surface at an adequate distance in an adequate amount of time. The reflectance value of the lighted surface must also be considered, since darker materials and colors will require more light than their lighter counterparts. Figure 1 illustrates the proper color and cosine corrected illumination meter position for the reading of horizontal footcandle levels on flat, vertical surfaces.

Surround Brightness and Uniformities

The brightness of the illuminated surface must be sufficient to stand out against the brightness of the surrounding area. A surface to surrounding brightness ratio of 2:1 or greater is recommended in all cases. This means that dependent upon the conditions under which it is viewed, the same type of sign or building may require two different levels of illumination. For example, an advertising billboard in a well-lighted central business district requires 50 to 100 footcandles of light to draw attention to it. The same billboard may require only 20 to 50 footcandles of illumination to create this brightness contrast when it is located in a dimly-lighted or rural area.

The maximum/minimum uniformity ratio occurring on the sign itself should be as close to 1:1 as

possible. This assures that there are no dark, difficult to read or view areas.

Scalloping. A low maximum/minimum uniformity ratio is not as important in exterior building lighting. In fact, maximum/minimum uniformity ratios of 10:1 or greater are often desired to produce scalloping effects on building walls. Scalloping reveals wall texture and relief through the use of shadowed and highlighted areas. Its principles are closely related to those used in the wall washing and shadowing of interior walls. (Refer to **Section II: Lighting for Interiors, Accent Lighting.**) The luminaire setback distance and the luminaire spacing distance are two key factors which have a decided effect on the uniformity ratios produced in exterior building lighting. More will be said about these factors later in this section.

COST FACTORS AND LAMP SELECTION

Controlling the overall cost of a sign or building lighting system is largely a function of the lamp selection process. Escalating energy costs have made operating costs the prime economic factor of any system. Maintenance costs, which depend solely upon lamp life and the hours of daily operation, are second in importance. So if you consider the low efficacy and relatively short lamp life of incandescent lamps, you can see why these lamps have fallen into disuse in sign and building lighting. Instead, clear mercury, metal halide, and high pressure sodium lamps of the high intensity discharge lamp group have become the lamps of choice in sign and build-

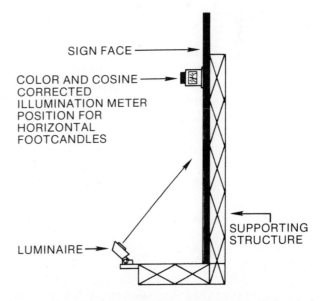

Fig. 1: When measuring the horizontal footcandle level of a vertical surface, position the illumination meter as shown.

Table 1: Roadway Sign Illumination Data		
Ambient Luminance Classification		
Low	**Medium**	**High**
Rural areas without illumination or areas of very low illumination, including rural interchanges.	Illuminated freeways and freeway interchanges with small commercial developments and minimum street lighting levels.	Central business districts with high street lighting levels and brightly lighted advertising signs.
Average Maintained Horizontal Footcandles		
10 footcandles	20 footcandles	40 footcandles

Note: A 6:1 maximum/minimum uniformity ratio is required within the sign border line on the sign face. See Fig. 4 (page 202) in the text.

Table 2: Advertising Sign Illumination Data		
Average Reflectance of Advertising Copy[1]	**Average Maintained Horizontal Footcandles**	
	Bright Surroundings	**Dark Surroundings[2]**
Low	100 footcandles	50 footcandles
High	50 footcandles	20 footcandles

Notes: 1. **Classification of Advertising Copy Reflectance:**
    Low—Less than 50% reflectivity. Colors such as black and dark reds, oranges, yellows, blues, greens, and browns.
    High—50% and higher reflectivity. Colors include white and light oranges, yellows, blues, greens, and tans.
2. **Classification of Surrounding Brightness:**
    Bright—Central business districts or other areas where there are many competitive advertising signs and brightly illuminated roadways, parking areas, and buildings.
    Dark—Remote or rural areas where there are few competitive signs and lower or non-illuminated areas.
3. **Uniformity:** A maximum/minimum uniformity ratio of 4:1 should be maintained over the entire message or advertising area.
4. **Basic Structure Sign Dimensions:** As set by the Outdoor Advertising Association of America: Poster Panels or Billboards—12-1/4' high x 24-1/2' long; Painted Bulletins—14' high x 48' long.
5. **Recommended Lamps:** Due to the wide variety of colors found on advertising signs, metal halide lamps are the only type of lamp recommended for use. This is due to the lamp's high color rendering characteristics.

ing floodlighting. These lamps have high efficacies, long lamp lives, and low lumen depreciations.

The third and least important economic factor is initial equipment and installation costs. Although high intensity discharge lighting equipment is more expensive than incandescent equipment on a per unit basis, the overall HID system cost is less due to reduced wiring requirements and a drop in the number of luminaires required to do the job.

Color Considerations

The primary color or colors of the sign or building being lighted must certainly be given consideration when selecting the proper HID lamp source. The color rendering characteristics of the lamp should complement the color scheme of the vertical surface (Table 4). Because of the high importance placed on the colors and graphic design of many advertising signs, metal halide lamps are the only lamp choice recommended for these applications. Clear mercury and high pressure sodium lamps do alter the appearance of certain colors, but they are otherwise fine for nearly all roadway sign and building lighting applications. Refer to Table 22 (page 26) in **Section I: Lamps and Ballasts** for a detailed description of the color rendering characteristics of these lamps.

THE POWER DRAWER SIGN LIGHT LUMINAIRE

The Power Drawer Sign Light (Fig. 2, page 202) is the only luminaire recommended for the sign and building applications described in this section. The Power Drawer Sign Light luminaire has a one-piece cast aluminum housing, and separate optical sys-

Table 3: Building Floodlighting Illumination Data

Surface Material Description and Color	Light Reflectance in Percent	Average Maintained Horizontal Footcandles Surrounding Area		Recommended HID Light Source		
		Bright	Dark	Clear Mercury	Metal Halide	High Pressure Sodium
Light Marble White Plaster White or Cream Terra Cotta Concrete	70%-85%	15	5	X X X X	X X X X	X X X X
Tinted Stucco Light Gray and Buff Sandstone Buff Face Brick	40%-70%	20	10		X X X	X X X
Medium Gray Limestone Common Tan Brick Sandstone	20%-45%	30	15	X	X X X	X X X
Common Red Brick Brownstone Stained Wood Shingles Dark Gray Brick	10%-20%*	50	20	X X	X X X X	X X X

*Buildings constructed of materials with light reflectances of less than 20% usually cannot be economically floodlighted unless the building contains a large amount of high-reflectance trim. In such cases, the trim, not the building surface, becomes the focal viewpoint.

Classification of Surrounding Areas: Bright—Central business districts or other areas where facilities are brightly illuminated.
Dark—Remote, rural, or other areas where there is no lighting. Areas where facilities are illuminated to low levels.

Table 4: Recommended Lamps for Various Sign Colors

Sign Color		Recommended Lamp Type		
Background	Copy	Clear Mercury	Clear Metal Halide	High Pressure Sodium
Green	White	X	X	X
Blue	White	X	X	X
Black	White	X	X	X
Yellow	Black		X	X
Multi-Colored Advertising Signs			X	

tems are available for use with clear or HID lamps. The Power Drawer ballast assembly allows for easy installation and maintenance, and the unit's adjustable aiming angle mechanism assures precise aiming and maximum system flexibility. The concealed light source eliminates glare and the need for auxiliary light baffles by directing the light upward and away from the viewer's field of vision.

USING THE POWER DRAWER SIGN LIGHT APPLICATION TABLE

Table 5 (page 203) lists all the pertinent data that a lighting designer requires to light roadway signs, advertising signs, and building exteriors. The table lists appropriate HID light sources, their wattage, designation, initial lumen production, and SPI Light-ing lamp-luminaire catalog number. The sign height and luminaire tilt angle (Fig. 3) are also given, and luminaire spacings of 4′, 5′, 6′, 8′, and 10′ are specified. Luminaire setback distances are specified in the notes beneath the table. Listed under each luminaire spacing are the exact footcandle levels which will be produced on the vertical surface for the given lamp, sign height, setback distance, and tilt angle combinations. All the lighting designer needs to do is determine the proper illumination and color requirements from Tables 1 through 4 and match them to the data found in Table 5. Several examples are given on the following pages.

Fig. 2: The Power Drawer Sign Light luminaire is the only luminaire recommended for the lighting of signs, building exteriors, and other vertical surfaces.

tering on a green background. Referring to Table 4, the designer decides to utilize an HID clear mercury lamp which will complement the sign's green background. Turning to Table 5, the designer then selects a 250-watt, H37KB-R250, clear mercury lamp. The table indicates that when used to light a 15' high sign, this lamp-luminaire combination should be positioned at a 4' setback distance and aimed at a 35° angle. By following this row across the table, the designer also learns that a 40 footcandle illumination level is achieved when the luminaires are spaced 8' apart. This spacing means that a luminaire should be located 2' in from each sign edge and all other luminaires spaced on 8' centers. This means that three luminaires will be required for this 20' long sign.

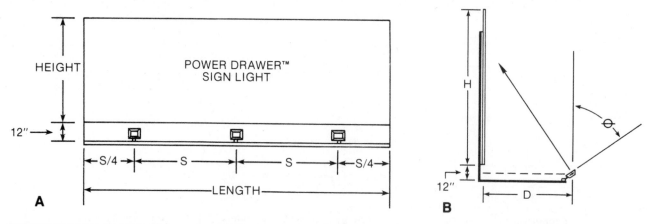

A

B

Fig. 3: (A) The height, length, and spacing dimensions of a sign lighting application. Note how the luminaires are positioned 12″ below the area to be illuminated. (B) The luminaire aiming angle. In this illustration, D equals the setback distance of the luminaire.

Roadway Sign Lighting

The project involves illuminating a roadway sign located in a busy central business district of a moderately large city. By referring to Table 1 (page 200) it is found that the ambient luminance of a busy central business district is classified as bright, and roadway signs in these areas require 40 footcandles of illumination for proper visibility. Figure 4 illustrates the correct roadway sign border line position as well as the area on the sign face where the correct maximum/minimum and average/minimum uniformities must be maintained. The designer also knows that the sign is 15' high, 20' long, and has white let-

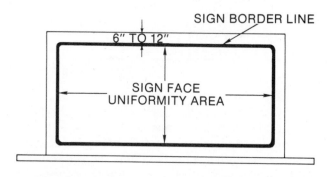

Fig. 4: The border margins and sign face area of typical roadway signs.

Advertising Sign Lighting

The same principles described under **Roadway Sign Lighting** also apply to advertising sign lighting, but in this case color rendering and color reflectance properties become even more important considerations. For example, the lighting designer just

Table 5: Sign Light Application Data

Type	Wattage	Designation	Lumens	Catalog Number	Sign Height	Tilt Angle	4'	5'	6'	8'	10'
Lamp Information							**Luminaire Spacing**				
							Footcandle Level				
Clear Mercury	175	H39KB-R175	7,450	FS1048	6'	52.5°	128	105	87	65	52
					9'	42.5°	87	70	59	44	36
					12'	37.5°	66	54	45	34	28
					15'	35°	54	45	38	29	23
					20'	35°	40	34	29	22	18
Clear Mercury	250	H37KB-R250	10,300	FS1058	6'	52.5°	178	144	120	90	72
					9'	42.5°	120	97	81	61	49
					12'	37.5°	91	74	63	47	38
					15'	35°	75	62	52	40	32
					20'	35°	56	47	40	31	25
Metal Halide	175	MS175/HOR	15,000	FS1148	6'	52.5°	259	210	175	131	105
					9'	42.5°	174	141	119	89	71
					12'*	37.5°	133*	108*	91*	69*	55*
					15'*	35°	109*	90*	75*	58*	46
					20'	35°	81	68	58	45	36
Metal Halide	250	MS250/HOR	23,000	FS1158	6'	52.5°	397	323	268	201	161
					9'	42.5°	267	216	182	137	110
					12'*	37.5°	204	166	140	106	85
					15'*	35°	167	138	116	88	71
					20'	35°	124	105	90	69	55
High Pressure Sodium	150	LU150	16,000	FS1838	6'	55°	278	226	187	140	113
					9'	42.5°	165	133	112	84	67
					12'	37.5°	126	102	87	66	52
					15'	35°	105	86	73	55	44
					20'	37.5°	86	73	62	47	38
High Pressure Sodium	250	LU250/S	30,000	FS1258	6'	55°	504	408	338	253	203
					9'	45°	331	267	224	168	135
					12'	40°	252	205	173	130	105
					15'	37.5°	208	171	144	109	87
					20'	37.5°	156	130	111	85	69

*Uniformity meets or exceeds the 4:1 maximum/minimum uniformity ratio recommended by the IES for Advertising Sign lighting. All other listings meet or exceed the 6:1 maximum/minimum uniformity ratio recommended by the IES for Roadway Sign lighting.

Notes:
1. All illumination levels are stated in average initial footcandles as measured on the vertical sign face. Included are readings taken 6" in from the sign edge.
2. Table data is based on luminaires located 12" below the sign's bottom edge and at a 4' setback distance out from the sign face for signs 6' through 15' in height. For signs 20' in height, the luminaire is located 12" below the sign's bottom edge and at a 5' setback distance from the sign face.
3. Lamp Proration: The listed footcandle values can be prorated down by substituting lamps of lower wattages. Use the lamp proration factors listed in Table 6 (page 205).

mentioned must now illuminate an advertising sign of the poster panel variety which utilizes dark reds, oranges, and browns in its color scheme. Again the sign is located in a central business district.

From Table 2 (page 200) the designer realizes that the dark earth-tone color scheme constitutes a low average reflectance of advertising copy, while the central business district is classified as a bright surrounding. Advertising signs of low reflectance located in bright surroundings require 100 or more footcandles of illumination. After reading the notes beneath Table 2, the designer also knows the dimensions of standard poster panel signs (12.25' high × 24.5' long). Table 4 (page 201) states that only metal halide lamps should be used in the lighting of advertising signs.

The designer now knows all he or she needs to know and can turn to Table 5 to quickly complete the

design. The designer selects a 250-watt, MS250/HOR, metal halide lamp. Table 5 indicates that when this particular lamp-luminaire combination is used to illuminate a 12' high sign, the unit should be positioned at a 4' setback distance and aimed at a 37.5° aiming angle. The table also states that a 106 footcandle illumination level is achieved when the luminaires are spaced 8' apart. This means that to achieve the finest lighting uniformity along this 24'6" long sign, a luminaire should be placed 4'3" in from each sign edge with a third luminaire located 8' farther in at the midpoint of the sign.

Exterior Building Lighting

In this application example, the lighting designer must illuminate a building wall 20' in height which is located in a bright surround area. The building is constructed of common tan brick, which Table 3 (page 201) indicates has a light reflectance of 20% to 45%. The required illumination level for this combination of surroundings and reflectance is listed as 30 footcandles. The table also recommends both metal halide and high pressure sodium lamps as possible light sources; but since the building is rather large and the client is concerned over system economics, the designer chooses to use HPS sources.

After studying Table 5 for a moment, the designer can see that 150-watt, LU150, high pressure sodium lamps are the logical choice. For a 20' wall height, luminaires equipped with 150-watt, HPS lamps would be set back from the wall a distance of 5' and aimed at a 37.5° angle. The luminaire spacing distance would be 10', and the illumination level created over the vertical surface would be approximately 38 footcandles.

OBTAINING LOWER LIGHT LEVELS

Table 5 does not list all of the possible HID lamps that can be used for these sign heights and luminaire spacings. Lamps of lower wattages and lamps of similar wattages but lower lumen outputs can be substituted for those listed in Table 5 to obtain lower illumination levels over the same area. The exact new footcandle level is calculated by multiplying the original footcandle level found in Table 5 by the correct lamp proration factor found in Table 6.

For example, in the exterior building lighting problem discussed, the building's bright surroundings forced the designer to use 150-watt, HPS lamps to produce an illumination level of 38 footcandles. However, if the same building were located in dark surroundings, Table 3 indicates that 15 footcandles would be sufficient illumination. Yet, as you can see, Table 5 does not list any HPS lamp capable of producing such *low* lighting levels.

Table 6 lists two possible HPS substitutes for the original 150-watt, HPS lamp. The 70-watt, LU70 design will produce light levels 0.363 times that of the 150-watt lamp. Substitution in this particular problem would mean 0.363 × 38 footcandles = 13.79 footcandles, a light level not quite meeting the 15 footcandle requirement. The second possible substitute, the 100-watt, LU100 design will produce 0.594 times as much light as the 150-watt lamp for a new level of 0.594 × 38 footcandles = 22.57 footcandles, a level which exceeds the minimum requirement. So, in this case, the 100-watt, HPS lamp is a viable substitute. Remember, when a substitution is made, only the illumination levels change; the tilting angle, setback distance, spacing distance, and uniformity ratios do not change.

LIGHTING LARGER SURFACES

Many surfaces are greater in area than the maximum areas listed in Table 5. For example, many buildings are higher than 20'. In these cases, the computer generated isofootcandle curve reference plots found in Appendix G can be used to work out an acceptable design. These footcandle plots, A through F, are based on the actual light patterns and levels produced when various HID lamps are placed in Power Drawer Sign Light luminaires and set at a specific setback distance and aiming angle.

The specifications for each individual footcandle plot are stated under Table 6. This information includes the lamp type, wattage, designation, and initial lumen production. The lamp-luminaire catalog number is included to assure easy cross-reference to other SPI Lighting publications. The exact luminaire tilt angle is given along with the average initial footcandles produced and the maximum/minimum uniformity ratio.

Footcandle plot A, shown in Fig. 5 (page 206), illustrates points common to all plots given in Appendix G. The luminaire is located 1' below the vertical surface, and the luminaire setback distance is 4' in all cases. All plots are divided into 1 square foot grids and measure 9' on a side for a total area of 81 square feet. Illumination levels expressed in horizontal footcandles are given at each of the 81 grid points, and points of equal illumination are connected with isofootcandle lines.

Original Lamp	Footcandle Plot*	Substitute Lamp Information				Proration Factor
		Type	Wattage	Designation	Lumens	
Clear Mercury 175-watt	A	Clear Mercury	100	H38HT-R100	3,900	.523
Metal Halide 175-watt (horizontal design)	C	Metal Halide	175	MVR175/U	12,000	.800
Metal Halide 250-watt (horizontal design)	D	Metal Halide	250	MVR250/U	19,500	.848
HPS 150-watt	E	HPS	70	LU70	5,800	.363
HPS 150-watt	E	HPS	100	LU100	9,500	.594
HPS 250-watt (superior design)	F	HPS	250	LU250	27,500	.917

*The isofootcandle curve reference plots A through F for sign lighting applications can be found in Appendix G of this handbook. Multiply all footcandle values appearing on the grid by the appropriate proration factor. The pertinent data concerning these plots is listed below.

Footcandle Plot A: 175-watt clear mercury, H39KB-R175 lamp producing 7,450 initial lumens. Catalog number FS1048. The luminaire setback distance is 4', and the luminaire tilt angle is 47.5°. The average initial footcandle level produced is 27.8, and the maximum/minimum uniformity ratio is 5.6:1.

Footcandle Plot B: 250-watt clear mercury H37KB-R250 lamp producing 10,300 initial lumens. Catalog number FS1058. The luminaire setback distance is 4', and the luminaire tilt angle is 47.5°. The average initial footcandle level produced is 38.4, and the maximum/minimum uniformity ratio is 5.6:1.

Footcandle Plot C: 175-watt metal halide MS175/HOR lamp producing 15,000 initial lumens. Catalog number FS1148. The luminaire setback distance is 4', and the luminaire tilt angle is 47.5°. The average initial footcandle level produced is 56.0, and the maximum/minimum uniformity ratio is 5.6:1.

Footcandle Plot D: 250-watt metal halide MS250/HOR lamp producing 23,000 initial lumens. Catalog number FS1158. The luminaire setback distance is 4', and the luminaire tilt angle is 47.5°. The average initial footcandle level produced is 85.8, and the maximum/minimum uniformity ratio is 5.6:1.

Footcandle Plot E: 150-watt high pressure sodium LU150 lamp producing 16,000 initial lumens. Catalog number FS1838. The luminaire setback distance is 4', and the luminaire tilt angle is 47.5°. The average initial footcandle level produced is 55.2, and the maximum/minimum uniformity ratio is 5.2:1.

Footcandle Plot F: 250-watt high pressure sodium LU250/S lamp producing 30,000 initial lumens. Catalog number FS1258. The luminaire setback distance is 4', and the luminaire tilt angle is 45°. The average initial footcandle level produced is 109.6, and the maximum/minimum uniformity ratio is 5.1:1.

Using the Isofootcandle Plots

The isofootcandle curve reference plots can be used in numerous ways to formulate sign and building lighting designs. As they are presented in Appendix G, these plots can be used to lay out surfaces measuring 9' × 9' to absolutely precise footcandle level and uniformity specifications. However, by simply altering the standard setback distance of 4', these **same footcandle plots** can be used to lay out vertical surfaces smaller and **very much larger** than the 9' × 9' areas gridded out on the plots. This is due to a very simple and predictable fact: As the setback distance between the luminaire and building or sign increases, the total area covered by the light emitted from the luminaire increases and the average light level over the area decreases (Fig. 6).

Because these relationships are directly and inversely proportionate to one another, a set of conversion factors can be tabulated which will accurately change the grid spacing and illumination levels appearing on the footcandle plots (Table 7, page 207). By working with the conversion factors

and the information found in Tables 1 through 6 and Appendix G, it is possible to illuminate just about any size area to any desired illumination level by simply altering the luminaire setback distance.

One point must never be forgotten. If the standard setback distance of 4' is changed, the grid spacing and illumination levels given on the plots **must also change.** If the setback distance is altered without changing the amount of area illuminated, the luminaire aiming angle must change and all illumination level values given on the footcandle plot become invalid. Consider the large area application discussed in the following paragraphs.

Large Area Application

A lighting designer must illuminate a 35' wall constructed of light marble which is located in a dark

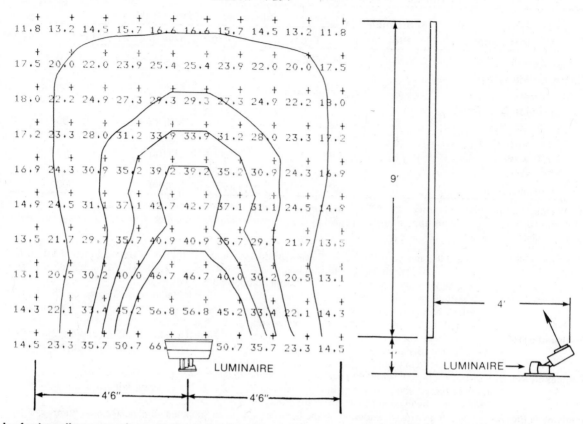

```
11.8  13.2  14.5  15.7  16.6  16.6  15.7  14.5  13.2  11.8

17.5  20.0  22.0  23.9  25.4  25.4  23.9  22.0  20.0  17.5

18.0  22.2  24.9  27.3  29.3  29.3  27.3  24.9  22.2  18.0

17.2  23.3  28.0  31.2  33.9  33.9  31.2  28.0  23.3  17.2

16.9  24.3  30.9  35.2  39.2  39.2  35.2  30.9  24.3  16.9

14.9  24.5  31.1  37.1  42.7  42.7  37.1  31.1  24.5  14.9

13.5  21.7  29.7  35.7  40.9  40.9  35.7  29.7  21.7  13.5

13.1  20.5  30.2  40.0  46.7  46.7  40.0  30.2  20.5  13.1

14.3  22.1  33.4  45.2  56.8  56.8  45.2  33.4  22.1  14.3

14.5  23.3  35.7  50.7  66.      50.7  35.7  23.3  14.5
```

LUMINAIRE

|← 4'6" →|← 4'6" →|

9'

4'

1'

LUMINAIRE →

Fig. 5: Isofootcandle curve reference plot A. Grid points are spaced 1' apart. The right side elevation of the illustration shows how this information would be utilized in an actual application.

surround area. From Table 3 (page 201) the designer realizes that the system must produce an average surface illumination of 5 footcandles. But the designer also realizes that the 35' height exceeds any height listed in Table 5 (page 203), and the 5 footcandle illumination level is also lower than any listed in Table 5.

One solution is as follows: The designer knows that the 35' wall height is essentially four times as great as the 9' heights gridded out on the footcandle plots given in Appendix G, so a new setback distance must be found which will increase the area covered by a factor of 4. By studying Table 7, the designer learns that increasing the setback distance to 16' will do just that. However, he or she must also note that increasing the setback distance by a factor of 4 will decrease the light levels produced by a factor of 0.063.

As previously stated, the final illumination level attained must be approximately 5 footcandles. By

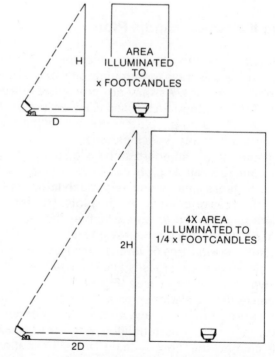

Fig. 6: As the setback distance increases, the area covered will increase and illumination levels on the vertical surface will decrease.

206 EXTERIOR LIGHTING

Table 7: Setback Distance Conversion Table		
Setback Distance from Vertical Surface	Illumination Conversion Factor	Grid Distance Conversion Factor
2'	4.000	.5
4' (standard)	1.000	1.0
6'	.444	1.5
8'	.250	2.0
10'	.160	2.5
12'	.111	3.0
14'	.082	3.5
16'	.063	4.0
18'	.049	4.5
20'	.040	5.0

Notes: 1. The distance between the grid points on the Isofootcandle Curve Reference Plots A through F found in Appendix G is 1'. These plots are based on a luminaire setback distance of 4'.

2. When a new setback distance is selected, multiply all footcandle levels found on the isofootcandle reference plot by the appropriate illumination conversion factor listed above. Also, find the new distance between the plot grid points by multiplying the original distance of 1' by the appropriate grid distance conversion factor listed above. For example: At a new setback distance of 16', all footcandle levels given on the isofootcandle curve reference plot must be multiplied by a 0.063 factor. The original 1' grid distance is also multiplied by a factor of 4. This new grid distance changes the overall area of the grid plot from 9' × 9' to 36' × 36'. Simply multiply all dimensions by the distance conversion factor of 4.

3. Do not change the luminaire setback distance without changing the area illuminated. If this is done, the aiming angles change and the illumination levels at all grid points and isofootcandle lines become invalid.

dividing this 5 footcandle illumination level by the light reduction factor of 0.063 (5 ÷ 0.063 = 79.3), the lighting designer finds that an original 9' × 9' footcandle plot with an average illumination level of 79.3 footcandles or more can easily be altered to accommodate the increased area. After checking the footcandle plot descriptions listed under Table 6 (page 205), the designer finds that footcandle plot D with an average illuminance of 85.8 footcandles closely matches his or her needs. (The actual new illumination level will be 85.8 footcandles × 0.063 = 5.4 footcandles.) From the information listed in the footcandle plot D description, the final design specifications will be as follows:

Power Drawer Sign Light luminaires will be equipped with 250-watt, MS250/HOR metal halide lamps. The luminaires will be positioned 1' below the vertical surface **and their setback distance will be 16'.** The aiming angle will be 47.5°. **The luminaires will be spaced on 36' centers, and the area covered by each luminaire will increase to 36' × 36' or 1,296 square feet. The illumination level maintained over this area will be 5.4 footcandles and the maximum/minimum uniformity ratio will be 5.6:1.**

The Grid Method Solution

A grid method very similar to that discussed earlier in Section II under **Parking Area Applications** can also be employed for vertical surface lighting. In this method, a layout drawing of the vertical surface is made and then gridded out to the scale corresponding to that of the isofootcandle curve reference plot. The footcandle levels occurring at each grid point on the reference plot are then transferred to the corresponding points on the layout drawing. Remember that the setback distance conversion factors listed in Table 7 make it possible to formulate numerous variations of the six basic reference plots given in Appendix G. Remember, too, that when the setback distance is changed from the standard of 4', all 81 illumination levels appearing on the footcandle plot must change along with the grid spacing scale.

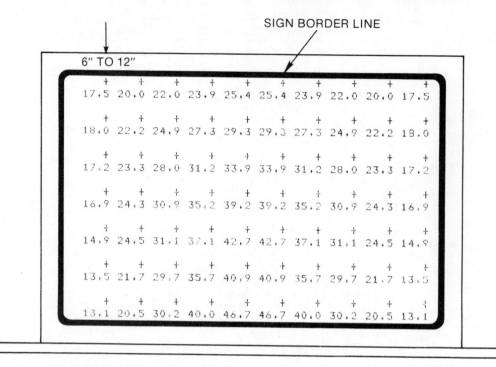

SIGN BORDER LINE

6" TO 12"

+	+	+	+	+	+	+	+	+	+
17.5	20.0	22.0	23.9	25.4	25.4	23.9	22.0	20.0	17.5
18.0	22.2	24.9	27.3	29.3	29.3	27.3	24.9	22.2	18.0
17.2	23.3	28.0	31.2	33.9	33.9	31.2	28.0	23.3	17.2
16.9	24.3	30.9	35.2	39.2	39.2	35.2	30.9	24.3	16.9
14.9	24.5	31.1	37.1	42.7	42.7	37.1	31.1	24.5	14.9
13.5	21.7	29.7	35.7	40.9	40.9	35.7	29.7	21.7	13.5
13.1	20.5	30.2	40.0	46.7	46.7	40.0	30.2	20.5	13.1

Fig. 7: Example of how a layout drawing of a proposed vertical surface can be gridded out to find exact footcandle levels at specific points.

Once the desired footcandle plot has been properly altered, its illumination values can be transferred to the layout drawing (Fig. 7). Luminaire spacing positions can be changed so that certain grid points overlap, thereby increasing the footcandle level at certain points on the vertical surface. Uniformities can be computed by using the same method described under **Parking Area Applications.**

The grid method is extremely accurate and easy to use once the designer understands its principles and practices the method. It is the finest method known for the lighting of irregularly sized or shaped surfaces and is often the only accurate means of lighting special one-of-a-kind applications. It is strongly recommended that you review the sections under **Parking Area Lighting** dealing with the use of isofootcandle curve reference plots. In this way you will have a better understanding of the design principles involved in the grid method of layout.

Security Lighting

There are two basic classifications of security lighting—surveillance lighting and protective lighting. **Surveillance security lighting** is used as part of an overall security system employed to visually observe potential intruders or escapees. The visual observance task is performed by guards at fixed stations or on patrol. Closed-circuit television systems are also commonly utilized. In this way, a single guard in a control room can visually monitor the activities in several areas.

Surveillance security systems are used where there are large open areas protected by barriers or fences or in smaller, confined spaces, such as walkways between buildings. Surveillance systems are often used for prisons, ammunition dumps or depots, storage depots, nuclear or fossil fuel electric generation stations, and other facilities which run a high risk of sabotage or theft. The lighting for such systems is uniquely fitted to the needs and physical dimensions of each individual facility, and no standard guidelines can be drawn. Due to the uniqueness of each surveillance security system, lighting for these applications **will not** be discussed in this handbook. Consult SPI Lighting for information and aid in the lighting of individual surveillance security systems.

PROTECTIVE SECURITY LIGHTING

Most buildings and facilities other than those already mentioned employ what is known as **protective security lighting.** These buildings and facilities have open access to the public and, as a result, can be vandalized or entered by intruders. In most cases, the protective security lighting system constitutes the building's entire security system. There are no special guards patrolling the perimeter areas as in surveillance systems.

Effective protective security lighting systems will discourage or deter intruder attempts by making the intruder believe that detection by building occupants, passing pedestrians, or regular night watchman or police patrols will be inevitable. An effective system should also **make detection inevitable** if entry into the area occurs. It should offer its users complete reliability, and failure of a lamp or lamps should not create a dark spot vulnerable to intrusion. Finally, protective lighting systems should not create glare or spill light which will annoy pedestrians, handicap roadway traffic, or pollute neighboring buildings or residential areas.

System Economics

Protective security lighting systems should be designed to provide the most economical operation available. As with all types of lighting systems, the three main economic factors listed in order of importance are (1) operating costs, (2) maintenance costs, and (3) initial equipment costs. The type of lamp selected for use in the system has a strong influence on operating and maintenance costs. That is why the HID high pressure sodium lamps are recommended for all protective security lighting systems. HPS lamps have the highest efficacy (lumens of light produced/watt of electricity consumed) of all lamp types, and HPS lamp life and lumen maintenance characteristics are also the finest available. Since color rendition is of no consequence in security lighting systems, the golden-white color of HPS light causes no problems.

To effectively utilize the tremendous light-producing capabilities of high pressure sodium lamps, the luminaires used should produce highly efficient asymmetrical light patterns. Specific equipment and illumination level requirements for both ground-mounted and building-mounted protective lighting systems will be discussed on the following pages.

PROTECTIVE LIGHTING METHODS

Any protective lighting system must provide adequate illumination in the area surrounding a building's perimeter. This illumination can be provided in one of two ways: from ground-mounted luminaires or from luminaires mounted on the building itself. Each method produces a different lighting effect.

The Shadow and Silhouette System

In the shadow and silhouette system of protective lighting, the building face or facade is illuminated from ground-mounted luminaires located away from the building. As shown in Fig. 1, any intruder passing between the luminaire and the building will cast a large shadow onto the illuminated building surface.

Fig. 1: An intruder passing between a ground-mounted luminaire and an illuminated building exterior will cast a long, obvious shadow.

Since this enlarged shadow signals the presence of a person in an area not normally open to regular pedestrian traffic, this type of lighting acts as a deterrent to an intruder and a vandal. Also, if the intruder is approaching but has not yet entered the area of illumination, his or her silhouette will stand out against the illuminated wall (Fig. 2). These shadows or silhouettes are easily detected by passing pedestrians, police patrols, or night watchmen.

Silhouette or shadowing effects are created by using the same lighting methods employed for building floodlighting discussed in the previous section, **Exterior Lighting: Sign and Building Lighting.** Follow the illumination requirements and design methods suggested for building lighting. Sign Light luminaires and high pressure sodium lamps should be used for all applications. While a ground-mounted protective security lighting system can add aesthetic beauty to a building's exterior, its primary purpose is to reveal the shadows and silhouettes of potential vandals and intruders. This means that the lighting level should be relatively uniform along the entire building face, a characteristic not necessary in some decorative building floodlighting applications.

The major drawback of the shadow and silhouette system is that its ground-mounted luminaires are easy targets for vandals and intruders. For this single reason, building facade- or parapet-mounted lighting systems are the preferred protective security lighting systems in use today.

Building Facade- or Parapet-Mounted Systems

The second and preferred method of protective security lighting involves mounting luminaires on the walls of the building itself (Fig. 3). In this type of system, the IES recommends that no less than

EXTERIOR LIGHTING

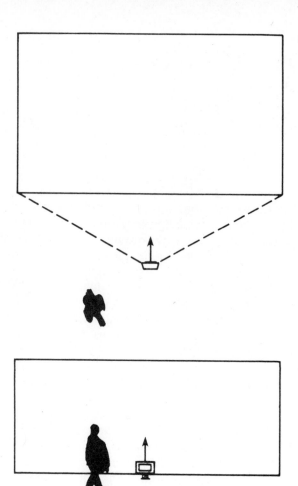

Fig. 2: As an intruder approaches the perimeter of a ground-mounted protective lighting system, his or her silhouette will stand out against the illuminated background of the building.

0.5 horizontal maintained footcandles be provided throughout the illuminated area. The width of this perimeter area will vary, but accepted field practice dictates that the illumination level should extend out from the building a minimum of 20′. No point within this area should be illuminated to a level below 0.5 footcandles, and reasonable uniformities should occur. It is also accepted field practice to provide a maximum/minimum uniformity ratio of 6:1 or less for proper visibility. The minimum lighting level of 0.5 footcandles should also extend up the building face for a distance of not less than 3′ (Fig. 4).

SPI Monitor Wall Light luminaires equipped with high pressure sodium lamps are recommended for all building facade- or parapet-mounted protective lighting systems (see page 99). When installed at the recommended spacing intervals and mounting heights, the Monitor Wall Light luminaire produces an asymmetrical light distribution ideally suited for these applications (Fig. 5).

Table 1 (page 212) contains all of the information needed to design building-mounted security light-

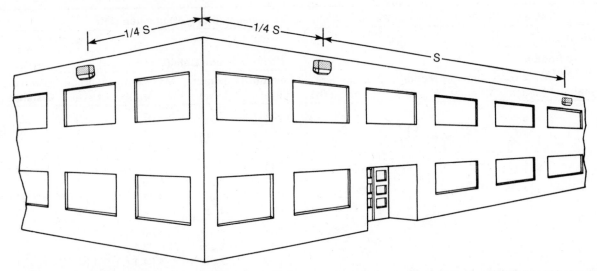

Fig. 3: Example of a building facade- or parapet-mounted protective lighting system. Note that the distance between the end luminaires and the building corner equals one-fourth that of the normal luminaire spacing distance.

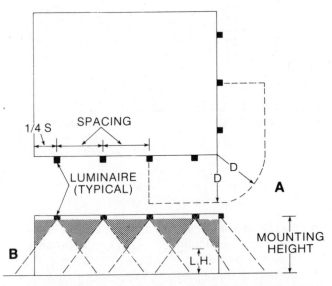

Fig. 4: (A) D equals the effective projection distance of the system. A minimum projection distance of 20' is recommended for any application and the maximum/minimum uniformity ratio within this area should not exceed 6:1. (B) The lighting height as measured on the face of the building. A minimum height of 3' is recommended in all cases.

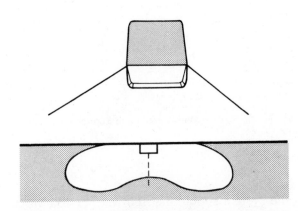

Fig. 5: The asymmetrical light pattern created by the Monitor Wall Light luminaire effectively lights the perimeter of building areas.

ing systems. The table lists the wattages, designations, and initial lumen productions of appropriate high pressure sodium lamps. The SPI Monitor Wall Light luminaire data includes the SPI Lighting lamp-luminaire catalog number, mounting height, and spacing distance. The illumination data lists the maximum, minimum, and average initial footcandle levels produced, and the maximum/minimum uniformity ratios which will occur when a particular set of design criteria is followed. As you can see, all minimum levels exceed the 0.5 minimum footcandle level recommended by the IES, and all uniformity ratios meet the 6:1 or better requirement. The effec-

tive projection distance given in the last column states the maximum distance from the building wall that the system will illuminate according to these IES standards.

For example, a lighting designer must design a protective lighting system for a building measuring 30' in height. The system must project adequate light to a point 30' from the building wall, and the client wants the finest light uniformity possible.

The lighting designer first determines that a luminaire mounting height of 24' (6' below the top edge of the building) will be satisfactory. The designer then locates the 24' mounting height listed in Table 1. As it reads from left to right, the table indicates

Table 1: Building Facade- or Parapet-Mounted Protective Lighting Application Data

Watts	Designation	Lumens	Catalog Number	Mounting Height (ft)	Luminaire Spacing (ft)	Minimum Level	Maximum Level	Max./Min. Uniformity	Average Level	Effective Projected Distance (ft)
	High Pressure Sodium (Medium Base)					**Illumination Data (footcandles)**				
35	LU35/MED	2,250	W2031	12	32	.524	2.66	5.07:1	1.30	21
				14	34	.525	2.12	4.05:1	1.14	21
				16	36	.532	1.71	3.22:1	1.02	21
50	LU50/MED	4,000	W2051	12	36	.738	4.47	6.00:1	2.06	28
				14	48	.507	3.07	6.00:1	1.44	20
				16	50	.525	2.34	4.47:1	1.30	21
				18	56	.493	1.86	3.79:1	1.09	20
70	LU70/MED	5,800	W2071	14	48	.735	4.45	6.00:1	2.09	30
				16	62	.558	3.23	5.78:1	1.53	21
				18	66	.518	2.56	4.94:1	1.34	21
				20	68	.509	2.15	4.24:1	1.22	22
100	LU100/MED	9,500	W2101	16	60	.870	5.30	6.00:1	2.39	33
				18	68	.735	4.29	5.84:1	1.98	30
				20	76	.585	3.47	5.93:1	1.67	26
				22	82	.513	2.85	5.56:1	1.47	26
150	LU150/MED	16,000	W2151	18	68	1.24	7.23	5.84:1	3.34	44
				20	76	.986	5.84	5.93:1	2.81	42
				22	84	.802	4.78	5.96:1	2.39	40
				24	92	.667	3.99	5.99:1	2.06	36
				26	100	.563	3.43	6.00:1	1.78	34

Notes: The illumination levels listed are the initial horizontal footcandles occurring (A) on the finished grade at a point out from the building equal to the effective projection distance and (B) at a point 3′ above the finished grade at the building wall. Refer to **Section I: Lamps and Ballasts** and **Section IV: System Maintenance and Economics** for details concerning lumen depreciation, lamp life, and system maintenance factors.

that the system should use 150-watt, LU150/MED, high pressure sodium lamps which produce 16,000 initial lumens. The SPI Lighting lamp-luminaire catalog number for this system is W2151.

The table lists a maximum spacing of 92′ between luminaires and indicates an effective projection distance of 36′, well within the 30′ projection range the designer requires. Closer spacings will result in higher illumination levels, lower uniformity ratios, and greater projection distances. As shown in Figs. 3 and 4, the distance between the building corner and the first luminaire should not exceed one-fourth of the suggested luminaire spacing distance. So for this particular application, the first luminaire on any wall must be located no more than 23′ (92′ ÷ 4) from the corner. If this one-fourth spacing guideline is disregarded, the illumination levels, uniformities, and effective projection distances produced will not meet the standards listed in Table 1.

System Maintenance and Economics

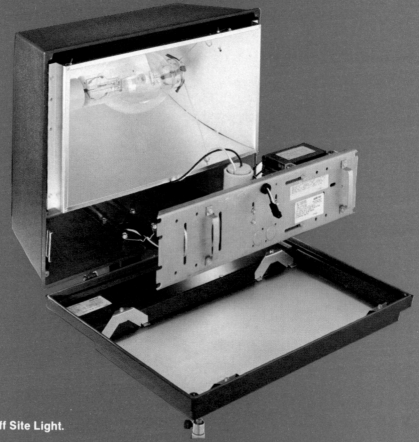

The Power Drawer Cutoff Site Light.

The Power Drawer Area Light.

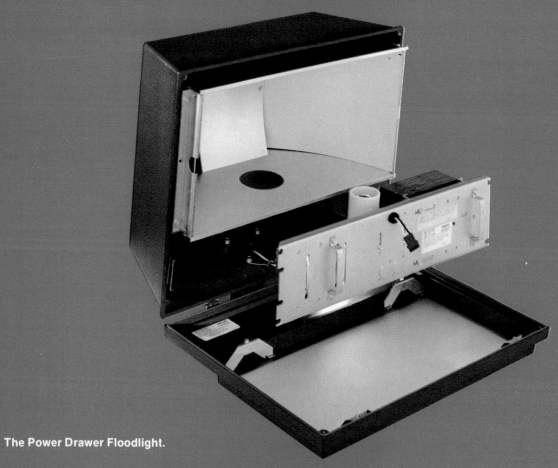

The Power Drawer Floodlight.

The Power Drawer Sign Light.

THE ADVANTAGES OF POWER DRAWER
LUMINAIRE BALLAST ASSEMBLY

- Contains all electrical components.
- Slides into luminaire housing and connects to power supply with polarized quick-disconnect plug assembly.
- Allows installation of housing without weight of ballast assembly.
- Allows a single housing to accommodate a variety of lamp and ballast types.

- Contains a prepositioned lamp and socket for maximum optical efficiency.
- Three housing sizes to accommodate ballasts for 100 through 1000 watt mercury, 70 through 1000 watt high pressure sodium, and 175 through 1500 watt metal halide lamps.
- Multi-tap ballasts available in most wattage sizes for different volt operations.

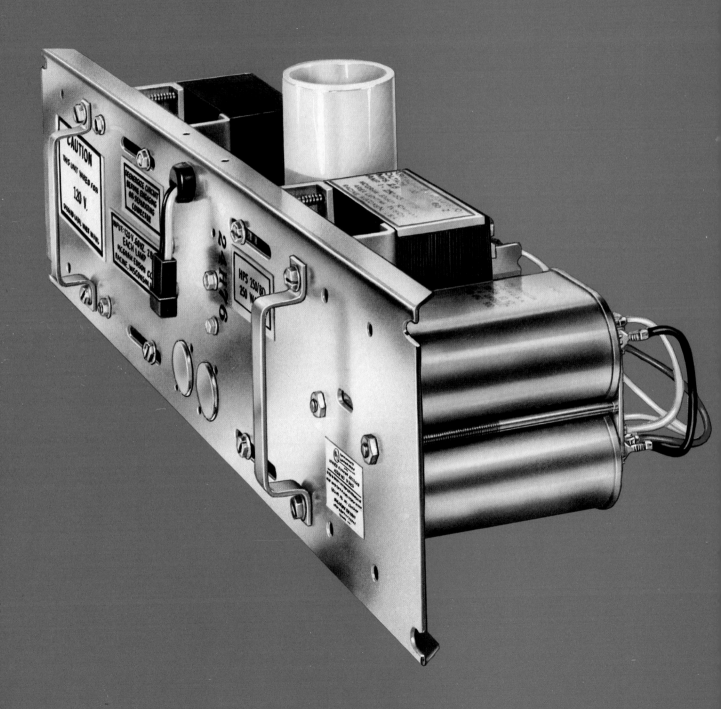

Lighting System Maintenance

The purpose of lighting system maintenance is to ensure the continued effectiveness and efficiency of the lighting installation. To achieve this goal, any practical methods which can be used to keep light output near its initial level should be investigated and implemented. Such maintenance techniques should maintain desired illumination levels or lighting effects while minimizing operational, energy, and maintenance costs.

LIGHT LOSS FACTORS

The fact that lighting designers must incorporate light loss factors into their initial design tabulations is in itself an admission that no amount of recurring maintenance can keep the output of a system to its initial level. Light loss factors, often expressed in terms of percentages, indicate the amount of expectably uncontrollable depreciation and the amount of projected effort that will be necessary to overcome this depreciation. A number of light loss factors were discussed in **Section I: Lamps and Ballasts**, and these and all other pertinent light loss factors are summarized in this section.

Lamp Lumen Depreciation

As explained in Section I, the light output of any lamp decreases as the lamp increases in age. This decrease, known as lamp lumen depreciation, can only be controlled by a carefully planned relamping program. Various tables found in Section I list the exact lamp lumen depreciation for specific lamp models, and when making any calculation concerning lumen depreciation, always remember to use the lamp's mean lumen value.

Voltage Drop

Voltage drop within a system can seriously lower light output. The National Electrical Code (N.E.C.) allows a 3% voltage drop within the wiring system, and since light output will decrease by about 1.5% for every 1% drop in line voltage, a possible lumen loss of 4.5% will occur by N.E.C. standards.

In addition to this drop, you must also be aware of possible drops in the service voltage. For example, if the utility company servicing an installation is forced by a lack of generating capacity to reduce the service voltage from 120 volts to 108 volts, an additional 15% (1.5 × 10%) lumen loss will result. When added to the 4.5% reduction from system voltage loss, a 19.5% reduction in light output is possible **before any lamp lumen depreciation occurs**. This means that a new 1000-watt metal halide lamp designed to produce 110,000 lumens will only produce 89,100 lumens. The importance of knowing the system voltage drop and the service voltage drop (if any) cannot be overemphasized.

The Ballast Factor

Light loss due to the operational characteristics of the lamp's ballast is usually only a problem in systems employing fluorescent lamps. The accepted ballast loss factor for fluorescent lighting systems is 0.90. This means that a light loss of roughly 10% can be attributed to ballast related problems. Ballast factors are not needed for HID lamps, a fact which distinctly shows the advantages of HID systems over fluorescent installations.

Luminaire Ambient Temperature. The surrounding ambient temperature can adversely affect the light output of a lamp. Cold weather can seriously reduce the light output of fluorescent lamps, and use of special protective jackets and special ballasts should be considered if fluorescent lamps are subject to cold temperatures.

Cold ambient temperatures do not affect the light output of high intensity discharge lamps or incandescent lamps, but exceedingly high temperatures can adversely affect the three major lamp groups. High ambient temperatures can lead to ballast overheating and malfunction. Exceeding the lamp's specified maximum operating temperature will also lead to lamp failure, and high ambient temperatures can adversely affect luminaire finishes. Refer to the lamp manufacturer's data sheet for specific information concerning any temperature related characteristics associated with a particular lamp model.

Lamp Tilt Factor. As explained fully in Section I, this factor is of particular importance when working with metal halide lamps. Refer to page 9 for details.

Luminaire Dirt Depreciation (LDD). A significant amount of light loss can be attributed to the accumu-

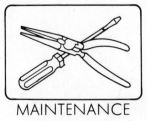

lation of dirt on the luminaire surface. The LDD is at best a very complicated and important factor. It is the multiplier used to relate the initial illumination provided by a clean luminaire to the reduced illumination provided by a dirty luminaire at the time of the anticipated cleaning. For example, if a luminaire generates 100,000 lumens when clean and the LDD for the installation is 0.80, the same luminaire will generate 80,000 lumens (100,000 × 0.80) at the time of its scheduled maintenance.

In order to determine a relatively accurate luminaire dirt depreciation factor, the lighting designer must know the ambient atmosphere contaminant level for the area in which the luminaire is located, the time interval between cleanings, and the exact construction characteristics of the luminaire in use. Table 1 lists the five major ambient atmosphere contaminant levels found in exterior commercial and industrial settings. Detailed research has found that over 90% of all applications fall into the moderate contaminant level of no more than 600 micrograms per cubic meter. Four-year relamping and cleaning intervals were also found to be the most prevalent.

Table 2 lists the five major ambient atmosphere contaminant classifications found in interior commercial and industrial settings. Studies have shown

Table 2: Indoor Ambient Atmosphere Contaminant Classifications

Classification	Description
1. Very Clean	High grade offices, not near production. Laboratories. Clean rooms.
2. Clean	Offices in older buildings or near production. Light assembly. Inspection.
3. Medium	Mill offices. Paper processing. Light machining.
4. Dirty	Heat treating. High speed printing. Rubber processing.
5. Very Dirty	Similar to dirty classification, but luminaires are within the immediate area of contamination.

that three-year cleaning and relamping cycles are most prevalent in interior applications.

Tables 3 and 4 list the main outdoor and indoor luminaire types and give typical lumen dirt depreciation factors based on the contaminant levels found in Tables 1 and 2. LDD factors are based on four-year maintenance cycles for exterior installations and three-year maintenance cycles for interior installations.

All illumination levels in interior and exterior lighting systems are subject to revision by these various light loss factors. For example, a system is designed to produce 10 initial footcandles. There is a 4.5% line voltage drop and the lamp lumen depreciation factor over four years is 0.75. The lumen dirt depreciation factor over the same time span is 0.85, therefore:

At the time of installation the system will produce 0.955 (Voltage drop factor) × 10 footcandles = 9.55 footcandles.

Table 1: Outdoor Ambient Atmosphere Contaminant Classifications

Classification	Description
1. Very Clean	No nearby smoke or dust generating activities and low ambient contaminant levels. Light traffic. Generally limited to residential or rural areas. The ambient particulate level is no more than 150 micrograms per cubic meter.
2. Clean	No nearby smoke or dust generating activities. Moderate to heavy traffic. The ambient particulate level is no more than 300 micrograms per cubic meter.
3. Moderate	Moderate smoke or dust generating activities nearby. The ambient particulate level is no more than 600 micrograms per cubic meter.
4. Dirty	Smoke or dust plumes generated by nearby activities may occasionally envelop the luminaire.
5. Very Dirty	Situations where the luminaire is commonly enveloped by smoke or dust plumes.

Table 3: Outdoor Luminaire Dirt Depreciation Factors

Luminaire Description*	O	G	GF	S
Open Bottom Refractor	30%	—	—	—
Post Top	51%	56%	—	—
Cobra Head Ovate	—	59%	80%	—
Cobra Head Flat Lens	—	62%	83%	—
Architectural Drop Lens	—	59%	80%	83%
Architectural Flat Lens	—	62%	83%	86%
High Mast Ovate	30%	59%	80%	—
High Mast Flat Lens	—	59%	80%	83%
Floodlights, Ribbed Lens	—	61%	82%	85%
Floodlights, Flat Lens	—	64%	85%	88%

*Key to luminaire descriptions: O = open
G = closed and gasketed
GF = closed, gasketed, and filtered
S = sealed

Note: All factors are based on a 4-year maintenance cycle and moderate atmospheric dirt conditions.

Table 4: Indoor Luminaire Dirt Depreciation Factors

Luminaire Description	Contaminant Classification				
	1	2	3	4	5
SPI HID Indirect w/lens	.95	.85	.82	.75	.70
Fluorescent Indirect w/lens	.85	.79	.75	.68	.61
Fluorescent Louvered Direct	.97	.85	.62	.53	.45
Fluorescent Direct w/lens	.85	.79	.75	.68	.61
Fluorescent Open Reflector	.97	.85	.62	.53	.45
Halo Recessed Open	.97	.85	.62	.53	.45
Halo Recessed w/lens	.85	.79	.75	.68	.61
Halo Sealed Beam Track Unit	.85	.79	.75	.68	.61

Note: All factors are based on three-year maintenance cycles.

After four years the system will produce 0.955 (Voltage drop factor) × 0.75 (LLD) × 0.85 (LDD) × 10 footcandles = 6.08 footcandles.

Room Surface Dirt Depreciation. It is a standard practice in all commercial and industrial installations to use wall and ceiling finishes with high light reflectance values. These light colored finishes help balance brightness levels and distribute light; they are particularly important in indirect lighting applications. Dirt collection on room surfaces reduces reflected light, and while regular building maintenance will eliminate room surface direct depreciation in most cases, increased cleaning may have to be scheduled in dirty to very dirty industrial environments. Each case should be assessed on an individual basis.

Luminaire Surface Depreciation. The reflective surfaces or lenses of luminaires can be adversely affected by exposure to certain chemicals or cleaning agents. Scratching or marring of these surfaces during cleaning or servicing can also lower the luminaire's ability to effectively distribute light. Careful servicing and periodic inspections of lighting equipment should prevent this type of light loss.

Lamp Burnouts. Lamp burnouts are an obvious source of light loss. As lamps within a system burn out, the average system illuminance decreases proportionately. To minimize burnouts and maintenance costs, it is recommended that a regular schedule of group lamp replacement is conducted in which all lamps are replaced at one time. The replacement timetable is based on the lamps' lumen depreciation and/or lamp life. Refer to the tables in Section I for precise lamp data.

RELAMPING AND CLEANING PRACTICES

It is the responsibility of the system designer to set a timetable for cleaning and relamping. For obvious economic reasons, cleaning and relamping are performed together; however, in some extremely dirty atmospheres, supplemental cleanings may be required between relampings. As was previously mentioned, most installations are maintained on three-year or four-year cleaning and relamping intervals. Longer intervals usually result in excessive lumen depreciation; shorter intervals often waste labor, equipment, and lamps.

Holding to a strict maintenance schedule has definite economic advantages. Because the illumination level can be predicted for any time within the maintenance cycle, the lighting designer can attain the desired results using the lowest possible number of luminaires and/or lower lamp wattages. The system need not be over-designed to compensate for unpredictable light loss or poor maintenance habits. This results in reduced capital investment, operating costs, and energy use.

As lighting systems become increasingly complex, the labor and equipment needed to service them also increase in complexity. The overall size of the lighting installation is the key factor in determining how efficiently it can be cleaned and serviced. The rate of dirt accumulation and the accessibility of the luminaires are two other important factors. Obviously, as the number of luminaires increases, the economic savings resulting from mechanization and worker training will also increase. However, the expense of renting special equipment, such as lift trucks, may make frequent cleaning cost prohibitive for smaller installations. As you can see, programs of cleaning and relamping must be carefully planned and balanced during the initial stages of system design.

Luminaire Cleaning

Using the correct cleaning compound will ensure fast, thorough luminaire cleaning. The following are summaries of the proper cleaning agents for the various luminaire materials.

Aluminum. Aluminum should be cleaned with very mild soap and cleaners. Such cleaning agents will not affect the surface finish if the aluminum is immediately rinsed with clean water. Never use strong alkaline cleaners on aluminum surfaces.

Porcelain Enamel. Porcelain enamel finishes are not damaged by nonabrasive cleaners. Most detergents, automobile cleaners, and glass cleaners can be used under average conditions.

Synthetic Enamel. Strong cleaners may damage this finish, particularly if the material is left to soak in the solution. While moderate detergents should be used, alcohol and abrasive cleansers must be avoided.

Glass. Most nonabrasive cleaners work quite well on glass surfaces. Dry cleaners are usually preferred on clear glass panels, but not on etched or sand-blasted surfaces. Most detergents will work well under average dirt conditions.

Plastics. Quite often plastic surfaces develop static electrical charges which attract dust particles. Most detergents cannot provide permanent anti-static protection, and most plastic surfaces should be cleaned twice a year to provide relief from static dust collection. Special anti-static agents are available which provide long-range static protection. Keep in mind that plastic surfaces should not be wiped dry after the application of a rinse solution.

Maintenance Equipment

Many different types of maintenance equipment are available to aid in cleaning procedures. The size of the installation, mounting height, and accessibility of luminaires will dictate the type of equipment best suited for maintenance operations.

Ladders. Light weight, low cost, and simplicity make ladders the logical choice for simple, low level maintenance tasks. However, safety and mobility restrictions often limit the extensive use of ladders in many situations.

Scaffolding. Scaffolding provides a solid working platform and is generally safer and more mobile than ladder setups. Portable scaffolding should be sturdy, lightweight, fully adjustable, and easily assembled and disassembled.

Special telescoping scaffolding is particularly useful in lighting maintenance work. It provides a fast means of reaching luminaires located at a variety of mounting heights. Such scaffolding devices are available in a number of sizes, and all have work platforms which are raised either manually or electrically.

Lift Trucks. Lift trucks are probably the most versatile and efficient devices used in lighting maintenance work. They are capable of placing a suitable work platform near almost any luminaire location in a matter of minutes. While the initial investment for such equipment is quite high, the maintenance savings realized often make lift trucks practical for larger installations.

Vacuum Cleaners and Blowers. Such machines are often used to remove heavy layers of dust and dirt from luminaires before washing. Periodic use of vacuum cleaners or blowers may extend the amount of time between complete washings.

Wash Tanks. Specially designed wash tanks reduce per unit cleaning time and are especially advantageous for large installations. Tanks should have wash and rinse sections and heating units to keep solutions and rinse water hot. Drying racks for luminaire louvers or reflectors are another desirable feature.

Ultrasonic Cleaning. Ultrasonic cleaning removes foreign matter from metals, plastics, glass, etc. through the use of ultrasonic sound waves. As these high frequency sound waves pass through the wash solution, they form countless microscopic bubbles which grow in size and then violently collapse. This produces a strong scrubbing action which removes surface dirt from any object immersed in the solution.

TROUBLESHOOTING LIGHTING SYSTEMS

While a regular schedule of cleaning and relamping will keep a lighting system operating near peak efficiency, it cannot guarantee completely trouble-free operation. Occasional electrical and lamp related situations may arise that will require immediate and knowledgeable attention. The following sections contain useful troubleshooting and maintenance information concerning each of the three major lamp groups.

TROUBLESHOOTING HID SYSTEMS

When troubleshooting high intensity discharge lamp lighting systems, it is essential that a thorough analysis of all operating conditions is made by qualified maintenance personnel. Because high voltages

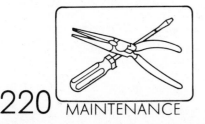

220 MAINTENANCE

are common in HID lighting systems, only qualified personnel should attempt to make electrical measurements or corrective maintenance. The HID troubleshooting chart found here can serve as a guide in determining possible causes of trouble within the system. It also suggests corrective maintenance procedures.

It should be noted that if a large percentage of lamps fail to operate in a new installation, it is likely that operating conditions are causing the problem, and the entire electrical installation should be thoroughly checked. In all cases, the following items should be checked before any replacement of lamps is made.

1. Is the power distribution system functioning properly? Is the power switch actuated?

2. Do the circuit breakers remain closed or is the circuit otherwise activated to the fixture when power is applied?

3. Is the electric eye or photocell functioning properly?

4. Is the proper line voltage available at the ballast primary? Any loss should not be greater than 10%.

5. If multiphase circuits are used, are all phases operating properly with all phase circuit breakers and grounds functioning properly?

6. Does the voltage rating given on the ballast nameplate agree with the line voltage and frequency available?

7. Is the ballast properly wired along with wiring to capacitors and lamp sockets?

8. Is the ballast properly grounded in the luminaire or to the mounting pole or hardware?

9. Are all socket components and leads in good condition?

10. Is the HID lamp compatible with the ballast being used?

11. Do the lamp and ballast wattage ratings agree?

12. Is the lamp being operated in the position specified by the lamp manufacturer?

13. Is the proper voltage and current available at the lamp socket as read on an RMS voltage meter?

Although many of these items appear too obvious or simple to be a cause of trouble, all items should be checked to avoid any unnecessary maintenance work or expense.

HID Troubleshooting Chart

Problem	Possible Cause	Corrective Maintenance
Lamp fails to start.	Normal end of lamp life.	Normal end of life occurs when the lamp's electrodes have aged sufficiently to prevent striking of the arc or lamp warming to full light output. A rise in arc tube starting voltage due to outgassing of contaminants also causes a normal end to lamp life. Refer to the lamp life tables found in Section I to find the normal life expectancy of HID lamps. Some lamps will fail before this rated life and others will exceed it. Correlate the number of failures, their time of occurrence, and the survival expectancy to determine if the lamp life of a particular system is within the expected range.
	Lamp loose in socket. Improper lamp insertion and seating.	Inspect the lamp base to see if there is any indication of arcing at the center contact button. Tighten the lamp to seat it properly, and if the lamp base is distorted and will not seat properly, replace the lamp.
	Electric eye inoperative.	Check for proper functioning by covering the electric eye to block out light as power is applied to the luminaire.
	Defective or improper wiring.	Check the wiring to assure it agrees with the wiring diagram on the ballast. Check the primary wiring to the ballast and from the ballast to the lamp socket to establish circuit continuity. Make certain all connections are secure. Check the wire size since too small of a wire may result in lowered voltage. Repair the circuit.

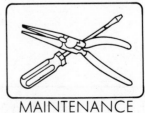

MAINTENANCE 221

Problem	Possible Cause	Corrective Maintenance
Lamp fails to start (continued).	Voltage at fixture too low.	Measure the line voltage at input of ballast. The measured line voltage should be within 10% of the nameplate rating. As is the case with many distribution systems, increasing the electrical load or demand may decrease the available voltage at the ballast primary. Because of this, the check should be made at a full load if possible. If a tapped ballast is used, match the ballast tap connection to the supply voltage measured at the ballast. Increase the supply voltage if feasible, or move the tap to the next position if possible.
	Improper ballasting.	Any HID lamp will perform erratically or fail to start if the wrong type of ballast is used. Make sure that the information on the ballast nameplate agrees with the line voltage and the type of lamp used. Premature failure is a common occurrence with improper ballasting. *Note:* While mercury lamps will successfully operate on metal halide ballasts of the same wattage, the reverse is not true.
	Shorted ballast.	A shorted ballast will often cause the seals at the end of the lamp's arc tube to rupture. Blackening around the seal area is a sign of this problem. The shorted condition may be due to shorted capacitors, shorted leads, or shorted windings.
	Improper lamp operating position (Metal Halide lamps only).	The operating position should agree with the information etched on the lamp bulb. A lamp operated beyond the specified operating position may not start or may degrade lamp performance if it does start. (See Section I.)
	Lamp has been operating. Insufficient cool-down time.	All HID lamp types require a period of time to re-establish optimum starting conditions after they have been operating and the supply line voltage has been interrupted. Mercury and metal halide lamps require from four to eight minutes cool-down time. High pressure sodium lamps require approximately one minute of cooling before restriking. In a luminaire, the restart time will vary according to the amount of ventilation, ambient temperatures, and draft conditions which exist within the luminaire.
	High restrike voltage (Metal Halide lamps only).	If the supply voltage to a metal halide lamp is interrupted during the warm-up period, the subsequent restrike voltage may be higher than that required for a lamp which has been allowed to stabilize (come up to full output normally or cool down to normal room temperature).
	Improper ballast for lamp operating condition.	Under extremely low ambient temperature conditions, the ballast may not supply sufficient voltage to start the lamp. At −20°F, ANSI specifications state that 90% of the lamps should start when proper lamp voltage is supplied. The same type of problem may exist at extremely high ambient temperatures. "Indoor" ballasts which are installed indoors but are connected to lamps which are located outdoors may not start the lamp due to insufficient secondary voltage. "Outdoor" ballasts are usually not adaptable for indoor use when the ambient temperature is extremely high.

Problem	Possible Cause	Corrective Maintenance
Lamp fails to start (continued).	End of ballast life.	Ballast appearance may indicate that a ballast has reached the end of its effective life. Charred ballasts may have been subject to sustained excessive heat, and swollen capacitors are another trouble indicator. Check the ballast with appropriate continuity testers, ammeters, and voltmeters. The failure process of a ballast is frequently capacitor failure with consequent low power factor operation and high current which leads to overheating of the core and coil and eventual failure.
	Defective starter (HPS lamps only).	High pressure sodium lamps depend on an external starting circuit to provide high voltage pulses necessary to start the lamp. If the pulse is not generated or is below a certain specified level, the lamp will not start. A starting circuit which is below specifications may start the lamp initially but may fail to start the lamp a second time when the lamp's required starting voltage increases as the lamp ages. To check the starting circuit, replace the lamp in question with a lamp known to be operative.
	Lamp defects. Arc tube leaks. Probe or cathode moly electrolysis. Quartz devitrification around rod. Open diode. Open welds. Diode or switch shorted. Sodium leaker.	Replace lamp. Mercury and metal halide tube leakers can be identified by sparking the base with a Tesla coil. The arc tube will not ignite. A shorted diode can be identified by using an ohmmeter. HPS tube leakers can be identified by sparking the base with a Tesla coil. The outer jacket will glow but the arc tube may or may not glow. All other types of defects can be identified by careful visual inspection of the lamp.
Short lamp life.	Lamp physically damaged. Lamp bulb leaks. Ring off.	Investigate the possibility of the outer bulb being damaged from handling or transportation which may have cracked the bulb glass. If air enters the outer bulb, the arc tube may continue to burn for up to 100 hours before failure. The bulb may be broken where the glass meets the base due to twisting the lamp into the socket too firmly or by scoring the glass where the socket inadvertently touches the bulb. Check for a broken arc tube or loose metal parts inside the bulb. A leak in the outer bulb will cause oxidation of the metal parts inside. In HPS lamps, the dark material in the neck of the bulb near the base will turn white or disappear. Replace the lamp for any of these problems.
	Improper ballasting.	Make certain the ballast nameplate information agrees with the line voltage and lamp type being used.
Lamp flicker. Lamp on-off cycling.	Improper ballasting.	With mercury lamps, improper ballasting can cause flickering or erratic operation. With metal halide lamps, the effect is most often noticeable during the start-up period when the lamp ignites, starts to warm up, and then extinguishes (cycling). This may be caused by improper voltage-current relationships delivered by the ballast. Wiring discontinuities will cause flicker. Under certain conditions new lamps may "cycle," but after three attempts to start at 30 to 60 second intervals, the lamps should stabilize and operate satisfactorily. High Pressure Sodium lamps will cycle on and off if the ballast does not have sufficient open circuit voltage to sustain the lamp.

Problem	Possible Cause	Corrective Maintenance
Lamp flicker. Lamp on-off cycling (continued).	High lamp operating voltage. Low open circuit voltage.	Measure the lamp's operating voltage. Measure the ballast's open circuit voltage. Replace as required.
	Variable voltage.	Heavy motor leads or welding equipment on line can cause lamp flickering during operation. Remove lighting circuits from the circuits servicing these devices. Provide voltage regulators. Check for loose connections.
	High-spike lamp.	The chemistry of a defective lamp may cause the lamp to require more voltage than the ballast can furnish with the result that the lamp will extinguish, cool, and repeat the cycle. Replace the lamp.
	High Pressure Sodium lamp cycling.	During its lifetime, the operating voltage of an HPS lamp will increase until a level is reached where the ballast cannot sustain the lamp. The lamp will begin to cycle on and off as a sign of its operating life being over. Replace the lamp after checking the ballast open circuit voltage and lamp operating voltage at wattage.
Lamp starts slowly. (Arc does not strike when the switch is first turned on.)	Hard starting lamp.	Hard starting lamps do not start rapidly and may glow for extended periods of time, resulting in destruction of the cathodes. After checking to make sure the problem is not ballast or voltage related, the hard starting lamp should be replaced.
Fuses blow or circuit breakers operate on lamp start.	Overloaded circuit.	Rewire to accommodate the starting current of the lamp-ballast combination.
	High momentary transient current.	This can be a result of reactor or autotransformer ballasts which draw initial high currents. Use circuit protective devices incorporating time delay elements. If this troubleshooting solution fails, change the ballast as high momentary transient current will affect lamp life. (Refer to **End of Ballast Life**.)
Low lamp light output.	Normal light output depreciation throughout lamp life.	Refer to the lumen maintenance characteristics found in the tables in Section I. If depreciation is within the range found on the table, replace the lamp. If not, proceed as outlined below.
	Improper ballasting.	Check the ballast nameplate to make sure the rating designation conforms to the lamp's rating designation.
	Incorrect voltage.	Check the line voltage at the ballast and set the ballast tap to voltage read. If not tapped, check the ballast voltage range against the input voltage. Check all wiring connections for voltage loss points, and check the socket contact point. Use a constant wattage ballast.
	Incorrect ballast output.	Check the ballast output to determine if it conforms to lamp requirements. If the voltage and current do not stabilize in 5 to 10 minutes of warm-up time, the ballast output is incorrect and an adjustment must be made. Check the capacitor wiring, if visibly possible, to determine if the capacitors are properly wired in.
	Dirt accumulation.	Check and clean luminaire and lamp. Reaccess the maintenance program if necessary to ensure adequate cleaning.

Problem	Possible Cause	Corrective Maintenance
Arc tube becomes blackened or swollen early in lamp life. Arc tube shows signs of scorching.	Overwattage operation. Improper ballasting.	Check to make sure that the lamp is not being operated on a ballast designed to accommodate a higher wattage lamp. Check ballast nameplate against the information etched on the lamp bulb.
	Excessive current or voltage. Shorted capacitor(s).	Check the voltage at the ballast. Check for the possibility of current or voltage surges which can damage the arc tube or seals or burn the connecting ribbons inside the lamp bulb. Check for shorted capacitors and replace the ballasts if shorts are found.
	"Glow-state" operation.	Under certain lamp and/or ballast conditions, the lamp may go into a partial discharge (dim glow) which will result in a darkening of the arc tube and a shorter lamp life. If this is the case, replace the lamp and check the ballast.
Lamp breakage occurs.	Scratched bulb.	Investigate for possible careless handling of luminaire or lamps. Make certain that the lamp socket does not contact the bulb as it may scratch the glass.
	Improper lamp insertion.	Screw the lamp into the lamp socket until firm contact is made and then stop.
Difference in lamp light color.	Normal maintenance.	In addition to the normal decrease in light output, a slight color shift can occur as the lamp ages. Spot replacement of burned out lamps may make the slight difference more apparent. Group relamping eliminates this problem.
	Mismatching of lamps.	Check the bulb etching on lamps which appear different to ensure that they are the same type of lamp having the same type of color rendering characteristics.
	Manufacturer tolerances.	Slight color variations may be caused by variations in the quantities of materials in the arc tubes of lamps. This is particularly true of metal halide lamps. Variations in the thickness of the phosphor coating of coated lamps can also cause very slight color variations. Lamp color is also affected by wattage variations, which can be as wide as $\pm 7.5\%$ according to ANSI standards. Interchanging different lamps may minimize apparent color differences.
	Dirty luminaires.	Dirt on the luminaire surface can also affect lamp light color. Practice regular maintenance.
	Variations in environment.	Color difference in walls, ceilings, office partitions, and floors, as well as different sources of illumination in the area, can affect apparent lamp color.
	Mismatching of lamp and socket (Certain super metal halide lamps only).	Certain super metal halide lamps have a special position oriented mogul base which must be matched with a corresponding position oriented mogul socket. If this is not done, arc tube orientation will not be correct and light output will be low. Early lamp failure will also be a problem.

TROUBLESHOOTING INCANDESCENT SYSTEMS

Over-Voltage or Over-Current Operation. The lamp rating should correspond with the actual circuit operating conditions. Over-voltage or over-current operation may drastically shorten lamp life. For example, when a 120-volt lamp is operated on a 125-volt circuit, it suffers a 40% loss in lamp life.

Sockets. Operating lamps designed for higher wattages in sockets designed for lower wattage models may result in excessively high socket temperatures which can affect lamp performance or shorten the life of insulated wire, sockets, and other components.

Luminaires. Use only those lamps recommended by the luminaire manufacturer. Also, contact between any metal part of the luminaire and the lamp may result in the violent failure of the lamp.

Cleaning and Replacement. Contact between a wet cleaning cloth and a hot lamp may result in the violent failure of the lamp. When relamping, be sure the power source to the luminaire is in the off position; replacing lamps with the power on may result in the drawing of an arc between the lamp base and socket. This is particularly true of high voltage lamps.

Burning Position. Lamps should be operated in the proper burning position specified by the lamp manufacturer. Operating the lamps in wrong positions may result in failure shortly after the lamp installation.

Tungsten Halogen Lamps. Tungsten halogen lamps should always be installed with the power off. Hold the lamp with a clear cloth or tissue to avoid fingerprints which could result in bulb discoloration and a subsequent reduction in light output. Follow any specific manufacturer's instructions.

TROUBLESHOOTING FLUORESCENT SYSTEMS

The following information is pertinent to the fluorescent applications described in this handbook. For systems employing a preheat starting fluorescent lamp:

1. Replace existing lamps with lamps that are known to be operative.

2. Replace existing starters with starters that are known to be operative. Blink starters are not recommended as replacement starters.

3. Examine the luminaire wiring for incorrect or loose connections or broken wires. Refer to the wiring diagram for the luminaire or ballast.

4. Replace the ballast with an appropriate model.

Lighting System Economics

As a lighting designer, it is your responsibility to create systems which provide sufficient amounts of quality light at a reasonable cost to your clients. Since most lighting requirements can be resolved in a number of ways, the deciding factor in favor of one method over another is often system cost.

This is not to say that the least expensive system is always the finest choice. Often, the client's desire for certain features or aesthetic effects will outweigh certain cost considerations, and you should never assume that a client will prefer the least expensive system. Rather, present a number of viable options and allow the client to be the final judge.

In order to cost rate lighting systems, set up economical maintenance schedules and give sound financial advice to clients. The lighting designer must be capable of performing detailed, accurate cost analysis and comparisons. Such analysis is highly useful in:

1. Comparing alternative systems as part of a decision-making process.
2. Evaluating various maintenance and relamping techniques.
3. Determining the impact of the lighting system on other building systems.
4. Managing budget and cash flow.
5. Helping determine the actual benefits of one system over another.
6. Simplifying the complexities of modern lighting systems into a basic language that clients can understand—cost.

The Cost-of-Lighting Concept

The process of providing light involves the spending of money on a number of goods, such as lamps, luminaires, and wire, and on a number of services, such as labor and electric power. All these costs are combined to generate a basic-cost-per-unit-of-light-delivered value. This traditional cost of light is expressed as cost per lumen-hour, or more precisely, the unit of dollars per million lumen-hours.

Cost-of-light data can be calculated for a luminaire by multiplying the average light output of the luminaire (lumens) by the life of the lamp(s) (hours) and dividing the result into the total costs (owning and operating) of the luminaire for the same time period. One relationship for this is expressed in the following equation:

$$U = 10/(Q \times D)[(P + h)/L + W \times R + (F + M)/H]$$

where
U = Unit cost of light in dollars per million lumen-hours.
Q = Mean lamp lumens.
D = Luminaire dirt depreciation (average between cleanings).
P = Lamp price in cents.
h = Cost to replace one lamp in cents.
L = Average rated lamp life in thousands of hours.
W = Mean luminaire input watts (lamps + ballast).
R = Energy cost in cents per kilowatt-hour.
F = Fixed or owning costs in cents per luminaire-year.
M = Cleaning cost in cents per luminaire-year.
H = Annual hours of operation in thousands of hours.

Lighting Cost Comparison

The factors in the cost-of-light formula can be expanded and reorganized in a way more suitable for system-to-system comparisons. Table 1 illustrates one method of setting up system-to-system comparisons which has become standard throughout the lighting industry.

In this annual cost model, both initial and recurring costs are placed on a "per year" basis. However, for such comparisons to be valid, each proposed system must provide the same amount of illuminance or the results must be normalized by dividing the various cost factors, such as total capital expense per year, total operating and maintenance expense per year, and total lighting expense per year, by the maintained illuminance.

Either individual (spot) or group relamping can be handled in this comparison model through the use of the following equations:

1. Individual replacement $= \dfrac{B}{R} (c + i)$ dollars per socket annually.

2. Group replacement (early burnouts replaced) $= \dfrac{B}{A} (c + g + KL + Ki)$ dollars per socket annually.

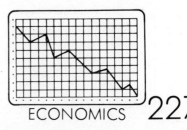

Table 1: Annual Lighting Cost Comparison

Item Description	Item Number	System A	System B
Installation Data			
Type of installation (office, industrial, etc.)	1	—	—
Luminaires per row	2	—	—
Number of rows	3	—	—
Total luminaires	4	—	—
Lamps per luminaire	5	—	—
Lamp type	6	—	—
Lumens per lamp	7	—	—
Watts per luminaire (including accessories)	8	—	—
Hours per start	9	—	—
Burning hours per year	10	—	—
Group relamping interval or rated life	11	—	—
Light loss factor	12	—	—
Coefficient of utilization	13	—	—
Illuminance, maintained	14	—	—
Capital Expenses			
Net cost per luminaire	15	—	—
Installation labor and wiring cost per luminaire	16	—	—
Cost per luminaire (luminaire plus labor and wiring)	17	—	—
Total cost of luminaires	18	—	—
Assumed years of luminaire life	19	—	—
Total cost per year of life	20	—	—
Interest on investment (per year)	21	—	—
Taxes (per year)	22	—	—
Insurance (per year)	23	—	—
Total capital expense per year	24	—	—
Annual Operating and Maintenance Expenses			
Energy expense			
Total watts	25	—	—
Average cost per kWh (including demand charges)	26	—	—
Total energy cost per year*	27	—	—
Lamp renewal expense			
Net cost per lamp	28	—	—
Labor cost each individual relamp	29	—	—
Labor cost each group relamp	30	—	—
Percent lamps that fail before group relamp	31	—	—
Renewal cost per lamp socket per year	32	—	—
Total number of lamps	33	—	—
Total lamp renewal expense per year	34	—	—
Cleaning expense			
Number of washings per year	35	—	—
Man-hours each (est.)	36	—	—
Man-hours for washing	37	—	—
Number of dustings per year	38	—	—
Man-hours per dusting each	39	—	—
Man-hours for dustings	40	—	—
Total man-hours	41	—	—
Expense per man-hour	42	—	—
Total cleaning expense per year	43	—	—
Repair expenses			
Repairs (based on experience, repairman's time, etc.)	44	—	—
Estimated total repair expense per year	45	—	—
Total operating and maintenance expense per year	46	—	—
Recapitulation			
Total capital expense per year	47	—	—
Total operating and maintenance expense per year	48	—	—
Total lighting expense per year	49	—	—

$$*\text{Total energy cost per year} = \frac{\text{Total watts} \times \text{burning hours per year} \times \text{cost per kWh}}{1,000}$$

Note: Items 38, 39, and 40 may be eliminated, and the word "washings" found in items 35 and 37 may be changed to "cleanings."

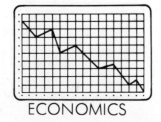

3. Group replacement (no replacement of early burnouts) $= \dfrac{B}{A}(c + g)$ dollars per socket annually.

where

B = burning hours per year.
R = rated average lamp life in hours.
A = burning time between replacements in hours.
c = net cost of lamps in dollars.
i = cost per lamp for replacing lamps individually in dollars.
g = cost per lamp for replacing lamps in a group in dollars.
K = proportion of lamps failing before group replacement (from lamp life mortality curve).
L = net cost of replacement lamps in dollars.

A specific rule cannot be given for the use of group replacements. Each installation should be considered separately. As a general rule, group lamp replacement should be considered when the individual replacement cost (i) is greater than half the cost (c) and the group replacement cost (g) is small in comparison to the individual replacement cost (i).

An iteration of equations 2 and 3 using various burning times between replacements (A) will indicate whether or not group relamping is economical. It will also find the best (lowest annual cost per socket) relamping interval.

As was discussed in the maintenance section, the choice of the periodical relamping or cleaning interval will have a direct bearing on the light loss factor. By weighing the various maintenance factors with the initial and recurring costs of equipment, a balance between lumen depreciation and cleaning and replacement costs can be struck. This balance guarantees a certain maintained footcandle level, using the fewest luminaires and the lowest possible lamp wattages. By making these comparisons during the planning stages of a system, it is possible to lower both initial as well as owning and operating costs over the entire life of the lighting system.

ECON II ECONOMIC ANALYSIS

SPI Lighting has developed a computerized program known as Econ II to help lighting designers draw economic comparisons between lighting systems. A typical program comparing three separate lighting systems is shown in Table 2. The analysis is based on data provided by the lighting designer as listed in point 13 of the table. The Econ II program details the various initial and recurring costs for the lighting system and its associated air-conditioning requirements.

The program also projects estimated annual energy costs over a ten-year period, and the cumulative cash flow of lighting and air-conditioning costs on a yearly basis. These long-term projections are extremely helpful in balancing initial cost considerations with long-term expenditures. Consult SPI Lighting with any questions concerning the setting up and interpretation of Econ II programs.

Table 2: SPI Lighting, ECON II Economic Analysis

ECONOMIC ANALYSIS

PREPARED BY: _____

1

```
JOB NAME:        WESTWOOD OFFICE COMPLEX
PROJECT NO:      399/79000
ADDRESS:         MILWAUKEE, WISC.
DATE:            12-SEP-80
```

2

	A UNIFORM 2×4 RECESSED FLUOR. TROUFFER 4L/F40T12CW	B UNIFORM SPI INDIRECT METAL HALIDE MS400C	C NON-UNIFORM SPI INDIRECT METAL HALIDE MS400C

FOR 100000.00 SQ. FT.

3

	A	B	C
CEILING HEIGHT: 9.00 FT.			
AVG. FC MAINTAINED	70.0	69.9	70.0
NUMBER OF LUMINAIRES REQD.—FIXED	1314	0	0
PORTABLE	0	402	325

INITIAL INSTALLATION COSTS

4

	A	B	C
CONNECTED LOAD—KW	262.8	182.9	147.9
LUMINAIRE COST—$ FIXED	72270.00	0.00	0.00
PORTABLE	0.00	135876.00	109850.00
WIRING COSTS—$ FIXED	23652.00	0.00	0.00
PORTABLE	0.00	4020.00	3250.00
INSTALL. LABOR COSTS—$ FIXED	36792.00	0.00	0.00
PORTABLE	0.00	4020.00	3250.00
INITIAL LAMP COST—$	5781.60	14070.00	11375.00

5

	A	B	C
TOTAL INITIAL COSTS—$	138495.61	157986.00	127725.00
RELATIVE INITIAL COSTS—%	100.00	114.07	92.22

1ST YEAR OPERATING COSTS

6

	A	B	C
ENERGY RATE—$ 0.040/KWH			
ANNUAL BURNING HOURS—3600			
PER LAMP REPLACEMENT LABOR COST—$	5.00	5.00	5.00

7

	A	B	C
ANNUAL LAMP COST—$	520.34	1266.30	1023.75

8

	A	B	C
ANNUAL MAINTENANCE LABOR—$	2365.20	180.90	146.25

9

	A	B	C
ANNUAL ENERGY COST—$	37843.20	26339.04	21294.00

10

	A	B	C
TOTAL OPERATING COST—$	40728.74	27786.24	22464.00
RELATIVE ANNUAL OPERATING—%	100.00	68.22	55.16

Notes:
1. Project identification.
2. Descriptions of the lighting systems analyzed. A maximum of three systems can be compared.
3. Lighting system data entered into computer.
4. Computer calculations based on the quantity of fixtures, fixture wattage, fixture costs, wiring materials costs, labor costs, and lamp costs. This information is found later in the printout under the heading of LIGHTING COST DATA USED IN ANALYSIS.
5. Acquisition or first cost totals (state and local taxes excluded).
6. Energy rate data entered into computer.
7. Value based on: [50% × (rated lamp life ÷ annual burning hours) × quantity of lamps] × lamp cost.
8. Value based on: [50% × (rated lamp life ÷ annual burning hours) × quantity of lamps] × labor costs.
9. Kilowatt hours (KWH) consumed × energy rate for the first year of operation.
10. First year operating cost (lighting).

1ST YEAR ANNUAL COSTS (LIGHTING ONLY)

1ST YEAR ANNUAL OWNING COST—$ FIXED	10653.51	0.00	0.00
PORTABLE	0.00	39496.50	31931.25

12

1ST YEAR TOTAL OWNING AND OPERATING COST—$	51382.25	67282.74	54395.25
RELATIVE 1ST YEAR TOTAL ANNUAL OWNING AND OPERATING—%	100.00	130.95	105.86

13

LIGHTING COST DATA USED IN ANALYSIS

AVG. FC—INITIAL	93.3	93.3	93.3
AVG. WATTS PER SQ. FT.	2.63	1.83	1.48
LAMPS REPLACED/YR.—TOTAL	473	36	29
INITIAL LAMP LUMENS	3150.00	40000.00	40000.00
# LAMPS PER FIXTURE	4	1	1
ESTIMATED LAMP LIFE	20000.00	20000.00	20000.00
FIXTURE INPUT WATTS	200.00	455.00	455.00
COEF. OF UTILIZATION	0.60	0.58	0.58
BALLAST FACTOR (FLUOR.)	0.94	1.00	1.00
MAINTENANCE FACTOR	0.75	0.75	0.75
FIXTURE COST EA. (NET $)	55.00	338.00	338.00
PER FIXTURE WIRING $ FIXED	18.00	0.00	0.00
PORTABLE	0.00	10.00	10.00
INSTALLATION LABOR $ FIXED	28.00	0.00	0.00
PORTABLE	0.00	10.00	10.00
LAMP NET $	1.10	35.00	35.00
DISCOUNT RATE $	0.10	0.10	0.10

INITIAL AND OPERATING COST OF AIR CONDITIONING SYSTEM TO COOL HEAT GAIN FROM LIGHTING

	SYSTEM A	SYSTEM B	SYSTEM C
HEAT GAIN FROM LIGHTING, SYSTEMS (1 WATT OF LIGHTING 3.413 BTU/HR.)	896936.44	624271.87	504697.41
TONS OF AIR CONDITIONING	74.74	52.02	42.06
KW OF ELECTRICAL POWER NEEDED FOR AIR CONDITIONING (1 TON-1.2 KW)	89.69	62.43	50.47

14

INITIAL COST OF AIR CONDITIONING EQUIPMENT TO COOL LIGHTING LOAD @ $1500/TON	112117.05	78033.98	63087.18
RELATIVE INITIAL COST OF AIR CONDITIONING TO COOL LIGHTING	100.00	69.60	56.27

(ASSUMING 1800 HR/YR. OPERATING OF A.C. SYSTEM)			
1ST YEAR ANNUAL OWNING COST—OF AIR CONDITIONING	8624.39	6002.61	4852.86
ANNUAL OPERATING COST OF AIR CONDITIONING TO COOL LIGHTING	6457.94	4494.76	3633.82

15

1ST YEAR TOTAL OWNING AND OPERATING COST OF AIR CONDITIONING	15082.33	10497.37	8486.68
RELATIVE 1ST YEAR TOTAL ANNUAL OWNING AND OPERATING COST	100.0	69.6	56.3

11. First year depreciation. Portable fixtures will show a greater owning cost due to accelerated depreciation. See additional notes (page 233).
12. First year operating costs and depreciation expense (lighting).
13. Lighting cost data entered into the computer.
14. Acquisition or first cost of air conditioning required to cool lighting induced heat gain.
15. First year operating cost and depreciating expense of the air conditioning required to cool lighting induced heat gain.

TOTAL COST OF LIGHTING INCLUDING AIR CONDITIONING SYSTEM TO COOL HEAT GAIN FROM LIGHTING

INITIAL LIGHTING COST	138495.61	157986.00	127725.00
INITIAL COST OF AIR CONDITIONING	112117.05	78033.98	63087.18

[16]

TOTAL INITIAL COST	250612.67	236019.98	190812.17
RELATIVE INITIAL COST	100.0	94.2	76.1

NORMAL OPERATING COST OF LIGHTING	40728.74	27786.24	22464.00
OPERATING COST OF AIR CONDITIONING	6457.94	4494.76	3633.82

[17]

1ST YEAR TOTAL OPERATING COST	47186.68	32281.00	26097.82
RELATIVE OPERATING COST	100.0	68.4	55.3

[18]

1ST YEAR ANNUAL OWNING COST	19277.90	45499.11	36784.11

[19]

1ST YEAR TOTAL OWNING AND OPERATING COST	66464.59	77780.11	62881.93
RELATIVE 1ST YEAR TOTAL OWNING AND OPERATING COST	100.0	117.0	94.6

ANNUAL ENERGY COSTS
OVER 10-YEAR PERIOD

[20]

ANNUAL ENERGY COSTS (1)	SYSTEM A (2)	SYSTEM B (3)	SYSTEM C (4)	MAXIMUM SAVINGS PER YEAR
1980@0.040 DOLLARS/KWH	$ 44301	$ 30833	$ 24927	$ 19374
1981@0.044 DOLLARS/KWH	$ 48731	$ 33916	$ 27419	$ 21312
1982@0.048 DOLLARS/KWH	$ 53604	$ 37307	$ 30160	$ 23444
1983@0.053 DOLLARS/KWH	$ 58964	$ 41037	$ 33176	$ 25788
1984@0.059 DOLLARS/KWH	$ 64860	$ 45140	$ 36493	$ 28367
1985@0.064 DOLLARS/KWH	$ 71346	$ 49654	$ 40142	$ 31204
1986@0.071 DOLLARS/KWH	$ 78480	$ 54619	$ 44156	$ 34324
1987@0.078 DOLLARS/KWH	$ 86328	$ 60080	$ 48571	$ 37757
1988@0.086 DOLLARS/KWH	$ 94960	$ 66088	$ 53428	$ 41532
1989@0.094 DOLLARS/KWH	$ 104456	$ 72696	$ 58770	$ 45686

[21]

MAXIMUM TOTAL 10-YEAR SAVINGS:	$ 308788

	A	B	C
NOTE: (1) A. CONNECTED KW LIGHTING LOAD 3600 HRS. USAGE/YEAR	262.8	182.9	147.9
B. CONNECTED KW A/C LOAD 1800 HRS. USAGE/YEAR	89.7	62.4	50.5

16. Total acquisition or first cost of lighting system and air conditioning required to cool lighting induced heat gain.
17. Total first year operating cost of lighting and air-conditioning systems.
18. Total first year depreciation expense of lighting and air-conditioning systems.
19. Total first year operating cost and depreciation expense.
20. Savings of lowest cost system over highest cost system.
21. Total possible energy savings. (Energy costs are based on initial energy rate and inflation rate selected.)

CUMULATIVE CASH FLOW OF LIGHTING AND AIR CONDITIONING COSTS BY YEAR

YEAR	SYSTEM A	SYSTEM B	SYSTEM C	
INVESTMENT (FIRST COST-INV. CR)	225551.41	212417.98	171730.95	22
1	240835.09	207364.53	167645.45	23
2	256488.92	205134.66	165842.69	24
3	272512.88	205728.36	166322.67	
4	288906.97	209145.64	169085.41	
5	305671.19	215386.52	174130.89	
6	322805.56	224450.97	181459.11	
7	340310.06	236339.00	191070.08	
8	358184.69	251050.61	202963.80	
9	376429.47	265877.47	214950.69	
10	395044.38	280819.59	227030.75	

PRESENT VALUE—CUMULATIVE CASH FLOW OF LIGHTING AND AIR CONDITIONING COSTS BY YEAR   25

PRESENT VALUE AT 0.100 DISCOUNT

	SYSTEM A	SYSTEM B	SYSTEM C
INVESTMENT (FIRST COST-INV. CR)	225551.41	212417.98	171730.95
1	239445.67	207823.94	168016.86
2	252382.72	205981.06	166526.97
3	264421.75	206427.13	166887.59
4	275619.13	208761.17	168774.58
5	286028.37	212636.27	171907.42
6	295700.28	217752.91	176044.02
7	304682.84	223853.34	180975.97
8	313021.50	230716.42	186524.47
9	320759.06	237004.45	191608.08
10	327935.91	242765.28	196265.47

22. Cumulative out-of-pocket expenditures: Year 0 = Acquisition cost – Investment tax credit.
23. Cumulative out-of-pocket expenditures: Year 1 = Year 0 + Δ_1
24. Cumulative out-of-pocket expenditures: Year n = Year (n – 1) + Δ_n
   Δ_n = (1 – tax rate) × (total operating cost) – (1 – tax rate) × (depreciation) or
   Δ_n = (1 – tax rate) × (total owning and operating cost) – depreciation.
   The tax rate is assumed to be 48%.
25. Cumulative present value: (out-of-pocket expenditures × discount rate). This involves discounting each year's out-of-pocket expenditures at some selected rate where the rate represents
   (a) cost of money,
   (b) inflation, and
   (c) corporate guidelines for payback for discriminating between investment alternatives.

Additional Notes:
   SPI Econ II depreciation—For **fixed lighting and air conditioning**, the depreciation rate is based on a 25-year life and the sum of the digits of the accelerated depreciation schedule. For **portable lighting** the depreciation rate is based on a seven-year life and the sum of the digits of the accelerated depreciation schedule.
   The term "owning cost" as used in the table has the same meaning as the accounting term "depreciation expense."

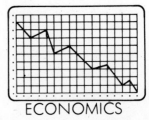

ECONOMICS 233

Appendix A

Commercial, Institutional, Residential, and Public Assembly Interior Illuminance Category Designations

Area/Activity	Illuminance Category
Auditoriums	
Assembly	C[1]
Social activity	B
Banks	
Lobby	
General	C
Writing area	D
Tellers' stations	E[2]
Barber shops and beauty parlors	E
Dance halls and discotheques	B
Drafting	
Mylar	
High contrast media; India ink, plastic leads, soft graphite leads	E[2]
Low contrast media; hard graphite leads	F[2]
Vellum	
High contrast	E[2]
Low contrast	F[2]
Tracing paper	
High contrast	E[2]
Low contrast	F[2]
Overlays[3]	
Light table	C
Printers	
Blue line	E
Blueprints	E
Sepia prints	F
Educational facilities	
Classrooms	
Science laboratories	E
Lecture rooms	
Demonstration	F
Sight saving rooms	F
Elevators, freight and passenger	C
Exhibition halls	C[1]
Food service facilities	
Dining areas	
Cashier	D
Cleaning	C
Dining	B[4]
Kitchen	E
Health care facilities	
Corridors[5]	
Nursing areas—day	C
Nursing areas—night	B
Operating areas, delivery, recovery,	

Area/Activity	Illuminance Category
and laboratory suites and service	E
Critical care areas[5]	
General	C
Examination	E
Surgical task lighting	H
Handwashing	F
Dental suite[5]	
General	D
Instrument tray	E
Oral cavity	H
Prosthetic laboratory, general	D
Prosthetic laboratory, workbench	E
Prosthetic laboratory, local	F
Recovery room, general	C
Recovery room, emergency examination	E
Elevators	C
Emergency outpatient[5]	
General	E
Local	F
Examination and treatment rooms[5]	
General	D
Local	E
Laboratories[5]	
Specimen collecting	E
Tissue laboratories	F
Microscopic reading room	D
Gross specimen review	F
Lobby	C
Locker rooms	C
Medical records	E
Nurseries[5]	
General[6]	C
Observation and treatment	E
Nursing stations[5]	
General	D
Desk	E
Corridors, day	C
Corridors, night	A
Medication station	E
Obstetric delivery suite[5]	
Labor rooms	
General	C
Local	E
Delivery area	
Scrub, general	G
General	G
Delivery table	(Consult Halo Lighting)
Resuscitation	G
Postdelivery recovery area	E
Substerilizing room	B

*Footnotes appear on page 240.

Area/Activity	Illuminance Category
Health care facilities (continued)	
Occupational therapy	
Work area, general	D
Work tables or benches	E
Patients' rooms[4]	
General[5]	B
Observation	A
Critical examination	E
Reading	D
Toilets	D
Pharmacy[4]	
General	E
Alcohol vault	D
Laminar flow bench	F
Night light	A
Parenteral solution room	D
Physical therapy departments	
Gymnasiums	D
Tank	D
Treatment cubicles	D
Stairways	C
Surgical suite	
Operating room, general	F
Operating table (Consult Halo Lighting)	
Scrub room[5]	E
Instruments and sterile supply room	D
Clean up room, instruments	E
Anesthesia storage	C
Substerilizing room	C
Toilets	C
Utility room	D
Waiting areas	
General	C
Local for reading	D
Hotels	
Bathrooms, for grooming	D
Bedrooms, for reading	D
Corridors, elevators and stairs	C
Front desk	E[2]
Linen room	
Sewing	F
General	C
Lobby	
General lighting	C
Reading and working areas	D
Libraries	
Book stacks (vertical 760 mm (30") above floor)	
Active stacks	D
Inactive stacks	B
Cataloging	D[2]
Card files	E
Circulation desks	D
Audiovisual areas	D
Audio listening areas	D

Area/Activity	Illuminance Category
Locker rooms	C
Merchandising spaces	
Alteration room	F
Fitting room	
Dressing areas	D
Fitting areas	F
Locker rooms	C
Stock rooms	D
Wrapping and packaging	D
Sales transaction area	E
Offices	
Accounting (see **Reading**)	
Drafting (see **Drafting**)	
General and private offices (see **Reading**)	
Libraries (see **Libraries**)	
Lobbies, lounges, and reception areas	C
Mail sorting	E
Offset printing and duplicating area	D
Reading	
Copied tasks	
Ditto copy	E[2]
Micro-fiche reader	B[7, 8]
Mimeograph	D
Photographs, moderate detail	E[8]
Thermal copy, poor copy	F[2]
Xerograph	D
Xerograph, 3rd generation and greater	E
Electronic data processing tasks	
CRT screens	B[7, 8]
Impact printer	
good ribbon	D
poor ribbon	E
2nd carbon and greater	E
Ink jet printer	D
Keyboard reading	D
Machine rooms	
Active operations	D
Tape storage	D
Machine area	C
Equipment service	E[9]
Thermal print	E
Handwritten tasks	
#3 pencil and softer leads	E[2]
#4 pencil and harder leads	F[2]
Ball-point pen	D[2]
Felt-tip pen	D
Handwritten carbon copies	E
Non photographically reproducible colors	F
Chalkboards	E[2]
Printed tasks	
6 point type	E[2]
8 and 10 point type	D[2]
Glossy magazines	D[8]

*Footnotes appear on page 240.

Area/Activity	Illuminance Category
Reading (continued)	
Maps	E
Newsprint	D
Typed originals	D
Typed 2nd carbon and later	E
Telephone books	E
Residences	
General lighting	
Conversation, relaxation, and entertainment	B
Passage areas	B
Specific visual tasks[10]	
Dining	C
Grooming	
Makeup and shaving	D
Full-length mirror	D
Handcrafts and hobbies	
Workbench hobbies	
Ordinary tasks	D
Difficult tasks	E
Critical tasks	F
Easel hobbies	E
Ironing	D
Kitchen duties	
Kitchen counter	
Critical seeing	E
Noncritical	D
Kitchen range	
Difficult seeing	E
Noncritical	D
Kitchen sink	
Difficult seeing	E
Noncritical	D
Laundry	
Preparation and tubs	D
Washer and dryer	D
Music study (piano or organ)	
Simple scores	D
Advanced scores	E
Substand size scores	F
Reading	
In a chair	
Books, magazines, and newspapers	D
Handwriting, reproductions, and poor copies	E
In bed	
Normal	D
Prolonged serious or critical	E
Desk	
Primary task plane, casual	D
Primary task plane, study	E
Sewing	
Hand sewing	
Dark fabrics, low contrast	F
Light to medium fabrics	E

Area/Activity	Illuminance Category
Occasional, high contrast	D
Machine sewing	
Dark fabrics, low contrast	F
Light to medium fabrics	E
Occasion, high contrast	D
Table games	D
Service spaces	
Stairways, corridors	C
Elevators, freight and passenger	C
Toilets and washrooms	C
Toilets and washrooms	C
Transportation terminals	
Waiting room and lounge	C
Ticket counters	E
Baggage checking	D
Rest rooms	C
Concourse	B
Boarding area	C
Industrial Group Activities	
Assembly	
Simple	D
Moderately difficult	E
Difficult	F
Very difficult	G
Exacting	H
Cleaning and pressing industry	
Checking and sorting	E
Dry and wet cleaning and steaming	E
Inspection and spotting	G
Pressing	F
Repair and alteration	F
Electric generating stations—interior	
Air-conditioning equipment, air preheater, and fan floor, ash sluicing	B
Auxiliaries, pumps, tanks, compressors, gauge area	C
Battery rooms	D
Boiler platforms	B
Burner platforms	C
Cable room	B
Coal handling systems	B
Coal pulverizer	C
Condensers, deaerator floor, evaporator floor, heater floors	B
Control rooms	
Main control boards	D[11]
Auxiliary control panels	D[11]
Operator's station	E[11]
Maintenance and wiring areas	D
Emergency operating lighting	C
Gauge reading	D
Hydrogen and carbon dioxide manifold area	C

*Footnotes appear on page 240.

237

Area/Activity	Illuminance Category
Electric generating stations—interior (continued)	
Laboratory	E
Precipitators	B
Screen house	C
Soot or slag blower platform	C
Steam headers and throttles	B
Switchgear and motor control centers	D
Telephone and communication equipment rooms	D
Tunnels or galleries, piping and electrical	B
Turbine building	
Operating floor	D
Below operating floor	C
Visitor's gallery	C
Water treating area	D
Flour mills	
Rolling, sifting, purifying	E
Packing	D
Product control	F
Cleaning, screens, man lifts, aisleways and walkways, bin checking	D
Forge shops	E
Foundries	
Annealing (furnaces)	D
Cleaning	D
Core making	
Fine	F
Medium	E
Grinding and chipping	F
Inspection	
Fine	G
Medium	F
Molding	
Medium	F
Large	E
Pouring	E
Sorting	E
Cupola	C
Shakeout	D
Garages—service	
Repairs	E
Active traffic areas	C
Write-up	D
Inspection	
Simple	D
Moderately difficult	E
Difficult	F
Very difficult	G
Exacting	H
Jewelry and watch manufacturing	G
Laundries	
Washing	D
Flat work ironing, weighing, listing, marking	D

Area/Activity	Illuminance Category
Machine and press finishing, sorting	E
Fine hand ironing	E
Leather manufacturing	
Cleaning, tanning and stretching, vats	D
Cutting, fleshing, and stuffing	D
Finishing and scarfing	E
Leather working	
Pressing, winding, glazing	F
Grading, matching, cutting, scarfing, sewing	G
Locker rooms	C
Machine shops	
Rough bench or machine work	D
Medium bench or machine work, ordinary automatic machines, rough grinding, medium buffing, and polishing	E
Fine bench or machine work, fine automatic machines, medium grinding, fine buffing, and polishing	G
Extra-fine bench or machine work, grinding, fine work	H
Materials handling	
Wrapping, packing, labeling	D
Picking stock, classifying	D
Loading, inside truck bodies and freight cars	C
Meat packing	
Slaughtering	D
Cleaning, cutting, cooking, grinding, canning, packing	D
Paint manufacturing	
Processing	D
Mix comparison	F
Paint shops	
Dipping, simple spraying, firing	D
Rubbing, ordinary hand painting and finishing art, stencil and special spraying	D
Fine hand painting and finishing	E
Extra-fine hand painting and finishing	G
Paper-box manufacturing	E
Paper manufacturing	
Beaters, grinding, calendering	D
Finishing, cutting, trimming, papermaking machines	E
Hand counting, wet end of paper machine	E
Paper machine reel, paper inspection, and laboratories	F
Rewinder	F
Plating	D
Poultry industry	
Brooding, production, and laying houses	

*Footnotes appear on page 240.

238

Area/Activity	Illuminance Category
Poultry industry (continued)	
Feeding, inspection, cleaning	C
Charts and records	D
Thermometers, thermostats, time clocks	D
Hatcheries	
General area and loading platform	C
Inside incubators	D
Dubbing station	F
Sexing	H
Egg handling, packing, and shipping	
General cleanliness	E
Egg quality inspection	E
Loading platform, egg storage area, etc.	C
Egg processing	
General lighting	E
Fowl processing plant	
General (excluding killing and unloading area)	E
Government inspection station and grading stations	E
Unloading and killing area	C
Feed storage	
Grain, feed rations	C
Processing	C
Charts and records	D
Machine storage area (garage and machine shed)	B
Printing industries	
Type foundries	
Matrix making, dressing type	E
Font assembly—sorting	D
Casting	E
Printing plants	
Color inspection and appraisal	F
Machine composition	E
Composing room	E
Presses	E
Imposing stones	F
Proofreading	F
Electrotyping	
Molding, routing, finishing, leveling molds, trimming	E
Blocking, tinning	D
Electroplating, washing, backing	D
Photoengraving	
Etching, staging, blocking	D
Routing, finishing, proofing	E
Tint laying, masking	E
Sawmills	
Secondary log deck	B
Head saw (cutting area viewed by sawyer)	E
Head saw outfeed	B
Machine in-feeds (bull edger, resaws, edgers, trim, hula saws, planers)	B

Area/Activity	Illuminance Category
Main mill floor (base lighting)	A
Sorting tables	D
Rough lumber grading	D
Finished lumber grading	F
Dry lumber warehouse (planer)	C
Dry kiln colling shed	B
Chipper infeed	B
Basement areas	
Active	A
Inactive	A
Filing room (work areas)	E
Service spaces	
Stairways, corridors	B
Elevators, freight and passenger	B
Toilets and washrooms	C
Sheet metal works	
Miscellaneous machines, ordinary bench work	E
Presses, shears, stamps, spinning, medium bench work	E
Punches	E
Tin plate inspection, galvanized	F
Scribing	F
Shoe manufacturing—leather	
Cutting and stitching	
Cutting tables	G
Making, buttonholing, skiving, sorting, vamping, counting	G
Stitching, dark materials	G
Making and finishing, nailers, sole layers, welt beaters and scarfers, trimmers, welters, lasters, edge setters, sluggers, randers, wheelers, treers, cleaning, spraying, buffing, polishing, embossing	F
Shoe manufacturing—rubber	
Washing, coating, mill run compounding	D
Varnishing, vulcanizing, calendering, upper and sole cutting	D
Sole rolling, lining, making and finishing processes	E
Storage rooms or warehouses	
Inactive	B
Active	
Rough, bulky items	C
Small items	D
Structural steel fabrication	E
Sugar refining	
Grading	E
Color inspection	F
Testing	
General	D
Exacting tests, extra-fine instruments, scales, etc.	F

*Footnotes appear on page 240.

Area/Activity	Illuminance Category	Area/Activity	Illuminance Category
Textile mills		bleaching, singeing, and mercerization)	D
Staple fiber preparation		Fabric dyeing (printing)	D
Stocking dyeing, tinting	D	Fabric finishing (calendaring, sanforizing,	
Sorting and grading (wood and cotton)	E[12]	sueding, chemical treatment)	E[12]
Yarn manufacturing		Inspection	G[12, 14]
Opening and picking (chute feed)	D	**Tobacco products**	
Carding (nonwoven web formation)	D[13]	Drying, stripping	D
Drawing (gilling, pin drafting)	D	Grading and sorting	F
Combing	D[13]	**Upholstering**	F
Roving (slubbing, fly frame)	E	**Welding**	
Spinning (cap spinning, twisting, texturing)	E	Orientation	D
Yarn preparation		Precision manual arc-welding	H
Winding, quilling, twisting	E	**Woodworking**	
Warping, (beaming, sizing)	F[12]	Rough sawing and bench work	D
Warp tie-in or drawing-in (automatic)	E	Sizing, planing, rough sanding, medium quality machine and bench work, gluing,	
Fabric production		veneering, cooperage	D
Weaving, knitting, tufting	F	Fine bench and machine work, fine sanding and finishing	E
Inspection	G[12]		
Finishing			
Fabric preparation (desizing, scouring,			

Notes:
1. Include provisions for higher levels for exhibitions.
2. Task subject to veiling reflections. Illuminance listed is not an Equivalent Sphere Illumination value. At the present time, insufficient experience in the use of ESI target values precludes the direct use of ESI in the present consensus approach to recommend illuminance values. Equivalent Sphere Illumination may be used as a tool in determining the effectiveness of controlling veiling reflections and as a part of the evaluation of lighting systems.
3. Degradation factors: Overlays—add 1 weighting factor for each overlay. Used materials—estimate additional factors.
4. Provide higher illumination levels over food service or selection areas.
5. Good to high color rendering capability should be considered in these areas. As lamps of higher luminous efficacy and higher color rendering capability become available and economically feasible, they should be applied in all health care facilities.
6. Light levels in these areas should be variable through either dimming or switching devices.
7. Veiling reflections may be produced on glass surfaces, and it may be necessary to treat plus weighting factors as minus factors in order to obtain the proper illuminance.
8. These situations are especially subject to veiling reflections, and it may be necessary to shield the task or reorient it.
9. Only required when actual equipment service is in progress. This level may be achieved through the regular lighting system or through the use of special portable equipment.
10. General lighting should not be less than 1/3 of visual task illuminance nor less than 20 footcandles (200 lux).
11. Maximum levels of a controlled system.
12. Supplementary lighting should be provided in this space to produce the higher lighting levels required for specific seeing tasks involved.
13. Additional lighting needs to be provided for maintenance only.
14. The color temperature of the light source is important for proper color matching.

Appendix B

The following isofootcandle curve reference plots, A through M, correspond to the information found in Table 5 on pages 68 and 69. Refer to Table 5 for specific lamp, luminaire, optical, and dimensional information pertinent to lighting design using these plots. For all plots in Appendix B, grid spacing is 2'. All footcandle levels are measured 2'6" above the floor surface.

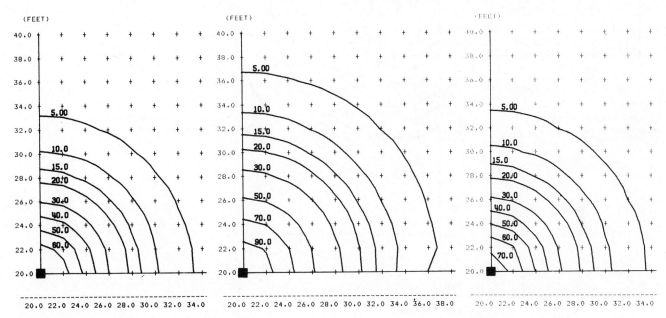

Plot A:
Symmetrical light pattern.

Plot B:
Symmetrical light pattern.

Plot C:
Symmetrical light pattern.

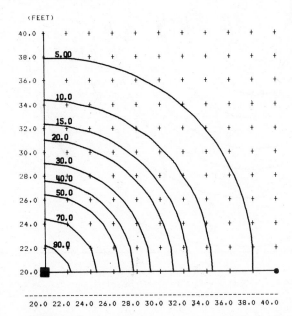

Plot D:
Symmetrical light pattern.

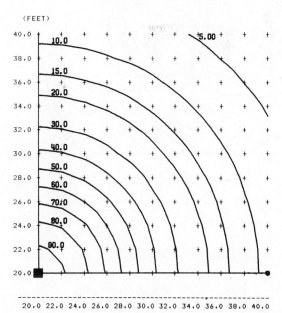

Plot E:
Symmetrical light pattern.

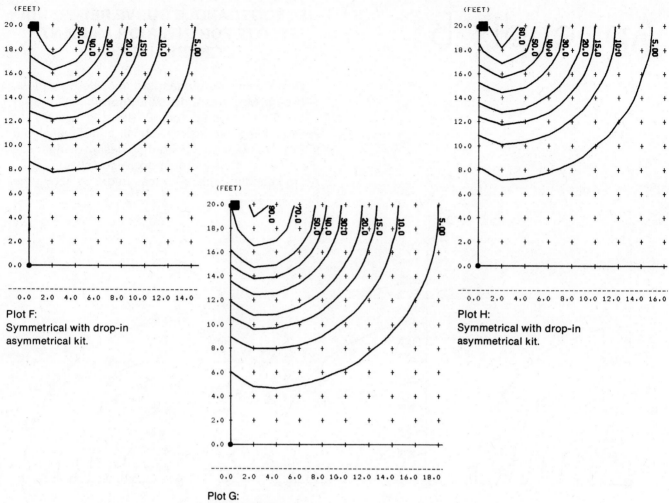

Plot F:
Symmetrical with drop-in
asymmetrical kit.

Plot G:
Symmetrical with drop-in
asymmetrical kit.

Plot H:
Symmetrical with drop-in
asymmetrical kit.

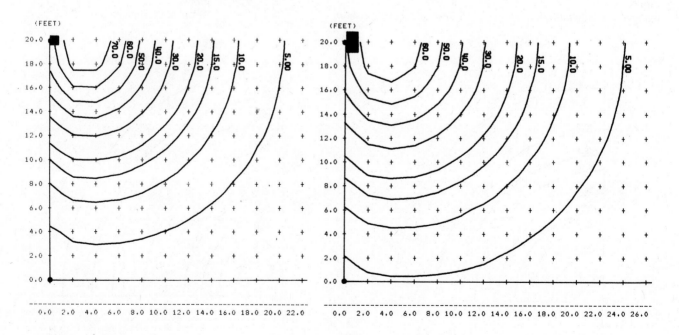

Plot I:
Symmetrical with drop-in
asymmetrical kit.

Plot J:
Asymmetrical forward-throw.

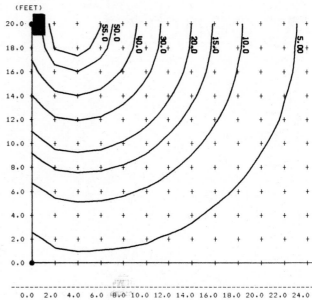

Plot K:
Asymmetrical forward-throw.

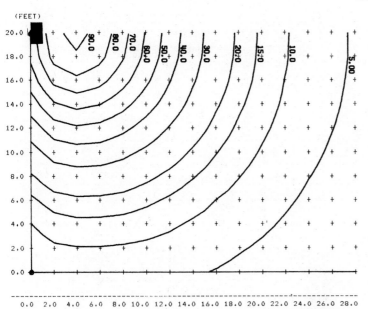

Plot L:
Asymmetrical forward-throw.

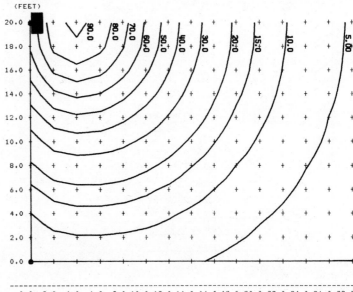

Plot M:
Asymmetrical forward-throw.

243

Appendix C

"CONES OF LIGHT" FOR HALO HID DOWNLIGHT FIXTURES

The following information corresponds to the data found in Table 8 on page 73. An explanation of how to use "Cones of Light" in designing lighting systems can also be found on page 73.

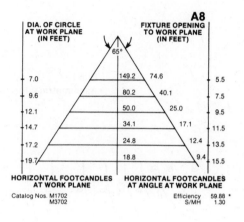

A5

DIA. OF CIRCLE AT WORK PLANE (IN FEET) / FIXTURE OPENING TO WORK PLANE (IN FEET)

65°

DIA.			OPENING
7.0	52.6	26.3	5.5
9.6	28.3	14.1	7.5
12.1	17.6	8.8	9.5
14.7	12.0	6.0	11.5
17.2	8.7	4.4	13.5
19.7	6.6	3.3	15.5

HORIZONTAL FOOTCANDLES AT WORK PLANE / HORIZONTAL FOOTCANDLES AT ANGLE AT WORK PLANE

Catalog Nos. M1400 M3400 Efficiency 63.95 S/MH 1.30

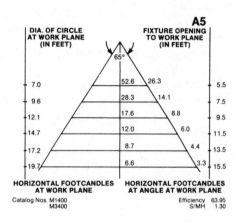

A6

DIA. OF CIRCLE AT WORK PLANE (IN FEET) / FIXTURE OPENING TO WORK PLANE (IN FEET)

65°

DIA.			OPENING
7.0	84.1	42.0	5.5
9.6	45.2	22.6	7.5
12.1	28.2	14.1	9.5
14.7	19.2	9.6	11.5
17.2	14.0	7.0	13.5
19.7	10.6	5.3	15.5

HORIZONTAL FOOTCANDLES AT WORK PLANE / HORIZONTAL FOOTCANDLES AT ANGLE AT WORK PLANE

Catalog Nos. M1401 M3401 Efficiency 63.14 S/MH 1.31

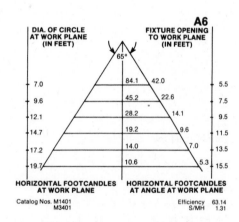

A7

DIA. OF CIRCLE AT WORK PLANE (IN FEET) / FIXTURE OPENING TO WORK PLANE (IN FEET)

65°

DIA.			OPENING
7.0	141.9	71.0	5.5
9.6	76.3	38.2	7.5
12.1	47.6	23.8	9.5
14.7	32.5	16.2	11.5
17.2	23.6	11.8	13.5
19.7	17.9	8.9	15.5

HORIZONTAL FOOTCANDLES AT WORK PLANE / HORIZONTAL FOOTCANDLES AT ANGLE AT WORK PLANE

Catalog Nos. M1402 M3402 Efficiency 62.77 * S/MH 1.31

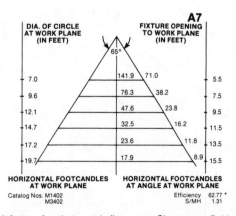

A8

DIA. OF CIRCLE AT WORK PLANE (IN FEET) / FIXTURE OPENING TO WORK PLANE (IN FEET)

65°

DIA.			OPENING
7.0	149.2	74.6	5.5
9.6	80.2	40.1	7.5
12.1	50.0	25.0	9.5
14.7	34.1	17.1	11.5
17.2	24.8	12.4	13.5
19.7	18.8	9.4	15.5

HORIZONTAL FOOTCANDLES AT WORK PLANE / HORIZONTAL FOOTCANDLES AT ANGLE AT WORK PLANE

Catalog Nos. M1702 M3702 Efficiency 59.88 * S/MH 1.30

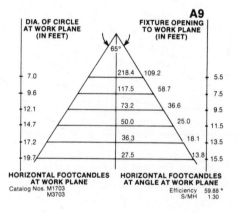

A9

DIA. OF CIRCLE AT WORK PLANE (IN FEET) / FIXTURE OPENING TO WORK PLANE (IN FEET)

65°

DIA.			OPENING
7.0	218.4	109.2	5.5
9.6	117.5	58.7	7.5
12.1	73.2	36.6	9.5
14.7	50.0	25.0	11.5
17.2	36.3	18.1	13.5
19.7	27.5	13.8	15.5

HORIZONTAL FOOTCANDLES AT WORK PLANE / HORIZONTAL FOOTCANDLES AT ANGLE AT WORK PLANE

Catalog Nos. M1703 M3703 Efficiency 59.88 * S/MH 1.30

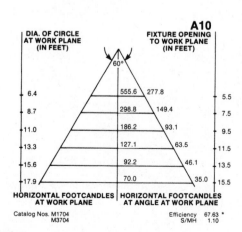

A10

DIA. OF CIRCLE AT WORK PLANE (IN FEET) / FIXTURE OPENING TO WORK PLANE (IN FEET)

60°

DIA.			OPENING
6.4	555.6	277.8	5.5
8.7	298.8	149.4	7.5
11.0	186.2	93.1	9.5
13.3	127.1	63.5	11.5
15.6	92.2	46.1	13.5
17.9	70.0	35.0	15.5

HORIZONTAL FOOTCANDLES AT WORK PLANE / HORIZONTAL FOOTCANDLES AT ANGLE AT WORK PLANE

Catalog Nos. M1704 M3704 Efficiency 67.63 * S/MH 1.10

*Consult factory for photometric figures on Champagne Gold and Anodized Black reflectors.

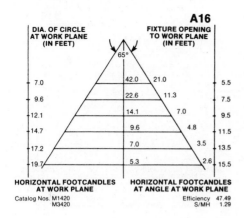

A16

DIA. OF CIRCLE AT WORK PLANE (IN FEET) — FIXTURE OPENING TO WORK PLANE (IN FEET) — 65°

7.0	42.0	21.0	5.5
9.6	22.6	11.3	7.5
12.1	14.1	7.0	9.5
14.7	9.6	4.8	11.5
17.2	7.0	3.5	13.5
19.7	5.3	2.6	15.5

HORIZONTAL FOOTCANDLES AT WORK PLANE — HORIZONTAL FOOTCANDLES AT ANGLE AT WORK PLANE

Catalog Nos. M1420 / M3420 — Efficiency 47.49 — S/MH 1.29

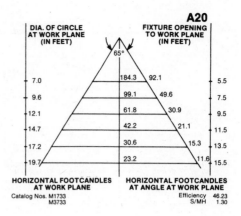

A20

DIA. OF CIRCLE AT WORK PLANE (IN FEET) — FIXTURE OPENING TO WORK PLANE (IN FEET) — 65°

7.0	184.3	92.1	5.5
9.6	99.1	49.6	7.5
12.1	61.8	30.9	9.5
14.7	42.2	21.1	11.5
17.2	30.6	15.3	13.5
19.7	23.2	11.6	15.5

HORIZONTAL FOOTCANDLES AT WORK PLANE — HORIZONTAL FOOTCANDLES AT ANGLE AT WORK PLANE

Catalog Nos. M1733 / M3733 — Efficiency 46.23 — S/MH 1.30

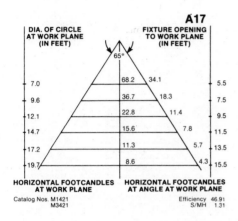

A17

DIA. OF CIRCLE AT WORK PLANE (IN FEET) — FIXTURE OPENING TO WORK PLANE (IN FEET) — 65°

7.0	68.2	34.1	5.5
9.6	36.7	18.3	7.5
12.1	22.8	11.4	9.5
14.7	15.6	7.8	11.5
17.2	11.3	5.7	13.5
19.7	8.6	4.3	15.5

HORIZONTAL FOOTCANDLES AT WORK PLANE — HORIZONTAL FOOTCANDLES AT ANGLE AT WORK PLANE

Catalog Nos. M1421 / M3421 — Efficiency 46.91 — S/MH 1.31

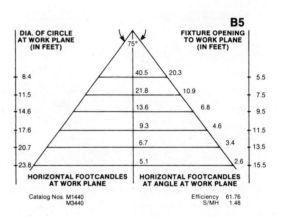

B5

DIA. OF CIRCLE AT WORK PLANE (IN FEET) — FIXTURE OPENING TO WORK PLANE (IN FEET) — 75°

8.4	40.5	20.3	5.5
11.5	21.8	10.9	7.5
14.6	13.6	6.8	9.5
17.6	9.3	4.6	11.5
20.7	6.7	3.4	13.5
23.8	5.1	2.6	15.5

HORIZONTAL FOOTCANDLES AT WORK PLANE — HORIZONTAL FOOTCANDLES AT ANGLE AT WORK PLANE

Catalog Nos. M1440 / M3440 — Efficiency 61.76 — S/MH 1.48

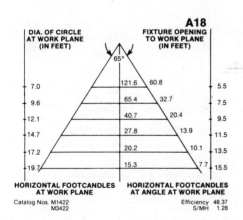

A18

DIA. OF CIRCLE AT WORK PLANE (IN FEET) — FIXTURE OPENING TO WORK PLANE (IN FEET) — 65°

7.0	121.6	60.8	5.5
9.6	65.4	32.7	7.5
12.1	40.7	20.4	9.5
14.7	27.8	13.9	11.5
17.2	20.2	10.1	13.5
19.7	15.3	7.7	15.5

HORIZONTAL FOOTCANDLES AT WORK PLANE — HORIZONTAL FOOTCANDLES AT ANGLE AT WORK PLANE

Catalog Nos. M1422 / M3422 — Efficiency 48.37 — S/MH 1.28

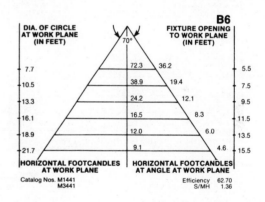

B6

DIA. OF CIRCLE AT WORK PLANE (IN FEET) — FIXTURE OPENING TO WORK PLANE (IN FEET) — 70°

7.7	72.3	36.2	5.5
10.5	38.9	19.4	7.5
13.3	24.2	12.1	9.5
16.1	16.5	8.3	11.5
18.9	12.0	6.0	13.5
21.7	9.1	4.6	15.5

HORIZONTAL FOOTCANDLES AT WORK PLANE — HORIZONTAL FOOTCANDLES AT ANGLE AT WORK PLANE

Catalog Nos. M1441 / M3441 — Efficiency 62.70 — S/MH 1.36

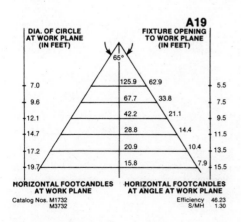

A19

DIA. OF CIRCLE AT WORK PLANE (IN FEET) — FIXTURE OPENING TO WORK PLANE (IN FEET) — 65°

7.0	125.9	62.9	5.5
9.6	67.7	33.8	7.5
12.1	42.2	21.1	9.5
14.7	28.8	14.4	11.5
17.2	20.9	10.4	13.5
19.7	15.8	7.9	15.5

HORIZONTAL FOOTCANDLES AT WORK PLANE — HORIZONTAL FOOTCANDLES AT ANGLE AT WORK PLANE

Catalog Nos. M1732 / M3732 — Efficiency 46.23 — S/MH 1.30

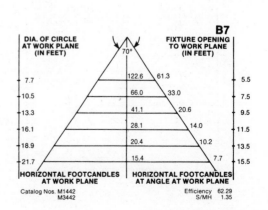

B7

DIA. OF CIRCLE AT WORK PLANE (IN FEET) — FIXTURE OPENING TO WORK PLANE (IN FEET) — 70°

7.7	122.6	61.3	5.5
10.5	66.0	33.0	7.5
13.3	41.1	20.6	9.5
16.1	28.1	14.0	11.5
18.9	20.4	10.2	13.5
21.7	15.4	7.7	15.5

HORIZONTAL FOOTCANDLES AT WORK PLANE — HORIZONTAL FOOTCANDLES AT ANGLE AT WORK PLANE

Catalog Nos. M1442 / M3442 — Efficiency 62.29 — S/MH 1.35

245

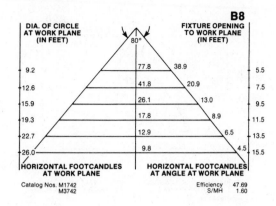

B8

DIA. OF CIRCLE
AT WORK PLANE
(IN FEET)

FIXTURE OPENING
TO WORK PLANE
(IN FEET)

80°

9.2	77.8	38.9	5.5
12.6	41.8	20.9	7.5
15.9	26.1	13.0	9.5
19.3	17.8	8.9	11.5
22.7	12.9	6.5	13.5
26.0	9.8	4.5	15.5

HORIZONTAL FOOTCANDLES
AT WORK PLANE

HORIZONTAL FOOTCANDLES
AT ANGLE AT WORK PLANE

Catalog Nos. M1742
M3742

Efficiency 47.69
S/MH 1.60

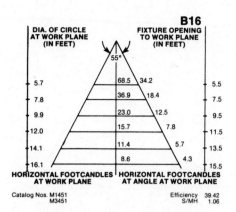

B16

DIA. OF CIRCLE
AT WORK PLANE
(IN FEET)

FIXTURE OPENING
TO WORK PLANE
(IN FEET)

55°

5.7	68.5	34.2	5.5
7.8	36.9	18.4	7.5
9.9	23.0	12.5	9.5
12.0	15.7	7.8	11.5
14.1	11.4	5.7	13.5
16.1	8.6	4.3	15.5

HORIZONTAL FOOTCANDLES
AT WORK PLANE

HORIZONTAL FOOTCANDLES
AT ANGLE AT WORK PLANE

Catalog Nos. M1451
M3451

Efficiency 39.42
S/MH 1.06

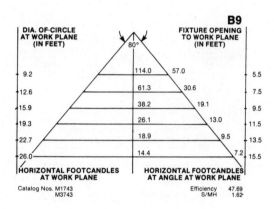

B9

DIA. OF CIRCLE
AT WORK PLANE
(IN FEET)

FIXTURE OPENING
TO WORK PLANE
(IN FEET)

80°

9.2	114.0	57.0	5.5
12.6	61.3	30.6	7.5
15.9	38.2	19.1	9.5
19.3	26.1	13.0	11.5
22.7	18.9	9.5	13.5
26.0	14.4	7.2	15.5

HORIZONTAL FOOTCANDLES
AT WORK PLANE

HORIZONTAL FOOTCANDLES
AT ANGLE AT WORK PLANE

Catalog Nos. M1743
M3743

Efficiency 47.69
S/MH 1.62

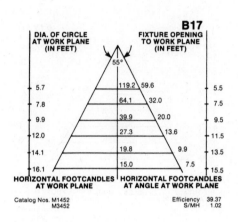

B17

DIA. OF CIRCLE
AT WORK PLANE
(IN FEET)

FIXTURE OPENING
TO WORK PLANE
(IN FEET)

55°

5.7	119.2	59.6	5.5
7.8	64.1	32.0	7.5
9.9	39.9	20.0	9.5
12.0	27.3	13.6	11.5
14.1	19.8	9.9	13.5
16.1	15.0	7.5	15.5

HORIZONTAL FOOTCANDLES
AT WORK PLANE

HORIZONTAL FOOTCANDLES
AT ANGLE AT WORK PLANE

Catalog Nos. M1452
M3452

Efficiency 39.37
S/MH 1.02

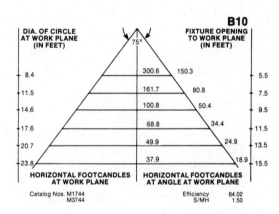

B10

DIA. OF CIRCLE
AT WORK PLANE
(IN FEET)

FIXTURE OPENING
TO WORK PLANE
(IN FEET)

75°

8.4	300.6	150.3	5.5
11.5	161.7	80.8	7.5
14.6	100.8	50.4	9.5
17.6	68.8	34.4	11.5
20.7	49.9	24.9	13.5
23.8	37.9	18.9	15.5

HORIZONTAL FOOTCANDLES
AT WORK PLANE

HORIZONTAL FOOTCANDLES
AT ANGLE AT WORK PLANE

Catalog Nos. M1744
M3744

Efficiency 64.02
S/MH 1.50

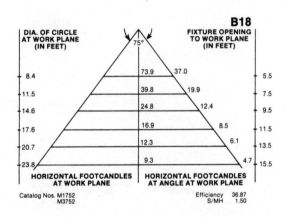

B18

DIA. OF CIRCLE
AT WORK PLANE
(IN FEET)

FIXTURE OPENING
TO WORK PLANE
(IN FEET)

75°

8.4	73.9	37.0	5.5
11.5	39.8	19.9	7.5
14.6	24.8	12.4	9.5
17.6	16.9	8.5	11.5
20.7	12.3	6.1	13.5
23.8	9.3	4.7	15.5

HORIZONTAL FOOTCANDLES
AT WORK PLANE

HORIZONTAL FOOTCANDLES
AT ANGLE AT WORK PLANE

Catalog Nos. M1752
M3752

Efficiency 36.87
S/MH 1.50

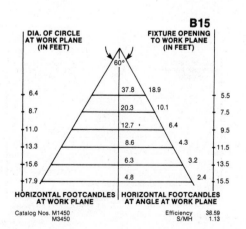

B15

DIA. OF CIRCLE
AT WORK PLANE
(IN FEET)

FIXTURE OPENING
TO WORK PLANE
(IN FEET)

60°

6.4	37.8	18.9	5.5
8.7	20.3	10.1	7.5
11.0	12.7	6.4	9.5
13.3	8.6	4.3	11.5
15.6	6.3	3.2	13.5
17.9	4.8	2.4	15.5

HORIZONTAL FOOTCANDLES
AT WORK PLANE

HORIZONTAL FOOTCANDLES
AT ANGLE AT WORK PLANE

Catalog Nos. M1450
M3450

Efficiency 38.59
S/MH 1.13

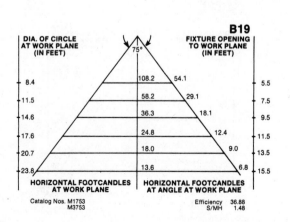

B19

DIA. OF CIRCLE
AT WORK PLANE
(IN FEET)

FIXTURE OPENING
TO WORK PLANE
(IN FEET)

75°

8.4	108.2	54.1	5.5
11.5	58.2	29.1	7.5
14.6	36.3	18.1	9.5
17.6	24.8	12.4	11.5
20.7	18.0	9.0	13.5
23.8	13.6	6.8	15.5

HORIZONTAL FOOTCANDLES
AT WORK PLANE

HORIZONTAL FOOTCANDLES
AT ANGLE AT WORK PLANE

Catalog Nos. M1753
M3753

Efficiency 36.88
S/MH 1.48

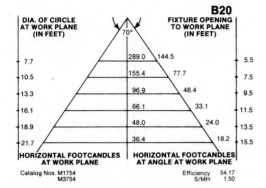

B20

DIA. OF CIRCLE AT WORK PLANE (IN FEET) — FIXTURE OPENING TO WORK PLANE (IN FEET)

70°

7.7	289.0 144.5	5.5
10.5	155.4 77.7	7.5
13.3	96.9 48.4	9.5
16.1	66.1 33.1	11.5
18.9	48.0 24.0	13.5
21.7	36.4 18.2	15.5

HORIZONTAL FOOTCANDLES AT WORK PLANE — HORIZONTAL FOOTCANDLES AT ANGLE AT WORK PLANE

Catalog Nos. M1754 M3754 Efficiency 54.17 S/MH 1.50

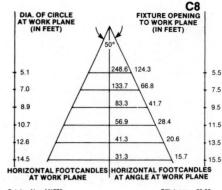

C8

DIA. OF CIRCLE AT WORK PLANE (IN FEET) — FIXTURE OPENING TO WORK PLANE (IN FEET)

50°

5.1	248.6 124.3	5.5
7.0	133.7 66.8	7.5
8.9	83.3 41.7	9.5
10.7	56.9 28.4	11.5
12.6	41.3 20.6	13.5
14.5	31.3 15.7	15.5

HORIZONTAL FOOTCANDLES AT WORK PLANE — HORIZONTAL FOOTCANDLES AT ANGLE AT WORK PLANE

Catalog Nos. M1772 M3772 Efficiency 60.20 S/MH 0.88

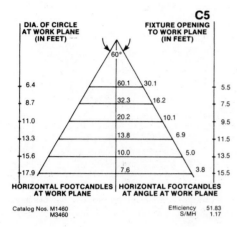

C5

DIA. OF CIRCLE AT WORK PLANE (IN FEET) — FIXTURE OPENING TO WORK PLANE (IN FEET)

60°

6.4	60.1 30.1	5.5
8.7	32.3 16.2	7.5
11.0	20.2 10.1	9.5
13.3	13.8 6.9	11.5
15.6	10.0 5.0	13.5
17.9	7.6 3.8	15.5

HORIZONTAL FOOTCANDLES AT WORK PLANE — HORIZONTAL FOOTCANDLES AT ANGLE AT WORK PLANE

Catalog Nos. M1460 M3460 Efficiency 51.83 S/MH 1.17

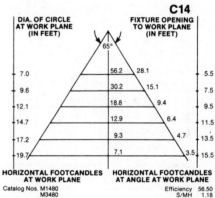

C9

DIA. OF CIRCLE AT WORK PLANE (IN FEET) — FIXTURE OPENING TO WORK PLANE (IN FEET)

50°

5.1	364.0 182.0	5.5
7.0	195.8 97.9	7.5
8.9	122.0 61.0	9.5
10.7	83.3 41.6	11.5
12.6	60.4 30.2	13.5
14.5	45.8 22.9	15.5

HORIZONTAL FOOTCANDLES AT WORK PLANE — HORIZONTAL FOOTCANDLES AT ANGLE AT WORK PLANE

Catalog Nos. M1773 .M3773 Efficiency 60.20 S/MH 0.88

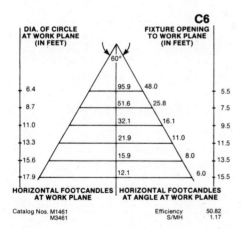

C6

DIA. OF CIRCLE AT WORK PLANE (IN FEET) — FIXTURE OPENING TO WORK PLANE (IN FEET)

60°

6.4	95.9 48.0	5.5
8.7	51.6 25.8	7.5
11.0	32.1 16.1	9.5
13.3	21.9 11.0	11.5
15.6	15.9 8.0	13.5
17.9	12.1 6.0	15.5

HORIZONTAL FOOTCANDLES AT WORK PLANE — HORIZONTAL FOOTCANDLES AT ANGLE AT WORK PLANE

Catalog Nos. M1461 M3461 Efficiency 50.82 S/MH 1.17

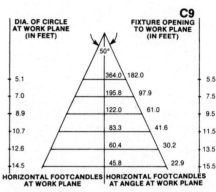

C14

DIA. OF CIRCLE AT WORK PLANE (IN FEET) — FIXTURE OPENING TO WORK PLANE (IN FEET)

65°

7.0	56.2 28.1	5.5
9.6	30.2 15.1	7.5
12.1	18.8 9.4	9.5
14.7	12.9 6.4	11.5
17.2	9.3 4.7	13.5
19.7	7.1 3.5	15.5

HORIZONTAL FOOTCANDLES AT WORK PLANE — HORIZONTAL FOOTCANDLES AT ANGLE AT WORK PLANE

Catalog Nos. M1480 M3480 Efficiency 56.50 S/MH 1.18

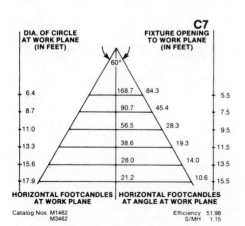

C7

DIA. OF CIRCLE AT WORK PLANE (IN FEET) — FIXTURE OPENING TO WORK PLANE (IN FEET)

60°

6.4	168.7 84.3	5.5
8.7	90.7 45.4	7.5
11.0	56.5 28.3	9.5
13.3	38.6 19.3	11.5
15.6	28.0 14.0	13.5
17.9	21.2 10.6	15.5

HORIZONTAL FOOTCANDLES AT WORK PLANE — HORIZONTAL FOOTCANDLES AT ANGLE AT WORK PLANE

Catalog Nos. M1462 M3462 Efficiency 51.98 S/MH 1.15

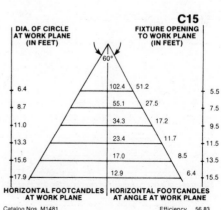

C15

DIA. OF CIRCLE AT WORK PLANE (IN FEET) — FIXTURE OPENING TO WORK PLANE (IN FEET)

60°

6.4	102.4 51.2	5.5
8.7	55.1 27.5	7.5
11.0	34.3 17.2	9.5
13.3	23.4 11.7	11.5
15.6	17.0 8.5	13.5
17.9	12.9 6.4	15.5

HORIZONTAL FOOTCANDLES AT WORK PLANE — HORIZONTAL FOOTCANDLES AT ANGLE AT WORK PLANE

Catalog Nos. M1481 M3481 Efficiency 56.83 S/MH 1.18

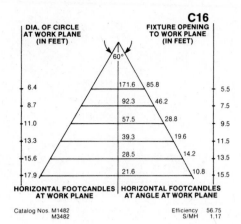

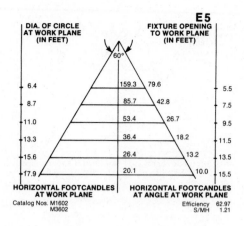

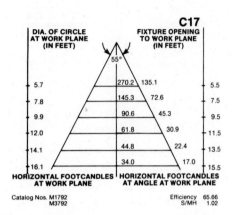

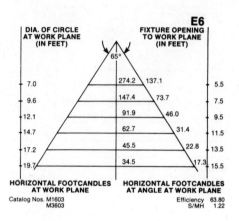

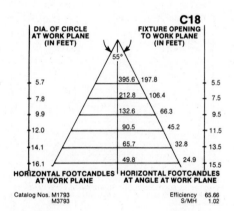

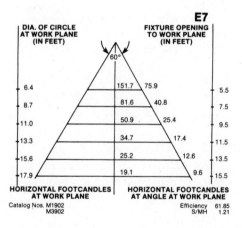

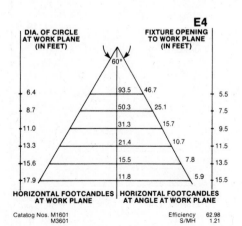

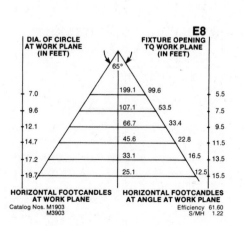

248

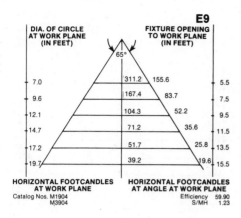

E9

DIA. OF CIRCLE
AT WORK PLANE
(IN FEET)

FIXTURE OPENING
TO WORK PLANE
(IN FEET)

65°

7.0	311.2 155.6	5.5
9.6	167.4 83.7	7.5
12.1	104.3 52.2	9.5
14.7	71.2 35.6	11.5
17.2	51.7 25.8	13.5
19.7	39.2 19.6	15.5

HORIZONTAL FOOTCANDLES
AT WORK PLANE

HORIZONTAL FOOTCANDLES
AT ANGLE AT WORK PLANE

Catalog Nos. M1904
M3904

Efficiency 59.90
S/MH 1.23

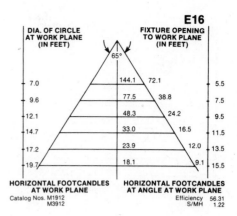

E16

DIA. OF CIRCLE
AT WORK PLANE
(IN FEET)

FIXTURE OPENING
TO WORK PLANE
(IN FEET)

65°

7.0	144.1 72.1	5.5
9.6	77.5 38.8	7.5
12.1	48.3 24.2	9.5
14.7	33.0 16.5	11.5
17.2	23.9 12.0	13.5
19.7	18.1 9.1	15.5

HORIZONTAL FOOTCANDLES
AT WORK PLANE

HORIZONTAL FOOTCANDLES
AT ANGLE AT WORK PLANE

Catalog Nos. M1912
M3912

Efficiency 56.31
S/MH 1.22

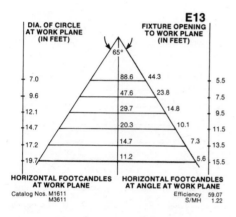

E13

DIA. OF CIRCLE
AT WORK PLANE
(IN FEET)

FIXTURE OPENING
TO WORK PLANE
(IN FEET)

65°

7.0	88.6 44.3	5.5
9.6	47.6 23.8	7.5
12.1	29.7 14.8	9.5
14.7	20.3 10.1	11.5
17.2	14.7 7.3	13.5
19.7	11.2 5.6	15.5

HORIZONTAL FOOTCANDLES
AT WORK PLANE

HORIZONTAL FOOTCANDLES
AT ANGLE AT WORK PLANE

Catalog Nos. M1611
M3611

Efficiency 59.07
S/MH 1.22

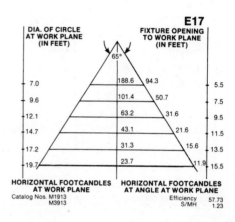

E17

DIA. OF CIRCLE
AT WORK PLANE
(IN FEET)

FIXTURE OPENING
TO WORK PLANE
(IN FEET)

65°

7.0	188.6 94.3	5.5
9.6	101.4 50.7	7.5
12.1	63.2 31.6	9.5
14.7	43.1 21.6	11.5
17.2	31.3 15.6	13.5
19.7	23.7 11.9	15.5

HORIZONTAL FOOTCANDLES
AT WORK PLANE

HORIZONTAL FOOTCANDLES
AT ANGLE AT WORK PLANE

Catalog Nos. M1913
M3913

Efficiency 57.73
S/MH 1.23

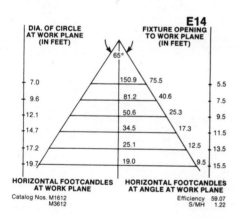

E14

DIA. OF CIRCLE
AT WORK PLANE
(IN FEET)

FIXTURE OPENING
TO WORK PLANE
(IN FEET)

65°

7.0	150.9 75.5	5.5
9.6	81.2 40.6	7.5
12.1	50.6 25.3	9.5
14.7	34.5 17.3	11.5
17.2	25.1 12.5	13.5
19.7	19.0 9.5	15.5

HORIZONTAL FOOTCANDLES
AT WORK PLANE

HORIZONTAL FOOTCANDLES
AT ANGLE AT WORK PLANE

Catalog Nos. M1612
M3612

Efficiency 59.07
S/MH 1.22

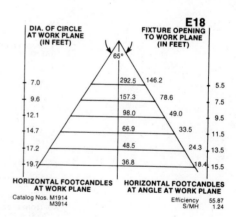

E18

DIA. OF CIRCLE
AT WORK PLANE
(IN FEET)

FIXTURE OPENING
TO WORK PLANE
(IN FEET)

65°

7.0	292.5 146.2	5.5
9.6	157.3 78.6	7.5
12.1	98.0 49.0	9.5
14.7	66.9 33.5	11.5
17.2	48.5 24.3	13.5
19.7	36.8 18.4	15.5

HORIZONTAL FOOTCANDLES
AT WORK PLANE

HORIZONTAL FOOTCANDLES
AT ANGLE AT WORK PLANE

Catalog Nos. M1914
M3914

Efficiency 55.87
S/MH 1.24

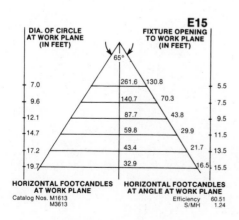

E15

DIA. OF CIRCLE
AT WORK PLANE
(IN FEET)

FIXTURE OPENING
TO WORK PLANE
(IN FEET)

65°

7.0	261.6 130.8	5.5
9.6	140.7 70.3	7.5
12.1	87.7 43.8	9.5
14.7	59.8 29.9	11.5
17.2	43.4 21.7	13.5
19.7	32.9 16.5	15.5

HORIZONTAL FOOTCANDLES
AT WORK PLANE

HORIZONTAL FOOTCANDLES
AT ANGLE AT WORK PLANE

Catalog Nos. M1613
M3613

Efficiency 60.51
S/MH 1.24

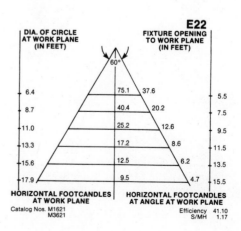

E22

DIA. OF CIRCLE
AT WORK PLANE
(IN FEET)

FIXTURE OPENING
TO WORK PLANE
(IN FEET)

60°

6.4	75.1 37.6	5.5
8.7	40.4 20.2	7.5
11.0	25.2 12.6	9.5
13.3	17.2 8.6	11.5
15.6	12.5 6.2	13.5
17.9	9.5 4.7	15.5

HORIZONTAL FOOTCANDLES
AT WORK PLANE

HORIZONTAL FOOTCANDLES
AT WORK PLANE

Catalog Nos. M1621
M3621

Efficiency 41.10
S/MH 1.17

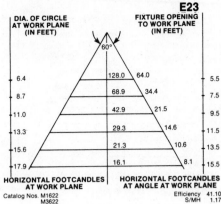

E23

DIA. OF CIRCLE
AT WORK PLANE
(IN FEET)

FIXTURE OPENING
TO WORK PLANE
(IN FEET)

60°

6.4	128.0	64.0	5.5
8.7	68.9	34.4	7.5
11.0	42.9	21.5	9.5
13.3	29.3	14.6	11.5
15.6	21.3	10.6	13.5
17.9	16.1	8.1	15.5

HORIZONTAL FOOTCANDLES
AT WORK PLANE

HORIZONTAL FOOTCANDLES
AT ANGLE AT WORK PLANE

Catalog Nos. M1622
M3622

Efficiency 41.10
S/MH 1.17

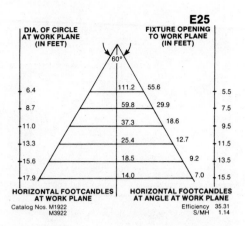

E25

DIA. OF CIRCLE
AT WORK PLANE
(IN FEET)

FIXTURE OPENING
TO WORK PLANE
(IN FEET)

60°

6.4	111.2	55.6	5.5
8.7	59.8	29.9	7.5
11.0	37.3	18.6	9.5
13.3	25.4	12.7	11.5
15.6	18.5	9.2	13.5
17.9	14.0	7.0	15.5

HORIZONTAL FOOTCANDLES
AT WORK PLANE

HORIZONTAL FOOTCANDLES
AT ANGLE AT WORK PLANE

Catalog Nos. M1922
M3922

Efficiency 35.31
S/MH 1.14

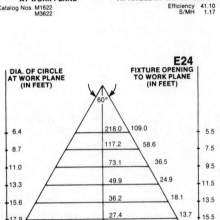

E24

DIA. OF CIRCLE
AT WORK PLANE
(IN FEET)

FIXTURE OPENING
TO WORK PLANE
(IN FEET)

60°

6.4	218.0	109.0	5.5
8.7	117.2	58.6	7.5
11.0	73.1	36.5	9.5
13.3	49.9	24.9	11.5
15.6	36.2	18.1	13.5
17.9	27.4	13.7	15.5

HORIZONTAL FOOTCANDLES
AT WORK PLANE

HORIZONTAL FOOTCANDLES
AT ANGLE AT WORK PLANE

Catalog Nos. M1623
M3623

Efficiency 39.15
S/MH 1.14

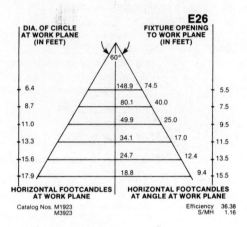

E26

DIA. OF CIRCLE
AT WORK PLANE
(IN FEET)

FIXTURE OPENING
TO WORK PLANE
(IN FEET)

60°

6.4	148.9	74.5	5.5
8.7	80.1	40.0	7.5
11.0	49.9	25.0	9.5
13.3	34.1	17.0	11.5
15.6	24.7	12.4	13.5
17.9	18.8	9.4	15.5

HORIZONTAL FOOTCANDLES
AT WORK PLANE

HORIZONTAL FOOTCANDLES
AT ANGLE AT WORK PLANE

Catalog Nos. M1923
M3923

Efficiency 36.38
S/MH 1.16

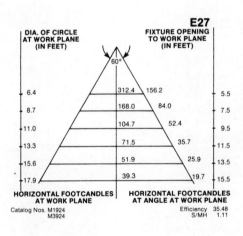

E27

DIA. OF CIRCLE
AT WORK PLANE
(IN FEET)

FIXTURE OPENING
TO WORK PLANE
(IN FEET)

60°

6.4	312.4	156.2	5.5
8.7	168.0	84.0	7.5
11.0	104.7	52.4	9.5
13.3	71.5	35.7	11.5
15.6	51.9	25.9	13.5
17.9	39.3	19.7	15.5

HORIZONTAL FOOTCANDLES
AT WORK PLANE

HORIZONTAL FOOTCANDLES
AT ANGLE AT WORK PLANE

Catalog Nos. M1924
M3924

Efficiency 35.48
S/MH 1.11

Vertical Illumination (Footcandles) (Direct Only)

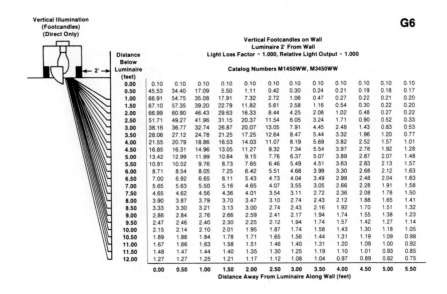

Vertical Footcandles on Wall
Luminaire 2′ From Wall
Light Loss Factor = 1.000, Relative Light Output = 1.000

Catalog Numbers M1450WW, M3450WW

Distance Below Luminaire (feet)	0.00	0.50	1.00	1.50	2.00	2.50	3.00	3.50	4.00	4.50	5.00	5.50
0.00	0.10	0.10	0.10	0.10	0.10	0.10	0.10	0.10	0.10	0.10	0.10	0.10
0.50	45.53	34.40	17.09	5.50	1.11	0.42	0.30	0.24	0.21	0.19	0.18	0.17
1.00	66.91	54.75	35.08	17.91	7.32	2.72	1.06	0.47	0.27	0.22	0.21	0.20
1.50	67.10	57.35	39.20	22.79	11.82	5.61	2.58	1.16	0.54	0.30	0.22	0.20
2.00	66.99	60.90	46.43	29.63	16.33	8.44	4.25	2.08	1.02	0.48	0.27	0.22
2.50	51.71	49.27	41.96	31.15	20.37	11.54	6.05	3.24	1.71	0.90	0.52	0.33
3.00	38.16	36.77	32.74	26.87	20.07	13.05	7.91	4.45	2.48	1.43	0.83	0.53
3.50	28.06	27.12	24.78	21.25	17.25	12.64	8.47	5.44	3.32	1.96	1.20	0.77
4.00	21.55	20.79	18.86	16.53	14.03	11.07	8.19	5.69	3.82	2.52	1.57	1.01
4.50	16.85	16.31	14.96	13.05	11.27	9.32	7.34	5.54	3.97	2.78	1.92	1.28
5.00	13.42	12.99	11.99	10.64	9.15	7.76	6.37	5.07	3.89	2.87	2.07	1.48
5.50	10.81	10.52	9.76	8.73	7.65	6.46	5.49	4.51	3.63	2.83	2.13	1.57
6.00	8.71	8.54	8.05	7.25	6.42	5.51	4.68	3.99	3.30	2.68	2.12	1.63
6.50	7.00	6.92	6.65	6.11	5.43	4.73	4.04	3.49	2.98	2.48	2.04	1.63
7.00	5.65	5.63	5.50	5.16	4.65	4.07	3.55	3.05	2.66	2.28	1.91	1.58
7.50	4.65	4.62	4.56	4.36	4.01	3.54	3.11	2.72	2.36	2.08	1.78	1.50
8.00	3.90	3.87	3.79	3.70	3.47	3.10	2.74	2.43	2.12	1.88	1.65	1.41
8.50	3.33	3.30	3.21	3.13	3.00	2.74	2.43	2.16	1.92	1.70	1.51	1.32
9.00	2.86	2.84	2.76	2.66	2.59	2.41	2.17	1.94	1.74	1.55	1.38	1.23
9.50	2.47	2.46	2.40	2.30	2.25	2.12	1.94	1.74	1.57	1.42	1.27	1.14
10.00	2.15	2.14	2.10	2.01	1.95	1.87	1.74	1.58	1.43	1.30	1.18	1.05
10.50	1.89	1.88	1.84	1.78	1.71	1.65	1.56	1.44	1.31	1.19	1.09	0.98
11.00	1.67	1.66	1.63	1.58	1.51	1.46	1.40	1.31	1.20	1.09	1.00	0.92
11.50	1.48	1.47	1.44	1.40	1.35	1.30	1.25	1.19	1.10	1.01	0.93	0.85
12.00	1.27	1.27	1.25	1.21	1.17	1.12	1.08	1.04	0.97	0.89	0.82	0.75

Distance Away From Luminaire Along Wall (feet)

Vertical Illumination (Footcandles) (Direct Only)

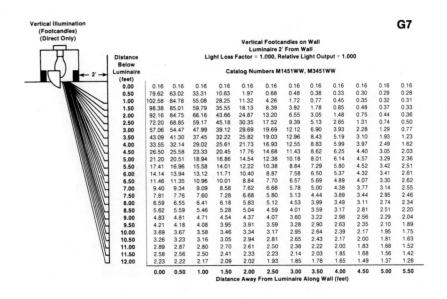

Vertical Footcandles on Wall
Luminaire 2′ From Wall
Light Loss Factor = 1.000, Relative Light Output = 1.000

Catalog Numbers M1451WW, M3451WW

Distance Below Luminaire (feet)	0.00	0.50	1.00	1.50	2.00	2.50	3.00	3.50	4.00	4.50	5.00	5.50
0.00	0.16	0.16	0.16	0.16	0.16	0.16	0.16	0.16	0.16	0.16	0.16	0.16
0.50	79.62	63.02	33.31	10.63	1.97	0.68	0.48	0.38	0.33	0.30	0.29	0.28
1.00	102.58	84.78	55.08	28.25	11.32	4.26	1.72	0.77	0.45	0.35	0.32	0.31
1.50	98.38	85.01	59.79	35.55	18.13	8.39	3.92	1.78	0.85	0.48	0.37	0.33
2.00	92.16	84.75	66.16	43.66	24.87	13.20	6.55	3.05	1.48	0.75	0.44	0.36
2.50	72.20	68.85	59.17	45.18	30.35	17.52	9.39	5.13	2.65	1.31	0.74	0.50
3.00	57.06	54.47	47.99	39.12	29.69	19.69	12.12	6.90	3.93	2.28	1.29	0.77
3.50	43.09	41.30	37.45	32.22	25.82	19.03	12.96	8.43	5.19	3.10	1.93	1.23
4.00	33.55	32.14	29.02	25.61	21.73	16.93	12.55	8.83	5.99	3.97	2.49	1.62
4.50	26.50	25.58	23.33	20.45	17.76	14.68	11.43	8.62	6.25	4.40	3.05	2.03
5.00	21.20	20.51	18.94	16.86	14.54	12.38	10.18	8.01	6.14	4.57	3.29	2.36
5.50	17.41	16.96	15.58	14.01	12.22	10.38	8.84	7.29	5.80	4.52	3.42	2.51
6.00	14.14	13.94	13.12	11.71	10.40	8.87	7.58	6.50	5.37	4.32	3.41	2.61
6.50	11.46	11.35	10.96	10.01	8.84	7.70	6.57	5.69	4.89	4.07	3.30	2.62
7.00	9.40	9.34	9.09	8.58	7.62	6.68	5.78	5.00	4.38	3.77	3.14	2.55
7.50	7.81	7.76	7.60	7.28	6.68	5.80	5.13	4.44	3.89	3.44	2.95	2.46
8.00	6.59	6.55	6.41	6.18	5.83	5.12	4.53	3.99	3.49	3.11	2.74	2.34
8.50	5.62	5.59	5.46	5.28	5.04	4.59	4.01	3.59	3.17	2.81	2.51	2.20
9.00	4.83	4.81	4.71	4.54	4.37	4.07	3.60	3.22	2.86	2.56	2.29	2.04
9.50	4.21	4.18	4.08	3.95	3.91	3.59	3.28	2.90	2.63	2.35	2.10	1.89
10.00	3.69	3.67	3.58	3.46	3.34	3.17	2.95	2.64	2.39	2.17	1.95	1.75
10.50	3.26	3.23	3.16	3.05	2.94	2.81	2.65	2.43	2.17	2.00	1.81	1.63
11.00	2.89	2.87	2.80	2.70	2.61	2.50	2.38	2.22	2.00	1.83	1.68	1.52
11.50	2.58	2.56	2.50	2.41	2.33	2.23	2.14	2.03	1.85	1.68	1.56	1.42
12.00	2.23	2.22	2.17	2.09	2.02	1.93	1.85	1.76	1.65	1.49	1.37	1.26

Distance Away From Luminaire Along Wall (feet)

Vertical Illumination (Footcandles) (Direct Only)

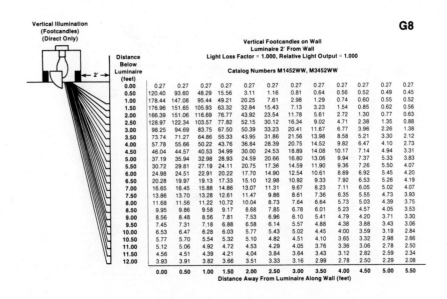

Vertical Footcandles on Wall
Luminaire 2′ From Wall
Light Loss Factor = 1.000, Relative Light Output = 1.000

Catalog Numbers M1452WW, M3452WW

Distance Below Luminaire (feet)	0.00	0.50	1.00	1.50	2.00	2.50	3.00	3.50	4.00	4.50	5.00	5.50
0.00	0.27	0.27	0.27	0.27	0.27	0.27	0.27	0.27	0.27	0.27	0.27	0.27
0.50	120.40	93.60	48.29	15.56	3.11	1.16	0.81	0.64	0.56	0.52	0.49	0.45
1.00	178.44	147.08	95.44	49.21	20.25	7.61	2.98	1.29	0.74	0.60	0.55	0.52
1.50	176.96	151.65	103.93	63.32	32.84	15.43	7.13	3.23	1.54	0.85	0.62	0.56
2.00	166.39	151.06	116.69	76.77	43.92	23.54	11.78	5.61	2.72	1.30	0.77	0.63
2.50	128.97	122.34	103.57	77.82	52.15	30.12	16.34	9.02	4.71	2.38	1.35	0.88
3.00	98.25	94.69	83.75	67.50	50.39	33.23	20.41	11.67	6.77	3.96	2.26	1.38
3.50	73.74	71.27	64.86	55.33	43.95	31.86	21.56	13.98	8.58	5.21	3.30	2.12
4.00	57.78	55.66	50.22	43.76	36.84	28.39	20.75	14.52	9.82	6.47	4.10	2.73
4.50	46.04	44.57	40.53	34.99	30.00	24.53	18.89	14.08	10.17	7.14	4.94	3.31
5.00	37.19	35.94	32.98	28.93	24.59	20.66	16.80	13.06	9.94	7.37	5.33	3.83
5.50	30.72	29.81	27.19	24.11	20.75	17.36	14.59	11.90	9.36	7.26	5.50	4.07
6.00	24.98	24.51	22.91	20.22	17.70	14.90	12.54	10.61	8.69	6.92	5.45	4.20
6.50	20.28	19.97	19.13	17.33	15.10	12.98	10.92	9.33	7.92	6.53	5.26	4.19
7.00	16.65	16.45	15.88	14.86	13.07	11.31	9.67	8.23	7.11	6.05	5.02	4.07
7.50	13.86	13.70	13.28	12.61	11.47	9.86	8.61	7.36	6.35	5.55	4.73	3.93
8.00	11.68	11.56	11.22	10.72	10.04	8.73	7.64	6.64	5.73	5.03	4.39	3.75
8.50	9.95	9.86	9.58	9.17	8.68	7.85	6.78	6.01	5.23	4.57	4.05	3.53
9.00	8.56	8.48	8.56	7.81	7.53	6.96	6.10	5.41	4.79	4.20	3.71	3.30
9.50	7.45	7.31	7.18	6.88	6.58	6.14	5.57	4.88	4.38	3.88	3.43	3.06
10.00	6.53	6.47	6.28	6.03	5.77	5.43	5.02	4.45	4.00	3.59	3.19	2.84
10.50	5.77	5.70	5.54	5.32	5.10	4.82	4.51	4.10	3.65	3.32	2.98	2.66
11.00	5.12	5.06	4.92	4.72	4.53	4.29	4.05	3.76	3.36	3.06	2.78	2.50
11.50	4.56	4.51	4.39	4.21	4.04	3.84	3.64	3.43	3.12	2.82	2.59	2.34
12.00	3.93	3.91	3.82	3.66	3.51	3.33	3.16	2.99	2.78	2.50	2.29	2.08

Distance Away From Luminaire Along Wall (feet)

G9

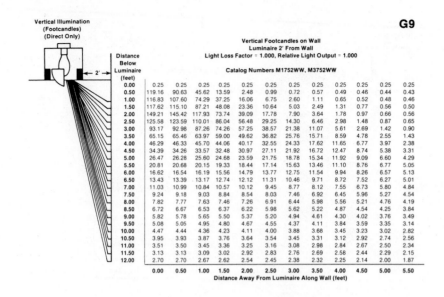

Vertical Illumination (Footcandles) (Direct Only)

Vertical Footcandles on Wall
Luminaire 2' From Wall
Light Loss Factor = 1.000, Relative Light Output = 1.000

Catalog Numbers M1752WW, M3752WW

Distance Below Luminaire (feet)	0.00	0.50	1.00	1.50	2.00	2.50	3.00	3.50	4.00	4.50	5.00	5.50
0.00	0.25	0.25	0.25	0.25	0.25	0.25	0.25	0.25	0.25	0.25	0.25	0.25
0.50	119.16	90.63	45.62	13.59	2.48	0.99	0.72	0.57	0.49	0.46	0.44	0.43
1.00	116.83	107.60	74.29	37.25	16.06	6.75	2.60	1.11	0.65	0.52	0.48	0.46
1.50	117.62	115.10	87.21	48.08	23.36	10.64	5.03	2.49	1.31	0.77	0.56	0.50
2.00	149.21	145.42	117.93	73.74	39.09	17.78	7.90	3.64	1.78	0.97	0.66	0.56
2.50	125.58	123.59	110.01	86.04	56.48	29.25	14.30	6.46	2.98	1.48	0.87	0.65
3.00	93.17	92.98	87.26	74.26	57.25	38.57	21.38	11.07	5.61	2.69	1.42	0.90
3.50	65.15	65.46	63.97	59.00	49.62	36.82	25.76	15.71	8.59	4.78	2.55	1.43
4.00	46.29	46.33	45.70	44.06	40.17	32.55	24.33	17.62	11.65	6.77	3.97	2.38
4.50	34.39	34.26	33.57	32.48	30.97	27.11	21.92	16.72	12.47	8.74	5.38	3.31
5.00	26.47	26.28	25.60	24.68	23.59	21.75	18.78	15.34	11.92	9.09	6.60	4.29
5.50	20.81	20.68	20.15	19.33	18.44	17.14	15.63	13.46	11.10	8.76	6.77	5.05
6.00	16.62	16.54	16.19	15.56	14.79	13.77	12.75	11.54	9.94	8.26	6.57	5.13
6.50	13.43	13.39	13.17	12.74	12.12	11.31	10.46	9.71	8.72	7.52	6.27	5.01
7.00	11.03	10.99	10.84	10.57	10.12	9.45	8.77	8.12	7.55	6.73	5.80	4.84
7.50	9.24	9.18	9.03	8.84	8.54	8.03	7.46	6.92	6.45	5.96	5.27	4.54
8.00	7.82	7.77	7.63	7.46	7.26	6.91	6.44	5.98	5.56	5.21	4.76	4.19
8.50	6.72	6.67	6.53	6.37	6.22	5.98	5.62	5.22	4.87	4.54	4.25	3.84
9.00	5.82	5.78	5.65	5.50	5.37	5.20	4.94	4.61	4.30	4.02	3.76	3.49
9.50	5.08	5.05	4.95	4.80	4.67	4.55	4.37	4.11	3.84	3.59	3.35	3.14
10.00	4.47	4.44	4.36	4.23	4.11	4.00	3.88	3.68	3.45	3.23	3.02	2.82
10.50	3.95	3.93	3.87	3.76	3.64	3.54	3.45	3.31	3.12	2.92	2.74	2.56
11.00	3.51	3.50	3.45	3.36	3.25	3.16	3.08	2.98	2.84	2.67	2.50	2.34
11.50	3.13	3.13	3.09	3.02	2.92	2.83	2.76	2.69	2.58	2.44	2.29	2.15
12.00	2.70	2.70	2.67	2.62	2.54	2.45	2.38	2.32	2.25	2.14	2.00	1.87

Distance Away From Luminaire Along Wall (feet)

G10

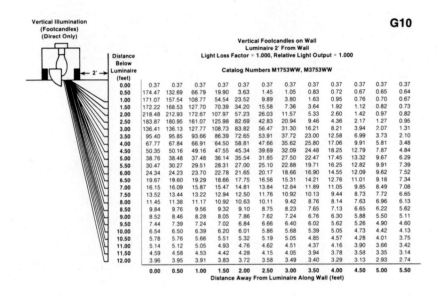

Vertical Illumination (Footcandles) (Direct Only)

Vertical Footcandles on Wall
Luminaire 2' From Wall
Light Loss Factor = 1.000, Relative Light Output = 1.000

Catalog Numbers M1753WW, M3753WW

Distance Below Luminaire (feet)	0.00	0.50	1.00	1.50	2.00	2.50	3.00	3.50	4.00	4.50	5.00	5.50
0.00	0.37	0.37	0.37	0.37	0.37	0.37	0.37	0.37	0.37	0.37	0.37	0.37
0.50	174.47	132.69	66.79	19.90	3.63	1.45	1.05	0.83	0.72	0.67	0.65	0.64
1.00	171.07	157.54	108.77	54.54	23.52	9.89	3.80	1.63	0.95	0.76	0.70	0.67
1.50	172.22	168.53	127.70	70.39	34.20	15.58	7.36	3.64	1.92	1.12	0.82	0.73
2.00	218.48	212.93	172.67	107.97	57.23	26.03	11.57	5.33	2.60	1.42	0.97	0.82
2.50	183.87	180.95	161.07	125.98	82.69	42.83	20.94	9.46	4.36	2.17	1.27	0.95
3.00	136.41	136.13	127.77	108.73	83.82	56.47	31.30	16.21	8.21	3.94	2.07	1.31
3.50	95.40	95.85	93.66	86.39	72.65	53.91	37.72	23.00	12.58	6.99	3.73	2.10
4.00	67.77	67.84	66.91	64.50	58.81	47.66	35.62	25.80	17.06	9.91	5.81	3.48
4.50	50.35	50.16	49.16	47.55	45.34	39.69	32.09	24.48	18.25	12.79	7.87	4.84
5.00	38.76	38.48	37.48	36.14	35.54	31.85	27.50	22.47	17.45	13.32	9.67	6.29
5.50	30.47	30.27	29.51	28.31	27.00	25.10	22.88	19.71	16.25	12.82	9.91	7.39
6.00	24.34	24.23	23.70	22.78	21.65	20.17	18.66	16.90	14.55	12.09	9.62	7.52
6.50	19.67	19.60	19.29	18.66	17.75	16.56	15.31	14.21	12.76	11.01	9.18	7.34
7.00	16.15	16.09	15.87	15.47	14.81	13.84	12.84	11.89	11.05	9.85	8.49	7.08
7.50	13.52	13.44	13.22	12.94	12.50	11.76	10.92	10.13	9.44	8.73	7.72	6.65
8.00	11.45	11.38	11.17	10.92	10.63	10.11	9.42	8.76	8.14	7.63	6.96	6.13
8.50	9.84	9.76	9.56	9.32	9.10	8.75	8.23	7.65	7.13	6.65	6.22	5.62
9.00	8.52	8.46	8.28	8.05	7.86	7.62	7.24	6.76	6.30	5.88	5.50	5.11
9.50	7.44	7.39	7.24	7.02	6.84	6.66	6.40	6.02	5.62	5.26	4.90	4.60
10.00	6.54	6.50	6.39	6.20	6.01	5.86	5.68	5.39	5.05	4.73	4.42	4.13
10.50	5.78	5.76	5.66	5.51	5.32	5.19	5.05	4.85	4.57	4.28	4.01	3.75
11.00	5.14	5.12	5.05	4.93	4.76	4.62	4.51	4.37	4.16	3.90	3.66	3.42
11.50	4.59	4.58	4.53	4.42	4.28	4.15	4.05	3.94	3.78	3.58	3.35	3.14
12.00	3.96	3.95	3.91	3.83	3.72	3.58	3.49	3.40	3.29	3.13	2.93	2.74

Distance Away From Luminaire Along Wall (feet)

G11

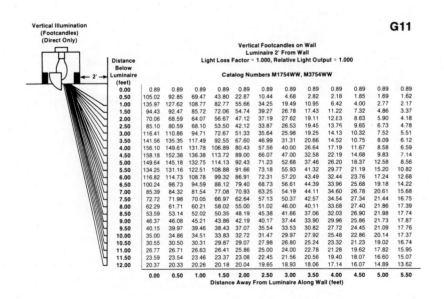

Vertical Illumination (Footcandles) (Direct Only)

Vertical Footcandles on Wall
Luminaire 2' From Wall
Light Loss Factor = 1.000, Relative Light Output = 1.000

Catalog Numbers M1754WW, M3754WW

Distance Below Luminaire (feet)	0.00	0.50	1.00	1.50	2.00	2.50	3.00	3.50	4.00	4.50	5.00	5.50
0.00	0.89	0.89	0.89	0.89	0.89	0.89	0.89	0.89	0.89	0.89	0.89	0.89
0.50	105.02	92.85	69.47	43.80	22.87	10.44	4.68	2.82	2.18	1.85	1.69	1.62
1.00	135.97	127.62	108.77	82.77	55.66	34.25	19.49	10.95	6.42	4.00	2.77	2.17
1.50	94.43	92.47	85.72	72.06	54.74	39.27	26.78	17.43	11.22	7.32	4.86	3.37
2.00	70.06	68.59	64.07	56.67	47.12	37.19	27.62	19.11	12.63	8.63	5.90	4.18
2.50	85.10	80.59	68.10	53.50	42.12	33.87	26.53	19.45	13.76	9.65	6.73	4.78
3.00	116.41	110.86	94.71	72.67	51.33	35.64	25.98	19.25	14.13	10.32	7.52	5.51
3.50	141.56	135.35	117.49	92.55	67.60	46.99	31.31	20.66	14.52	10.75	8.09	6.12
4.00	156.10	149.61	131.78	106.89	80.43	57.56	40.00	26.64	17.19	11.67	8.58	6.59
4.50	158.18	152.38	136.38	113.72	89.00	66.07	47.00	32.58	22.19	14.68	9.83	7.14
5.00	149.64	145.18	132.75	114.13	92.43	71.23	52.68	37.46	26.20	18.37	12.58	8.56
5.50	134.25	131.16	122.51	108.88	91.66	73.18	55.93	41.32	29.77	21.19	15.20	10.82
6.00	116.82	114.73	108.78	99.32	86.91	72.31	57.20	43.49	32.44	23.76	17.24	12.68
6.50	100.24	98.73	94.59	88.12	79.40	68.73	56.61	44.39	33.96	25.68	19.18	14.22
7.00	85.39	84.32	81.54	77.08	70.93	63.25	54.19	44.11	34.60	26.78	20.61	15.68
7.50	72.72	71.98	70.05	66.97	62.64	57.13	50.37	42.57	34.54	27.34	21.44	16.75
8.00	62.29	61.71	60.21	58.02	55.00	51.02	46.00	40.11	33.68	27.40	21.86	17.39
8.50	53.59	53.14	52.00	50.35	48.19	45.38	41.66	37.06	32.03	26.90	21.98	17.74
9.00	46.37	46.08	45.21	43.86	42.19	40.17	37.44	33.90	29.96	25.86	21.73	17.87
9.50	40.15	39.97	39.46	38.43	37.07	35.54	33.53	30.82	27.72	24.45	21.09	17.76
10.00	35.00	34.86	34.51	33.83	32.72	31.47	29.97	27.98	25.48	22.80	20.14	17.37
10.50	30.55	30.50	30.31	29.87	29.07	27.98	26.80	25.24	23.32	21.23	19.02	16.74
11.00	26.77	26.71	26.63	26.41	25.86	25.00	24.00	22.78	21.28	19.62	17.82	15.95
11.50	23.59	23.54	23.46	23.37	23.08	22.45	21.56	20.56	19.40	18.07	16.60	15.07
12.00	20.37	20.33	20.26	20.18	20.04	19.65	18.93	18.06	17.14	16.07	14.89	13.62

Distance Away From Luminaire Along Wall (feet)

Appendix D

The following information corresponds to the data found in Table 9 on page 75. An explanation of how to use "Cones of Light" in designing lighting systems can be found on page 73.

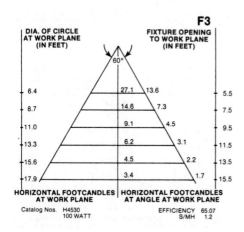

F3

DIA. OF CIRCLE AT WORK PLANE (IN FEET) — FIXTURE OPENING TO WORK PLANE (IN FEET)

60°

6.4	27.1	13.6	5.5
8.7	14.6	7.3	7.5
11.0	9.1	4.5	9.5
13.3	6.2	3.1	11.5
15.6	4.5	2.2	13.5
17.9	3.4	1.7	15.5

HORIZONTAL FOOTCANDLES AT WORK PLANE — HORIZONTAL FOOTCANDLES AT ANGLE AT WORK PLANE

Catalog Nos. H4530 100 WATT — EFFICIENCY 65.07 S/MH 1.2

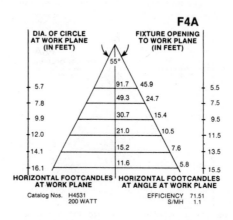

F4A

DIA. OF CIRCLE AT WORK PLANE (IN FEET) — FIXTURE OPENING TO WORK PLANE (IN FEET)

55°

5.7	91.7	45.9	5.5
7.8	49.3	24.7	7.5
9.9	30.7	15.4	9.5
12.0	21.0	10.5	11.5
14.1	15.2	7.6	13.5
16.1	11.6	5.8	15.5

HORIZONTAL FOOTCANDLES AT WORK PLANE — HORIZONTAL FOOTCANDLES AT ANGLE AT WORK PLANE

Catalog Nos. H4531 200 WATT — EFFICIENCY 71.51 S/MH 1.1

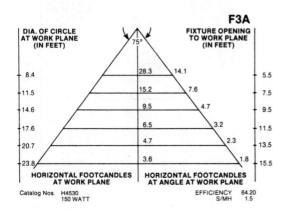

F3A

DIA. OF CIRCLE AT WORK PLANE (IN FEET) — FIXTURE OPENING TO WORK PLANE (IN FEET)

75°

8.4	28.3	14.1	5.5
11.5	15.2	7.6	7.5
14.6	9.5	4.7	9.5
17.6	6.5	3.2	11.5
20.7	4.7	2.3	13.5
23.8	3.6	1.8	15.5

HORIZONTAL FOOTCANDLES AT WORK PLANE — HORIZONTAL FOOTCANDLES AT ANGLE AT WORK PLANE

Catalog Nos. H4530 150 WATT — EFFICIENCY 64.20 S/MH 1.5

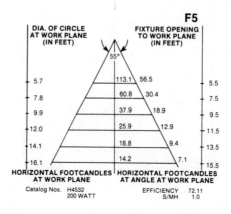

F5

DIA. OF CIRCLE AT WORK PLANE (IN FEET) — FIXTURE OPENING TO WORK PLANE (IN FEET)

55°

5.7	113.1	56.5	5.5
7.8	60.8	30.4	7.5
9.9	37.9	18.9	9.5
12.0	25.9	12.9	11.5
14.1	18.8	9.4	13.5
16.1	14.2	7.1	15.5

HORIZONTAL FOOTCANDLES AT WORK PLANE — HORIZONTAL FOOTCANDLES AT ANGLE AT WORK PLANE

Catalog Nos. H4532 200 WATT — EFFICIENCY 72.11 S/MH 1.0

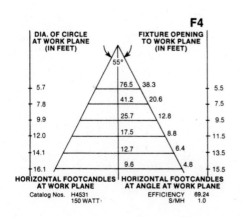

F4

DIA. OF CIRCLE AT WORK PLANE (IN FEET) — FIXTURE OPENING TO WORK PLANE (IN FEET)

55°

5.7	76.5	38.3	5.5
7.8	41.2	20.6	7.5
9.9	25.7	12.8	9.5
12.0	17.5	8.8	11.5
14.1	12.7	6.4	13.5
16.1	9.6	4.8	15.5

HORIZONTAL FOOTCANDLES AT WORK PLANE — HORIZONTAL FOOTCANDLES AT ANGLE AT WORK PLANE

Catalog Nos. H4531 150 WATT — EFFICIENCY 69.24 S/MH 1.0

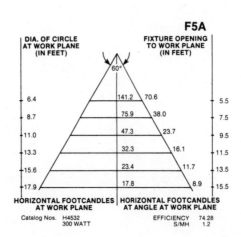

F5A

DIA. OF CIRCLE AT WORK PLANE (IN FEET) — FIXTURE OPENING TO WORK PLANE (IN FEET)

60°

6.4	141.2	70.6	5.5
8.7	75.9	38.0	7.5
11.0	47.3	23.7	9.5
13.3	32.3	16.1	11.5
15.6	23.4	11.7	13.5
17.9	17.8	8.9	15.5

HORIZONTAL FOOTCANDLES AT WORK PLANE — HORIZONTAL FOOTCANDLES AT ANGLE AT WORK PLANE

Catalog Nos. H4532 300 WATT — EFFICIENCY 74.28 S/MH 1.2

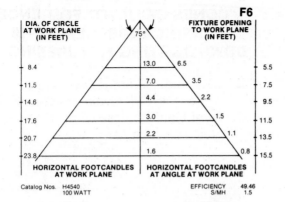

F6

DIA. OF CIRCLE
AT WORK PLANE
(IN FEET)

FIXTURE OPENING
TO WORK PLANE
(IN FEET)

75°

8.4	13.0	6.5	5.5
11.5	7.0	3.5	7.5
14.6	4.4	2.2	9.5
17.6	3.0	1.5	11.5
20.7	2.2	1.1	13.5
23.8	1.6	0.8	15.5

HORIZONTAL FOOTCANDLES
AT WORK PLANE

HORIZONTAL FOOTCANDLES
AT ANGLE AT WORK PLANE

Catalog Nos. H4540
100 WATT

EFFICIENCY 49.46
S/MH 1.5

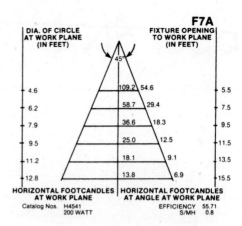

F7A

DIA. OF CIRCLE
AT WORK PLANE
(IN FEET)

FIXTURE OPENING
TO WORK PLANE
(IN FEET)

45°

4.6	109.2	54.6	5.5
6.2	58.7	29.4	7.5
7.9	36.6	18.3	9.5
9.5	25.0	12.5	11.5
11.2	18.1	9.1	13.5
12.8	13.8	6.9	15.5

HORIZONTAL FOOTCANDLES
AT WORK PLANE

HORIZONTAL FOOTCANDLES
AT ANGLE AT WORK PLANE

Catalog Nos. H4541
200 WATT

EFFICIENCY 55.71
S/MH 0.8

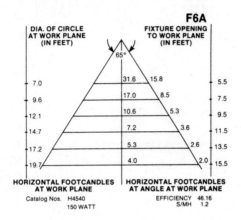

F6A

DIA. OF CIRCLE
AT WORK PLANE
(IN FEET)

FIXTURE OPENING
TO WORK PLANE
(IN FEET)

65°

7.0	31.6	15.8	5.5
9.6	17.0	8.5	7.5
12.1	10.6	5.3	9.5
14.7	7.2	3.6	11.5
17.2	5.3	2.6	13.5
19.7	4.0	2.0	15.5

HORIZONTAL FOOTCANDLES
AT WORK PLANE

HORIZONTAL FOOTCANDLES
AT ANGLE AT WORK PLANE

Catalog Nos. H4540
150 WATT

EFFICIENCY 46.16
S/MH 1.2

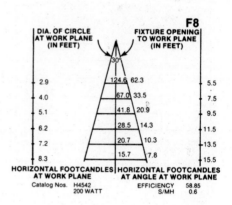

F8

DIA. OF CIRCLE
AT WORK PLANE
(IN FEET)

FIXTURE OPENING
TO WORK PLANE
(IN FEET)

30°

2.9	124.6	62.3	5.5
4.0	67.0	33.5	7.5
5.1	41.8	20.9	9.5
6.2	28.5	14.3	11.5
7.2	20.7	10.3	13.5
8.3	15.7	7.8	15.5

HORIZONTAL FOOTCANDLES
AT WORK PLANE

HORIZONTAL FOOTCANDLES
AT ANGLE AT WORK PLANE

Catalog Nos. H4542
200 WATT

EFFICIENCY 58.85
S/MH 0.6

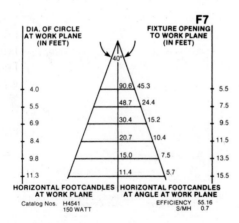

F7

DIA. OF CIRCLE
AT WORK PLANE
(IN FEET)

FIXTURE OPENING
TO WORK PLANE
(IN FEET)

40°

4.0	90.6	45.3	5.5
5.5	48.7	24.4	7.5
6.9	30.4	15.2	9.5
8.4	20.7	10.4	11.5
9.8	15.0	7.5	13.5
11.3	11.4	5.7	15.5

HORIZONTAL FOOTCANDLES
AT WORK PLANE

HORIZONTAL FOOTCANDLES
AT ANGLE AT WORK PLANE

Catalog Nos. H4541
150 WATT

EFFICIENCY 55.16
S/MH 0.7

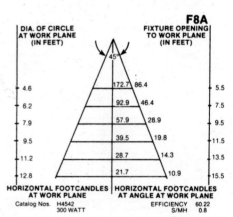

F8A

DIA. OF CIRCLE
AT WORK PLANE
(IN FEET)

FIXTURE OPENING
TO WORK PLANE
(IN FEET)

45°

4.6	172.7	86.4	5.5
6.2	92.9	46.4	7.5
7.9	57.9	28.9	9.5
9.5	39.5	19.8	11.5
11.2	28.7	14.3	13.5
12.8	21.7	10.9	15.5

HORIZONTAL FOOTCANDLES
AT WORK PLANE

HORIZONTAL FOOTCANDLES
AT ANGLE AT WORK PLANE

Catalog Nos. H4542
300 WATT

EFFICIENCY 60.22
S/MH 0.8

Appendix E

The Data Key Table given in this appendix lists specific mounting and spacing distances and aiming angles for the most popular types of PAR, R, ER, and MR-16 lamps used in accent and downlighting applications. The individual plot numbers given in the table key this information to a specific computer generated isofootcandle curve illustrated later. The grid spacing (in feet) for each curve printout is also given in the first column of the table.

Knowing this information, it is possible to predict the exact light patterns and illumination levels these lamps, when mounted at a specific position and aiming angle, will produce on a given wall or floor. Simply transpose the isofootcandle curve grid to the appropriate area on the wall or floor. A straight line bisecting the center of the fixture and running to the illuminated surface will indicate the point on the surface which corresponds to the center point of the isofootcandle reference plot. On the plots, this center point is indicated by a heavy black dot. Because all of the isofootcandle curve plots given in this appendix are symmetrical around this dot, only one-half of the total plot is illustrated in some cases. The lighting designer can quickly work up the total light pattern from the information given.

Modifying the Curves. Not all application will fall into the guidelines set up in the Data Key. Changing the given fixture mounting distance will change the size of the light pattern produced and the illumination levels. However, through the use of two simple formulas it is possible to compute the exact extent of these changes so that the curves can be modified to fit thousands of applications.

Formula #1: Determining the new grid spacing for the modified curve.

$$\frac{\text{New mounting distance}}{\text{Old mounting distance}} \times \text{Old grid spacing} = \text{New grid spacing}$$

Formula #2: Determining the new illumination levels at the new grid points.

$$\frac{\text{Old mounting distance}^2}{\text{New mounting distance}^2} \times \text{Old illumination level} = \text{New illumination level}$$

Example: A Halo Power-Trac fixture #L1762 equipped with an MR-16, 42-watt, 42EYS/NFL lamp positioned at a 45° aiming angle is used to illuminate an 18″ high by 12″ wide wall display. The mounting distance from the wall is 2′6″, and since the fixture is mounted 4″ below an 8′4″ ceiling, the actual mounting height is 8′ (Fig. E1). Determine the illumination levels and the maximum/minimum uniformity ratio occurring on the display.

Step 1: Refer to the Data Key Table and locate the listing for the 42EYS/NFL lamp. You can see that the isofootcandle curve reference plot listed under the 45° aiming angle is 45C. For plot 45C the mounting distance from the wall (D) is listed as 5′, and the grid increment spacing used in the generation of the plot is 0.5′ or 6″.

Step 2: Locate plot 45C illustrated later in this appendix. The light pattern and intensities shown are those which will be generated when the fixture is aimed at 45° and mounted 5′ from the wall. The plot must now be converted to that which would appear if the fixture were aimed at 45° and mounted 2′6″ from the wall.

Step 3: Use formula #1 to determine the new grid increment spacing.

$$\frac{\text{New mounting distance}}{\text{Old mounting distance}} = \frac{2.5'}{5.0'} =$$

.5 × .5′ original grid spacing = .25′ or 3″ new grid spacing

Since the display is 12″ wide, you must plot 12″ ÷ 3″ = 4 columns of grid points (two to the right of the center column and two to the left of the center column). Counting the center column of grid points, there will be five columns of grid points. Since the display is 18″ high, you must plot 18″ ÷ 3″ = 6 rows of grid points (three below the center row and three above the center row). So overall, there will be seven rows of grid points with five grid points in each row (Fig. E2).

Step 4: Use formula #2 to determine the new footcandle levels at the new grid points.

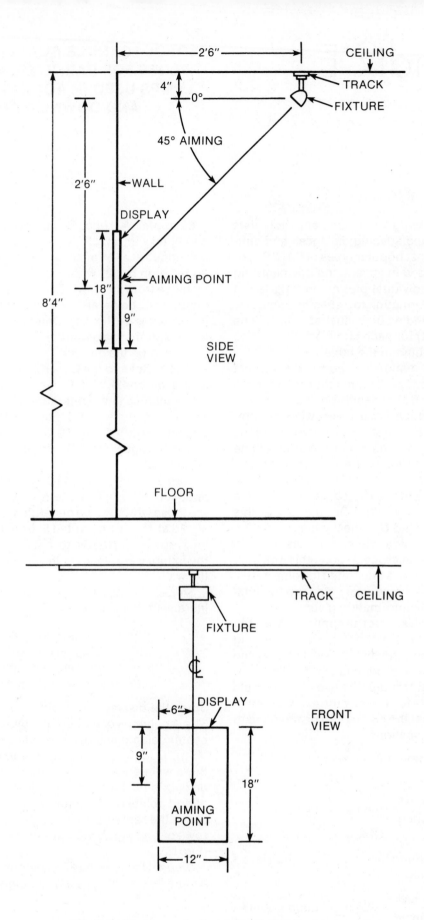

Fig. E-1: Aiming and dimensional details for sample problem.

24" (12")

36" (18")

20.0 (80.0)	27.0 (108.0)	29.0 (116.0)	27.0 (108.0)	20.0 (80.0)
24.4 (97.6)	30.9 (123.6)	31.8 (127.2)	30.9 (123.6)	24.4 (97.6)
25.9 (103.6)	31.8 (127.2)	32.7 (130.8)	31.8 (127.2)	25.9 (103.6)
24.7 (98.8)	29.3 (117.2)	31.8 (127.2)	29.3 (117.2)	24.7 (98.8)
20.6 (82.4)	23.9 (95.6)	24.6 (98.4)	23.9 (95.6)	20.6 (82.4)
16.3 (65.2)	18.5 (74.0)	18.7 (74.8)	18.5 (74.0)	16.3 (65.2)
12.2 (48.8)	13.8 (55.2)	14.2 (56.8)	13.8 (55.2)	12.2 (48.8)

Fig. E2: Top distance and footcandle values represent those found on the original isofootcandle curve reference plot 45C. Fixture to surface distance is 5′. Grid spacing is 6″. Distance and footcandle values in parentheses are the new values generated when the fixture to surface distance is altered to 2.5′. Grid spacing distance is then 3″.

$$\frac{\text{Old mounting distance}^2}{\text{New mounting distance}^2} = \frac{5^2}{2.5^2} = \frac{25}{6.25} = 4.0$$

Multiply all appropriate original footcandle levels appearing on plot 45C by a factor of 4.0 to determine the new footcandle levels at the new grid spacing points. By doing this, you can determine the precise light levels over the entire display areas (Fig. E2).

Step 5: Determine the maximum/minimum uniformity ratio for the display area by dividing the maximum footcandle reading at a given point by the minimum footcandle reading at a given point. In this case:

$$\frac{130.8 \text{ footcandles}}{48.8 \text{ footcandles}} =$$

2.68:1 maximum/minimum uniformity

Alternate Method for Quick Checks. As you can see by referring to plot 45C, dark circular lines are used to connect points of equal illumination, such as 30 footcandles, 20 footcandles, etc. As a quick alternate method to the grid point by grid point method just described, these isofootcandle lines can be plotted onto a properly scaled drawing of the illuminated area. While not as precise as the previous method, this method often provides approximations accurate enough to be used in many applications.

Remember, if the mounting distance is altered, a new grid spacing must be found and an illumination level modifying factor must be determined. The new scale must be used on all layouts and the values of the isofootcandle lines must be multiplied by the modifying factor.

Fixture Spacing for Uniform Lighting. When uniform lighting is desired, it is standard practice to provide a maximum/minimum uniformity ratio of 2:1 or less. The Data Key Table lists the spacing (S) for each lamp at each aiming angle which will provide for uniform lighting. For example, for lamp 42EYS/NFL aimed at 45° and mounted 5′ from the wall, the spacing between fixtures to provide uniform lighting will be 4′. If the mounting distance changes, the spacing for uniform lighting will also change by the same modifying factor found using Formula #1. So, the previous example can be calculated in the following manner:

$$\frac{\text{New mounting distance}}{\text{Old mounting distance}} = \frac{2.5'}{5.0'} =$$

$.5 \times 4'$ fixture spacing =

2′ new fixture spacing

Data Key to PAR, R, ER, and MR-16 Lamp Isofootcandle Curve Reference Plots

Lamp Designation	Grid Spacing	0° Aiming			30° Aiming			45° Aiming			60° Aiming		
		Plot #	D^1	S^2	Plot #	D^1	S^2	Plot #	D^1	S^2	Plot #	D^1	S^2
25PAR36VNSP	.2′	1A	25	1.5	1B	20	1.7	1C	15	1.6	1D	10	1.5
25PAR36NSP	.5′	2A	12	3.8	2B	11	4	2C	9	4	2D	5	3
25PAR36WFL	.5′	3A	6	4	3B	6	5	3C	4	4	3D	3	2.8
25PAR36VWFL	.5′	4A	4	3.5	4B	4	3.8	4C	4	4.6	4D	3	4.4
25PAR46VNSP	.2′	5A	25	1.5	5B	20	1.7	5C	15	1.6	5D	10	1.5
50PAR36VNSP	.5′	6A	25	3.4	6B	20	3.2	6C	15	2.9	6D	10	2.7
50PAR36NSP(Z3)	.5′	7A	16	4.7	7B	15	5	7C	10	4	7D	5	2.8
50PAR36WFL	.5′	8A	7	4.8	8B	7	5.6	8C	4	3.8	8D	3	3.5
50PAR36VWFL	.5′	9A	5	4.3	9B	5	4.8	9C	4	4.7	9D	3	4.4
75PAR38/SP	1.0′	10A	12	5.2	10B	10	4.8	10C	9	5.2	10D	5	3.8
75PAR38/FL	1.0′	11A	8	5.6	11B	7	5.6	11C	5	4.7	11D	4	4.8
150PAR38/SP	1.0′	12A	20	7.6	12B	16	6.4	12C	11	5.6	12D	6	4.4
150PAR38/FL	1.0′	13A	12	8.2	13B	11	9	13C	8	7.5	13D	4	4.8
200PAR46/3NSP	1.0′	14A	25	7.6	14B	20	7.6	14C	15	7	14D	10	6.6
200PAR46/3MFL	1.0′	15A	20	11	15B	16	10.4	15C	11	8.8	15D	6	6.8
300PAR56/NSP	1.0′	16A	30	6.2	16B	24	5.6	16C	18	5.2	16D	12	5
300PAR56/MFL	1.0′	17A	48	12.3	17B	20	11.4	17C	15	10.4	17D	15	14.6
300PAR56/WFL	1.0′	18A	20	17.6	18B	16	16.8	18C	12	13.4	18D	7	11
500PAR64/NSP	1.0′	19A	36	8.8	19B	27	7.8	19C	21	7.1	19D	15	7.2
500PAR64/MFL	1.0′	20A	30	16	20B	25	15.6	20C	17	13.2	20D	11	11.6
500PAR64/WFL	1.0′	21A	24	24	21B	18	20.2	21C	16	21.4	21D	8	13.6
Q250PAR38/SP	1.0′	22A	25	5.2	22B	20	5.6	22C	15	4.6	22D	10	4.5
Q250PAR38/FL	1.0′	23A	16	11.8	23B	12	10.4	23C	10	9.6	23D	5	6
Q500PAR56/NSP	1.0′	24A	36	17.6	24B	27	15.2	24C	21	14.1	24D	15	14.2
Q500PAR56/MFL	1.0′	25A	30	18.2	25B	25	17.6	25C	17	14.5	25D	11	12.4
Q500PAR56/WFL	1.0′	26A	24	22.8	26B	18	19.4	26C	16	20	26D	8	12.6
15R14SC/SP	.5′	27A	9	4.4	27B	8	4.4	27C	5	3.2	27D	4	3.3
25R14SC/SP	.5′	28A	9	4.5	28B	8	4.3	28C	5	3.3	28D	4	3.6
25R14/N(Z11)	1.0′	29A	5	7	29B	5	6.5	29C	4	6	29D	3	4.8
30R20/FL	.5′	30A	4	3	30B	4	3.6	30C	4	4.4	30D	3	3.6
40R16/FL(Z9)	.5′	31A	8	9	31B	7	9	31C	5	7.4	31D	4	7
50R20/FL	1.0′	32A	5	4.4	32B	5	4.6	32C	4	4.6	32D	3	4
75R30/SP	1.0′	33A	8	5.2	33B	7	5.5	33C	5	4.6	33D	4	4.4
75R30/FL	1.0′	34A	5	8.6	34B	5	8	34C	4	7.6	34D	3	6.2
100R25/FL(Z10)	1.0′	35A	8	10	35B	7	10	35C	5	7.6	35D	4	5
150R40/SP	1.0′	36A	16	8.4	36B	15	9.2	36C	10	7.4	36D	5	5.2
150R40/FL	1.0′	37A	8	13	37B	7	11.4	37C	5	8	37D	4	7.4
300R40/SP	1.0′	38A	20	11.6	38B	16	11	38C	11	9	38D	6	6.4
300R40/FL	1.0′	39A	10	16.4	39B	9	16	39C	6	11	39D	4	7.8
75ER30	1.0′	40A	8	6	40B	7	6	40C	5	5	40D	4	5.5
120ER40	1.0′	41A	11	7.6	41B	10	8	41C	7	7	41D	4	5
20ESX/NSP(Z30)	.5′	42A	12	2.6	42B	11	2.5	42C	10	2.8	42D	9	3.6
20BAB/FL (Z35)	.5′	43A	10	6.4	43B	9	6.4	43C	5	4.2	43D	4	3.8
42EPZ/NSP(Z20)	.5′	44A	16	3.8	44B	15	4.2	44C	10	3.5	44D	5	2.5
42EYS/NFL(Z25)	.5′	45A	10	5.6	45B	9	6	45C	5	4	45D	4	4.2
50EXT/NSP	.5′	46A	16	4.4	46B	15	4.8	46C	10	4	46D	5	2.5
50EXZ/NFL(Z26)	.5′	47A	10	6.6	47B	9	6.4	47C	5	4.5	47D	4	4.8
50EXN/FL(Z31)	.5′	48A	10	6.4	48B	9	6.8	48C	5	4.4	48D	4	4.6
75EYE/NSP	.5′	49A	16	4.4	49B	7	6	49C	5	5.2	49D	4	4.6
75EYC/FL	.5′	50A	8	6.1	50B	15	4.5	50C	10	3.6	50D	5	2.5

Notes: 1. Distance in feet from the fixture to the wall or floor.
2. Spacing between fixtures (feet) to ensure uniform lighting (2:1 maximum/minimum uniformity ratio).

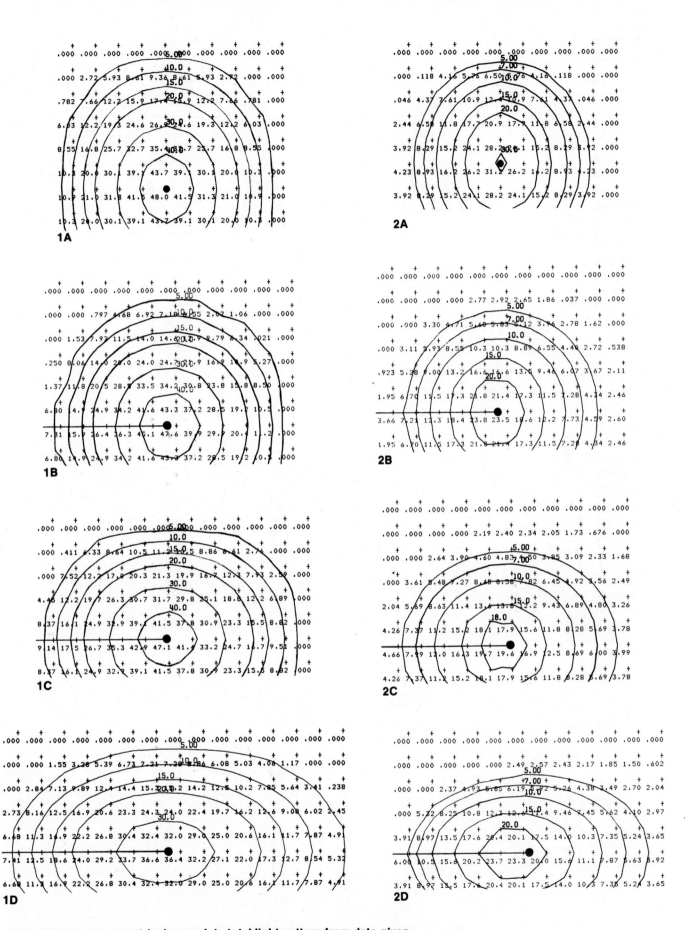

Note: All curves symmetrical; complete total light pattern from data given.

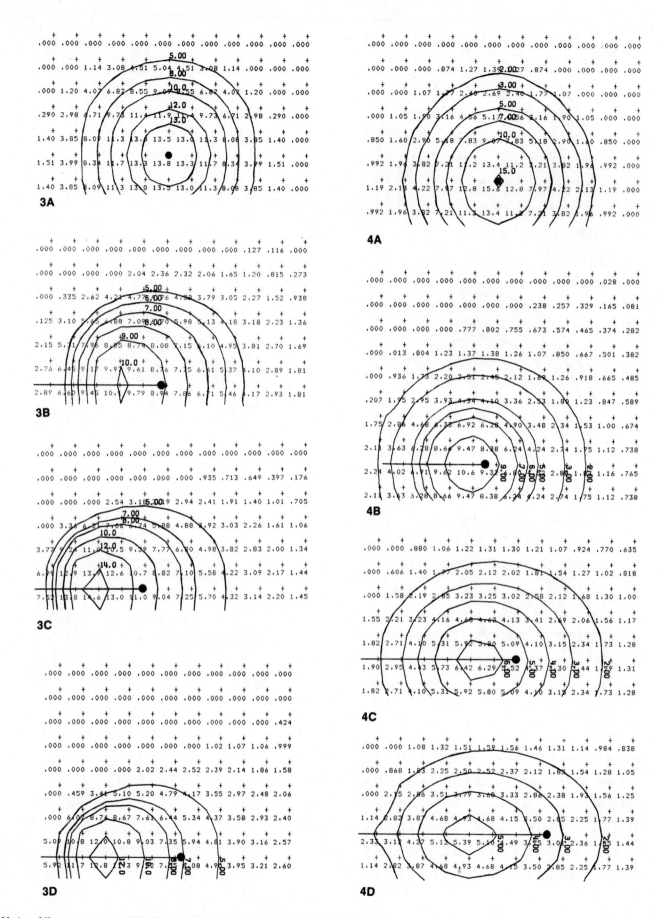

Note: All curves symmetrical; complete total light pattern from data given.

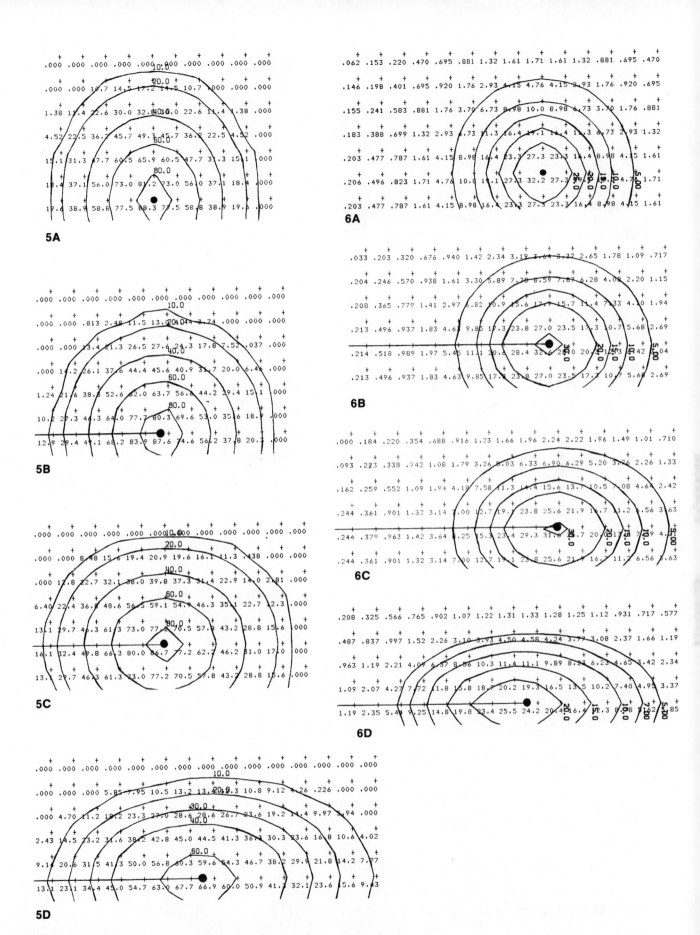

Note: All curves symmetrical; complete total light pattern from data given.

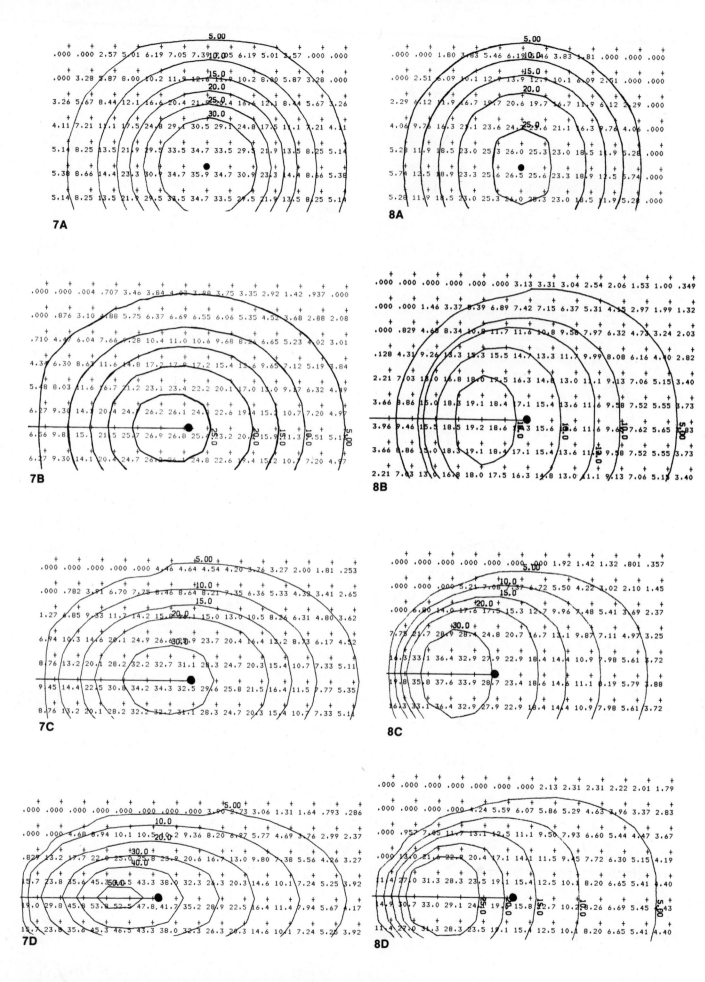

Note: All curves symmetrical; complete total light pattern from data given.

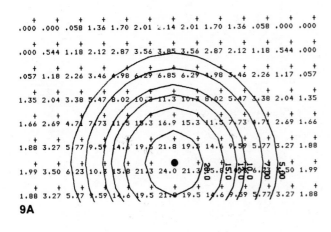

9A

9B

9C

9D

10A

10B

10C

10D

Note: All curves symmetrical; complete total light pattern from data given.

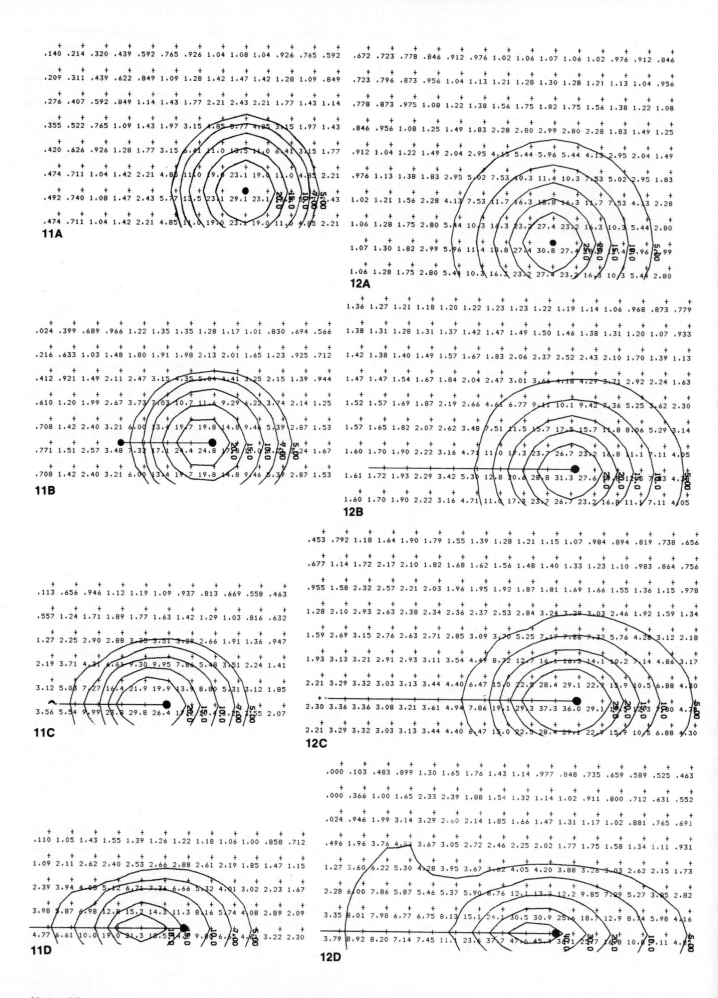

Note: All curves symmetrical; complete total light pattern from data given.

13A

```
536 .658 .795 .937 1.07 1.20 1.31 1.38 1.40 1.38 1.31 1.20 1.07 .937 .795
658 .809 .977 1.15 1.33 1.50 1.66 1.77 1.82 1.77 1.66 1.50 1.33 1.15 .977
795 .977 1.18 1.40 1.64 1.90 2.19 2.43 2.55 2.43 2.19 1.90 1.64 1.40 1.18
937 1.15 1.40 1.68 2.04 2.51 3.15 3.77 4.10 3.77 3.15 2.51 2.04 1.68 1.40
.07 1.33 1.64 2.04 2.68 4.09 6.04 7.76 8.60 7.76 6.04 4.09 2.68 2.04 1.64
.20 1.50 1.90 2.51 4.09 7.01 10.4 13.1 14.4 13.1 10.4 7.01 4.09 2.51 1.90
.31 1.66 2.19 3.15 6.04 10.4 15.1 18.7 20.8 18.7 15.1 10.4 6.04 3.15 2.19
.38 1.77 2.43 3.77 7.76 13.1 18.9 23.8 26.4 23.8 18.9 13.1 7.76 3.77 2.43
.40 1.82 2.55 4.10 8.60 14.4 20.8 26.4 29.2 26.4 20.8 ... 4.00 2.55
.38 1.77 2.43 3.77 7.76 13.1 18.9 23.8 26.4 23.8 18.9 13.1 7.76 3.77 2.43
```

13B

```
.909 1.05 1.16 1.23 1.26 1.26 1.22 1.17 1.10 1.01 .905 .804 .714 .631
1.18 1.35 1.48 1.57 1.61 1.61 1.58 1.50 1.38 1.29 1.15 1.00 .861 .736
1.50 1.71 1.87 1.98 2.05 2.21 2.33 2.29 2.07 1.79 1.49 1.29 1.07 .883
1.86 2.13 2.37 2.66 3.06 3.40 3.93 4.03 3.65 3.11 2.43 1.86 1.36 1.06
2.26 2.60 3.07 4.13 5.68 6.95 7.53 7.20 6.15 4.99 3.80 2.80 1.95 1.44
2.64 3.17 4.36 7.03 9.94 11.6 12.1 11.1 9.30 7.36 5.50 3.90 2.63 1.86
3.00 3.90 6.55 10.9 14.8 16.8 17.0 15.3 12.4 9.63 7.13 5.03 3.39 2.30
3.28 4.66 8.68 14.2 18.7 21.0 21.1 18.6 14.8 11.2 8.19 5.74 3.87 2.59
3.40 5.05 9.72 15.8 20.7 23.3 23.3 20.5 16.1 ... 5.11 2.73
3.28 4.66 8.68 14.2 18.7 21.0 21.1 18.6 14.8 11.2 8.19 5.74 3.87 2.59
```

13C

```
.206 .740 1.03 1.25 1.39 1.44 1.43 1.37 1.29 1.20 1.08 .965 .887 .784 .684
.728 1.14 1.51 1.77 1.91 1.94 1.91 1.83 1.71 1.67 1.56 1.38 1.18 1.02 .911
1.09 1.68 2.14 2.44 2.57 2.60 2.67 2.84 2.86 2.63 2.57 2.33 1.95 1.57 1.25
1.61 2.35 2.92 3.26 3.49 3.81 4.59 5.56 5.90 5.47 4.66 3.88 3.09 2.43 1.88
2.19 3.10 3.79 4.23 4.96 7.23 9.90 10.8 10.5 9.15 7.50 5.96 4.45 3.45 2.56
2.76 3.84 4.63 5.53 8.59 14.1 17.1 17.3 15.9 13.1 10.3 7.96 5.97 4.44 3.24
3.18 4.37 5.34 7.25 13.7 20.5 23.4 23.2 20.7 16.5 12.6 9.47 6.94 5.07 3.67
3.35 4.57 5.63 8.22 16.2 23.5 27.0 26.7 23.2 ... 4.39 5.89
3.18 4.37 5.34 7.25 13.7 20.5 23.6 23.2 20.7 16.5 12.6 9.47 6.94 5.07 3.67
```

13D

```
.000 .000 .886 1.22 1.35 1.33 1.24 1.11 .989 .871 .750 .686 .603 .520
.000 1.00 1.81 2.14 2.15 1.99 1.78 1.57 1.38 1.28 1.11 .991 .906 .793
.280 2.49 3.44 3.61 3.36 3.03 2.87 2.73 2.43 2.38 2.07 1.71 1.43 1.21
2.67 5.15 6.03 5.83 5.91 6.07 7.00 6.51 5.48 4.56 3.62 2.87 2.29 1.80
5.73 9.20 9.85 11.9 16.6 18.0 15.9 12.6 9.62 7.27 5.39 4.06 3.09 2.36
9.62 13.6 15.9 37.6 37.5 33.5 26.4 19.0 13.4 9.59 6.84 4.97 3.68 2.75
11.5 15.8 23.9 46.1 49.9 42.4 ... 4.10 .7 .56 5.42 3.96 2.94
```

14A

```
.472 .601 .680 .778 .919 1.08 1.22 1.28 1.22 1.08 .919 .778 .680 .601 .472
.608 .689 .815 1.06 1.42 1.85 2.27 2.47 2.27 1.85 1.42 1.06 .815 .689 .608
.677 .797 1.10 1.65 2.61 4.18 5.81 6.71 5.81 4.18 2.61 1.65 1.10 .797 .677
.739 1.00 1.61 2.81 5.29 8.89 11.9 13.7 11.9 8.89 5.29 2.81 1.61 1.00 .739
.833 1.32 2.40 4.67 8.83 15.1 21.3 24.1 21.3 15.1 8.83 4.67 2.40 1.32 .833
.963 1.67 3.29 6.19 11.8 22.1 31.5 36.1 31.5 22.1 11.8 6.19 3.29 1.67 .963
1.06 1.94 3.93 7.16 13.6 26.7 40.6 49.5 40.6 26.7 13.6 7.16 3.93 1.94 1.06
1.11 2.10 4.18 7.45 14.1 28.1 44.9 59.0 ... 2.10 1.11
1.06 1.94 3.93 7.16 13.6 26.7 40.6 49.5 40.6 26.7 13.6 7.16 3.93 1.94 1.06
```

14B

```
.000 .659 .861 .968 1.08 1.27 1.48 1.70 1.80 1.69 1.43 1.16 .922 .718 .575
.480 .935 1.03 1.24 1.67 2.30 3.33 4.36 4.71 4.12 3.11 2.15 1.49 1.05 .764
.933 1.07 1.24 1.91 3.25 5.77 8.75 11.0 11.2 9.20 6.82 4.34 2.64 1.66 1.07
1.09 1.20 1.73 3.25 6.48 11.6 17.7 21.4 21.1 17.3 11.6 7.22 4.29 2.51 1.49
1.15 1.38 2.39 4.98 9.91 18.6 28.6 34.1 33.0 26.3 17.4 9.66 5.57 3.29 1.92
1.19 1.57 2.96 6.41 12.1 23.4 37.7 47.8 46.1 33.8 20.9 11.0 6.36 3.81 2.23
1.20 1.65 3.29 6.86 12.6 24.6 41.2 55.8 53.9 ... 3.59 3.90 2.37
1.19 1.57 2.96 6.41 12.1 23.4 37.7 47.8 46.1 33.8 20.9 11.0 6.36 3.81 2.23
```

14C

```
.000 .589 .887 .959 1.00 1.05 1.16 1.22 1.18 1.12 1.02 .896 .754 .616 .506
.378 1.06 1.16 1.28 1.57 1.99 2.38 2.59 2.62 2.57 2.16 1.68 1.27 .945 .732
1.20 1.32 1.54 2.27 3.53 5.39 7.15 8.35 7.75 6.46 4.98 3.47 2.37 1.57 1.11
1.44 1.67 2.58 4.72 8.75 13.3 16.8 18.1 18.0 12.7 8.98 6.00 3.95 2.51 1.63
1.57 2.32 4.41 8.79 15.9 24.8 30.2 31.1 26.5 20.4 13.8 8.34 5.22 3.27 2.13
1.66 3.05 6.37 11.7 21.7 35.1 44.1 46.2 37.2 26.5 16.8 9.72 5.99 3.76 2.47
1.72 3.46 7.10 12.5 23.0 38.3 51.4 57.9 ... 10. 6.22 3.71 2.59
1.66 3.05 6.37 11.7 21.7 35.1 44.1 46.2 37.2 26.5 16.8 9.72 5.99 3.76 2.47
```

14D

```
.218 1.00 1.04 1.07 1.15 1.27 1.39 1.61 1.68 1.59 1.67 1.59 1.40 1.17 .953 .837
1.29 1.36 1.47 1.82 2.27 3.24 4.34 5.13 5.23 4.90 4.38 3.73 3.06 2.39 1.85 1.46
1.68 1.92 2.72 4.46 7.34 9.94 11.6 12.8 12.1 10.5 8.86 6.93 5.29 3.97 2.93 2.22
2.05 3.39 6.15 10.5 16.0 21.3 23.8 23.9 21.6 17.9 14.3 10.7 7.83 5.44 3.79 2.80
2.74 5.39 9.64 15.4 24.8 33.0 36.8 36.4 32.3 25.1 18.9 13.4 9.39 6.31 4.29 3.15
3.14 6.42 10.8 16.9 27.2 37.2 43.9 46.4 ... 28.4 20.2 14.0 9.70 6.55 4.32 3.25
```

Note: All curves symmetrical; complete total light pattern from data given.

265

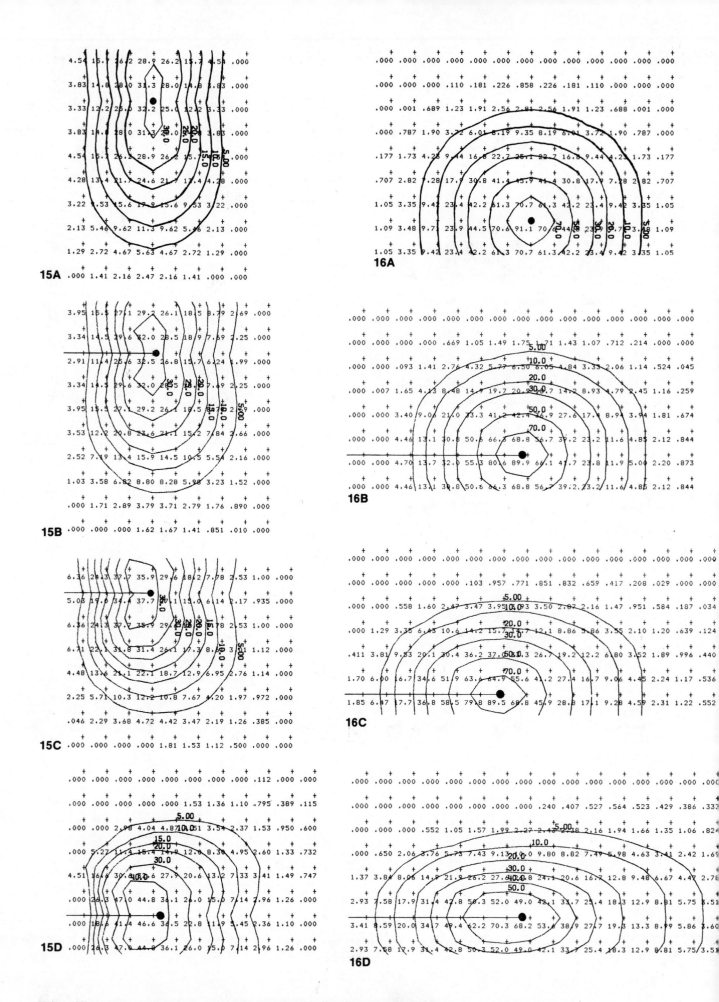

Note: All curves symmetrical; complete total light pattern from data given.

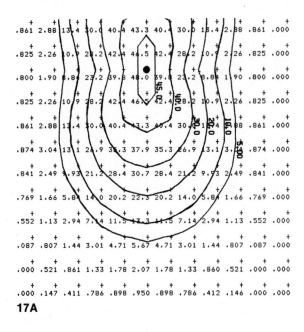

17A

17B

17C

17D

18A

Note: All curves symmetrical; complete total light pattern from data given.

267

18B

18C

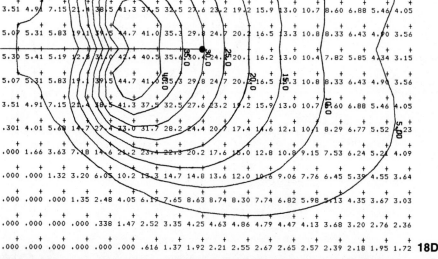

18D

Note: All curves symmetrical; complete total light pattern from data given.

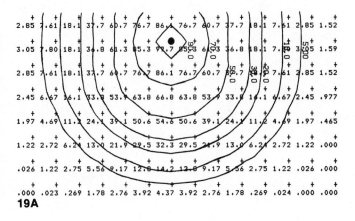

19A

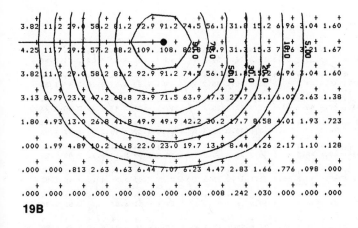

19B

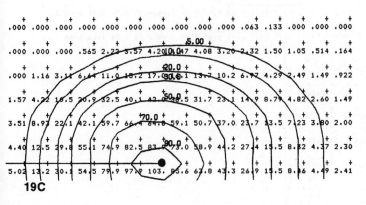

19C

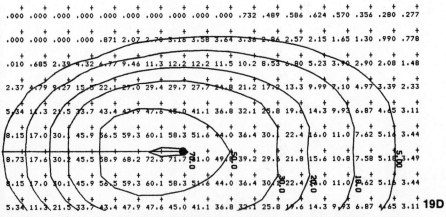

19D

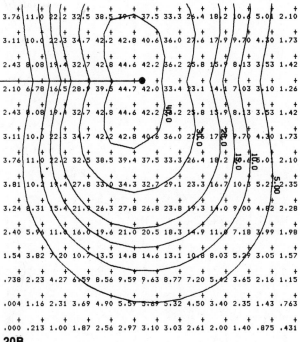

20A

20B

Note: All curves symmetrical; complete total light pattern from data given.

269

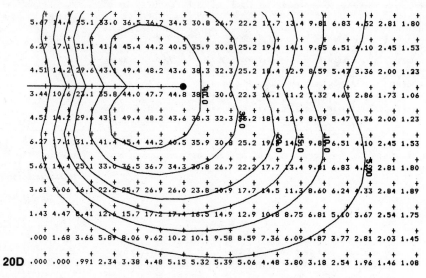

```
6.52 19.4 36.4 48.4 51.1 48.5 43.4 36.0 26.4 17.0 9.50 4.55 2.09
4.84 15.8 33.9 49.1 54.2 51.5 45.8 36.2 24.8 15.0 7.87 3.67 1.65
3.79 12.4 28.3 42.8 52.6 52.7  .7 32.5 21.7 12.9 6.61 3.14 1.41
4.84 15.8 33.9 49.1 54.2 51.5 45.8 36.2 24.8 15.0 7.87 3.67 1.65
6.52 19.4 36.4 48.4 51.1 48.5 43.4 36.0 26.4 17.0 9.50 4.55 2.09
6.89 18.3 31.7 41.0 44.2 42.8 38.5 32.1 24.5 16.7 10.5 5.17 2.49
5.58 13.9 23.9 31.3 34.5 34.2 31.1 26.2 20.4 14.4 9.21 5.09 2.59
3.55 8.93 15.7 21.4 24.4 24.8 23.0 19.6 15.6 11.3 7.47 4.38 2.35
1.92 4.88 8.88 12.7 15.4 16.2 15.4 13.4 10.8 8.06 5.47 3.36 1.88
.358 2.27 4.40 6.63 8.45 9.42 9.32 8.29 6.76 5.18 3.63 2.32 1.36
.000 .278 1.90 3.05 3.99 4.76 4.95 4.56 3.82 3.02 2.21 1.46 .895
.000 .000 .396 1.00 1.65 2.13 2.35 2.25 1.93 1.61 1.22 .848 .517   20C
```

```
5.67 14.4 25.1 33.0 36.5 36.7 34.3 30.8 26.7 22.2 17.7 13.4 9.81 6.83 4.52 2.81 1.80
6.27 17.1 31.1 41.1 45.4 44.2 40.5 35.9 30.8 25.2 19.4 14.1 9.85 6.51 4.10 2.45 1.53
4.51 14.2 29.6 43.1 49.4 48.2 43.6 38.3 32.3 25.2 18.4 12.9 8.59 5.47 3.36 2.00 1.23
3.44 10.6 23.1 35.8 44.0 47.7 44.8    30.0 22.3 16.1 11.2 7.32 4.63 2.86 1.73 1.06
4.51 14.2 29.6 43.1 49.4 48.2 43.6 38.3 32.3 25.2 18.4 12.9 8.59 5.47 3.36 2.00 1.23
6.27 17.1 31.1 41.4 45.4 44.2 40.5 35.9 30.8 25.2 19.4 14.1 9.85 6.51 4.10 2.45 1.53
5.67 14.4 25.1 33.0 36.5 36.7 34.3 30.8 26.7 22.2 17.7 13.4 9.81 6.83 4.   2.81 1.80
3.61 9.06 16.1 22.2 25.7 26.9 26.0 23.8 20.9 17.7 14.5 11.3 8.60 6.24 4.33 2.84 1.89
1.43 4.47 8.41 12.6 15.7 17.2 17.4 16.5 14.9 12.9 10.8 8.75 6.81 5.10 3.67 2.54 1.75
.000 1.68 3.66 5.87 8.06 9.62 10.2 10.1 9.58 8.59 7.36 6.09 4.87 3.77 2.81 2.03 1.45
20D  .000 .000 .991 2.34 3.38 4.48 5.15 5.32 5.39 5.06 4.48 3.80 3.18 2.54 1.96 1.46 1.08
```

```
5.25 8.98 13.2 16.9 19.5 21.3 22.2 22.7 22.9 22.7 22.2 21.3 19.5 16.9 13.2 8.97 5.25 2.88
4.50 7.86 12.1 16.4 19.7 21.7 22.9 23.4 23.6 23.4 22.9 21.7 19.7 16.4 12.1 7.86 4.50 2.42
3.87 6.63 10.4 14.9 18.7 21.5 23.0 23.8 24.0 23.8 23.0 21.5 18.7 14.9 10.4 6.63 3.87 2.18
3.52 5.92 9.44 13.6 17.7 20.9 22.9 23.9 24.3 23.9 22.9 20.9 17.7 13.6 9.44 5.92 3.52 2.06
3.87 6.63 10.4 14.9 18.7 21.5 23.0 23.8 24.0 23.8 23.0 21.5 18.7 14.9 10.4 6.63 3.87 2.18
4.50 7.86 12.1 16.4 19.7 21.7 22.9 23.4 23.6 23.4 22.9 21.7 19.7 16.4 12.1 7.86 4.50 2.42
5.25 8.98 13.2 16.9 19.5 21.3 22.2 22.7 22.9 22.7 22.2 21.3 19.5 16.9 13.2 8.97 5.25 2.88
5.71 9.35 13.2 16.5 18.8 20.4 21.3 21.8 22.0 21.8 21.3 20.4 18.8 16.5 13.2 9.35 5.71 3.18
5.71 9.11 12.6 15.6 17.7 19.2 20.1 20.6 20.8 20.6 20.1 19.2 17.7 15.6 12.6 9.11 5.71 3.23
5.27 8.36 11.4 14.2 16.3 17.7 18.7 19.2 19.4 19.2 18.7 17.7 16.3 14.2 11.4 8.36 5.27 3.04
4.44 7.20 9.95 12.4 14.5 16.0 17.0 17.5 17.7 17.5 17.0 16.0 14.5 12.4 9.95 7.20 4.44 2.63
3.60 5.75 8.18 10.4 12.3 13.8 14.9 15.4 15.6 15.4 14.9 13.8 12.3 10.4 8.18 5.75 3.60 2.14
2.77 4.36 6.36 8.36 10.1 11.5 12.5 13.1 13.3 13.1 12.5 11.5 10.1 8.36 6.36 4.36 2.77 1.70
1.98 3.09 4.57 6.31 7.86 9.13 10.0 10.6 10.8 10.6 10.0 9.13 7.86 6.31 4.57 3.09 1.98 1.27
1.46 2.19 3.18 4.35 5.63 6.77 7.61 8.10 8.29 8.10 7.61 6.77 5.63 4.35 3.18 2.19 1.46 .546
.878 1.51 2.15 2.91 3.84 4.70 5.33 5.74 5.91 5.74 5.33 4.70 3.84 2.91 2.15 1.51 .878 .154   21A
```

Note: All curves symmetrical; complete total light pattern from data given.

21B

```
7.33 14.6 22.3 27.5 29.3 29.2 28.2 26.7 24.9 22.9 20.8 18.6 16.2 13.6 10.8 8.01 5.58 3.69
6.06 12.7 21.2 27.7 30.5 30.5 29.4 27.8 25.8 23.7 21.5 19.0 16.2 13.2 10.1 7.13 4.82 3.13
4.79 10.1 17.9 25.5 29.7 30.8 30.1 28.4 26.4 24.1 21.6 18.6 15.4 12.0 8.76 6.03 4.04 2.66
4.31 8.41 15.1 22.7 28.1 30.2 30.1 28.7 26.6 24.1 21.2 18.0 14.5 11.0 7.90 5.42 3.62 2.42
4.79 10.1 17.9 25.5 29.7 30.8 30.1 28.4 26.4 24.1 21.6 18.6 15.4 12.0 8.76 6.03 4.04 2.66
6.06 12.7 21.2 27.7 30.5 30.5 29.4 27.8 25.8 23.7 21.5 19.0 16.2 13.2 10.1 7.13 4.82 3.13
7.33 14.6 22.3 27.5 29.3 29.2 28.2 26.7 24.9 22.9 20.8 18.6 16.2 13.6 10.8 8.01 5.58 3.69
7.55 14.4 21.1 25.8 27.3 27.3 26.5 25.2 23.6 21.8 19.8 17.7 15.6 13.3 10.9 8.30 6.00 4.09
6.48 12.5 18.4 22.5 24.5 24.9 24.4 23.3 21.9 20.2 18.5 16.6 14.6 12.5 10.4 8.13 6.06 4.39
5.21 9.64 14.8 18.7 21.0 21.9 21.8 21.0 19.8 18.4 16.8 15.1 13.3 11.4 9.54 7.59 5.79 4.18
3.60 6.76 10.8 14.4 16.8 18.2 18.6 18.1 17.3 16.1 14.8 13.3 11.7 10.1 8.40 6.72 5.17 3.78
2.57 4.44 7.20 10.2 12.6 14.1 14.7 14.8 14.3 13.5 12.5 11.3 9.92 8.52 7.08 5.70 4.42 3.27
1.02 2.84 4.32 6.31 8.47 10.0 10.7 11.3 11.1 10.7 9.97 9.02 7.97 6.86 5.72 4.62 3.59 2.63
.348 1.32 2.54 3.73 5.14 6.40 7.39 7.96 8.11 7.90 7.44 6.80 6.05 5.23 4.36 3.48 2.71 2.08
.000 .031 1.52 2.26 3.00 3.64 4.22 4.83 5.19 5.25 5.11 4.77 4.22 3.62 3.08 2.55 2.01 1.58
```

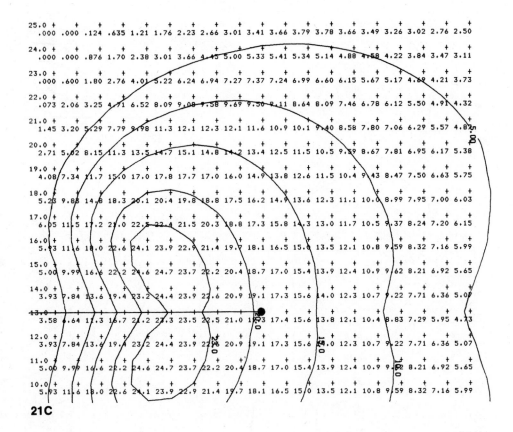

21C

```
25.0  .000 .000 .124 .635 1.21 1.76 2.23 2.66 3.01 3.41 3.66 3.79 3.78 3.66 3.49 3.26 3.02 2.76 2.50
24.0  .000 .000 .876 1.70 2.38 3.01 3.66 4.45 5.00 5.33 5.41 5.34 5.14 4.88 4.58 4.22 3.84 3.47 3.11
23.0  .000 .600 1.80 2.76 4.01 5.22 6.24 6.94 7.27 7.37 7.24 6.99 6.60 6.15 5.67 5.17 4.69 4.21 3.73
22.0  .073 2.06 3.25 4.71 6.52 8.09 9.08 9.58 9.69 9.50 9.11 8.64 8.09 7.46 6.78 6.12 5.50 4.91 4.32
21.0  1.45 3.20 5.29 7.79 9.98 11.3 12.1 12.3 12.1 11.6 10.9 10.1 9.40 8.58 7.80 7.06 6.29 5.57 4.87
20.0  2.71 5.02 8.15 11.3 13.5 14.7 15.1 14.8 14.2 13.4 12.5 11.5 10.5 9.59 8.67 7.81 6.95 6.17 5.38
19.0  4.08 7.34 11.7 15.0 17.0 17.8 17.7 17.0 16.0 14.9 13.8 12.6 11.5 10.4 9.43 8.47 7.50 6.63 5.75
18.0  5.23 9.88 14.8 18.3 20.1 20.4 19.8 18.8 17.5 16.2 14.9 13.6 12.3 11.1 10.0 8.99 7.95 7.00 6.03
17.0  6.05 11.5 17.2 21.0 22.5 22.4 21.5 20.3 18.8 17.3 15.8 14.3 13.0 11.7 10.5 9.37 8.24 7.20 6.15
16.0  5.93 11.6 18.0 22.6 24.1 23.9 22.9 21.4 19.7 18.1 16.5 15.0 13.5 12.1 10.8 9.59 8.32 7.16 5.99
15.0  5.00 9.99 16.6 22.2 24.6 24.7 23.7 22.2 20.4 18.7 17.0 15.4 13.9 12.4 10.9 9.62 8.21 6.92 5.65
14.0  3.93 7.84 13.6 19.4 23.2 24.4 23.9 22.6 20.9 19.1 17.3 15.6 14.0 12.3 10.7 9.22 7.71 6.36 5.07
13.0  3.58 6.64 11.3 16.7 21.2 23.3 23.5 22.5 21.0 18.3 17.4 15.6 13.8 12.1 10.4 8.83 7.29 5.95 4.73
12.0  3.93 7.84 13.6 19.4 23.2 24.4 23.9 22.6 20.9 19.1 17.3 15.6 14.0 12.3 10.7 9.22 7.71 6.36 5.07
11.0  5.00 9.99 16.6 22.2 24.6 24.7 23.7 22.2 20.4 18.7 17.0 15.4 13.9 12.4 10.9 9.62 8.21 6.92 5.65
10.0  5.93 11.6 18.0 22.6 24.1 23.9 22.9 21.4 19.7 18.1 16.5 15.0 13.5 12.1 10.8 9.59 8.32 7.16 5.99
```

Note: All curves symmetrical; complete total light pattern from data given.

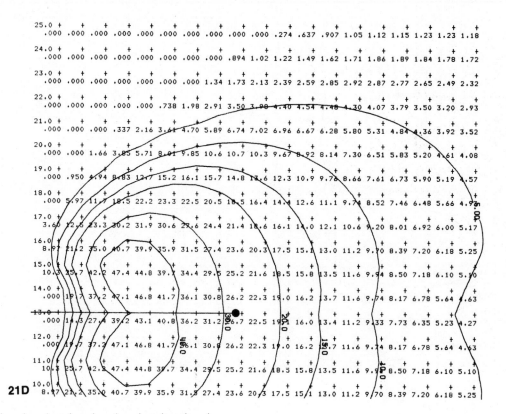

21D

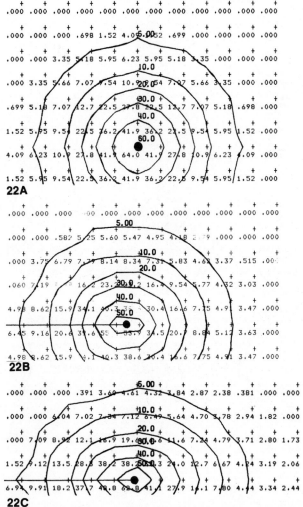

22A

22B

22C

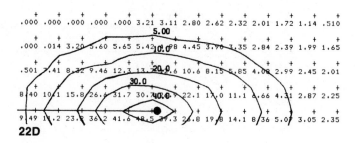

22D

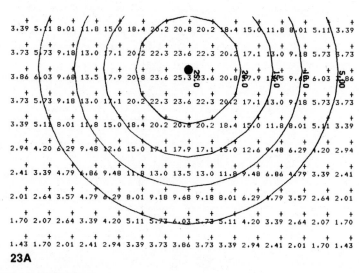

23A

Note: All curves symmetrical; complete total light pattern from data given.

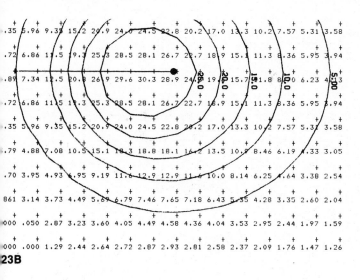

23B

```
.35  5.96  9.33  15.2  20.9  24.0  24.5  22.8  20.2  17.0  13.3  10.2  7.57  5.31  3.58
.72  6.86  11.5  19.3  25.3  28.5  28.1  26.7  22.7  18.9  15.1  11.3  8.36  5.95  3.94
.89  7.34  12.5  20.8  26.9  29.6  30.3  28.9  24.0  19.2  15.7  11.8  8.00  6.23  4.00
.72  6.86  11.5  19.3  25.3  28.5  28.1  26.7  22.7  18.9  15.1  11.3  8.36  5.95  3.94
.35  5.96  9.35  15.2  20.9  24.0  24.5  22.8  20.2  17.0  13.3  10.2  7.57  5.31  3.58
.79  4.88  7.08  10.5  15.1  18.3  18.8  18.1  16.2  13.5  10.9  8.46  6.19  4.33  3.05
.70  3.95  4.93  6.95  9.19  11.6  12.9  12.9  11.6  10.0  8.14  6.25  4.64  3.38  2.54
861  3.14  3.73  4.49  5.69  6.79  7.46  7.65  7.18  6.43  5.35  4.28  3.35  2.60  2.04
.000 .050  2.87  3.23  3.60  4.05  4.49  4.58  4.36  4.04  3.53  2.95  2.44  1.97  1.59
.000 .000  1.29  2.44  2.64  2.72  2.87  2.93  2.81  2.58  2.37  2.09  1.76  1.47  1.26
```
Scale: 25.0 20.0 15.0 10.0 5.00

24A

```
10.4  16.6  25.3  39.0  51.3  61.0  64.8  61.0  51.3  39.0  25.3  16.6  10.4  .000
9.33  14.2  22.5  36.0  53.3  67.4  71.9  67.4  53.3  36.0  22.5  14.2  9.33  .000
8.69  12.5  20.5  32.2  53.1  70.6  75.6  70.6  53.1  32.2  20.5  12.5  8.69  .000
9.33  14.2  22.5  36.0  53.3  67.4  71.9  67.4  53.3  36.0  22.5  14.2  9.33  .000
10.4  16.6  25.3  39.0  51.3  61.0  64.8  61.0  51.3  39.0  25.3  16.6  10.4  .000
11.5  18.3  25.9  37.7  47.0  52.1  53.5  52.1  47.0  37.7  25.9  18.3  11.5  .000
12.0  18.4  24.8  33.6  41.6  45.6  47.0  45.6  41.6  33.6  24.8  18.4  12.0  .000
11.8  17.5  22.9  28.9  35.0  39.0  40.5  39.0  35.0  28.9  22.9  17.5  11.8  .000
11.1  15.9  20.4  24.4  28.3  31.9  33.3  31.9  28.3  24.4  20.4  15.9  11.1  .000
9.82  13.8  17.7  20.7  23.3  24.9  25.6  24.9  23.3  20.7  17.7  13.8  9.82  .000
8.71  11.4  14.8  17.6  19.7  21.0  21.5  21.0  19.7  17.6  14.8  11.4  8.71  .000
7.53  9.53  11.8  14.3  16.1  17.2  17.6  17.2  16.1  14.3  11.8  9.53  7.53  .000
6.31  7.88  9.41  11.2  12.7  13.6  14.0  13.6  12.7  11.2  9.41  7.88  6.31  .000
5.07  6.47  7.69  8.68  9.46  10.2  10.5  10.2  9.46  8.68  7.69  6.47  5.07  .000
1.51  5.08  6.17  7.05  7.71  8.21  8.38  8.21  7.71  7.05  6.17  5.08  1.50  .000
```
Scale: 70.0 50.0 30.0 20.0 10.0 8.00

23C

```
.000  .000  .000  .000  .000  1.38  1.76  1.74  1.68  1.60  1.56  1.44  1.33  1.25  1.12  .988
.000  .000  .000  .820  2.08  2.34  2.33  2.40  2.44  2.36  2.28  2.12  1.93  1.73  1.52  1.33
.000  .000  .218  2.84  3.06  3.24  3.47  3.76  3.79  3.70  3.51  3.17  2.74  2.40  2.07  1.75
.000  .000  2.81  3.85  4.40  5.20  5.89  6.26  6.32  6.10  5.61  4.93  4.14  3.46  2.86  2.34
.000  2.91  4.54  5.52  7.05  8.74  10.3  10.8  10.4  9.43  8.28  7.15  5.90  4.79  3.83  3.06
.032  4.85  5.93  8.40  11.5  14.9  16.2  15.7  14.6  12.8  10.9  9.00  7.37  5.97  4.79  3.78
2.51  5.84  8.08  12.1  17.8  20.7  21.9  20.4  19.2  15.7  13.2  10.9  8.69  6.92  5.51  4.33
5.08  6.55  9.99  16.0  22.4  25.5  25.3  23.5  21.1  17.6  14.5  11.9  9.61  7.62  5.93  4.64
5.30  6.85  10.7  17.7  23.9  27.2  26.7  25.2  22.9  18.8  15.3  12.2  9.90  7.89  6.10  4.78
5.08  6.55  9.99  16.0  22.4  25.5  25.3  23.5  21.1  17.6  19.5  11.9  9.61  7.62  5.93  4.64
```
Scale: 25.0 20.0 15.0 10.0 5.00

23D

```
.000  .000  .000  .000  .000  2.17  2.05  1.89  1.82  1.69  1.61  1.47  1.33  1.18  1.06
.000  .000  .000  3.09  3.44  3.32  3.31  3.23  3.03  2.83  2.51  2.22  1.96  1.70  1.46
.000  .654  5.59  5.69  6.04  6.34  6.39  5.92  5.50  4.87  4.14  3.50  2.95  2.46  2.04
.000  8.65  9.61  11.7  13.1  13.9  12.9  11.0  9.22  7.63  6.12  4.96  4.02  3.27  2.67
7.58  14.4  20.5  27.1  27.5  24.3  20.4  16.3  12.7  10.0  7.84  6.14  4.88  3.92  3.16
16.5  25.4  40.6  44.3  40.1  32.8  26.0  19.8  15.2  11.9  9.14  7.12  5.52  4.31  3.41
18.7  32.4  59.1  52.1  58.4  29.7  21.8  15.3  12.3  9.41  7.46  5.75  4.47  3.52
16.5  25.4  40.6  44.3  40.1  32.8  26.0  19.8  15.2  11.9  9.14  7.12  5.52  4.31  3.41
```
Scale: 50.0 25.0 20.0 10.0 5.00

24B

```
17.5  27.5  37.3  50.5  57.8  58.6  56.5  52.1  44.5  33.6  23.4  17.0  11.2  7.54
16.0  26.0  38.3  55.7  66.1  71.0  68.9  60.1  48.7  34.7  22.7  15.4  9.91  6.67
13.8  22.0  34.7  54.9  72.7  82.0  79.5  66.8  49.6  31.7  20.4  13.0  8.76  5.78
12.4  18.4  30.4  49.5  75.2  87.2  84.3  69.4  47.9  28.2  18.3  11.3  8.10  5.24
13.8  22.0  34.7  54.9  72.7  82.0  79.5  66.8  49.6  31.7  20.4  13.0  8.76  5.78
16.0  26.0  38.3  55.7  66.1  71.0  68.9  60.1  48.7  34.7  15.4  9.91  6.67
17.5  27.5  37.3  50.5  57.8  58.6  56.5  52.1  44.5  33.6  23.4  11.2  7.54
17.5  26.2  33.6  42.1  48.2  50.2  48.8  44.4  38.5  29.6  22.3  16.8  11.6
16.0  23.1  29.0  33.6  38.0  40.4  39.7  35.8  30.4  25.1  20.3  15.7  11.2  7.91
13.9  19.2  24.2  27.6  29.5  30.1  29.8  27.9  25.0  21.5  17.8  14.0  10.2  7.54
11.8  15.2  19.2  22.2  24.0  24.5  24.1  22.6  20.6  18.0  15.0  11.9  9.01  6.90
9.56  11.9  14.4  16.9  18.7  19.3  19.1  18.1  16.6  14.5  12.1  9.78  7.69  6.15
6.10  9.44  11.0  12.3  13.6  14.4  14.5  13.8  12.7  11.2  9.39  7.95  6.59  5.28
1.76  6.75  8.49  9.55  10.2  10.7  10.7  10.1  9.34  8.58  7.64  6.56  5.47  4.35
.000  .524  5.45  7.10  7.77  8.09  8.12  7.88  7.44  6.82  6.07  5.24  4.08  2.79
.000  .000  .000  .000  .000  .000  6.04  5.93  5.65  5.19  3.77  3.26  2.58  .032
```
Scale: 70.0 50.0 30.0 20.0 10.0 8.00

Note: All curves symmetrical; complete total light pattern from data given.

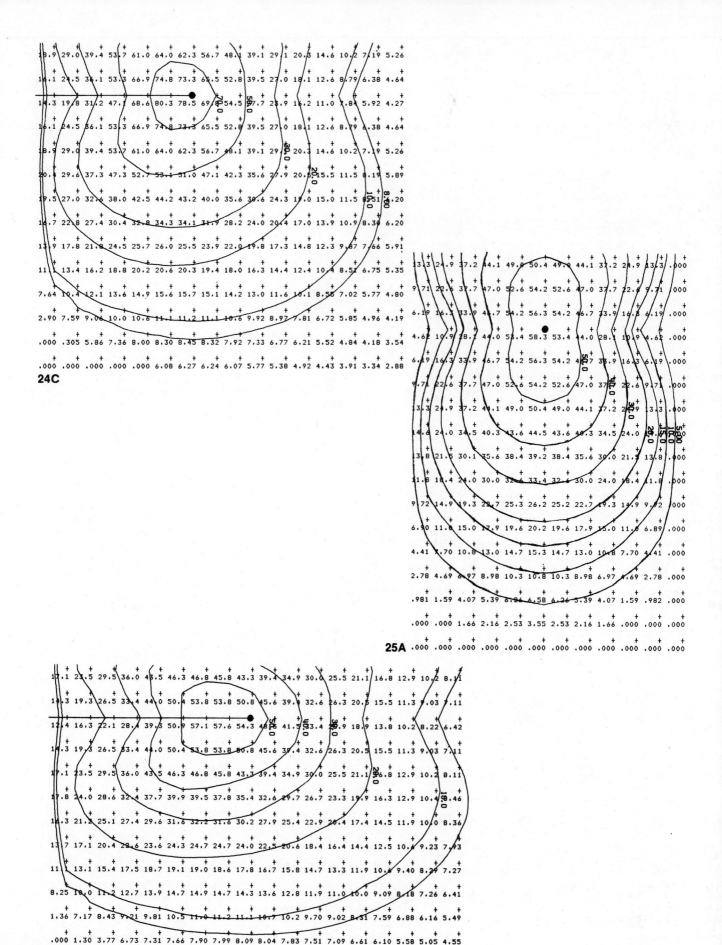

24C

25A

24D

Note: All curves symmetrical; complete total light pattern from data given.

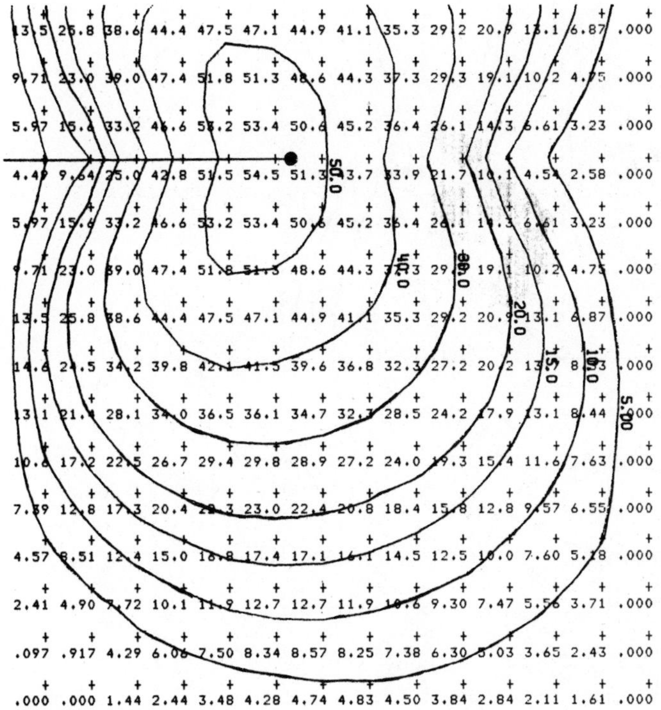

25B

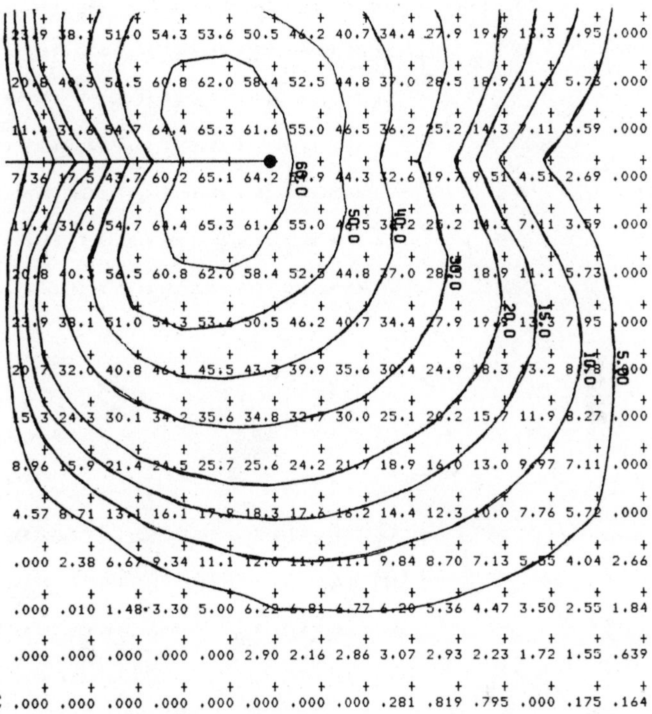

25C

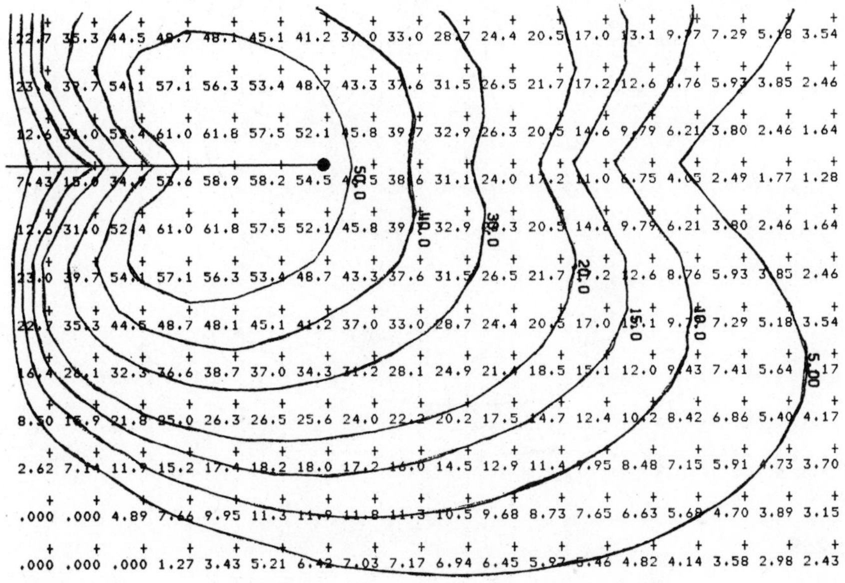

25D

Note: All curves symmetrical; complete total light pattern from data given.

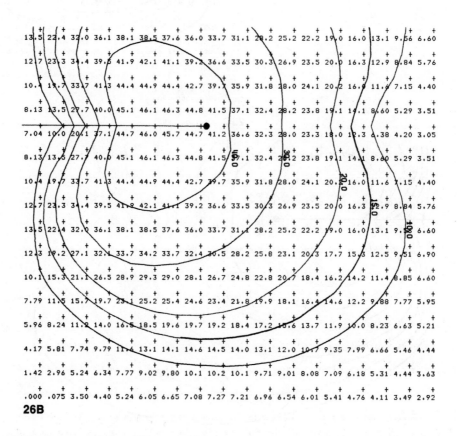

26A

26B

Note: All curves symmetrical; complete total light pattern from data given.

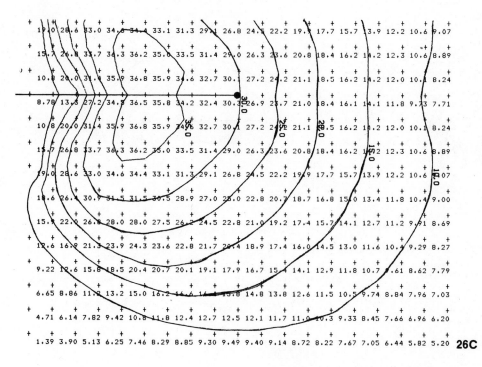

```
17.0 28.6 33.0 34.6 34.4 33.1 31.3 29.1 26.8 24.5 22.2 19.9 17.7 15.7 13.9 12.2 10.6 9.07

15.7 26.8 33.7 36.3 36.2 35.6 33.5 31.4 29.0 26.3 23.6 20.8 18.4 16.2 14.2 12.3 10.6 8.89

10.8 20.0 31.4 35.9 36.8 35.9 34.6 32.7 30.1 27.2 24.2 21.1 18.5 16.2 14.2 12.0 10.1 8.24

8.78 13.3 27.2 34.8 36.5 35.8 34.2 32.4 30.3 30.0 26.9 23.7 21.0 18.4 16.1 14.1 11.8 9.73 7.71

10.8 20.0 31.4 35.9 36.8 35.9 34.6 32.7 30.1 27.2 24.2 21.1 18.5 16.2 14.2 12.0 10.1 8.24

15.7 26.8 33.7 36.3 36.2 35.0 33.5 31.4 29.0 26.3 23.6 20.8 18.4 16.2 14.2 12.3 10.6 8.89

19.0 28.6 33.0 34.6 34.4 33.1 31.3 29.1 26.8 24.5 22.2 19.9 17.7 15.7 13.9 12.2 10.6 9.07

18.6 26.4 30.9 31.5 31.5 30.5 28.9 27.0 25.0 22.8 20.7 18.7 16.8 15.0 13.4 11.8 10.4 9.00

15.7 22.0 26.8 28.0 28.0 27.5 26.2 24.5 22.8 21.0 19.2 17.4 15.7 14.1 12.7 11.2 9.91 8.69

12.6 16.9 21.3 23.9 24.3 23.6 22.8 21.7 20.4 18.9 17.4 16.0 14.5 13.0 11.6 10.4 9.29 8.27

9.22 12.6 15.8 18.5 20.4 20.7 20.1 19.1 17.9 16.7 15.4 14.1 12.9 11.8 10.7 9.61 8.62 7.79

6.65 8.86 11.2 13.2 15.0 16.2 16.6 16.1 15.8 14.8 13.8 12.6 11.5 10.5 9.74 8.84 7.96 7.03

4.71 6.14 7.82 9.42 10.8 11.8 12.4 12.7 12.5 12.1 11.7 11.0 10.3 9.33 8.45 7.66 6.96 6.20

1.39 3.90 5.13 6.25 7.46 8.29 8.85 9.30 9.49 9.14 8.72 8.22 7.67 7.05 6.44 5.82 5.20    26C
```

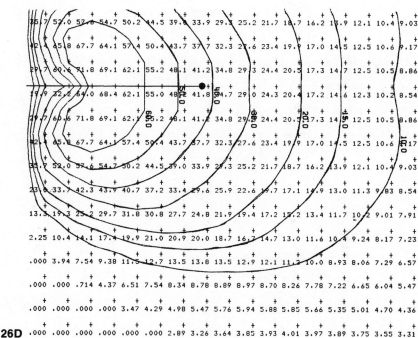

```
35.7 52.0 57.6 54.7 50.2 44.5 39.6 33.9 29.3 25.2 21.7 18.7 16.2 13.9 12.1 10.4 9.03

42.4 65.8 67.7 64.1 57.4 50.4 43.7 37.7 32.3 27.6 23.4 19.9 17.0 14.5 12.5 10.6 9.17

29.7 60.6 71.8 69.1 62.1 55.2 48.1 41.2 34.8 29.3 24.4 20.5 17.3 14.7 12.5 10.5 8.86

19.9 32.2 64.0 68.4 62.1 55.0 48.2 41.8 34.7 29.0 24.3 20.4 17.2 14.6 12.3 10.2 8.54

29.7 60.6 71.8 69.1 62.1 55.2 48.1 41.2 34.8 29.0 24.4 20.5 17.3 14.7 12.5 10.5 8.86

42.4 65.8 67.7 64.1 57.4 50.4 43.7 37.7 32.3 27.6 23.4 19.9 17.0 14.5 12.5 10.6 9.17

35.7 52.0 57.6 54.7 50.2 44.5 39.6 33.9 29.3 25.2 21.7 18.7 16.2 13.9 12.1 10.4 9.03

23.0 33.7 42.3 43.9 40.7 37.2 33.4 29.6 25.9 22.6 19.7 17.1 14.9 13.0 11.3 9.83 8.54

13.3 19.3 25.2 29.7 31.8 30.8 27.7 24.8 21.9 19.4 17.2 15.2 13.4 11.7 10.2 9.01 7.91

2.25 10.4 14.1 17.4 19.9 21.0 20.9 20.0 18.7 16.7 14.7 13.0 11.6 10.4 9.24 8.17 7.23

.000 3.94 7.54 9.38 11.5 12.7 13.5 13.8 13.5 12.9 12.1 11.2 10.0 8.93 8.06 7.29 6.57

.000 .000 .714 4.37 6.51 7.54 8.34 8.78 8.89 8.97 8.70 8.26 7.78 7.22 6.65 6.04 5.47

.000 .000 .000 .000 3.47 4.29 4.98 5.47 5.76 5.94 5.88 5.85 5.66 5.35 5.01 4.70 4.36

26D  .000 .000 .000 .000 .000 .000 2.89 3.26 3.64 3.85 3.93 4.01 3.97 3.89 3.75 3.55 3.31
```

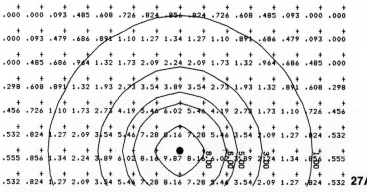

```
.000 .000 .093 .485 .608 .726 .824 .856 .824 .726 .608 .485 .093 .000 .000

.000 .093 .479 .686 .891 1.10 1.27 1.34 1.27 1.10 .891 .686 .479 .093 .000

.000 .485 .686 .964 1.32 1.73 2.09 2.24 2.09 1.73 1.32 .964 .686 .485 .000

.298 .608 .891 1.32 1.93 2.73 3.54 3.89 3.54 2.73 1.93 1.32 .891 .608 .298

.456 .726 1.10 1.73 2.73 4.19 5.46 6.02 5.46 4.19 2.73 1.73 1.10 .726 .456

.532 .824 1.27 2.09 3.54 5.46 7.28 8.16 7.28 5.46 3.54 2.09 1.27 .824 .532

.555 .856 1.34 2.24 3.89 6.02 8.16 9.87 8.16 6.02 3.89 2.24 1.34 .856 .555

.532 .824 1.27 2.09 3.54 5.46 7.28 8.16 7.28 5.46 3.54 2.09 1.27 .824 .532    27A
```

Note: All curves symmetrical; complete total light pattern from data given.

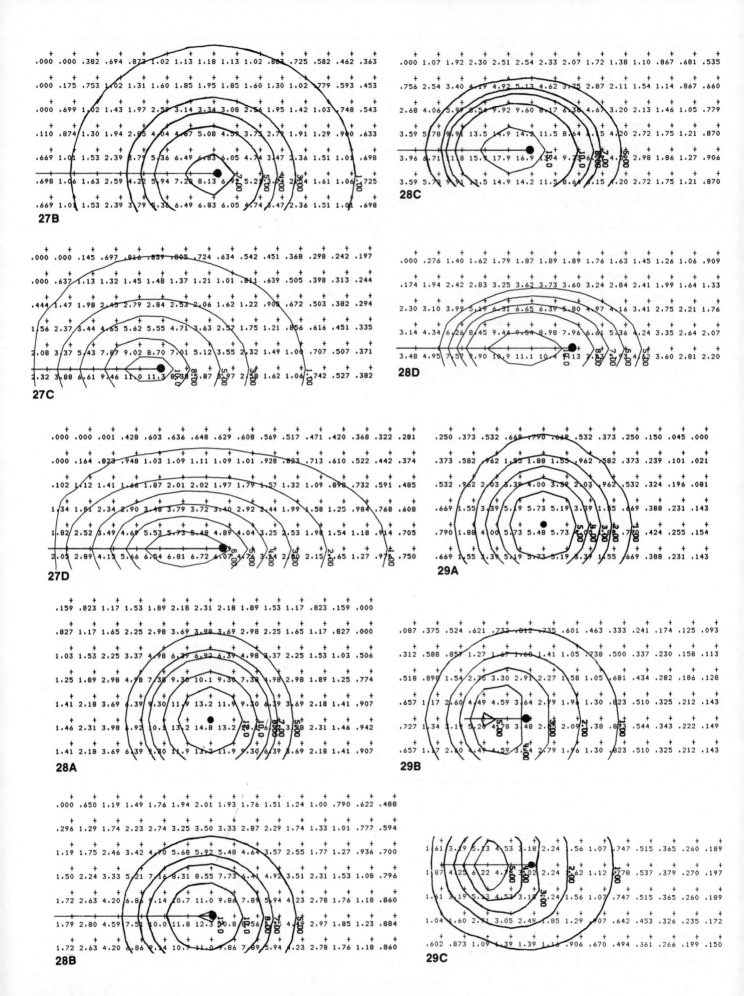

Note: All curves symmetrical; complete total light pattern from data given.

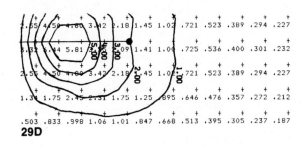

29D

```
2.55 4.50 4.80 3.42 2.18 1.45 1.02 .721 .523 .389 .294 .227
6.32 6.44 5.81 ... .09 1.41 1.06 .725 .536 .400 .301 .232
2.55 4.50 4.80 3.42 2.18 1.45 1.02 .721 .523 .389 .294 .227
1.31 1.75 2.45 2.31 1.75 1.25 .895 .646 .476 .357 .272 .212
.503 .833 .998 1.06 1.01 .847 .668 .513 .395 .305 .237 .187
```

30A

```
1.16 1.66 2.67 4.95 9.38 14.6 16.6 14.6 9.38 4.95 2.67 1.66      .852
1.21 1.77 2.94 5.14 11.0 16.6 18.7 16.6 ...          1.77 1.21 .888
1.16 1.66 2.67 4.95 9.38 14.6 16.6 14.6 9.38 4.95 2.67 1.66 1.16 .852
1.06 1.47 2.17 3.58 6.18 9.38 11.0 9.38 6.18 3.58 2.17 1.47 1.06 .782
.913 1.24 1.67 2.41 3.58 4.95 5.74 4.95 3.58 2.41 1.67 1.24 .913 .685
.765 1.00 1.28 1.67 2.17 2.67 2.94 2.67 2.17 1.67 1.28 1.00 .765 .564
.593 .783 1.00 1.24 1.47 1.66 1.77 1.66 1.47 1.24 1.00 .783 .593 .429
```

30B

```
1.20 1.36 1.46 1.56 1.61 1.54 1.40 1.21 1.00 .805 .646 .518 .419
1.57 1.83 2.13 2.47 2.67 2.57 2.25 1.85 1.43 1.06 .815 .623 .491
1.99 2.56 3.38 4.33 4.88 4.45 3.82 2.91 2.09 1.45 1.04 .753 .566
2.56 3.59 5.55 7.64 8.51 7.76 6.08 4.32 2.91 1.89 1.28 .883 .638
3.03 4.73 8.11 11.2 11.7 10.3 7.99 5.54 3.61 2.27 1.47 .985 .693
3.28 5.41 9.48 12.7 12.9 ...            2.48 1.57 1.04 .720
```

30C

```
.643 .944 1.12 1.21 1.27 1.31 1.36 1.42 1.39 1.26 1.15 1.00 .854 .712
.933 1.25 1.44 1.56 1.77 1.97 2.18 2.31 2.29 2.04 1.72 1.45 1.18 .960
1.26 1.61 1.82 2.14 2.58 3.20 3.66 3.81 3.62 3.12 2.56 2.05 1.60 1.24
1.55 1.90 2.28 2.86 3.87 5.10 5.81 5.68 5.10 4.24 3.40 2.65 2.01 1.52
1.71 2.12 2.64 3.63 5.24 6.78 7.67 7.13 6.16 5.02 3.97 3.05 2.29 1.72
1.81 2.23 2.83 4.05 6.03 7.89 8.41 7.68 6.43 ... 3.20 ... 2.42 1.81
```

30D

```
.385 1.19 1.51 1.55 1.56 1.59 1.65 1.68 1.71 1.64 1.49 1.32 1.14 .990 .849
.981 1.79 2.05 2.12 2.26 2.53 2.78 2.86 2.79 2.56 2.23 1.89 1.56 1.30 1.08
1.60 2.41 2.68 2.94 3.47 4.21 4.62 4.56 4.10 3.53 2.94 2.41 1.97 1.62 1.31
2.05 2.89 3.17 3.82 4.98 6.09 6.42 5.99 5.10 4.22 3.42 2.75 2.20 1.78 1.43
2.25 3.12 3.45 4.31 5.84 7.05 7.20 ... 5.51 3.63 ... 2.30 1.86 1.49
2.05 2.89 3.17 3.82 4.98 6.09 6.42 5.99 5.10 4.22 3.42 2.75 2.20 1.78 1.43
```

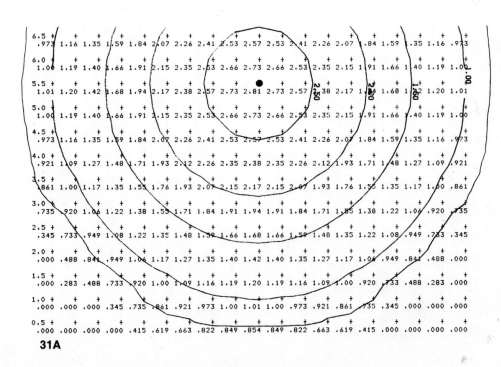

```
6.5  .973 1.16 1.35 1.59 1.84 2.07 2.26 2.41 2.53 2.57 2.53 2.41 2.26 2.07 1.84 1.59 1.35 1.16 .973
6.0  1.00 1.19 1.40 1.66 1.91 2.15 2.35 2.53 2.66 2.73 2.66 2.53 2.35 2.15 1.91 1.66 1.40 1.19 1.00
5.5  1.01 1.20 1.42 1.68 1.94 2.17 2.38 2.57 2.73 2.81 2.73 2.57 2.38 2.17 1.94 1.68 1.42 1.20 1.01
5.0  1.00 1.19 1.40 1.66 1.91 2.15 2.35 2.53 2.66 2.73 2.66 2.53 2.35 2.15 1.91 1.66 1.40 1.19 1.00
4.5  .973 1.16 1.35 1.59 1.84 2.07 2.26 2.41 2.53 2.57 2.53 2.41 2.26 2.07 1.84 1.59 1.35 1.16 .973
4.0  .921 1.09 1.27 1.48 1.71 1.93 2.12 2.26 2.35 2.38 2.35 2.26 2.12 1.93 1.71 1.48 1.27 1.09 .921
3.5  .861 1.00 1.17 1.35 1.55 1.76 1.93 2.07 2.15 2.17 2.15 2.07 1.93 1.76 1.55 1.35 1.17 1.00 .861
3.0  .735 .920 1.06 1.22 1.38 1.55 1.71 1.84 1.91 1.94 1.91 1.84 1.71 1.55 1.38 1.22 1.06 .920 .735
2.5  .345 .733 .949 1.08 1.22 1.35 1.48 1.59 1.66 1.68 1.66 1.59 1.48 1.35 1.22 1.08 .949 .733 .345
2.0  .000 .488 .841 .949 1.06 1.17 1.27 1.35 1.40 1.42 1.40 1.35 1.27 1.17 1.04 .949 .841 .488 .000
1.5  .000 .283 .488 .733 .920 1.00 1.09 1.16 1.19 1.20 1.19 1.16 1.09 1.00 .920 .733 .488 .283 .000
1.0  .000 .000 .000 .345 .735 .861 .921 .973 1.00 1.01 1.00 .973 .921 .861 .735 .345 .000 .000 .000
0.5  .000 .000 .000 .415 .619 .663 .822 .849 .854 .849 .822 .663 .619 .415 .000 .000 .000 .000
```

31A

Note: All curves symmetrical; complete total light pattern from data given.

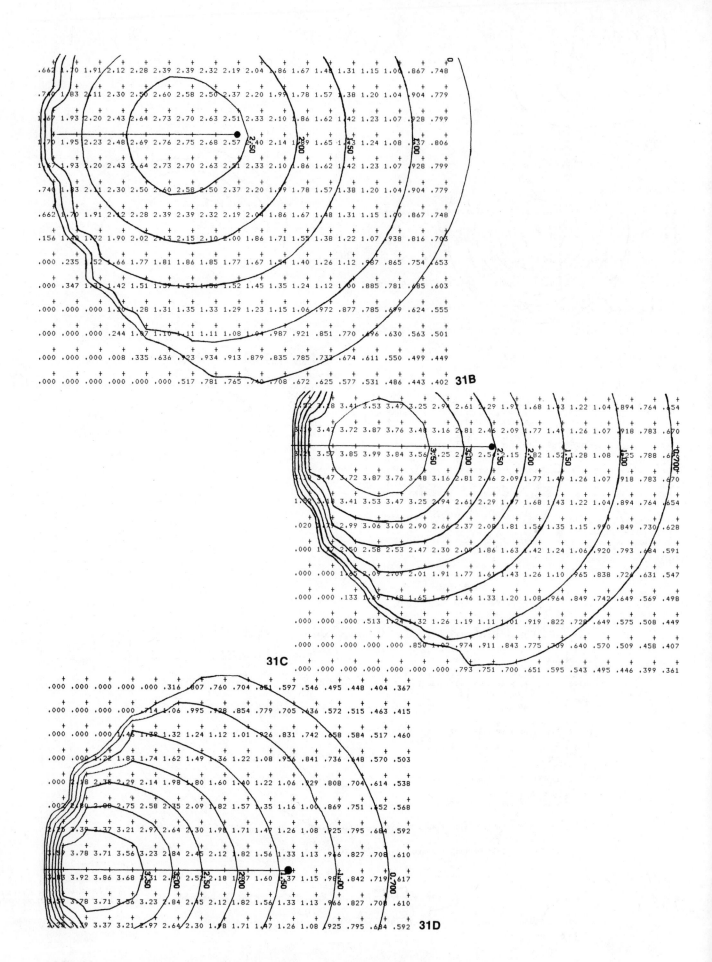

31B

31C

31D

Note: All curves symmetrical; complete total light pattern from data given.

32A

```
.414  .728  1.06  1.33  1.46  1.33  1.06  .728  .414  .194  .050  .000
.728  1.17  1.72  2.33  2.64  2.33  1.72  1.17  .728  .386  .138  .023
1.06  1.72  2.81  4.78  6.38  4.78  2.81  1.72  1.06  .608  .306  .108
1.33  2.33  4.78  11.7  17.0  11.7  4.78  2.33  1.33  .777  .414  .201
1.46  2.64  6.38  17.0  21.6  17.0  6.38  2.64  1.46  .849  .460  .223
1.33  2.33  4.78  11.7  17.0  11.7  4.78  2.33  1.33  .777  .414  .201
```

32B

```
.571  1.02  1.25  1.33  1.27  1.10  .902  .690  .528  .400  .304  .233  .181
1.10  1.70  2.09  2.34  2.26  1.95  1.42  .995  .696  .497  .362  .270  .205
1.79  2.65  3.67  5.23  5.50  4.01  2.53  1.50  .918  .601  .422  .301  .226
2.37  3.79  7.15  12.1  11.4  7.77  4.20  2.12  1.15  .691  .467  .326  .240
2.61  4.41  9.96  16.6  15.6  12.8              2.44  1.27  .728  .482  .333  .245
```

32C

```
3.75  5.98  12.0  16.0              2.70  1.50  .903  .566  .387
3.17  4.87  7.92  11.6  9.95  6.66  4.04  2.32  1.33  .823  .527  .367
1.86  3.07  3.73  4.49  4.59  3.48  2.40  1.55  .993  .660  .443  .322
```

32D

```
6.51  8.91  14.1  12.3              3.50  2.31  1.57  1.08
5.07  6.19  8.31  9.14  8.87  4.65  3.15  2.08  1.41  .977
2.38  3.31  3.36  3.47  3.30  2.66  2.00  1.45  1.03  .751
.608  1.64  1.68  1.54  1.36  1.22  1.02  .832  .650  .512
```

33A

```
1.77  2.59  4.20  7.85  14.9  19.2  14.9  7.85  4.20  2.59  1.77  1.28
1.84  2.76  4.69  9.89  19.0  25.5  19.0  9.89  4.69  2.76  1.84  1.31
1.77  2.59  4.20  7.85  14.9  19.2  14.9  7.85  4.20  2.59  1.77  1.28
1.57  2.19  3.25  5.02  7.85  8.89  7.85  5.02  3.25  2.19  1.57  1.17
1.34  1.77  2.39  3.25  4.20  4.69  4.20  3.25  2.39  1.77  1.34  1.03
```

33B

```
1.42  1.72  1.97  2.20  2.39  2.44  2.39  2.15  1.80  1.43  1.11  .869  .677
1.78  2.17  2.58  3.07  3.60  4.01  4.06  3.49  2.68  1.97  1.44  1.06  .799
2.09  2.63  3.31  4.30  5.78  7.72  8.53  6.64  4.39  2.82  1.84  1.27  .919
2.34  3.00  4.00  5.76  9.57  15.4  16.4  11.9  7.04  3.88  2.23  1.44  1.00
2.43  3.14  4.30  6.47  12.5  20.3  21.7              2.43  1.51  1.04
2.34  3.00  4.00  5.76  9.57  15.4  16.4  11.9  7.04  3.88  2.23  1.44  1.00
```

33C

```
1.57  2.32  2.38  2.34  2.20  2.01  1.72  1.45  1.17  .928  .731  .580  .459
2.94  3.35  3.55  3.64  3.64  3.32  2.85  2.25  1.67  1.26  .938  .714  .546
4.06  4.73  5.40  6.32  6.89  7.21  5.66  3.88  2.53  1.73  1.18  .859  .629
5.03  6.17  8.01  11.8  16.9  16.3  11.1  6.68  3.75  2.26  1.41  .980  .687
5.46  6.87  9.55  17.4  25.1  23.1              2.57  1.53  1.03  .712
```

33D

```
7.64  8.21  9.58  13.8  17.2  14.1              2.76  2.53  1.74  1.23
6.80  7.12  7.63  9.49  11.0  11.5  9.42  6.74  4.64  3.21  2.21  1.54  1.10
5.01  5.13  5.07  5.18  5.14  5.34  4.88  3.86  2.92  2.20  1.62  1.19  .887
3.08  3.41  3.23  3.01  2.83  2.53  2.32  1.96  1.61  1.34  1.07  .842  .657
```

34A

```
2.45  3.85  5.59  9.22  12.6  14.2  12.6  9.22  5.59  3.85  2.45  1.59
2.61  4.17  5.85  10.3  14.2  15.9  14.2  10.3  5.85  4.17  2.61  1.69
2.45  3.85  5.59  9.22  12.6  14.2  12.6  9.22  5.59  3.85  2.45  1.59
2.09  3.15  4.74  6.56  9.22  10.3  9.22  6.56  4.74  3.15  2.09  1.37
1.64  2.40  3.45  4.74  5.59  5.85  5.59  4.74  3.45  2.40  1.64  1.06
1.19  1.74  2.40  3.15  3.85  4.17  3.85  3.15  2.40  1.74  1.19  .753
```

34B

```
3.29  3.66  3.61  3.16  2.61  2.19  1.74  1.34  1.04  .822  .654  .514
5.03  5.48  5.30  4.88  4.08  3.05  2.22  1.62  1.21  .939  .728  .563
7.10  8.06  8.45  7.25  5.57  4.06  2.85  1.98  1.42  1.02  .765  .596
9.14  11.4  11.1  9.24  6.81  4.78  3.31  2.30  1.55  1.05  .792  .621
9.73  12.8  12.6  10.4  7.34              3.49  2.41  1.58  1.06  .804  .632
```

34C

```
.491  1.08  2.28  3.18  3.40  3.26  2.68  2.09  1.75  1.40  1.06  .829  .656
.761  1.99  4.22  5.40  5.50  4.63  4.07  3.32  2.52  1.84  1.38  1.03  .772
1.12  3.51  7.01  8.73  8.48  8.00  6.24  4.53  3.23  2.29  1.65  1.20  .904
1.56  5.35  10.0  12.3  13.2  11.0  8.08  5.52  3.79  2.61  1.84  1.32  .980
1.82  6.87  11.5  13.2  15.3  14.            2.74  1.92  1.37  1.01
1.56  5.35  10.0  12.3  13.2  11.0  8.08  5.52  3.79  2.61  1.84  1.32  .980
```

34D

```
.898  1.90  2.81  2.76  2.46  1.89  1.47  1.25  1.02  .821  .644  .515  .421
1.85  4.06  5.15  4.60  3.48  2.93  2.33  1.73  1.30  1.00  .770  .601  .477
4.18  8.97  9.33  7.64  6.05  4.15  3.07  2.17  1.57  1.16  .874  .670  .523
3.64  15.3  14.1  12.0  8.32  5.54  3.68  2.50  1.76  1.27  .943  .714  .552
      13.2  18.3  14.            3.93  2.64  1.85  1.32  .975  .735  .566
```

Note: All curves symmetrical; complete total light pattern from data given.

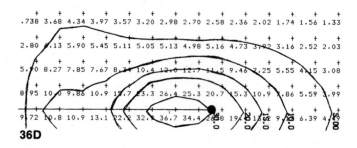

35A

35B

35C

35D

36A

36B

36C

36D

37A

Note: All curves symmetrical; complete total light pattern from data given.

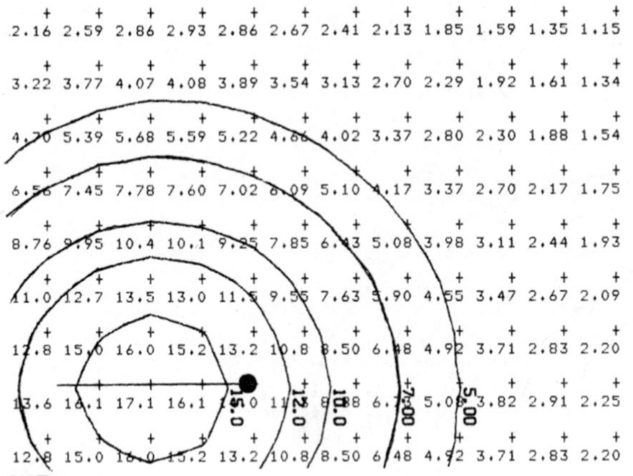

37B

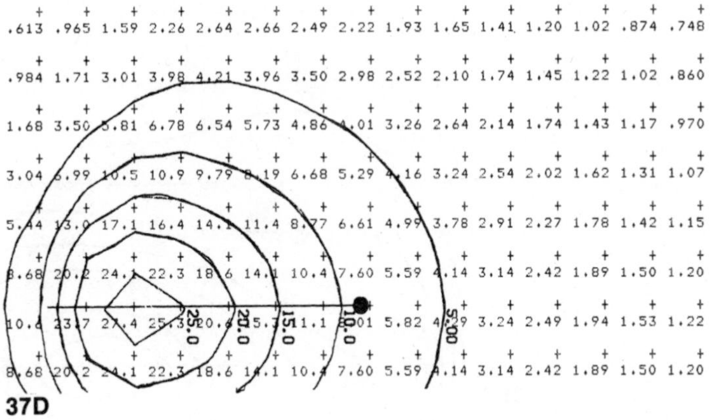

37D

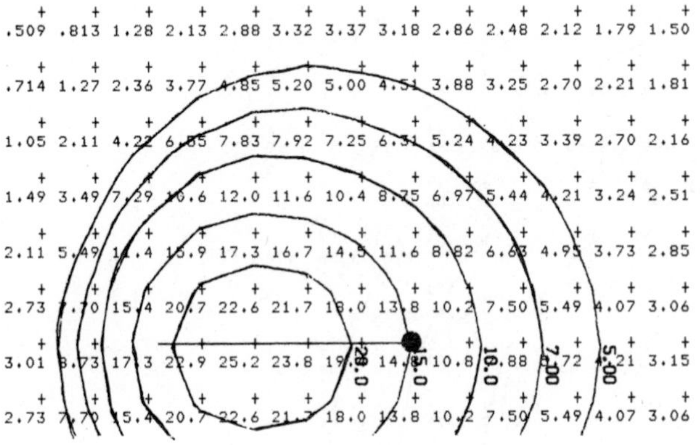

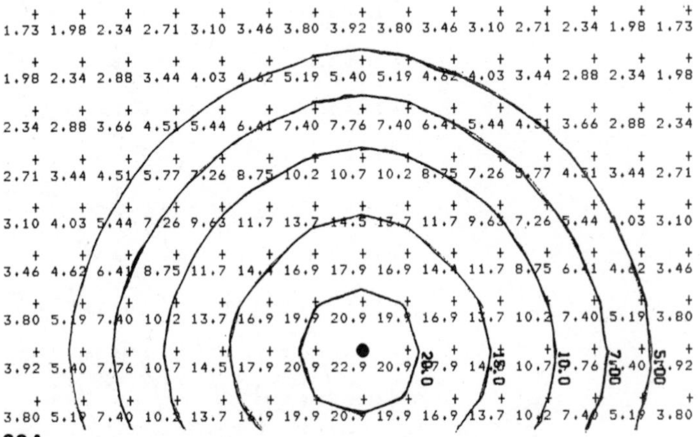

38A

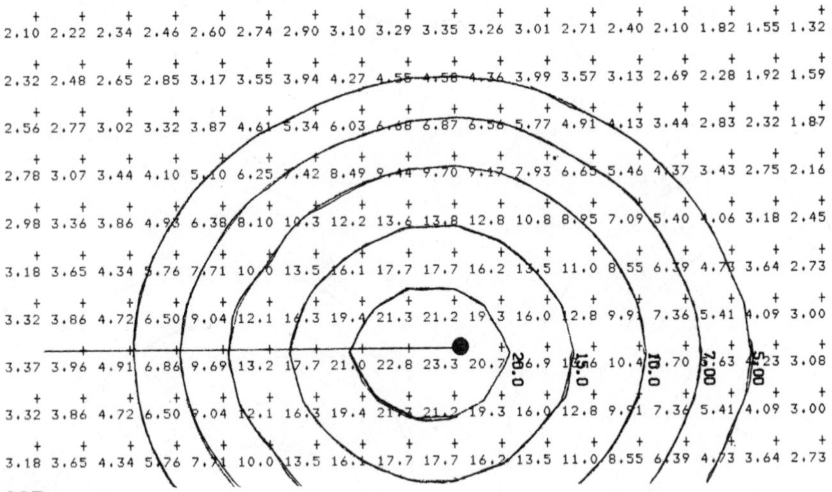

38B

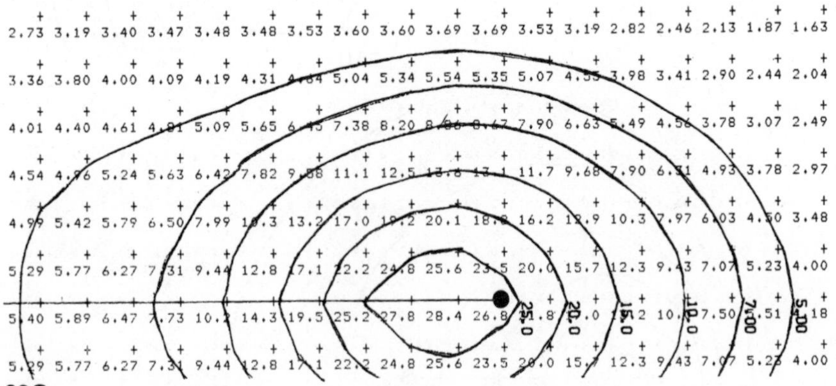

38C

Note: All curves symmetrical; complete total light pattern from data given.

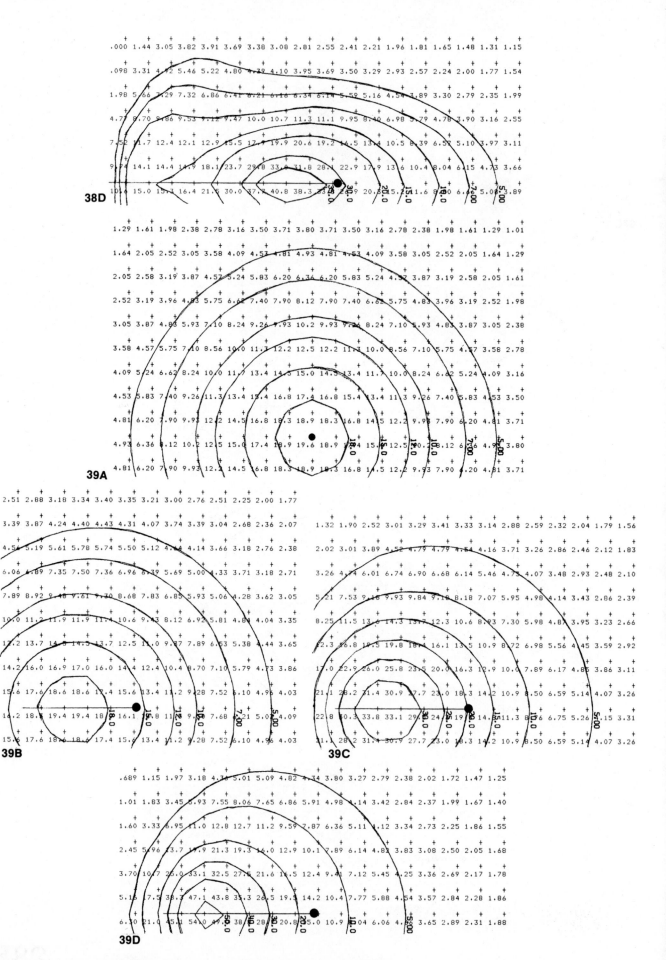

Note: All curves symmetrical; complete total light pattern from data given.

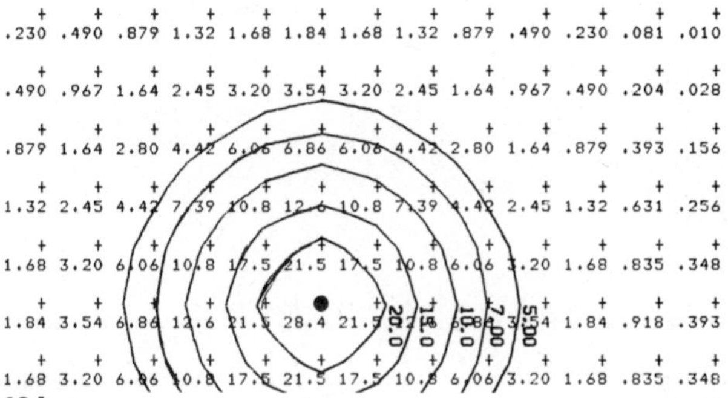

40A

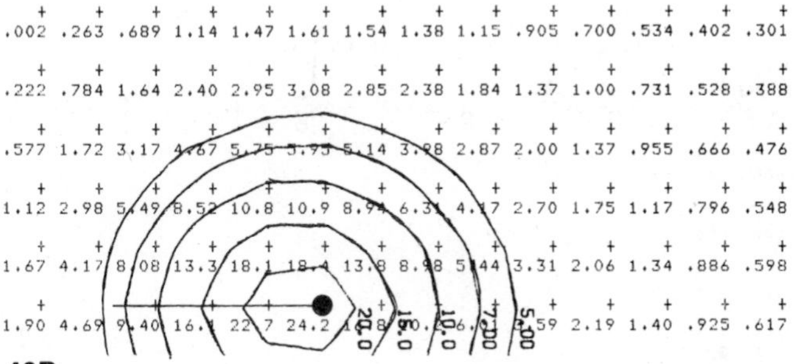

40B

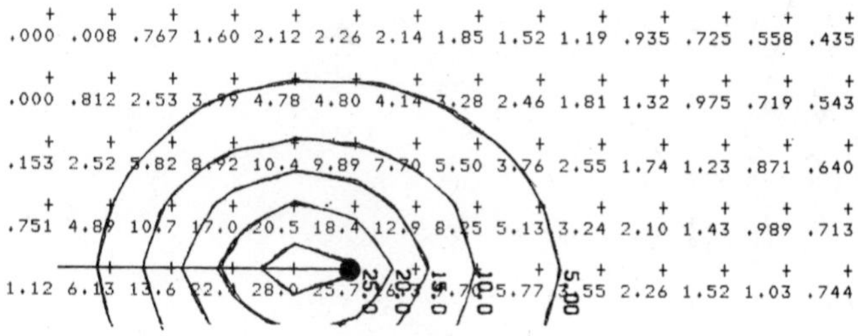

40C

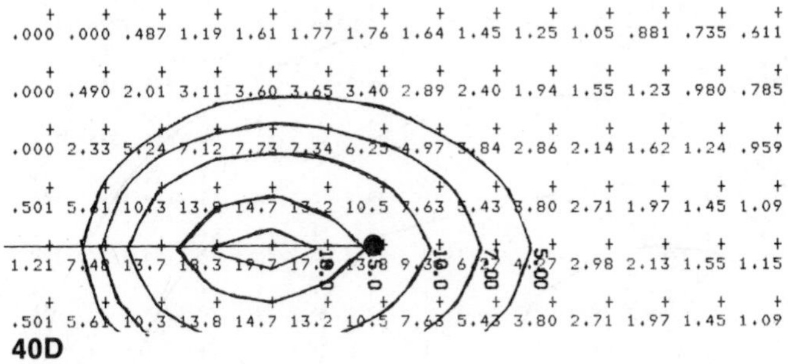

40D

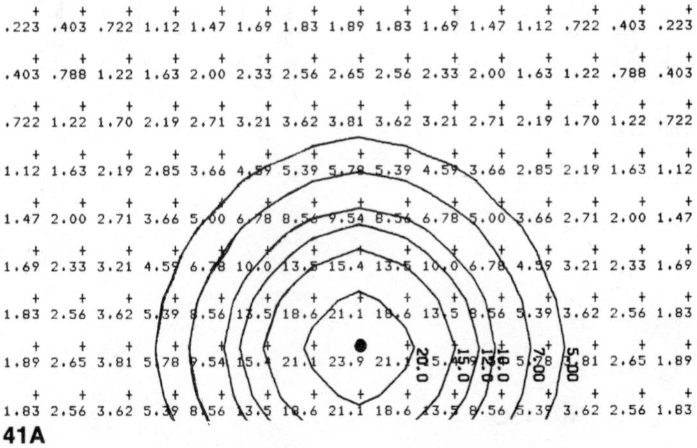

41A

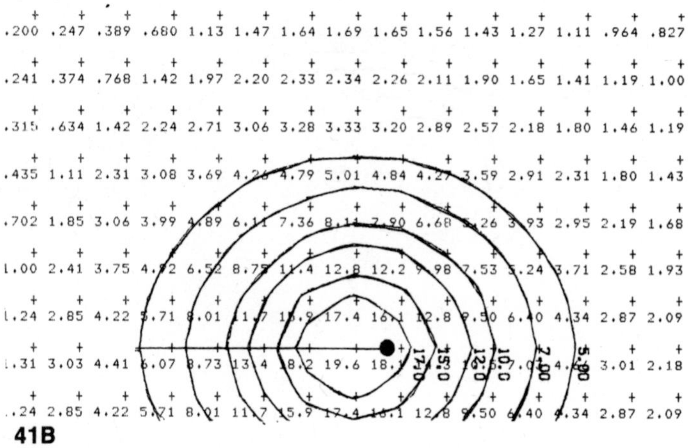

41B

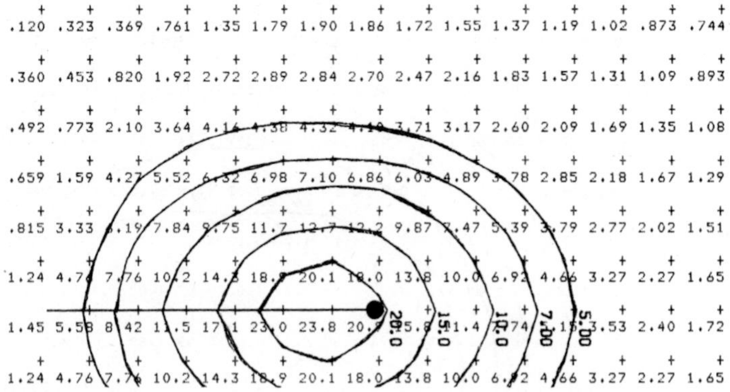

41C

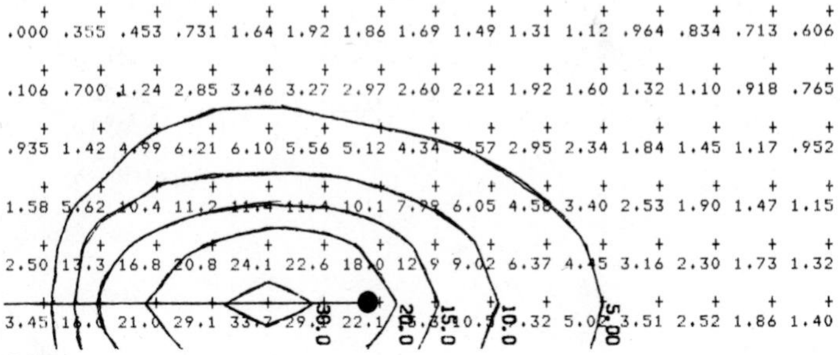

41D

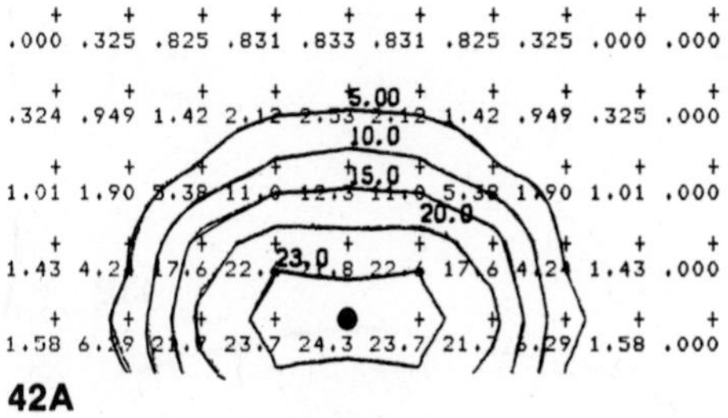

42A

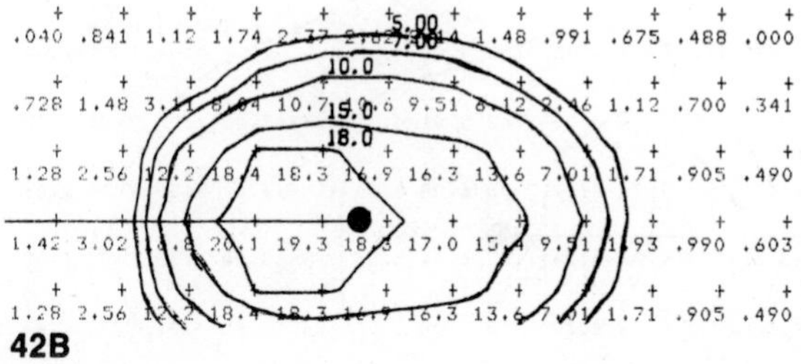

42B

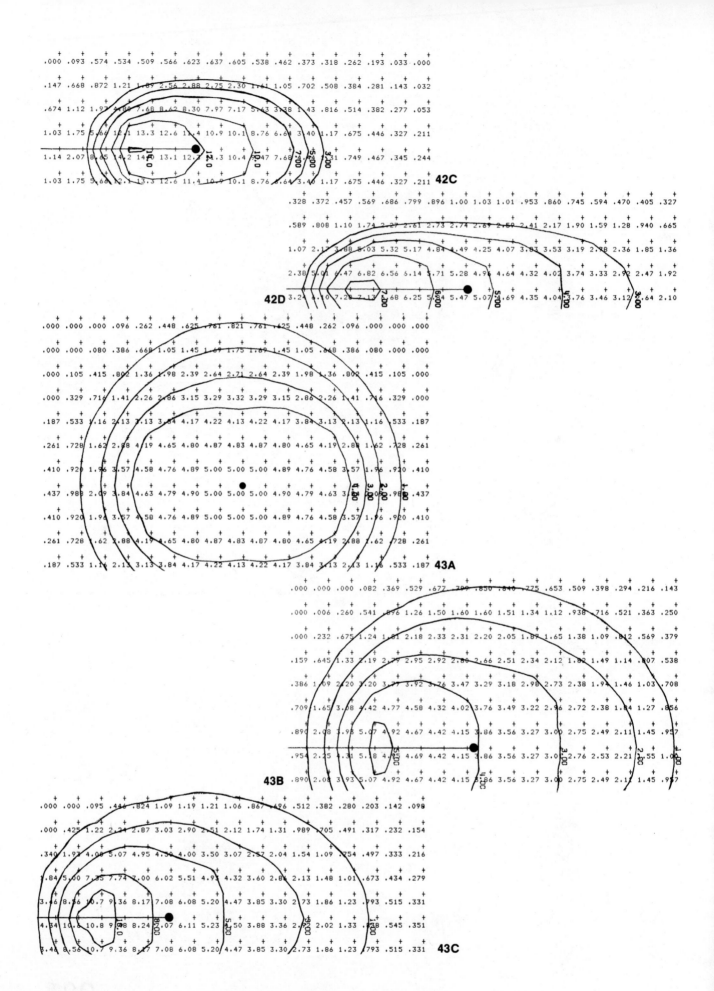

.000 .093 .574 .534 .509 .566 .623 .637 .605 .538 .462 .373 .318 .262 .193 .033 .000

.147 .668 .872 1.21 1.89 2.56 2.88 2.75 2.30 1.61 1.05 .702 .508 .384 .281 .143 .032

.674 1.12 1.97 4.80 7.68 8.62 8.30 7.97 7.17 5.43 3.38 1.43 .816 .514 .382 .277 .053

1.03 1.75 5.68 12.1 13.3 12.6 11.4 10.9 10.1 8.76 6.64 3.40 1.17 .675 .446 .327 .211

1.14 2.07 8.65 4.2 14.0 13.1 12.7 10.4 9.47 7.68 31 .749 .467 .345 .244

1.03 1.75 5.68 12.1 13.3 12.6 11.4 10.9 10.1 8.76 6.64 3.40 1.17 .675 .446 .327 .211   **42C**

.328 .372 .457 .569 .686 .799 .896 1.00 1.03 1.01 .953 .860 .745 .594 .470 .405 .327

.589 .808 1.10 1.74 2.27 2.61 2.73 2.74 2.69 2.59 2.41 2.17 1.90 1.59 1.28 .940 .665

1.07 2.11 3.88 5.03 5.32 5.17 4.84 4.49 4.25 4.07 3.83 3.53 3.19 2.78 2.36 1.85 1.36

2.38 5.01 6.47 6.82 6.56 6.14 5.71 5.28 4.96 4.64 4.32 4.02 3.74 3.33 2.92 2.47 1.92

42D 3.24 4.10 7.28 7.13 6.84 6.25 5.47 5.07 4.69 4.35 4.04 3.76 3.46 3.12 3.64 2.10

.000 .000 .000 .096 .262 .448 .625 .761 .821 .761 .625 .448 .262 .096 .000 .000 .000

.000 .000 .080 .386 .668 1.05 1.45 1.69 1.75 1.69 1.45 1.05 .668 .386 .080 .000 .000

.000 .105 .415 .802 1.36 1.98 2.39 2.64 2.71 2.64 2.39 1.98 1.36 .802 .415 .105 .000

.000 .329 .716 1.41 2.26 2.86 3.15 3.29 3.32 3.29 3.15 2.86 2.26 1.41 .716 .329 .000

.187 .533 1.16 2.13 3.13 3.84 4.17 4.22 4.13 4.22 4.17 3.84 3.13 2.13 1.16 .533 .187

.261 .728 1.62 2.88 4.19 4.65 4.80 4.87 4.83 4.87 4.80 4.65 4.19 2.88 1.62 .728 .261

.410 .920 1.96 3.57 4.58 4.76 4.89 5.00 5.00 5.00 4.89 4.76 4.58 3.57 1.96 .920 .410

.437 .988 2.09 3.84 4.63 4.79 4.90 5.00 5.00 5.00 4.90 4.79 4.63 3.84 2.09 .988 .437

.410 .920 1.96 3.57 4.58 4.76 4.89 5.00 5.00 5.00 4.89 4.76 4.58 3.57 1.96 .920 .410

.261 .728 1.62 2.88 4.19 4.65 4.80 4.87 4.83 4.87 4.80 4.65 4.19 2.88 1.62 .728 .261

.187 .533 1.16 2.13 3.13 3.84 4.17 4.22 4.13 4.22 4.17 3.84 3.13 2.13 1.16 .533 .187   **43A**

.000 .000 .000 .082 .369 .529 .677 .799 .850 .840 .775 .653 .509 .398 .294 .216 .143

.000 .006 .260 .541 .876 1.26 1.50 1.60 1.60 1.51 1.34 1.12 .938 .716 .521 .363 .250

.000 .232 .675 1.24 1.81 2.18 2.33 2.31 2.20 2.05 1.87 1.65 1.38 1.09 .812 .569 .379

.159 .645 1.33 2.19 2.79 2.95 2.92 2.88 2.66 2.51 2.34 2.12 1.82 1.49 1.14 .807 .538

.386 1.09 2.20 3.20 3.77 3.92 3.76 3.47 3.29 3.18 2.98 2.73 2.38 1.94 1.46 1.03 .708

.709 1.65 3.08 4.42 4.77 4.58 4.32 4.02 3.76 3.49 3.22 2.96 2.72 2.38 1.84 1.27 .856

.890 2.08 3.93 5.07 4.92 4.67 4.42 4.15 3.86 3.56 3.27 3.00 2.75 2.49 2.11 1.45 .957

.954 2.25 4.31 5.18 4.95 4.69 4.42 4.15 3.86 3.56 3.27 3.00 2.76 2.53 2.21 1.55 1.00

43B .890 2.08 3.93 5.07 4.92 4.67 4.42 4.15 3.86 3.56 3.27 3.00 2.75 2.49 2.11 1.45 .957

.000 .000 .095 .446 .824 1.09 1.19 1.21 1.06 .867 .696 .512 .382 .280 .203 .142 .098

.000 .425 1.22 2.21 2.87 3.03 2.90 2.51 2.12 1.74 1.31 .989 .705 .491 .317 .232 .154

.340 1.93 4.08 5.07 4.95 4.50 4.00 3.50 3.07 2.57 2.04 1.54 1.09 .754 .497 .333 .216

1.84 5.00 7.35 7.74 7.00 6.02 5.51 4.91 4.32 3.60 2.84 2.13 1.48 1.01 .673 .434 .279

3.16 8.56 10.7 9.36 8.17 7.08 6.08 5.20 4.47 3.85 3.30 2.73 1.86 1.23 .793 .515 .331

4.34 10.8 10.8 9.26 8.24 7.07 6.11 5.23 4.50 3.88 3.36 2.85 2.02 1.33 .868 .545 .351

3.46 8.56 10.7 9.36 8.17 7.08 6.08 5.20 4.47 3.85 3.30 2.73 1.86 1.23 .793 .515 .331   **43C**

Note: All curves symmetrical; complete total light pattern from data given.

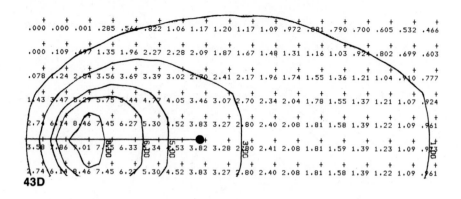

43D

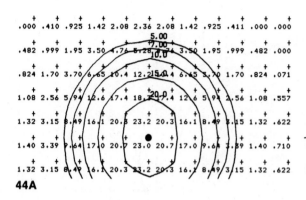

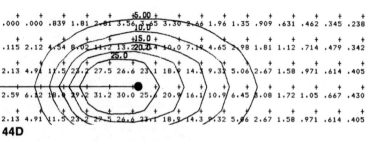

44A

44D

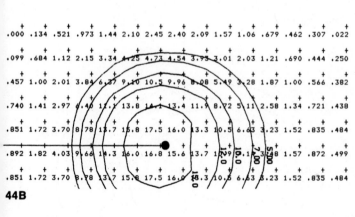

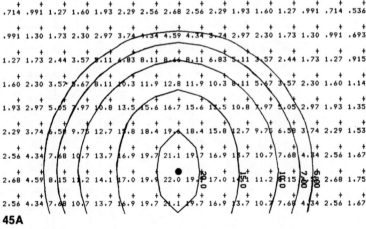

44B

45A

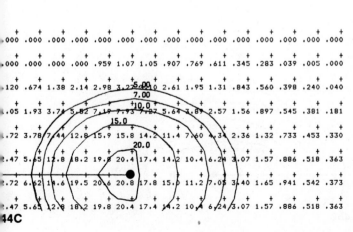

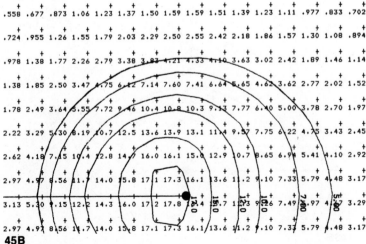

44C

45B

287

Note: All curves symmetrical; complete total light pattern from data given.

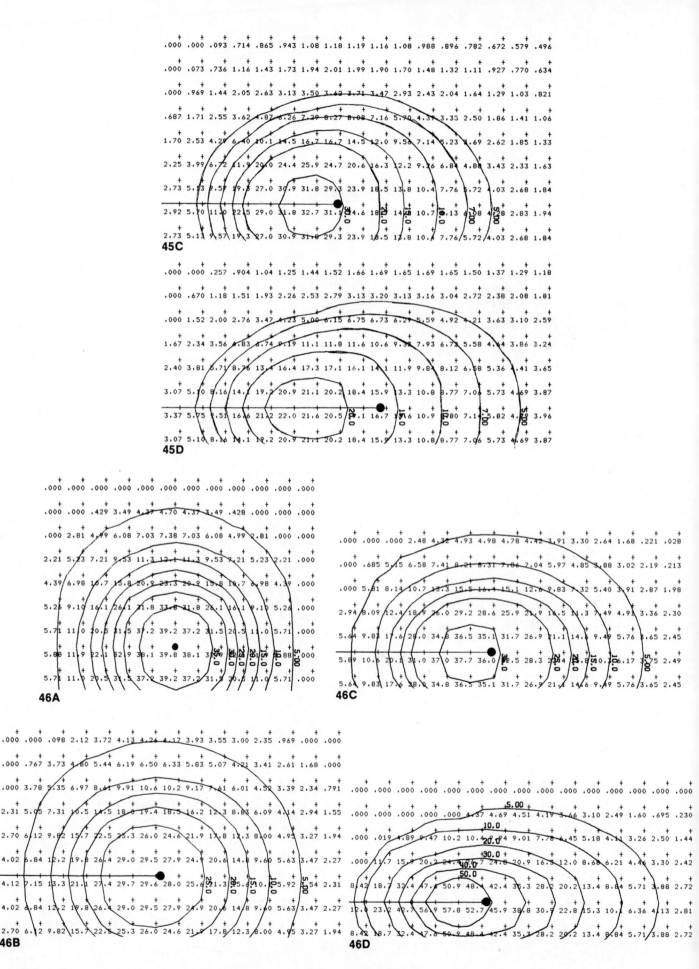

45C

45D

46A

46C

46B

46D

Note: All curves symmetrical; complete total light pattern from data given.

47A

```
  +    +    +    +    +    +    +    +    +    +    +    +    +    +    +    +    +    +
.000 .000 .000 .000 .000 .000 .000 .000 .000 .000 .000 .000 .000 .000 .000 .000 .000 .000

  +    +    +    +    +    +    +    +    +    +    +    +    +    +    +    +    +    +
.000 .000 .000 .000 .000 1.31 1.57 2.59 2.76 2.59 1.57 1.31 .000 .000 .000 .000 .000 .000

  +    +    +    +    +    +    +    +    +    +    +    +    +    +    +    +    +    +
.000 .000 .000 .859 2.15 3.39 4.95 6.13 6.59 6.13 4.95 3.39 2.15 .859 .000 .000 .000 .000

  +    +    +    +    +    +    +    +    +    +    +    +    +    +    +    +    +    +
.000 .000 .634 2.79 4.57 7.02 9.43 11.3 12.1 11.3 9.43 7.02 4.57 2.79 .634 .000 .000 .000

  +    +    +    +    +    +    +    +    +    +    +    +    +    +    +    +    +    +
.000 .859 2.78 4.80 7.62 11.0 14.8 17.4 18.5 17.4 14.8 11.0 7.62 4.80 2.78 .859 .000 .000

  +    +    +    +    +    +    +    +    +    +    +    +    +    +    +    +    +    +
.000 2.15 4.25 7.06 10.6 15.4 20.1 23.2 24.3 23.2 20.1 15.4 10.6 7.06 4.25 2.15 .000 .000

  +    +    +    +    +    +    +    +    +    +    +    +    +    +    +    +    +    +
1.31 3.22 5.75 8.83 13.4 19.2 24.8 27.3 28.2 27.3 24.8 19.2 13.4 8.83 5.75 3.22 1.31 .000

  +    +    +    +    +    +    +    +    +    +    +    +    +    +    +    +    +    +
1.57 4.12 6.82 10.2 15.4 21.3 26.8 30.4 31.3 30.4 26.8 21.3 15.4 10.2 6.82 4.12 1.57 .000

  +    +    +    +    +    +    +    +    +    +    +    +    +    +    +    +    +    +
2.59 4.68 7.45 11.1 16.4 22.1 28.0 31.8 32.7 31.8 28.0 22.1 16.4 11.1 7.45 4.68 2.59 .000

  +    +    +    +    +    +    +    +    +    +    +    +    +    +    +    +    +    +
2.71 4.88 7.66 11.3 16.6 22.0 27.7 31.5 33.7 31.5 27.7 22.0 16.6 11.3 7.66 4.88 2.71 .000

  +    +    +    +    +    +    +    +    +    +    +    +    +    +    +    +    +    +
2.59 4.68 7.45 11.1 16.4 22.1 28.0 31.8 32.7 31.8 28.0 22.1 16.4 11.1 7.45 4.68 2.59 .000

  +    +    +    +    +    +    +    +    +    +    +    +    +    +    +    +    +    +
1.57 4.12 6.82 10.2 15.4 21.3 26.8 30.4 31.3 30.4 26.8 21.3 15.4 10.2 6.82 4.12 1.57 .000
```

47B

```
  +    +    +    +    +    +    +    +    +    +    +    +    +    +    +    +    +    +
.000 .000 .000 .000 .300 .981 2.25 2.54 2.76 2.92 2.79 2.38 1.82 1.54 1.27 .764 .395 .000

  +    +    +    +    +    +    +    +    +    +    +    +    +    +    +    +    +    +
.000 .000 .000 .675 3.01 4.25 5.45 6.25 6.39 6.02 5.29 4.41 3.51 2.67 1.97 1.47 1.00 .647

  +    +    +    +    +    +    +    +    +    +    +    +    +    +    +    +    +    +
.000 .046 2.09 4.03 6.23 8.39 9.99 10.8 10.6 9.60 8.25 6.75 5.30 4.04 3.02 2.19 1.57 1.11

  +    +    +    +    +    +    +    +    +    +    +    +    +    +    +    +    +    +
.000 1.80 4.45 7.42 10.4 13.3 15.3 15.9 15.2 13.8 11.7 9.30 7.16 5.37 4.00 2.98 2.15 1.53

  +    +    +    +    +    +    +    +    +    +    +    +    +    +    +    +    +    +
1.29 3.98 7.30 10.8 15.0 18.4 20.3 20.5 19.1 17.0 14.5 11.7 8.99 6.64 4.79 3.62 2.68 1.90

  +    +    +    +    +    +    +    +    +    +    +    +    +    +    +    +    +    +
2.54 6.10 9.70 14.1 19.2 22.6 23.9 23.5 21.9 19.6 16.7 13.5 10.3 7.69 5.54 4.11 3.08 2.24

  +    +    +    +    +    +    +    +    +    +    +    +    +    +    +    +    +    +
4.27 7.72 11.5 16.5 21.5 25.2 26.5 25.9 24.0 21.3 18.1 14.6 11.1 8.39 6.12 4.42 3.35 2.48

  +    +    +    +    +    +    +    +    +    +    +    +    +    +    +    +    +    +
4.93 8.68 12.5 17.7 22.3 26.3 27.7 26.9 24.9 22.1 18.5 14.8 11.3 8.68 6.42 4.58 3.51 2.62

  +    +    +    +    +    +    +    +    +    +    +    +    +    +    +    +    +    +
5.20 9.00 12.8 18.0 22.3 26.0 27.4 27.1 25.0 21.8 18.3 14.7 11.3 8.77 6.52 4.10 3.57 2.68

  +    +    +    +    +    +    +    +    +    +    +    +    +    +    +    +    +    +
4.93 8.68 12.5 17.7 22.3 26.3 27.7 26.9 24.9 22.1 18.5 14.8 11.3 8.68 6.42 4.58 3.51 2.62

  +    +    +    +    +    +    +    +    +    +    +    +    +    +    +    +    +    +
4.27 7.72 11.5 16.5 21.5 25.2 26.5 25.9 24.0 21.3 18.1 14.6 11.1 8.39 6.12 4.42 3.35 2.48
```

47C

```
  +    +    +    +    +    +    +    +    +    +    +    +    +    +    +
.000 .000 .000 .000 .000 2.93 3.07 2.82 3.02 2.49 2.12 1.79 1.31 1.02 .520

  +    +    +    +    +    +    +    +    +    +    +    +    +    +    +
.000 .000 .869 3.92 6.70 8.82 9.18 8.42 7.10 5.65 4.35 3.28 2.40 1.77 1.32

  +    +    +    +    +    +    +    +    +    +    +    +    +    +    +
.000 3.81 8.91 15.1 19.1 20.2 18.4 15.7 12.2 9.26 6.77 5.01 3.68 2.69 1.93

  +    +    +    +    +    +    +    +    +    +    +    +    +    +    +
2.61 12.3 22.0 30.6 34.2 32.4 28.3 23.0 17.7 12.9 9.17 6.40 4.71 3.46 2.52

  +    +    +    +    +    +    +    +    +    +    +    +    +    +    +
11.3 22.4 35.5 44.5 45.1 40.9 34.9 28.0 21.5 15.5 10.9 7.62 5.46 3.98 2.94

  +    +    +    +    +    +    +    +    +    +    +    +    +    +    +
17.1 29.4 42.9 51.6 51.5 45.7 38.5 30.4 23.0 16.3 11.8 8.39 5.89 4.29 3.19

  +    +    +    +    +    +    +    +    +    +    +    +    +    +    +
19.3 31.4 43.9 51.9 51.9 45.7 38.5 30.2 23.0 16.4 12.0 8.60 6.01 4.38 3.28

  +    +    +    +    +    +    +    +    +    +    +    +    +    +    +
17.1 29.4 42.9 51.6 51.5 45.7 38.5 30.4 23.0 16.3 11.8 8.39 5.89 4.29 3.19
```

47D

```
  +    +    +    +    +    +    +    +    +    +    +    +    +    +    +    +
.000 .000 .000 .000 .000 1.96 2.60 3.34 3.95 4.14 4.01 3.73 3.39 3.01 2.63 2.30 1.99 1.71

  +    +    +    +    +    +    +    +    +    +    +    +    +    +    +    +    +
.000 .000 .007 2.59 4.67 6.60 7.87 8.30 8.10 7.51 6.73 5.96 5.11 4.35 3.69 3.10 2.61 2.20

  +    +    +    +    +    +    +    +    +    +    +    +    +    +    +    +    +
.000 .978 5.50 9.41 12.6 14.4 14.9 14.3 12.9 11.4 9.85 8.29 7.04 5.75 4.73 3.90 3.22 2.66

  +    +    +    +    +    +    +    +    +    +    +    +    +    +    +    +    +
.619 8.13 14.3 19.4 22.9 23.2 21.9 19.5 16.7 14.3 12.2 10.1 8.31 6.79 5.55 4.52 3.69 3.03

  +    +    +    +    +    +    +    +    +    +    +    +    +    +    +    +    +
9.11 16.7 23.5 29.5 31.0 29.5 26.5 23.1 19.6 16.5 13.6 11.2 9.25 7.41 5.96 4.86 3.97 3.26

  +    +    +    +    +    +    +    +    +    +    +    +    +    +    +    +    +
14.6 23.0 29.8 34.0 35.1 32.7 28.9 24.8 20.9 17.5 14.3 11.7 9.54 7.59 6.07 4.97 4.08 3.36

  +    +    +    +    +    +    +    +    +    +    +    +    +    +    +    +    +
16.3 23.4 31.1 34.3 35.2 32.8 29.2 25.6 21.0 17.3 14.1 11.6 9.50 7.57 6.07 4.11 3.39

  +    +    +    +    +    +    +    +    +    +    +    +    +    +    +    +    +
14.6 22.0 29.8 34.0 35.1 32.7 28.9 24.8 20.9 17.5 14.3 11.7 9.54 7.59 6.07 4.97 4.08 3.36
```

Note: All curves symmetrical; complete total light pattern from data given.

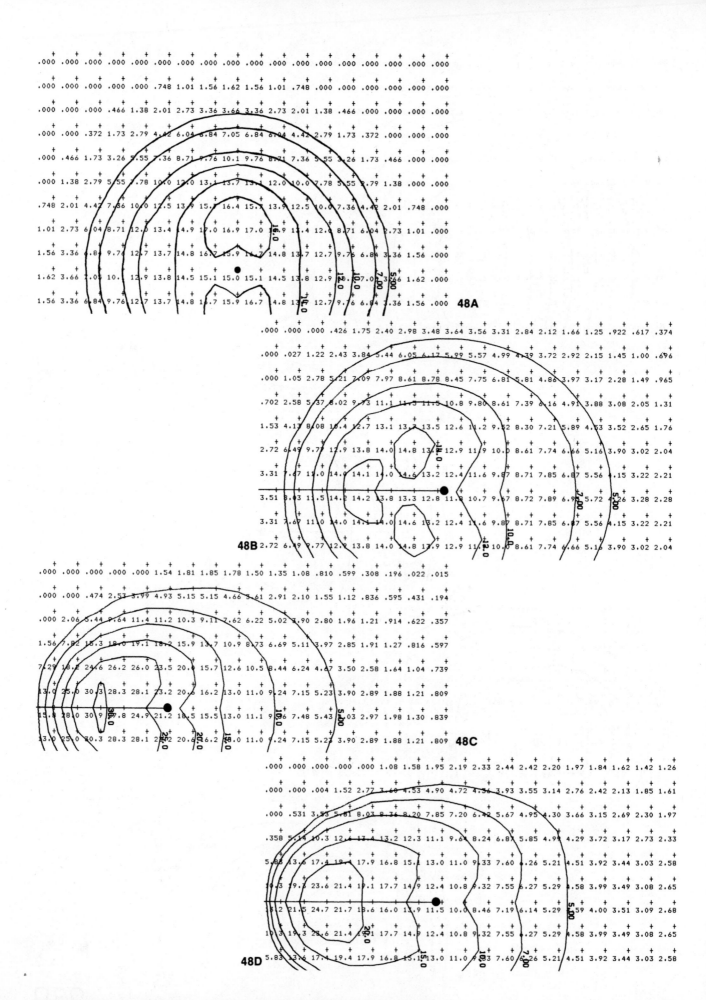

Note: All curves symmetrical; complete total light pattern from data given.

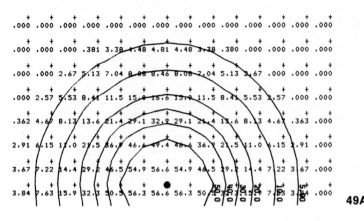

```
  +     +     +     +     +     +     +     +     +     +     +     +     +     +
.000  .000  .000  .000  .000  .000  .000  .000  .000  .000  .000  .000  .000  .000

  +     +     +     +     +     +     +     +     +     +     +     +     +     +
.000  .000  .000  .381  3.38  4.48  4.81  4.48  3.38  .380  .000  .000  .000  .000

  +     +     +     +     +     +     +     +     +     +     +     +     +     +
.000  .000  2.67  5.13  7.04  8.08  8.46  8.08  7.04  5.13  2.67  .000  .000  .000

  +     +     +     +     +     +     +     +     +     +     +     +     +     +
.000  2.57  5.53  8.41  11.5  15.6  16.6  13.8  11.5  8.41  5.53  2.57  .000  .000

 +     +     +     +     +     +     +     +     +     +     +     +     +     +
.362  4.67  8.13  13.6  21.4  29.1  32.9  29.1  21.4  13.6  8.13  4.67  .363  .000

  +     +     +     +     +     +     +     +     +     +     +     +     +     +
2.91  6.15  11.0  21.5  36.9  46.4  49.4  46.4  36.9  21.5  11.0  6.15  2.91  .000

  +     +     +     +     +     +     +     +     +     +     +     +     +     +
3.67  7.22  14.4  29.2  46.5  54.9  56.6  54.9  46.5  29.2  14.4  7.22  3.67  .000

  +     +     +     +     +     •     +     +     +     +     +     +     +     +
3.84  7.63  15.9  32.3  50.5  56.3  56.6  56.3  50.5  32.3  15.9  7.63  3.84  .000
```

49A

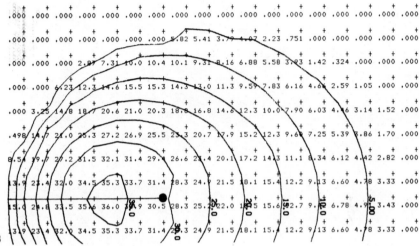

```
  +     +     +     +     +     +     +     +     +     +     +     +     +     +     +     +     +     +
.000  .000  .000  .000  .000  .000  .000  .000  .000  .000  .000  .000  .000  .000  .000  .000  .000  .000

  +     +     +     +     +     +     +     +     +     +     +     +     +     +     +     +     +     +
.000  .000  .000  .000  .000  .000  .000  5.82  5.41  3.79  4.07  2.23  .751  .000  .000  .000  .000  .000

  +     +     +     +     +     +     +     +     +     +     +     +     +     +     +     +     +     +
.000  .000  .000  2.97  7.31  10.0  10.4  10.1  9.31  8.16  6.88  5.58  3.73  1.42  .324  .000  .000  .000

  +     +     +     +     +     +     +     +     +     +     +     +     +     +     +     +     +     +
.000  .000  6.23  12.3  14.6  15.5  15.3  14.3  13.0  11.3  9.59  7.83  6.16  4.64  2.59  1.05  .000  .000

  +     +     +     +     +     +     +     +     +     +     +     +     +     +     +     +     +     +
.000  3.25  14.8  18.7  20.6  21.0  20.3  18.8  16.8  14.6  12.3  10.0  7.90  6.03  4.46  3.14  1.52  .000

  +     +     +     +     +     +     +     +     +     +     +     +     +     +     +     +     +     +
.498  14.7  21.0  25.3  27.2  26.9  25.5  23.3  20.7  17.9  15.2  12.3  9.68  7.25  5.39  3.86  1.70  .000

  +     +     +     +     +     +     +     +     +     +     +     +     +     +     +     +     +     +
8.51  19.7  27.2  31.5  32.1  31.4  29.1  26.6  23.4  20.1  17.2  14.3  11.1  8.34  6.12  4.42  2.82  .000

  +     +     +     +     +     +     +     +     +     +     +     +     +     +     +     +     +     +
13.9  23.4  32.0  34.5  35.3  33.7  31.4  28.3  24.9  21.5  18.1  15.4  12.2  9.13  6.60  4.78  3.33  .000

  +     +     +     +     +     +     +     +     +     +     +     +     +     +     +     +     •     +
15.0  24.4  31.5  35.4  36.0  35.9  30.5  28.3  25.2  22.0  18.15 15.6  12.7  9.85  6.78  4.9   3.43  .000

  +     +     +     +     +     +     +     +     +     +     +     +     +     +     +     +     +     +
13.9  23.4  32.0  34.5  35.3  33.7  31.4  24.9  21.5  18.1  15.1  12.2  9.13  6.60  4.78  3.33  .000
```

49B

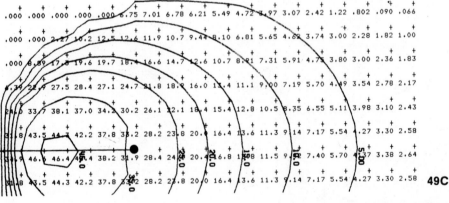

```
  +     +     +     +     +     +     +     +     +     +     +     +     +     +     +     +     +
.000  .000  .000  .000  .000  6.75  7.01  6.78  6.21  5.49  4.72  3.97  3.07  2.42  1.22  .802  .090  .066

  +     +     +     +     +     +     +     +     +     +     +     +     +     +     +     +     +
.000  .000  2.27  10.2  12.5  12.6  11.9  10.7  9.44  8.10  6.81  5.65  4.62  3.74  3.00  2.28  1.82  1.00

  +     +     +     +     +     +     +     +     +     +     +     +     +     +     +     +     +
.000  8.89  17.8  19.6  19.7  18.4  16.6  14.7  12.6  10.7  8.91  7.31  5.91  4.75  3.80  3.00  2.36  1.83

 +     +     +     +     +     +     +     +     +     +     +     +     +     +     +     +     +
6.38  22.9  27.5  28.4  27.1  24.7  21.8  18.9  16.0  13.4  11.1  9.00  7.19  5.70  4.49  3.54  2.78  2.17

 +     +     +     +     +     +     +     +     +     +     +     +     +     +     +     +     +
28.0  33.7  38.1  37.0  34.2  30.2  26.1  22.1  18.4  15.4  12.8  10.5  8.35  6.55  5.11  3.98  3.10  2.43

 +     +     +     +     +     +     +     +     +     +     +     +     +     +     +     +     +
31.8  43.5  44.7  42.2  37.8  33.2  28.2  23.8  20.6  16.4  13.6  11.3  9.14  7.17  5.54  4.27  3.30  2.58

 +     +     +     +     +     •     +     +     +     +     +     +     +     +     +     +     +
34.9  46.6  46.4  45.4  38.2  31.9  28.4  24.5  20.4  16.8  11.5  9.8   7.40  5.70  4.37  3.38  2.64

 +     +     +     +     +     +     +     +     +     +     +     +     +     +     +     +     +
31.8  43.5  44.3  42.2  37.8  33.2  28.2  23.8  20.0  16.4  13.6  11.3  9.14  7.17  5.54  4.27  3.30  2.58
```

49C

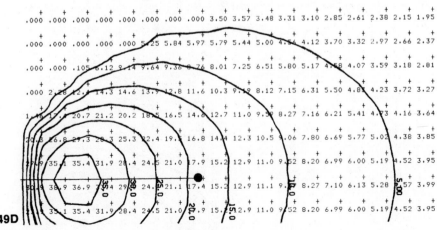

```
  +     +     +     +     +     +     +     +     +     +     +     +     +     +     +     +     +     +
.000  .000  .000  .000  .000  .000  .000  .000  3.50  3.57  3.48  3.31  3.10  2.85  2.61  2.38  2.15  1.95

  +     +     +     +     +     +     +     +     +     +     +     +     +     +     +     +     +     +
.000  .000  .000  .000  .000  5.25  5.84  5.97  5.79  5.44  5.00  4.56  4.12  3.70  3.32  2.97  2.66  2.37

  +     +     +     +     +     +     +     +     +     +     +     +     +     +     +     +     +     +
.000  .000  .105  6.76  9.14  9.64  9.38  8.76  8.01  7.25  6.51  5.80  5.17  4.58  4.07  3.59  3.18  2.81

  +     +     +     +     +     +     +     +     +     +     +     +     +     +     +     +     +     +
.000  2.28  12.4  14.3  14.6  13.9  12.8  11.6  10.3  9.19  8.12  7.15  6.31  5.50  4.85  4.23  3.72  3.27

  +     +     +     +     +     +     +     +     +     +     +     +     +     +     +     +     +     +
1.15  17.1  20.7  21.2  20.2  18.5  16.5  14.6  12.7  11.0  9.52  8.27  7.16  6.21  5.41  4.73  4.16  3.64

  +     +     +     +     +     +     +     +     +     +     +     +     +     +     +     +     +     +
30.3  26.8  27.3  28.3  25.3  22.4  19.5  16.8  14.4  12.3  10.5  9.06  7.80  6.69  5.77  5.02  4.38  3.85

  +     +     +     +     +     +     +     +     +     +     +     +     +     +     +     +     +     +
37.9  35.5  35.4  31.9  28.4  24.5  21.0  17.9  15.2  12.9  11.0  9.52  8.20  6.99  6.00  5.19  4.52  3.95

  +     +     +     +     +     •     +     +     +     +     +     +     +     +     +     +     +     +
30.9  38.9  36.9  35.4  29.9  24.5  21.1  17.4  15.2  12.9  11.1  9.5   8.27  7.10  6.13  5.28  4.57  3.99

  +     +     +     +     +     +     +     +     +     +     +     +     +     +     +     +     +     +
35.1  35.4  31.9  28.4  24.5  21.0  17.9  15.2  12.9  11.0  9.52  8.20  6.99  6.00  5.19  4.52  3.95
```

49D

Note: All curves symmetrical; complete total light pattern from data given.

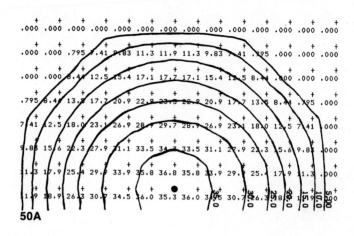

50A

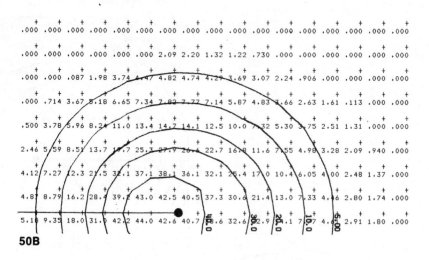

50B

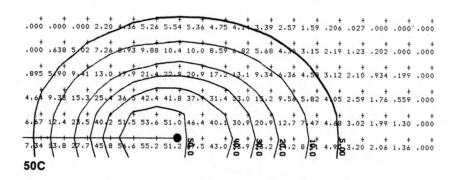

50C

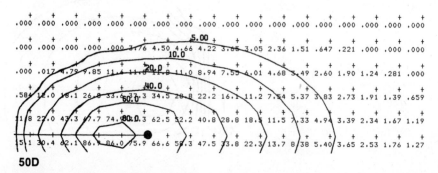

50D

Note: All curves symmetrical; complete total light pattern from data given.

Appendix F

Power Drawer Cutoff Site Light

The following isofootcandle curve reference plots A through G (one luminaire/pole) and A-1 through G-1 (four luminaires/pole) correspond to the information found in Table 2 on page 110. Refer to Table 2 for complete design details. All curves given are symmetrical; complete the total curve from the information given.

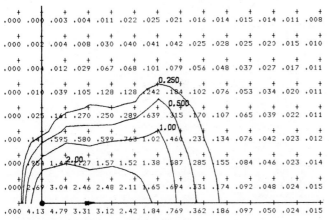

A. Grid spacing = 12.5'; 1" = 50'

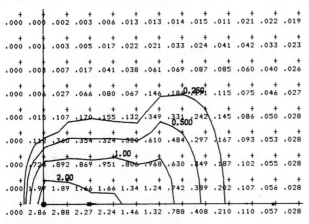

B. Grid spacing = 12.5'; 1" = 50'

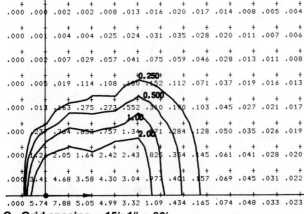

C. Grid spacing = 15'; 1" = 60'

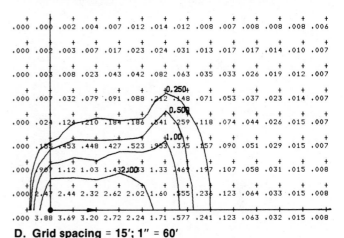

D. Grid spacing = 15'; 1" = 60'

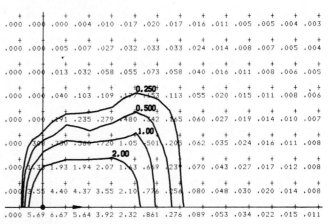

E. Grid spacing = 25'; 1" = 100'

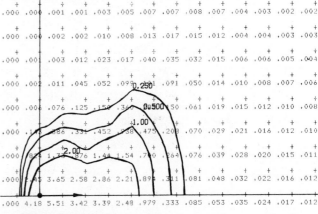

F. Grid spacing = 20'; 1" = 80'

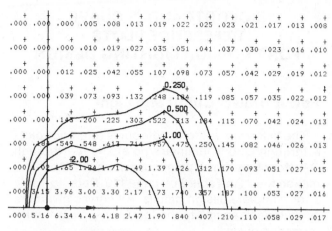

G. Grid spacing = 30'; 1" = 120'

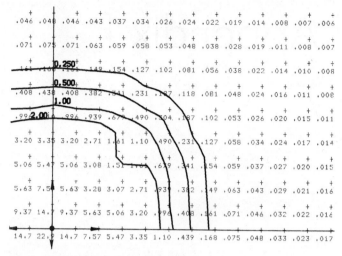

C-1. Grid spacing = 15'; 1" = 60'

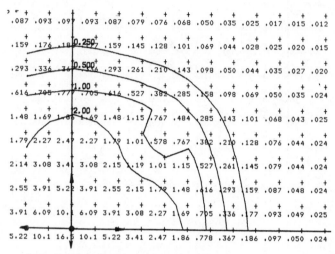

A-1. Grid spacing = 12.5'; 1" = 50'

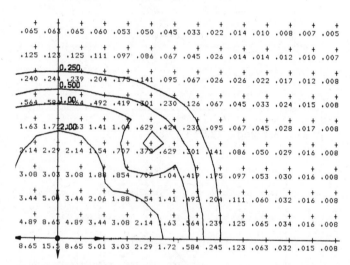

D-1. Grid spacing = 15'; 1" = 60'

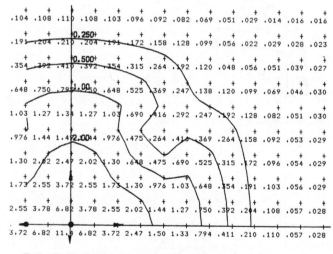

B-1. Grid spacing = 12.5'; 1" = 50'

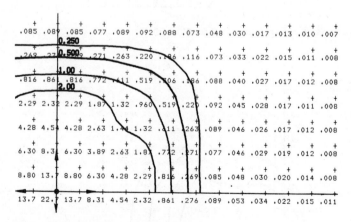

E-1. Grid spacing = 25'; 1" = 100'

294

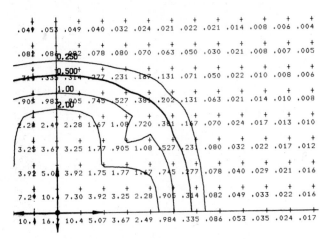

F-1. Grid spacing = 20'; 1" = 80'

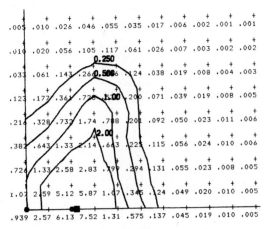

A. Grid spacing = 12.5'; 1" = 50'

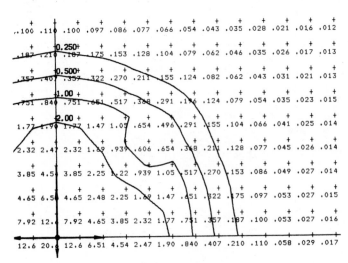

G-1. Grid spacing = 30'; 1" = 120'

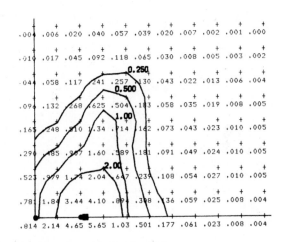

B. Grid spacing = 12.5'; 1" = 50'

Power Drawer Concourse Design 20

The following isofootcandle curve reference plots A through G (one luminaire/pole), A-1 through G-1 (two luminaires/pole), and A-2 through G-2 (four luminaires/pole) correspond to the information found in Table 3 on page 111. Refer to Table 3 for complete design details. All curves given are symmetrical; complete the total curve from the information given.

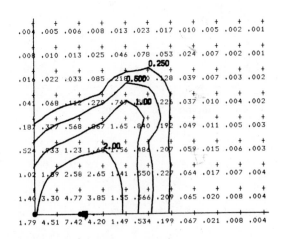

C. Grid spacing = 15'; 1" = 60'

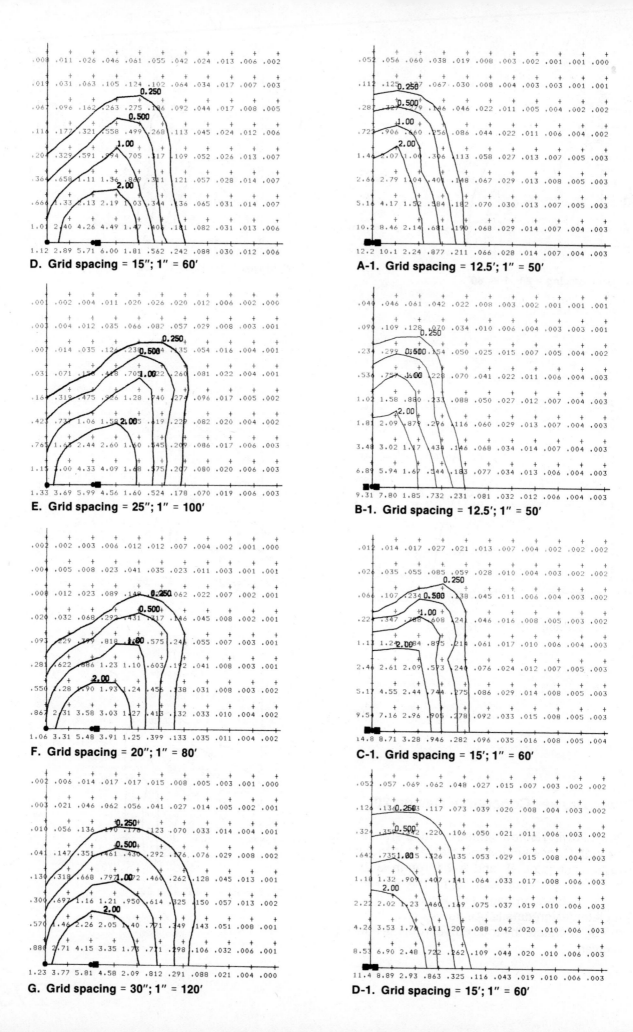

D. Grid spacing = 15″; 1″ = 60′

E. Grid spacing = 25″; 1″ = 100′

F. Grid spacing = 20″; 1″ = 80′

G. Grid spacing = 30″; 1″ = 120′

A-1. Grid spacing = 12.5′; 1″ = 50′

B-1. Grid spacing = 12.5′; 1″ = 50′

C-1. Grid spacing = 15′; 1″ = 60′

D-1. Grid spacing = 15′; 1″ = 60′

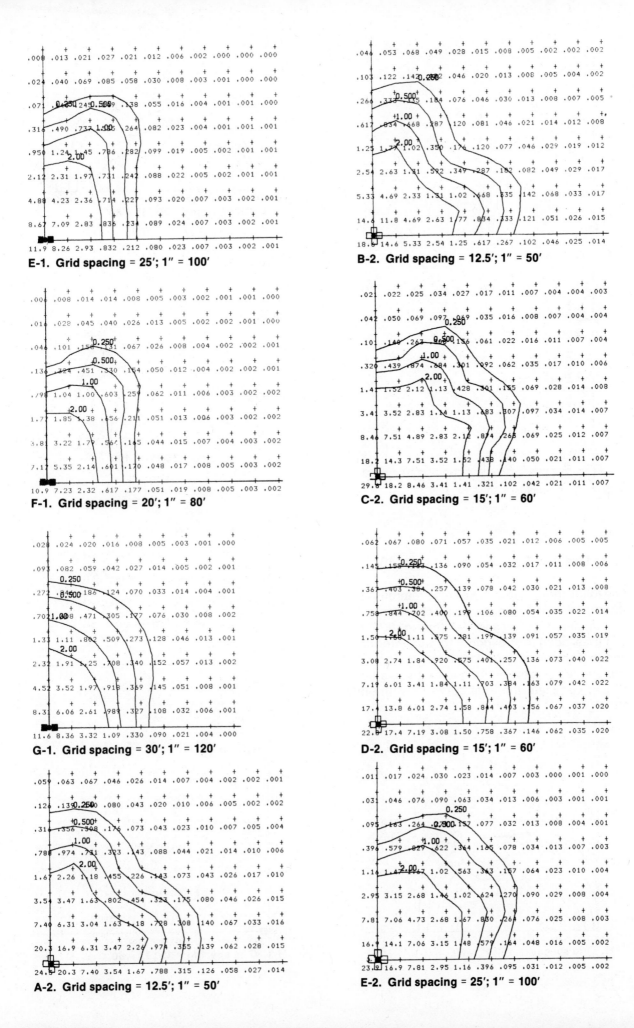

E-1. Grid spacing = 25'; 1" = 100'

F-1. Grid spacing = 20'; 1" = 80'

G-1. Grid spacing = 30'; 1" = 120'

A-2. Grid spacing = 12.5'; 1" = 50'

B-2. Grid spacing = 12.5'; 1" = 50'

C-2. Grid spacing = 15'; 1" = 60'

D-2. Grid spacing = 15'; 1" = 60'

E-2. Grid spacing = 25'; 1" = 100'

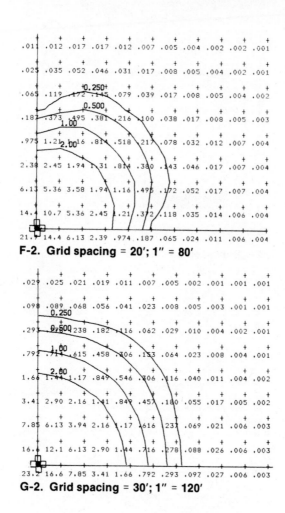

F-2. Grid spacing = 20'; 1" = 80'

G-2. Grid spacing = 30'; 1" = 120'

Power Drawer Concourse Design 40

The following isofootcandle curve reference plots H through K (one luminaire/pole), H-1 through K-1 (two luminaires/pole), and H-2 through K-2 (four luminaires/pole) correspond to the information found in Table 4 on page 112. Refer to Table 4 for complete design details. All curves given are symmetrical; complete the total curve from the information given.

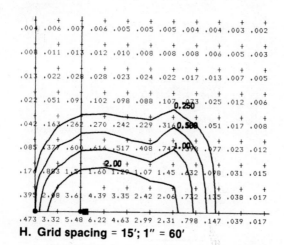

H. Grid spacing = 15'; 1" = 60'

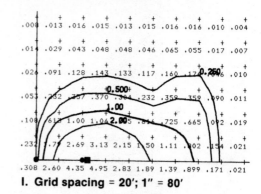

I. Grid spacing = 20'; 1" = 80'

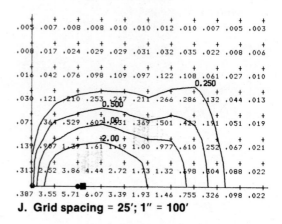

J. Grid spacing = 25'; 1" = 100'

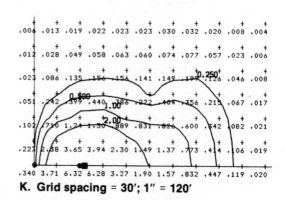

K. Grid spacing = 30'; 1" = 120'

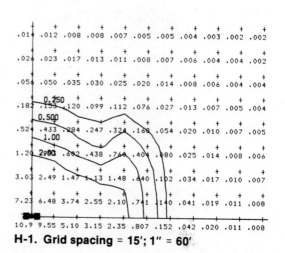

H-1. Grid spacing = 15'; 1" = 60'

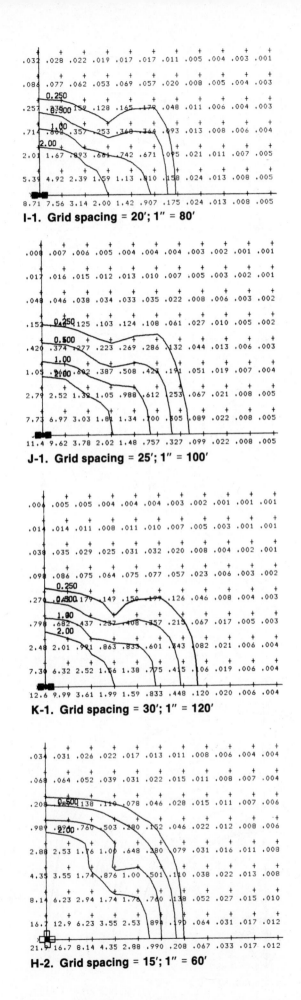

I-1. Grid spacing = 20'; 1" = 80'

J-1. Grid spacing = 25'; 1" = 100'

K-1. Grid spacing = 30'; 1" = 120'

H-2. Grid spacing = 15'; 1" = 60'

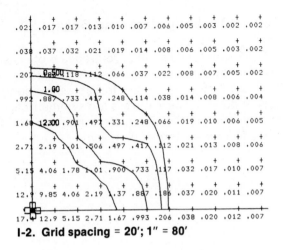

I-2. Grid spacing = 20'; 1" = 80'

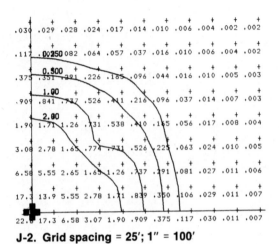

J-2. Grid spacing = 25'; 1" = 100'

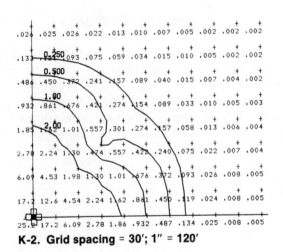

K-2. Grid spacing = 30'; 1" = 120'

Power Drawer Concourse Design 50

The isofootcandle curve reference plots C and F given below correspond to the information found in Table 5 on page 113. Refer to Table 5 for complete design details. These curves are symmetrical completely around the luminaire; complete the total curve from the information given.

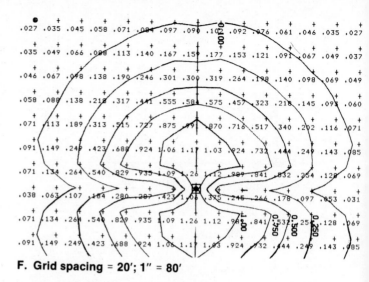

F. Grid spacing = 20'; 1" = 80'

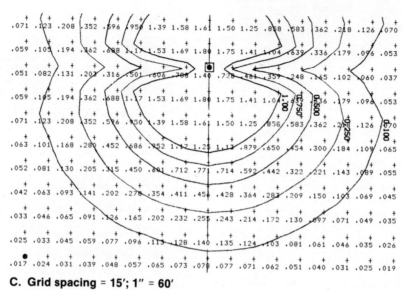

C. Grid spacing = 15'; 1" = 60'

Conquest Landscape

The isofootcandle curve reference plots A, B, C, E, and F given here correspond to the information found in Table 6 on page 114. Refer to Table 6 for complete design details. These curves are symmetrical completely around the luminaire; complete the total curve from the information given.

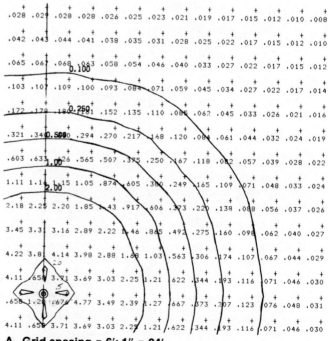

A. Grid spacing = 6'; 1" = 24'

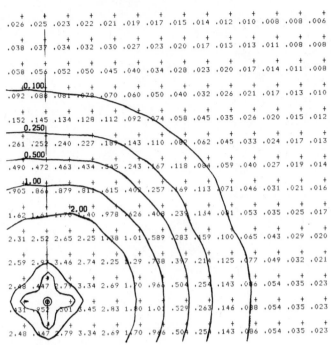

```
 .026  .025  .023  .022  .021  .019  .017  .015  .014  .012  .010  .008  .008  .006

 .038  .037  .034  .032  .030  .027  .023  .020  .017  .015  .013  .011  .008  .008

 .058  .056  .052  .050  .045  .040  .034  .028  .023  .020  .017  .014  .011  .008
      0.100
 .092  .088  .081  .078  .070  .060  .050  .040  .032  .026  .021  .017  .013  .010

 .152  .145  .134  .128  .112  .092  .074  .058  .045  .035  .026  .020  .015  .012
      0.250
 .261  .252  .240  .227  .187  .143  .110  .082  .062  .045  .033  .024  .017  .013
      0.500
 .490  .472  .463  .434  .345  .243  .167  .118  .084  .059  .040  .027  .019  .014
      1.00
 .903  .866  .879  .811  .615  .407  .257  .169  .113  .071  .046  .031  .021  .016

1.62  1.61  1.70  1.40  .978  .626  .408  .239  .134  .081  .053  .035  .025  .017
                 2.00
2.31  2.52  2.65  2.25  1.38  1.01  .589  .283  .159  .100  .065  .043  .029  .020

2.59  2.9   3.46  2.74  2.25  1.29  .738  .397  .214  .125  .077  .049  .032  .021

2.48  .447  2.79  3.34  2.69  1.70  .966  .504  .254  .143  .086  .054  .035  .023

 .231  .952  .301  3.45  2.83  1.80  1.01  .529  .263  .146  .088  .054  .035  .023

2.48  .447  2.79  3.34  2.69  1.70  .966  .504  .254  .143  .086  .054  .035  .023
```

B. Grid spacing = 6'; 1" = 24'

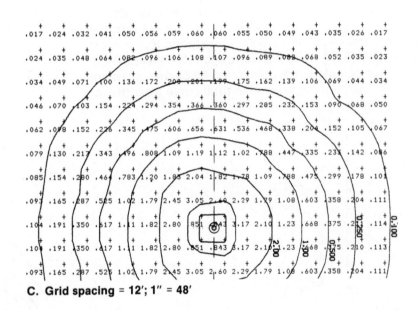

```
 +    +    +    +    +    +    +    +    +    +    +    +    +    +    +    +
.017 .024 .032 .041 .050 .056 .059 .060 .060 .055 .050 .049 .043 .035 .026 .017

 +    +    +    +    +    +    +    +    +    +    +    +    +    +    +    +
.024 .035 .048 .064 .082 .096 .106 .108 .107 .096 .089 .082 .068 .052 .035 .023

 +    +    +    +    +    +    +    +    +    +    +    +    +    +    +    +
.034 .049 .071 .100 .136 .172 .208 .201 .199 .175 .162 .139 .106 .069 .044 .034

 +    +    +    +    +    +    +    +    +    +    +    +    +    +    +    +
.046 .070 .103 .154 .224 .294 .354 .366 .360 .297 .285 .232 .153 .090 .068 .050

 +    +    +    +    +    +    +    +    +    +    +    +    +    +    +    +
.062 .098 .152 .226 .345 .475 .606 .656 .631 .536 .468 .338 .204 .152 .105 .067

 +    +    +    +    +    +    +    +    +    +    +    +    +    +    +    +
.079 .130 .217 .343 .496 .808 1.09 1.19 1.12 1.02 .788 .447 .335 .233 .142 .086

 +    +    +    +    +    +    +    +    +    +    +    +    +    +    +    +
.085 .154 .280 .464 .783 1.20 1.83 2.04 1.82 1.78 1.09 .788 .475 .299 .178 .101

 +    +    +    +    +    +    +    +    +    +    +    +    +    +    +    +
.093 .165 .287 .525 1.02 1.79 2.45 3.05 2.60 2.29 1.79 1.08 .603 .358 .204 .111

 +    +    +    +    +    +    +    +    +    +    +    +    +    +    +    +
.104 .191 .350 .617 1.11 1.82 2.80 .851 .843 3.17 2.10 1.23 .668 .375 .2    .114

 +    +    +    +    +    +    +    +    +    +    +    +    +    +    +    +
.10  .191 .350 .617 1.11 1.82 2.80 .851 .843 3.17 2.10 1.23 .668 .210 .113

 +    +    +    +    +    +    +    +    +    +    +    +    +    +    +    +
.093 .165 .287 .525 1.02 1.79 2.45 3.05 2.60 2.29 1.79 1.08 .603 .358 .204 .111
```

C. Grid spacing = 12'; 1" = 48'

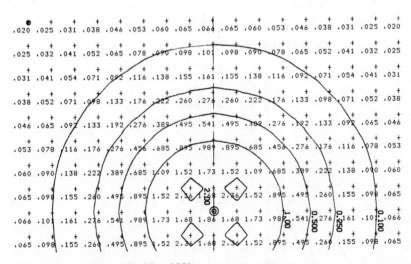

```
 •    +    +    +    +    +    +    +    +    +    +    +    +    +    +    +
.020 .025 .031 .038 .046 .053 .060 .065 .066 .065 .060 .053 .046 .038 .031 .025 .020

 +    +    +    +    +    +    +    +    +    +    +    +    +    +    +    +
.025 .032 .041 .052 .065 .078 .090 .098 .101 .098 .090 .078 .065 .052 .041 .032 .025

 +    +    +    +    +    +    +    +    +    +    +    +    +    +    +    +
.031 .041 .054 .071 .092 .116 .138 .155 .161 .155 .138 .116 .092 .071 .054 .041 .031

 +    +    +    +    +    +    +    +    +    +    +    +    +    +    +    +
.038 .052 .071 .098 .133 .176 .222 .260 .276 .260 .222 .176 .133 .098 .071 .052 .038

 +    +    +    +    +    +    +    +    +    +    +    +    +    +    +    +
.046 .065 .092 .133 .192 .276 .389 .495 .541 .495 .389 .276 .192 .133 .092 .065 .046

 +    +    +    +    +    +    +    +    +    +    +    +    +    +    +    +
.053 .078 .116 .176 .276 .456 .685 .875 .989 .895 .685 .456 .276 .176 .116 .078 .053

 +    +    +    +    +    +    +    +    +    +    +    +    +    +    +    +
.060 .090 .138 .222 .389 .685 1.09 1.52 1.73 1.52 1.09 .685 .389 .222 .138 .090 .060

 +    +    +    +    +    +    +    +    +    +    +    +    +    +    +    +
.065 .098 .155 .260 .495 .895 1.52 2.36 2.76 2.36 1.52 .895 .495 .260 .155 .098 .065

 +    +    +    +    +    +    +    +    +    +    +    +    +    +    +    +
.066 .101 .161 .276 .541 .989 1.73 1.68 1.86 1.68 1.73 .989 .541 .276 .161 .101 .066

 +    +    +    +    +    +    +    +    +    +    +    +    +    +    +    +
.065 .098 .155 .260 .495 .895 1.52 2.36 1.68 2.36 1.52 .895 .495 .260 .155 .098 .065
```

E. Grid spacing = 25'; 1" = 100'

301

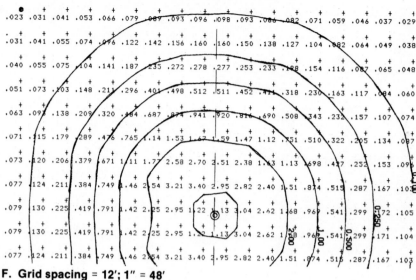

F. Grid spacing = 12'; 1" = 48'

Power Drawer Area Light

The following isofootcandle curve reference plots A through G (one luminaire/pole) and A-1 through G-1 (four luminaires/pole) correspond to the information found in Table 7 on page 115. Refer to Table 7 for complete design details. All curves given are symmetrical; complete the total curve from the information given.

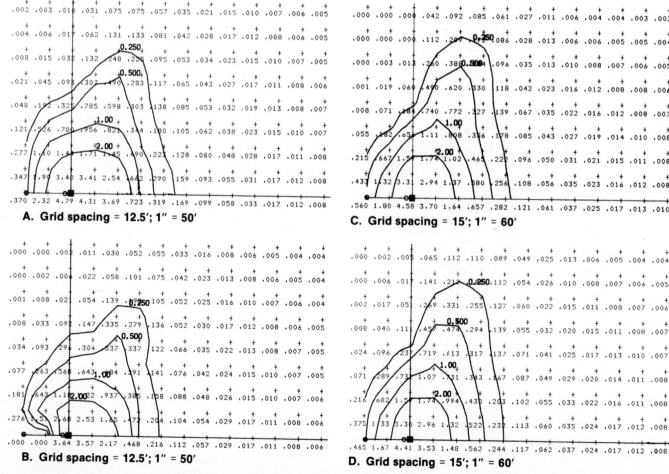

A. Grid spacing = 12.5'; 1" = 50'

C. Grid spacing = 15'; 1" = 60'

B. Grid spacing = 12.5'; 1" = 50'

D. Grid spacing = 15'; 1" = 60'

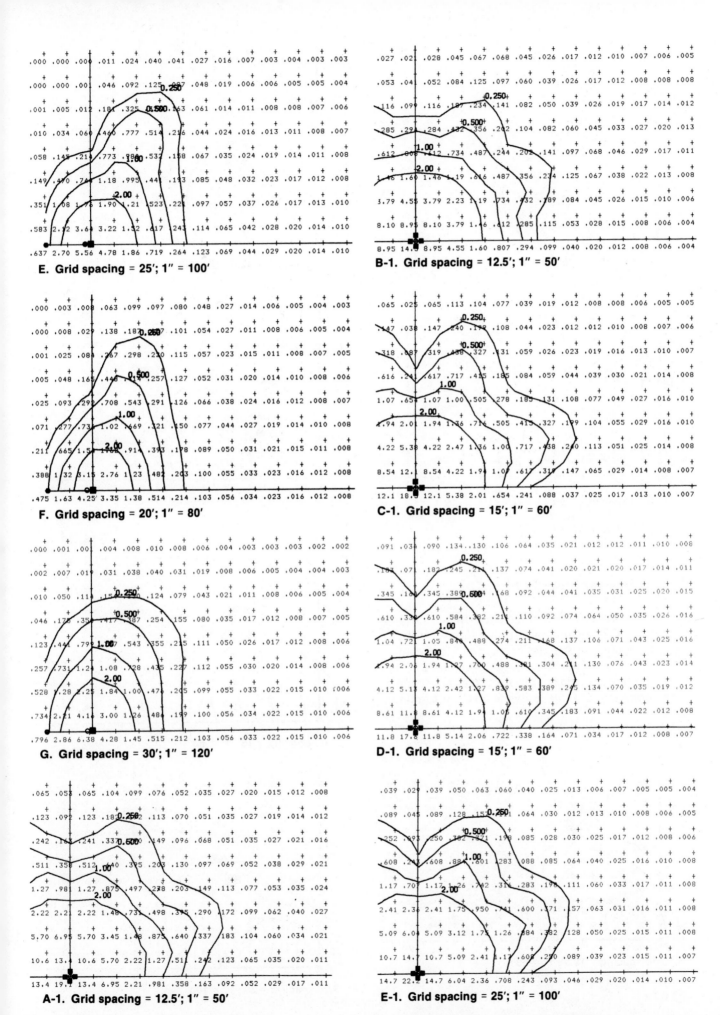

E. Grid spacing = 25'; 1" = 100'

B-1. Grid spacing = 12.5'; 1" = 50'

F. Grid spacing = 20'; 1" = 80'

C-1. Grid spacing = 15'; 1" = 60'

G. Grid spacing = 30'; 1" = 120'

D-1. Grid spacing = 15'; 1" = 60'

A-1. Grid spacing = 12.5'; 1" = 50'

E-1. Grid spacing = 25'; 1" = 100'

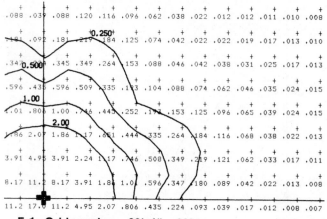

F-1. Grid spacing = 20'; 1" = 80'

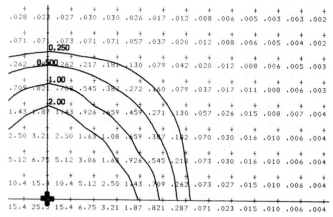

G-1. Grid spacing = 30'; 1" = 120'

Power Drawer Floodlight

The following isofootcandle curve reference plots A through G (one luminaire/pole) and A-1 through G-1 (four luminaires/pole) correspond to the information found in Table 8 on page 116. Refer to Table 8 for complete design details. All curves are symmetrical; complete the total curve from the information given.

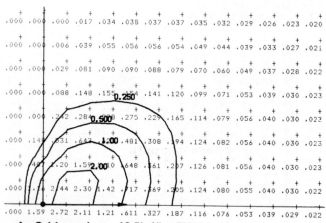

A. Grid spacing = 12.5'; 1" = 50'

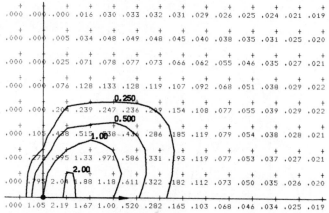

B. Grid spacing = 12.5'; 1" = 50'

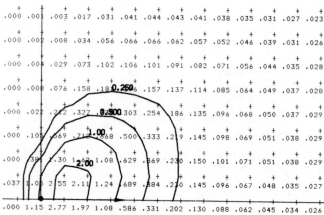

C. Grid spacing = 15'; 1" = 60'

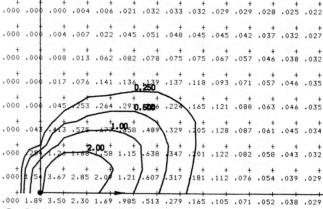

D. Grid spacing = 15'; 1" = 60'

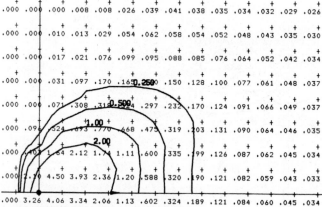

E. Grid spacing = 25'; 1" = 100'

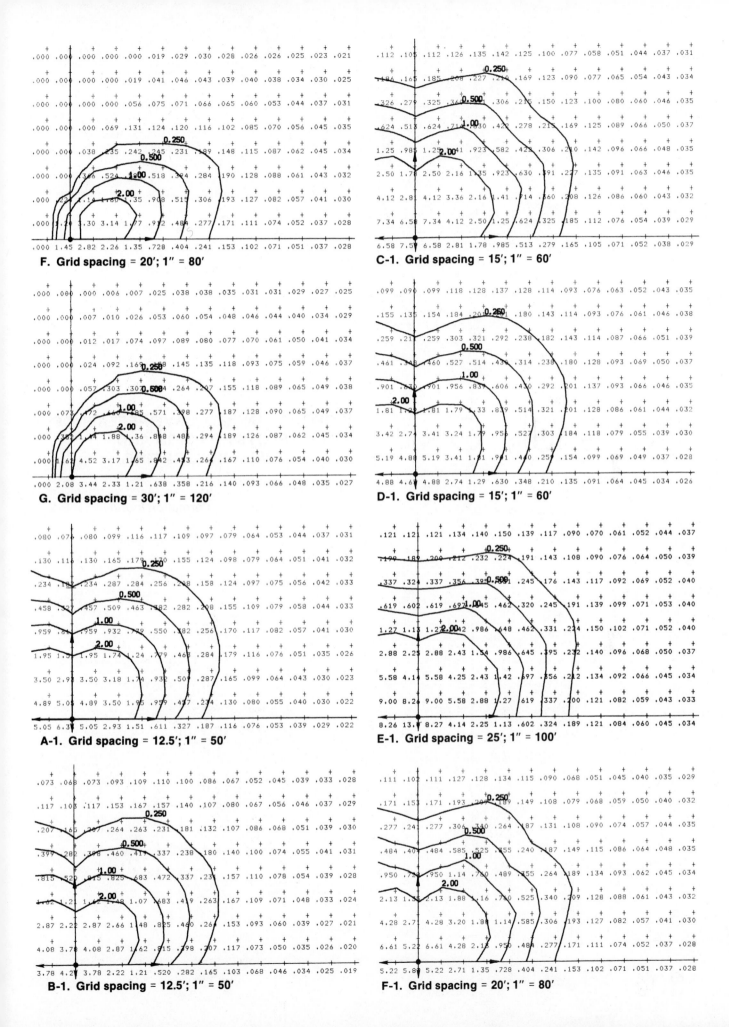

F. Grid spacing = 20'; 1" = 80'

G. Grid spacing = 30'; 1" = 120'

A-1. Grid spacing = 12.5'; 1" = 50'

B-1. Grid spacing = 12.5'; 1" = 50'

C-1. Grid spacing = 15'; 1" = 60'

D-1. Grid spacing = 15'; 1" = 60'

E-1. Grid spacing = 25'; 1" = 100'

F-1. Grid spacing = 20'; 1" = 80'

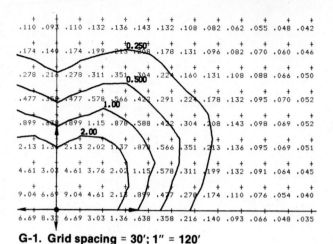

G-1. Grid spacing = 30'; 1" = 120'

Appendix G

ISOFOOTCANDLE CURVE REFERENCE PLOTS FOR SIGN AND BUILDING LIGHTING

The isofootcandle curve reference plots given here correspond to the information found in Table 6 on page 205. Complete details on the use of these plots in sign and building lighting can be found on pages 204-208.

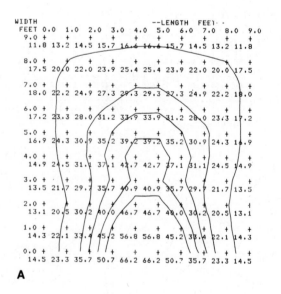

A

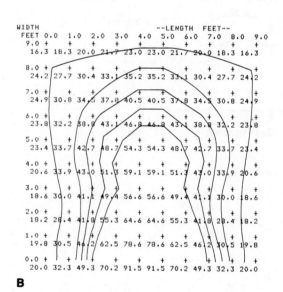

B

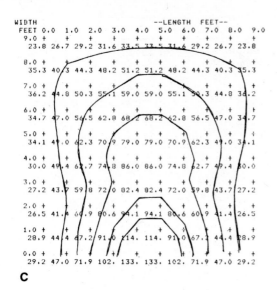

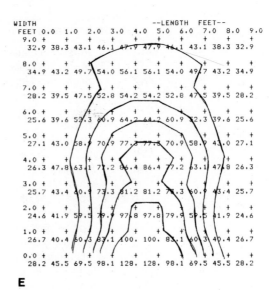

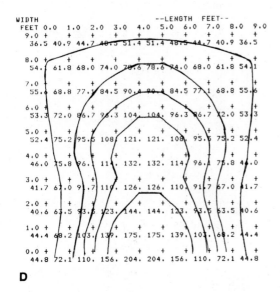

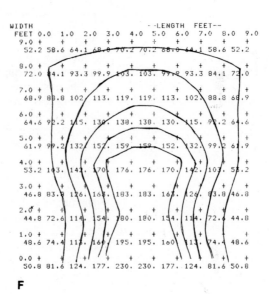

List of Several Common Abbreviations and Acronyms

ANSI	American National Standards Institute
BCD	borderline between comfort and discomfort
BCP	beam candlepower
CBU	coefficient of beam utilization
CCR	ceiling cavity ratio
cos	cosine
cp	candlepower
CRF	contrast retention factor
CRI	color rendering index
CRT	cathode ray tube
CU	coefficient of utilization
CW	cool white
CWX	cool white deluxe
DGF	disabling glare factor
DGR	disabling glare rating
DIC	direct illumination component
ESI	equivalent sphere illumination
FCR	floor cavity ratio
G.E.	General Electric
HID	high intensity discharge
HPS	high pressure sodium
IES	Illuminating Engineering Society
IERI	Illuminating Engineering Research Institute
K	kelvin
kW	kilowatt
kWh	kilowatt-hour
LDD	luminaire dirt depreciation
LEF	lighting effectiveness factor
LLD	lamp lumen depreciation
LLF	light loss factor
LPS	low pressure sodium
max	maximum
MF	maintenance factor
MH	mounting height
min	minimum
NEC	National Electrical Code
NEMA	National Electrical Manufacturers Association
NIOSH	National Institute of Occupational Safety and Health
pf	power factor
RCR	room cavity ratio
RSDD	room surface dirt depreciation
sin	sine
sq	square
TAF	transient adaptation factor
UV	ultraviolet
UL	Underwriters Laboratories
V	volt
VCP	visual comfort probability
W	watt
WW	warm white
WWX	warm white deluxe

Glossary

Accent Lighting: Directional lighting to emphasize a particular object or to draw attention to a part of the field of view. See *Directional Lighting*.

Adaptation: The process by which the visual system becomes accustomed to more or less light or light of a different color than it was exposed to during an immediately preceding period. It results in a change in the sensitivity of the eye to light. *Note:* Adaptation is also used to refer to the final state of the process, as reaching a condition of dark adaptation or light adaptation.

Ambient Lighting: Lighting throughout an area that produces general illumination.

Ambient-Task Lighting: A combination of ambient lighting and task lighting within an area such that the general level of ambient lighting is lower than and complementary to the task lighting.

Arc Discharge: An electric discharge characterized by high cathode current densities and a low voltage drop at the cathode.

Average Luminance (of a luminaire): The luminous intensity at a given angle divided by the projected area of the luminaire at that angle.

Backlight: Illumination from behind a subject directed substantially parallel to a vertical plane through the optical axis of the camera.

Ballast: A device used with an electric-discharge lamp to obtain the necessary circuit conditions (voltage, current, and wave form) for starting and operating.

Ballast-Factor: The fractional loss of task illuminance due to use of a ballast other than the standard one.

Bare (Exposed) Lamp: A light source with no shielding.

Beam Spread (in any plane): The angle between the two directions in the plane in which the intensity is equal to a stated percentage of the maximum beam intensity. The percentage typically is 10% for floodlights and 50% for photographic lights.

Blackbody: A temperature radiator of uniform temperature which has a radiant existence in all parts of the spectrum that is the maximum obtainable from any temperature radiator at the same temperature. Such a radiator is called a blackbody because it will absorb all the radiant energy that falls upon it. All other temperature radiators may be classed as nonblackbodies. They radiate less in some or all wavelength intervals than a blackbody of the same size and the same temperature. *Note:* The blackbody is practically realized in the form of a cavity with opaque walls at a uniform temperature and with a small opening for observation purposes. It also is referred to as a full radiator, a standard radiator, a complete radiator, or an ideal radiator.

Blackbody (Planckian) Locus: The locus of points on a chromaticity diagram representing the chromaticities of blackbodies having various (color) temperatures.

Blinding Glare: Glare which is so intense that for an appreciable length of time after it has been removed, no object can be seen.

Borderline Between Comfort and Discomfort (BCD): The average luminance of a source in a field of view which produces a sensation between comfort and discomfort.

Brightness: See *Luminance* and *Veiling Luminance*.

Candela (cd): The SI unit of luminous intensity. One candela is one lumen per steradian. Formerly, candle.

Candlepower (cp): $I = d\phi/d\omega$: Luminous intensity expressed in candelas.

Candlepower (intensity) Distribution Curve: A curve, generally polar, representing the variation of luminous intensity of a lamp or luminaire in a plane through the light center.

Cavity Ratio (CR): A number indicating cavity proportions calculated from length, width, and height. See *Ceiling Cavity Ratio, Floor Cavity Ratio,* and *Room Cavity Ratio.*

Ceiling Area Lighting: A general lighting system in which the entire ceiling is, in effect, one large luminaire.

Ceiling Cavity: The cavity formed by the ceiling, the plane of the luminaires, and the wall surfaces between these two planes.

Ceiling Cavity Ratio (CCR): A number indicating ceiling cavity proportions calculated from length, width, and height.

Ceiling Ratio: The ratio of the luminous flux reaching the ceiling directly to the upward component from the luminaire.

Chromaticity of a Color: Consists of the dominant or complementary wavelength and purity aspects of the color taken together or the aspects specified by the chromaticity coordinates of the color taken together.

Coefficient of Beam Utilization (CBU): The ratio of the luminous flux (lumens) reaching a specified area directly from a floodlight or projector to the total beam luminous flux (lumens).

Coefficient of Utilization (CU): The ratio of the luminous flux (lumens) from a luminaire calculated as received on the work plane to the luminous flux emitted by the luminaire's lamps alone.

Color: The characteristics of light by which a human observer may distinguish between two structure-free patches of light of the same size and shape.

Color Comparison or Color Grading (CIE, object color inspection): The judgment of equality, or of the amount and character of difference, of the color of two objects viewed under identical illumination.

Color Discrimination: The perception of differences between two or more colors.

Colorimetry: The measurement of color.

Color Rendering: General expression for the effect of a light source on the color appearance of objects in conscious or subconscious comparison with their color appearance under a reference light source.

Color Rendering Index (of a light source) (CRI): Measure of the degree of color shift that objects undergo when illuminated by the light source as compared with the color of those same objects when illuminated by a reference source of comparable color temperature.

Color Temperature of a Light Source: The absolute temperature of a blackbody radiator having a chromaticity equal to that of the light source. See *Correlated Color Temperature* and *Distribution Temperature.*

Complete Diffusion: Diffusion in which the diffusing medium redirects the flux incident by scattering in such a manner that none is in an image-forming state.

Contrast Rendition Factor (CRF): The ratio of visual task contrast with a given lighting environment to the contrast with sphere illumination. Also known as contrast rendering factor.

Correlated Color Temperature (of a light source): The absolute temperature of a blackbody which has a chromaticity most nearly resembling that of the light source.

Cosine Law: The law that the illuminance on any surface varies as the cosine of the angle of incidence. The angle of incidence θ is the angle between the normal to the surface and the direction of the incident light. The inverse-square law and the cosine law can be combined as $E = (I \cos \theta)/d^2$. See *Cosine-Cubed Law* and *Inverse-Square Law*.

Cosine-Cubed Law: An extension of the cosine law in which the distance d between the source and surface is replaced by $h/\cos \theta$, where h is the perpendicular distance of the source from the plane in which the point is located. It is expressed by $E = (I \cos^3 \theta)/h^2$.

Cut-Off Angle (of a luminaire): The angle, measured up from nadir, between the vertical axis and the first line of sight at which the bare source is not visible.

Diffused Lighting: Lighting, provided on the work plane or on an object, that is not predominantly incident from any particular direction.

Direct Component: That portion of the light from a luminaire which arrives at the work plane without being reflected by room surfaces. See *Indirect Component*.

Direct Glare: Glare resulting from high luminances or insufficiently shielded light sources in the field of view. It usually is associated with bright areas, such as luminaires, ceilings, and windows which are outside the visual task or region being viewed.

Directional Lighting: Lighting provided on the work plane or on an object predominantly from a preferred direction. See *Accent Lighting* and *Key Light*.

Direct Lighting: Lighting by luminaires distributing 90 to 100% of the emitted light in the general direction of the surface to be illuminated. The term usually refers to light emitted in a downward direction.

Disabling Glare: Glare resulting in reduced visual performance and visibility. It often is accompanied by discomfort.

Disabling Glare Factor (DGF): A measure of the visibility of a task in a given lighting installation in comparison with its visibility under reference lighting conditions, expressed in terms of the ratio of luminance contrasts having an equivalent effect upon task visibility. The value of DGF takes account of the equivalent veiling luminance produced in the eye by the pattern of luminances in the task surround.

Discomfort Glare: Glare producing discomfort. It does not necessarily interfere with visual performance or visibility.

Discomfort Glare Factor: The numerical assessment of the capacity of a single source of brightness, such as a luminaire, in a given visual environment for producing discomfort. (This term is obsolete and is retained for reference and literature searches.) See *Discomfort Glare* and *Glare*.

Discomfort Glare Rating (DGR): A numerical assessment of the capacity of a number of sources of luminance, such as luminaires, in a given visual environment for producing discomfort. It is the net effect of the individual values of index of sensation for all luminous areas in the field of view. See *Discomfort Glare Factor*.

Distribution Temperature (of a light source): The absolute temperature of a blackbody which has a relative spectral distribution that is the same (or nearly so) in the visible region of the spectrum as that of the light source.

Downlight: A small, direct lighting unit which guides the light downward. It can be recessed, surface mounted, or suspended.

Downward Component: That portion of the luminous flux from a luminaire emitted at angles below the horizontal. See *Upward Component*.

Effective Ceiling Cavity Reflectance, ρ_{CC}: A number giving the combined reflectance effect of the walls and ceiling of the ceiling cavity. See *Ceiling Cavity Ratio*.

Effective Floor Cavity Reflectance, ρ_{FC}: A number giving the combined reflectance effect of the walls and floor of the floor cavity. See *Floor Cavity Ratio*.

Efficacy: See *Luminous Efficacy of a Source of Light*.

Efficiency: See *Luminaire Efficiency* and *Luminous Efficacy of a Source of Light*.

Electric Discharge: See *Gaseous Discharge*.

Electric Discharge Lamp: A lamp in which light (or energy near the visible spectrum) is produced by the passage of an electric current through a gas. See *Fluorescent Lamp* and *High Intensity Discharge Lamp*. Note: Electric discharge lamps may be named after the filling gas that is responsible for the major portion of the light energy; for example, mercury lamps, sodium lamps, neon lamps, argon lamps, etc. A second method of designating electric discharge lamps is by physical dimensions or operating parameters; for example, short arc lamps, high pressure lamps, low pressure lamps, etc. A third method of designating electric discharge lamps is by their application; in addition to lamps for illumination, there are photochemical lamps, bactericidal lamps, blacklight lamps, sun lamps, etc.

Equivalent Sphere Illumination (ESI): The level of sphere illumination which would produce task visibility equivalent to that produced by a specific lighting environment.

Fill Light: Supplementary illumination to reduce shadow or contrast range.

Fixed Light: A light having a constant luminous intensity when observed from a fixed point.

Fixture: See *Luminaire*.

Floodlight: A projector designed for lighting a scene or object to a luminance considerably greater than its surroundings. It usually is capable of being pointed in any direction and is constructed of weatherproof materials. See *General Purpose Floodlight* and *Heavy-Duty Floodlight*.

Floodlighting: A system designed for lighting a scene or object to a luminance greater than its surroundings. It may be for utility, advertising, or decorative purposes.

Floor Cavity: The cavity formed by the work plane, the floor, and the wall surfaces between these two planes.

Floor Cavity Ratio (FCR): A number indicating floor cavity proportions calculated from length, width, and height.

Fluorescence: The emission of light (luminescence) as the result of, and only during, the absorption of light energy of other (mostly shorter) wavelengths.

Fluorescent Lamp: A low pressure mercury, electric discharge lamp in which a fluorescing coating (phosphor) transforms some of the ultraviolet energy generated by the discharge into light. See *Preheat (switch start) Fluorescent Lamp* and *Rapid Start Fluorescent Lamp*.

Flush Mounted or Recessed: A luminaire which is mounted above the ceiling (or behind a wall or other surface) with the opening of the luminaire level with the surface.

Flux Transfer Theory: A method of calculating the illuminance in a room by taking into account the interreflection of the light flux from the room surfaces based on the average flux transfer between surfaces.

Footcandle (fc): The unit of illuminance when the foot is taken as the unit of length. It is the illuminance on a surface one square foot in area on which there is a uniformly distributed flux of one lumen or the illuminance produced on a surface all points of which are at a distance of 1' from a directionally uniform point source of one candela.

Footcandle Meter: See *Illuminance Meter.*

Footlambert (fL): A unit of luminance equal to $1/\pi$ candela per square foot, to the uniform luminance of a perfectly diffusing surface emitting or reflecting light at the rate of one lumen per square foot, or to the average luminance of any surface emitting or reflecting light at that rate. See *Units of Luminance.* (The use of this unit is depreciated.) *Note:* The average luminance of any reflecting surface in footlamberts is, therefore, the product of the illumination in footcandles and the luminous reflectance of the surface.

Gaseous Discharge: The emission of light from gas atoms excited by an electric current.

General Color Rendering Index (R_a): Measure of the average shift of eight standardized colors chosen to be of intermediate saturation and spread throughout the range of hues. If the Color Rendering Index is not qualified as to the color samples used, R_a is assumed.

General Diffuse Lighting: Lighting involving luminaires which distribute 40 to 60% of the emitted light downward and the balance upward, sometimes with a strong component at 90° (horizontal).

General Lighting: Lighting designed to provide a substantially uniform level of illumination throughout an area, exclusive of any provision for special local requirements.

General Purpose Floodlight (GP): A weatherproof unit constructed in such a way that the housing forms the reflecting surface. The assembly is enclosed by a cover glass.

Glare: The sensation produced by luminance within the visual field that is sufficiently greater than the luminance to which the eyes are adapted to cause annoyance, discomfort, or loss in visual performance and visibility. See *Blinding Glare, Direct Glare, Disabling Glare, Discomfort Glare.* *Note:* The magnitude of the sensation of glare depends upon such factors as the size, position, and luminance of a source; the number of sources; and the luminance to which the eyes are adapted.

Heavy-Duty Floodlight (HD): A weatherproof unit having a substantially constructed metal housing into which a separate and removable reflector is placed. A weatherproof, hinged door with cover glass encloses the assembly but provides an unobstructed light opening at least equal to the effective diameter of the reflector.

High Intensity Discharge (HID) Lamp: An electric discharge lamp in which the light producing arc is stabilized by wall temperature and the arc tube has a bulb wall loading in excess of 3 watts per square centimeter. HID lamps include groups of lamps known as mercury, metal halide, and high pressure sodium.

High Mast Lighting: Illumination of a large area by means of a group of luminaires which are designed to be mounted in fixed orientation on the top of a high mast, generally 80' (24.4m) or higher.

High Pressure Sodium (HPS) Lamp: High intensity discharge (HID) lamp in which light is produced from sodium gas operating at a partial pressure of about 1.33 × 10⁴ Pa (100 torr). Clear and diffuse-coated lamps are included.

Illuminance, $E = d\phi/dA$: The density of the luminous flux incident on a surface; it is the quotient of the luminous flux multiplied by the area of the surface when the latter is uniformly illuminated.

Illuminance (lux or footcandle) Meter: An instrument for measuring illuminance on a plane. Instruments which accurately respond to more than one spectral distribution are color corrected, for example, the spectral response is balanced to V (λ) or V' (λ). Instruments which accurately respond to more than one spatial distribution of incident flux are cosine corrected, for example, the response to a source of unit luminous intensity, illuminating the detector from a fixed distance and from different directions decreases as the cosine of the angle between the incident direction and the normal to the detector surface. The instrument is comprised of some form of photodetector, with or without a filter, driving a digital or analog readout through appropriate circuitry.

Illumination: The act of illuminating or the state of being illuminated. This term has been used for density of luminous flux on a surface (illuminance) and such use should be depreciated.

Incandescence: The self-emission of light energy in the visible spectrum due to the thermal excitation of atoms or molecules.

Incandescent Filament Lamp: A lamp in which light is produced by a filament heated to incandescence by an electric current.

Indirect Component: The portion of the luminous flux from a luminaire arriving at the work plane after being reflected by room surfaces. See *Direct Component.*

Indirect Lighting: Lighting by luminaires distributing 90 to 100% of the emitted light upward.

Intensity: A shortening of the terms luminous intensity and radiant intensity. Often misused for level of illumination or illuminance.

Interflectance Method: A lighting design procedure for predetermining the luminances of walls, ceiling, and floor and the average illuminance on the work plane based on integral equations. It takes into account both direct and reflected flux.

Interflected Component: The portion of the luminous flux from a luminaire arriving at the work plane after being reflected one or more times from room surfaces, as determined by the flux transfer theory.

Interflection: The multiple reflection of light by the various room surfaces before it reaches the work plane or other specified surface of a room.

Inverse-Square Law: The law stating that the illuminance E at a point on a surface varies directly with the intensity I of a point source and inversely as the square of the distance d between the source and the point. If the surface at the point is normal to the direction of the incident light, the law is expressed by $E = I/d^2$.

Isocandela Line: A line plotted on any appropriate set of coordinates to show directions in space, about a source of light, in which the intensity is the same. A series of such curves, usually for equal increments of intensity, is called an isocandela diagram.

Isolux (isofootcandle) Line: A line plotted on any appropriate set of coordinates to show all the points on a surface where the illuminance is the same. A series of such lines for various illuminance values is called an isolux (isofootcandle) diagram.

Key Light: The apparent principal source of directional illumination falling upon a subject or area.

Lamp: A generic term for a man-made source of light.

Lamp Lumen Depreciation Factor (LLD): The multiplier to be used in illumination calculations to relate the initial rated output of light sources to the anticipated minimum rated output based on the relamping program to be used.

Lamp Shielding Angle: The angle between the plane of the baffles or louver grid and the plane most nearly horizontal that is tangent to both the lamps and the louver blades.

Level of Illumination: See *Illuminance*.

Light: Energy that is capable of exciting the retina and producing a visual sensation. The visible portion of the electromagnetic spectrum extends from about 380 to 770 nm.

Light Center (of a lamp): The center of the smallest sphere that would completely contain the light-emitting element of the lamp.

Light Center Length (of a lamp): The distance from the light center to a specified reference point on the lamp.

Lighting Effectiveness Factor (LEF$_v$): The ratio of equivalent sphere illumination to ordinary measured or calculated illumination.

Light Loss Factor (LLF): A factor used in calculating illuminance after a given period of time and under given conditions. It takes into account temperature and voltage variations, dirt accumulation on luminaire and room surfaces, lamp depreciation, maintenance procedures, and atmosphere conditions. Formerly called maintenance factor.

Light-Source Color: The color of the light emitted by the source.

Localized General Lighting: Lighting that utilizes luminaires above the visual task and contributes also to the illumination of the surrounding area.

Local Lighting: Lighting designed to provide illuminance over a relatively small area or confined space without providing any significant general surrounding lighting.

Louver: A series of baffles used to shield a source from view at certain angles or to absorb unwanted light. The baffles usually are arranged in a geometric pattern.

Louver Shielding Angle, θ: The angle between the horizontal plane of the baffles or louver grid and the plane at which the louver conceals all objects above. See *Lamp Shielding Angle*.

Low Pressure Sodium Lamp: A discharge lamp in which light is produced from sodium gas operating at a partial pressure of 0.13 to 1.3 Pa (10^{-3} to 10^{-2} torr).

Lumen (lm): SI unit of luminous flux. Radiometrically, it is determined from the radiant power. Photometrically, it is the luminous flux emitted within a unit solid angle (one steradian) by a point source having a uniform luminous intensity of one candela.

Luminaire: A complete lighting unit consisting of a lamp or lamps together with the parts designed to distribute the light, to position and protect the lamps, and to connect the lamps to the power supply.

Luminaire Ambient Temperature Factor: The fractional loss of task illuminance due to improper operating temperature of a gas discharge lamp.

Luminaire Dirt Depreciation Factor (LDD): The multiplier to be used in illuminance calculations to relate the initial illuminance provided by clean, new luminaires to the reduced illuminance that they will provide due to dirt collection on the luminaires at the time at which it is anticipated that cleaning procedures will be instituted.

Luminaire Efficiency: The ratio of luminous flux (lumens) emitted by a luminaire to that emitted by the lamp or lamps used therein.

Luminaire Surface Depreciation Factor: The loss of task illuminance due to permanent deterioration of luminaire surfaces.

Luminance, $L = d^2\phi/(d\omega\, dA \cos\theta)$ **(in a direction and at a point of a real or imaginary surface):** The quotient of the luminous flux at an element of the surface surrounding the point, and propagated in directions defined by an elementary cone containing the given direction, multiplied by the product of the solid angle of the cone and the area of the orthogonal projection of the element of the surface on a plane perpendicular to the given direction. The luminous flux may be leaving, passing through, and/or arriving at the surface. Formerly, photometric brightness. By introducing the concept of luminous intensity, luminance may be expressed as $L = dI\,(dA \cos\theta)$. Here luminance at a point of a surface in a direction is interpreted as the quotient of luminous intensity in the given direction produced by an element of the surface surrounding the point by the area of the orthogonal projection of the element of surface on a plane perpendicular to the given direction. Luminance may be measured at a receiving surface by using $L = dE/(d\omega \cos\theta)$. This value may be less than the luminance of the emitting surface due to the attenuation of the transmitting media. *Note:* In common usage the term "brightness" usually refers to the strength of sensation which results from viewing surfaces or spaces from which light comes to the eye. This sensation is determined in part by the definitely measurable luminance defined previously and in part by conditions of observation such as the state of adaptation of the eye. In much of the literature, the term brightness, used alone, refers to both luminance and sensation. The context usually indicates which meaning is intended.

Luminance Contrast: The relationship between the luminances of an object and its immediate background.

Luminance Difference: The difference in luminance between two areas. It usually is applied to contiguous areas, such as the detail of a visual task and its immediate background, in which case it is quantitatively equal to the numerator in the formula for luminance contrast.

Luminance Ratio: The ratio between the luminances of any two areas in the visual field.

Luminous Efficacy of a Source of Light: The quotient of the total luminous flux emitted by the total lamp power input. It is expressed in lumens per watt. *Note:* The term luminous efficiency has in the past been extensively used for this concept.

Lux (lx): The SI unit of illuminance. One lux is one lumen per square meter (lm/m²).

Lux Meter: See *Illuminance Meter*.

Maintenance Factor (MF): A factor formerly used to denote the ratio of the illuminance on a given area after a period of time to the initial illuminance on the same area. See *Light Loss Factor*.

Matte Surface: One from which the reflection is predominantly diffuse, with or without a negligible specular component.

Mercury Lamp: A high intensity discharge (HID) lamp in which the major portion of the light is produced by mercury operating at a partial pressure in excess of 1.013 × 10⁵ Pa (1 atmosphere). Includes clear, phosphor coated, and self-ballasted lamps.

Metal Halide Lamp: A high intensity discharge (HID) lamp in which the major portion of the light is produced from metal halides and their products of dissociation— possibly in combination with metallic gases such as mercury. Includes clear and phosphor coated lamps.

Nit (Nt): A unit of luminance equal to one candela per square meter. *Note:* Candela per square meter is the International Standard (SI) unit of luminance.

Non-Uniform Lighting: Variation of light levels determined by task requirements.

Orientation: The relation of a building with respect to compass directions.

Point by Point Method: A method of lighting calculation now called point method.

Point Method: A lighting design procedure for predetermining the illuminance at various locations in lighting installations, by use of luminaire photometric data. *Note:* The direct component of illuminance due to the luminaires and the interreflected component of illuminance due to the room surfaces are calculated separately. The sum is the total illuminance at a point.

Pole (Roadway Lighting): A standard support generally used where overhead lighting distribution circuits are employed.

Portable Luminaire: A lighting unit that is not permanently fixed in place.

Position Index (P): A factor which represents the relative average luminance for a sensation at the borderline between comfort and discomfort (BCD) for a source located anywhere within the visual field.

Preheat (switch start) Fluorescent Lamp: A fluorescent lamp designed for operation in a circuit requiring a manual or automatic starting switch to preheat the electrodes in order to start the arc.

Primary Line of Sight: The line connecting the point of observation and the point of fixation.

Protective Lighting: A system intended to facilitate the nighttime policing of industrial and other properties.

Pupil (pupillary aperture): The opening in the iris that admits light into the eye.

Quality of Lighting: Pertains to the distribution of luminance in a visual environment. The term is used in a positive sense and implies that all luminances contribute favorably to visual performance, visual comfort, ease of seeing, safety, and aesthetics for the specific visual tasks involved.

Quantity of Light (luminous energy, $Q = \int \phi dt$): The product of the luminous flux multiplied by the time it is maintained. It is the time integral of luminous flux. (Compare light and luminous flux.)

Quartz-Iodine Lamp: An obsolete term for tungsten halogen lamp.

Rapid Start Fluorescent Lamp: A fluorescent lamp designed for operation with a ballast that provides a low voltage winding for preheating the electrodes and initiating the arc without a starting switch or the application of high voltage.

Reaction Time: The interval between the beginning of a stimulus and the beginning of the response from an observer.

Recessed Luminaire: See *Flush Mounted or Recessed*.

Recoverable Light Loss Factors: Factors which give the fractional light loss that can be recovered by cleaning or lamp replacement.

Reflectance Factor (R): Ratio of the radiant (or luminous) flux reflected in directions delimited to that reflected in the same directions by a perfect reflecting diffuser identically irradiated (or illuminated).

Reflectance of a Surface or Medium, $\rho = \phi_r/\phi_i$: The ratio of the reflected flux to the incident flux.

Reflected Glare: Glare resulting from specular reflections of high luminances in polished or glossy surfaces in the field of view. It usually is associated with reflections from within a visual task or areas in close proximity to the region being viewed. See *Veiling Reflection*.

Reflection: A general term for the process by which the incident flux leaves a surface or medium from the incident side, without change in frequency. *Note:* Reflection is usually a combination of regular and diffuse reflection.

Reflector: A device used to redirect the luminous flux from a source by the process of reflection.

Refractor: A device used to redirect the luminous flux from a source, primarily by the process of refraction.

Regular (specular) Reflectance: The ratio of the flux leaving a surface or medium by regular (specular) reflection to the incident flux. See *Regular (specular) Reflection*.

Regular (specular) Reflection: That process by which incident flux is redirected at the specular angle. See *Specular Angle*.

Room Cavity: The cavity formed by the plane of the luminaires, the work plane, and the wall surfaces between these two planes.

Room Cavity Ratio (RCR): A number indicating room cavity proportions calculated from length, width, and height.

Room Index: A letter designation for a range of room ratios.

Room Ratio: A number indicating room proportions, calculated from the length, width, and ceiling height (or luminaire mounting height) above the work plane.

Room Surface Dirt Depreciation (RSDD): The fractional loss of task illuminance due to dirt on the room surface.

Spacing: For roadway lighting, the distance between successive lighting units, measured along the center line of the street.

Spacing-to-Mounting Height Ratio (S/MH$_{wp}$): The ratio of the distance between luminaire centers to the mounting height above the work plane.

Specular Angle: The angle between the perpendicular to the surface and the reflected ray that is numerically equal to the angle of incidence and that lies in the same plane as the incident ray and the perpendicular but on the opposite side of the perpendicular to the surface.

Specular Reflection: See *Regular (specular) Reflection*.

Sphere Illumination: The illumination on a task from a source providing equal luminance in all directions about that task, such as an illuminated sphere with the task located at the center.

313

Standard Source: In colorimetry, a source that has a specified spectral distribution and is used as a standard.

Standard Source A: A tungsten filament lamp operated at a color temperature of 2,856°K, approximating a black-body operating at that temperature.

Starter: A device used in conjunction with a ballast for the purpose of starting an electric discharge lamp.

Street Lighting Luminaire: A complete lighting device consisting of a light source and ballast, where appropriate, together with its direct appendages such as globe, reflector, refractor housing, and support that is integral with the housing. The pole, post, or bracket is not considered part of the luminaire.

Street Lighting Unit: The assembly of a pole or lamp post with a bracket and a luminaire.

Supplementary Lighting: Lighting used to provide an additional quantity and quality of illumination that cannot readily be obtained by a general lighting system and that supplements the general lighting level, usually for specific work requirements.

Surface Mounted Luminaire: A luminaire mounted directly on the ceiling.

Suspended (pendant) Luminaire: A luminaire hung from a ceiling by supports.

Switch Start Fluorescent Lamps: See *Preheat (switch start) Fluorescent Lamp.*

Task Lighting: Lighting directed to a specific surface or area that provides illumination for visual tasks.

Torchère: An indirect floor lamp sending all or nearly all of its light upward.

Troffer: A recessed lighting unit, usually long and installed with the opening flush with the ceiling. The term is derived from "trough" and "coffer."

Tungsten Halogen Lamp: A gas filled tungsten incandescent lamp containing a certain proportion of halogens. *Note:* The tungsten-iodine lamp (UK) and quartz-iodine lamp (USA) belong to this category.

Units of Luminance: The luminance of a surface in a specified direction may be expressed in luminous intensity per unit of projected area of surface or in luminous flux per unit of solid angle and per unit of projected surface area. *Note:* Typical units are the candela per square meter (lumen per steradian and per square meter) and the candela per square foot (lumen per steradian and per square foot).

Unrecoverable Light Loss Factors: Factors which give the fractional light loss that cannot be recovered by cleaning or lamp replacement.

Upward Component: That portion of the luminous flux from a luminaire emitted at angles above the horizontal. See *Downward Component.*

Veiling Luminance: A luminance superimposed on the retinal image which reduces its contrast. It is this veiling effect produced by bright sources or areas in the visual field that results in decreased visual performance and visibility.

Veiling Reflection: Regular reflections superimposed upon diffuse reflections from an object that partially or totally obscure the details to be seen by reducing the contrast. This sometimes is called reflected glare.

Visibility: The quality or state of being perceivable by the eye. In many outdoor applications, visibility is defined in terms of the distance at which an object can be just perceived by the eye. In indoor applications it usually is defined in terms of the contrast or size of a standard test object, observed under standardized view conditions, having the same threshold as the given object.

Visibility Level (VL): A contrast multiplier to be applied to the visibility reference function to provide the luminance contrast required at different levels of task background luminance to achieve visibility for specified conditions relating to the task and observer.

Visual Comfort Probability (VCP): The rating of a lighting system expressed as a percent of people who, when viewing from a specified location and in a specified direction, will be expected to find it acceptable in terms of discomfort glare. Visual comfort probability is related to discomfort glare rating (DGR).

Visual Field: The locus of objects or points in space that can be perceived when the head and eyes are kept fixed. The field may be monocular or binocular.

Visual Performance: The quantitative assessment of the performance of a visual task, taking into consideration speed and accuracy.

Visual Surround: Includes all portions of the visual field except the visual task.

Visual Task: Conventionally designates those details and objects that must be seen for the performance of a given activity and includes the immediate background of the details or objects. *Note:* The term visual task as used is a misnomer because it refers to the visual display itself and not the task of extracting information from it. The task of extracting information also has to be differentiated from the overall task performed by the observer.

Voltage to Luminaire Factor: The fractional loss of task illuminance due to improper voltage at the luminaire.

Wide Angle Luminaire: A luminaire distributing the light through a comparatively large, solid angle.

Work Plane: The plane at which work is usually done and on which the illuminance is specified and measured. Unless otherwise indicated, this is assumed to be a horizontal plane 30" (0.76m) above the floor.

Zonal-Cavity Interreflectance Method: A procedure for calculating coefficients of utilization, wall luminance coefficients, and ceiling cavity luminance coefficients taking into consideration the luminaire intensity distribution, room size and shape (cavity ratio concepts), and room reflectances. It is based on flux transfer theory.

Angular Measure, Temperature, and Power Conversion Equations

Angle
   1 radian = 57.29578 degrees
Temperature
   (F to C) $C = 5/9 (F - 32)$
   (C to F) $F = 9/5\ C + 32$
   (C to K) $K = C + 273$
Power
   1 kilowatt = 1.341 horsepower
            = 56.89 Btu per minute

Luminance Conversion Factors

Multiply Number of → To Obtain Number of ↓	Footlambert By ↓	Nit	Millilambert	Candela/ square inch	Candela/ square foot	Stilb
Footlambert	1	0.2919	0.929	452	3.142	2,919
Nit	3.426	1	3.183	1,550	10.76	10,000
Millilambert	1.076	0.3142	1	487	3.382	3,142
Candela/square inch	0.00221	0.000645	0.00205	1	0.00694	6.45
Candela/square foot	0.3183	0.0929	0.2957	144	1	929
Stilb	0.00034	0.0001	0.00032	0.155	0.00108	1

Note: 1 nit = 1 candela/square meter
   1 stilb = 1 candela/square centimeter
   1 apostilb (international) = 0.1 millilambert = 1 blondel
   1 apostilb (German Hefner) = 0.09 millilambert
   1 lambert = 1,000 millilamberts

Conversion Factors for Units of Length

	Millimeters	Centimeters	Meters	Kilometers	Mils	Inches	Feet	Miles
Millimeters	1	10	10^3	10^6	2.540×10^{-2}	2.540×10	3.048×10^2	1.609×10^6
Centimeters	10^{-1}	1	10^2	10^5	2.540×10^{-3}	2.540	3.048×10	1.609×10^5
Meters	10^{-3}	10^{-2}	1	10^3	2.540×10^{-5}	2.540×10^{-2}	3.048×10^{-1}	1.609×10^3
Kilometers	10^{-6}	10^{-5}	10^{-3}	1	2.540×10^{-8}	3.048×10^{-5}	3.048×10^{-4}	1.609
Mils	3.937×10	3.937×10^2	3.937×10^4	3.937×10^7	1	10^3	1.2×10^4	6.336×10^7
Inches	3.937×10^{-2}	3.937×10^{-1}	3.937×10	3.937×10^4	10^{-3}	1	12	6.336×10^4
Feet	3.281×10^{-3}	3.281×10^{-2}	3.281	3.281×10^3	8.333×10^{-5}	8.333×10^{-2}	1	5.280×10^3
Miles	6.214×10^{-7}	6.214×10^{-6}	6.214×10^{-4}	6.214×10^{-1}	1.578×10^{-8}	1.578×10^{-5}	1.894×10^{-4}	1

Index

319